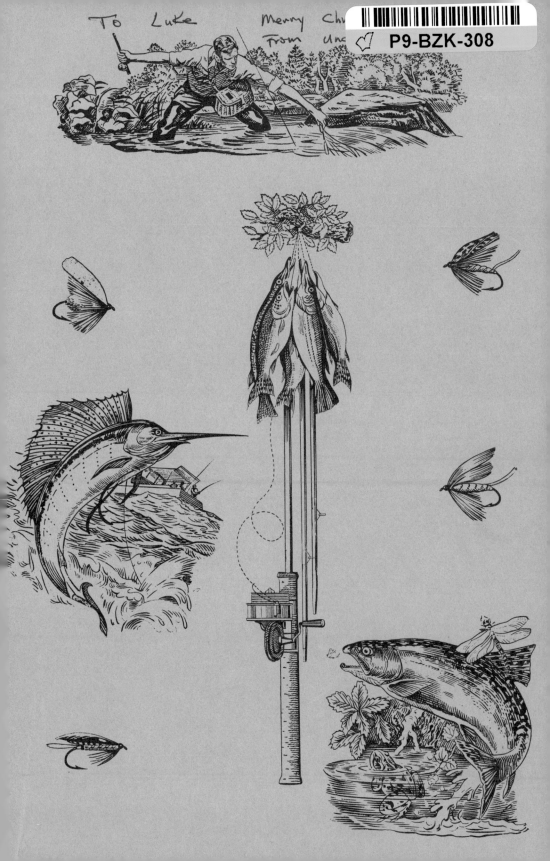

Books by Raymond R. Camp

ALL SEASONS AFIELD

FISHING THE SURF

DUCK BOATS

BLINDS AND DECOYS

RAY CAMP'S HUNTING BOOK

THE HUNTER'S ENCYCLOPEDIA

THE COLLIER'S BOOK OF HUNTING AND FISHING

GAME COOKERY

The Fireside Book

of

FISHING

A Selection

from the Great Literature of Angling

Edited by

RAYMOND R. CAMP

ILLUSTRATIONS BY WILLIAM K. PLUMMER

Simon and Schuster

New York

1959

Acknowledgments

For arrangements made with various authors, their representatives and publishers, where copyrighted material was permitted to be reprinted, and for the courtesy extended by them, the following acknowledgments are gratefully made:

Alfred A. Knopf, Inc., for "In the Rainbow Kingdom," from *Hunting and Fishing in Alaska* by Russell Annabel, © 1948 by Russell Annabel; "Some Field Problems and Their Solutions," from *Just Fishing* by Ray Bergman, © 1932 by Alfred A. Knopf, Inc.; and for "Bonefish," from *Salt Water Fishing* by Van Campen Heilner, © 1937 by Alfred A. Knopf, Inc.

Farrar and Rinehart for "Daniel Webster and the Sea Serpent," from *Thirteen O'Clock* by Stephen Vincent Benét, © 1937 by Stephen Vincent Benét.

Charles Scribner's Sons for "The Rajah's Rock," from *The Glorious Mornings* by Paul Hyde Bonner, © 1933 by Lilly M. Bonner; "Big Two-Hearted River" by Ernest Hemingway, © 1930 by Charles Scribner's Sons; "Introduction," from *The Complete Fly Fisherman* by John McDonald, © 1947 by John McDonald; and for "Black Salmon," from *Tutt, Tutt, Mr. Tutt* by Arthur Train, © 1937 by Arthur Train.

Alvin Redman for selections from *The Shining Tides* by Win Brooks, © 1953 by Win Brooks.

Field & Stream Magazine for "Dirty Work at the Covered Bridge" by Paul Brown, © 1932 by Henry Holt & Company.

Houghton Mifflin for "The Old Etonian Tramp," from *John Macnab* by John Buchan, © 1925 by John Buchan; and for "Chet McAusland of Fraternity," from *Fraternity Village* by Ben Ames Williams, © 1949 by Ben Ames Williams.

Outdoor Life Magazine for "Stouthearted Men" by Raymond R. Camp, © 1954 by *Outdoor Life* Magazine.

Coward McCann for "Peru," from *Fishing the Pacific* by S. Kip Farrington, © 1942 by Coward McCann; and for "Bass Are Bass," from *Dud Dean and His Country* by Arthur MacDougal, Jr., © 1946 by Arthur MacDougal.

The Derrydale Press for "Angler, Beware!" from *The One-Eyed Poacher of Privilege* by Edmund Ware Smith, © 1936 by Edmund Ware Smith.

R. Bently for "Trouting along the Catasauqua" by Frank Forester, 1849.

William Morrow & Co. for "When Is a Rainbow," from *Fisherman's Spring* by Roderick Haig-Brown, © 1951 by Roderick Haig-Brown.

vi

J. W. Arrowsmith for "Storytelling on the Thames," from *Three Men in a Boat* by Jerome K. Jerome, © 1889 by J. W. Arrowsmith.

G. P. Putnam's Sons for "Fishing the Dry Fly on Quiet Waters," from *A Modern Dry Fly Code* by Vincent Marinaro, © 1950 by Vincent Marinaro.

Prentice-Hall for "History," from *Spinning for Fresh and Salt Water Fish in North America* by A. J. McClane, © 1952 by Prentice-Hall.

Seeley, Service & Co. for "Mr. Theodore Castwell," from *Sidelines, Sidelights and Reflections* by G. E. M. Skues, © 1947 by G. E. M. Skues.

Alfred W. Miller for "The Lotus Eaters" and for "Murder," from *Fishless Days* by Sparse Grey Hackle, © 1954 by Alfred W. Miller.

Duell, Sloane & Pearce for "In Defense of Worms," from *In Defense of Worms* by Frederic F. Van de Water, © 1949 by Frederic F. Van de Water.

The Macmillan Company for "Old Poacher's Return," from *Big Stony* by Howard T. Walden II, © 1940 by Howard T. Walden II.

W. & R. Chambers for "Thomasheen James and the Absent-Minded Professor," from *Thomasheen James, Man of No Work,* by Maurice Walsh, © 1941 by Maurice Walsh.

Little, Brown & Co. for "The Redds," from *Salar the Salmon* by Henry Williamson, © 1935 by Henry Williamson.

Rinehart & Co., Inc., for "The Visiting Fire-Eater," from *The Big Ones Get Away* by Philip Wylie, © 1939 by Philip Wylie.

Appleton-Century for "The Truth about Izaak Walton," from *To Hell with Fishing* by Ed Zern, © 1945 by Ed Zern.

Contents

Introduction

AN ANTHOLOGIST *is faced with a paradox: he is given the agreeable task of delving into his preferred field of literature, rereading old favorites and discovering new treasures, and then, if he is to stay within the bounds of a reasonable volume, he has the arduous responsibility of selecting only a relative sample of these for inclusion.*

In choosing the material for this book, I have tried to cover every form of angling, in order to satisfy any fishing buff who may glance herein. I have also tried to avoid the temptation of studding the table of contents with "name" authors merely for the sake of the name, and only included those whose contribution to fishing lore warranted it. On the other hand, I hope I am introducing the reader to a few heretofore unknown but extremely fine writers.

While I attempted to maintain a proper proportion of both fact and fiction, I occasionally found, as I suspect many a fishing wife could have told me, that the distinction between these two, in this field, is frequently quite nebulous and sometimes even nonexistent.

There is no instructional section as such, since long acquaintance with dedicated anglers has taught me that not one of them will ever admit to needing to learn anything. I wish to go on record, however, as being conscious of the existence of a considerable measure of valuable instruction cannily worked into some of these pages by the different contributors.

The exigencies of space prevented me from using larger portions of certain books, but I am satisfied that I have at least brought them to the reader's attention and feel he will be stimulated to read the complete original in many cases. I hope that I have fulfilled my goal of offering a representative collection of angling literature: of the old and the new, of fact and imagination, of lake, stream, river and ocean.

RAYMOND R. CAMP

Owen's Adventure

ROBERT ALLAN

["A Cosmopolite"]

Robert Allan's fierce indictments against British landlordism, in the Ireland of the mid-nineteenth century, stamped him as a belligerent crusader. The tale of "Owen's Adventure" is one of his less contentious writings, although force is not lacking even in this lighter-touch story.

I CANNOT TELL whether dyspeptic people ever become fishermen, or whether fishermen can ever become dyspeptic; but it would be as hard a trial as any I can conceive—even to one of the guards who finished at the battle of Waterloo the tender discipline of the Peninsular war—to drink whisky punch all night in a cabin, and set forth at daybreak, for the enlivening purpose of traversing a bog, of twenty miles extent, saturated with rain. If the powers of digestion are a little irregular and fastidious, perhaps this would be an occasion to call forth some of these extraordinary antics their defective subordination so frequently suggests.

Owen's face looked, if possible, more lengthy than ever; and I thought I could discover in the major's eye somewhat of the golden tinge, which, though in the main rather a pretty color, is not highly esteemed even by gentlemen from India, who come to drink Epsom salt water at that pleasant vortex for invalids—Cheltenham. But I was afraid to venture an observation, fully impressed with the conviction that the *Tu quoque* would form a just rejoinder. I won't say that I was quite well, or that a good bed, with a nice clean-capped chambermaid lighting me thereto, and fumbling about the clothes with an old frying-pan, with holes in the lid, would not have o'ertopped the hopes of the *fresh* in the river. But here was nothing but the wild heath, the resounding river, now charged to its banks' edge, bursting through the chasms of solid granite, and in the stillness of the dawn roaring through the glens. The mists still covered the tops of the mountains, and showed forth the dreariness and desolation of an unexplored expanse.

Nature has made some little confusion in what philosopher Square calls "the eternal fitness of things"; the heat without is by no means in a proper ratio of that within the body; for, though both the major and myself had taken especial care and used considerable diligence in fortifying the inner man with all the warmth which new whisky could possibly excite, it is a curious fact in physics, for which I am wholly incompetent to account, that the exterior man did shiver most intolerably. There was a disinclination to parlance also—at other times little to be charged on the major; and I believe, friends as we were, nothing would have been more easy at that moment than to have concocted a very nice quarrel. None of us were quarrelsome, but the discourse was monosyllabic, and our words were chilled; but neither dared confess the discomfort under which we all three labored.

I thought of nothing but the twenty miles, and continued to occupy myself in ratiocinative deductions, arising from the fact that a man had been known to achieve the distance even without once throwing himself horizontally on a wet bog—an inclination, however, which, ever and anon, assumed considerable force. Not unfrequently did I persuade myself that I could walk, and sustain the dignity of the *ad sidera vultus,* with my eyes shut. Nothing could be seen; the bog was level; nor was I roused from the favorable view I had been induced to take of this very pernicious fallacy but by the practical squash into the morass, which generally invited the other foot to the rescue of the offending member, which it was not then exactly convenient to amputate. There was no inequality of wretchedness, therefore, both feet being well saturated with the porterlike overflowing of the bog.

As to Owen, I had conceived hopes that he at least would break down, and give me some color for following his example. The imperturbable villain had secured a piece of lighted turf, and, as I looked behind to observe how he got on, I had the mortification of witnessing a countenance of the utmost complacency, in the principal feature of which was stuck a short black pipe, and out of which very principal feature issued long volumes of detestable-looking smoke. There was no chance from him. There was nothing for it but to push on.

The river was swollen to a flood; but, as the rain had now ceased and the fall was rapid, we anticipated a good cast by midday. The major grumbled at the disappointment, as he had determined to carry into the town the wherewith of a good dinner. I found in this state of the water the roe useless—the fish were scattered by the extended volume of the stream. We were at least three hours too early, as the major ventured to observe after a few casts.

"It's a glorious morning, however," said he.

"Splendid."

"The fresh morning air is very refreshing."

"I daresay it is."

"This is a grand specimen of the fisherman's life. Now, I just observe to you that nothing gives a greater relish to a breakfast than the mountain air—it's perfectly astonishing what it will do for the health."

"And the comfort too."

"Why, I was thinking that the smallest drop of whisky might do no great hurt, and help us onward."

This was the point the gallant officer had been aiming at ever since our departure. I could not resist the temptation of assuring him that it was, of all things in the world, the proper thing: the stimulus should be kept up when there was no sport to enliven the labors. The major's draught was *not loud but deep;* and there was a manifestation of enterprise almost simultaneously engendered.

"Huzza for the lob-trouts this day!—the thick water will be off in an hour. It was just after such a day that I grabbled fifty of the best salmon I ever saw—all fresh run from the sea."

"What is the process of grabbling?"

"After a fresh flood, the salmon come up in shoals to the falls, and there rest till they are sufficiently recovered to make the leap. They are then sulky—will take neither bait nor fly, but stick like logs under the fall. I then quietly take a dozen large cod hooks, tie them back to back, and, with a stout stick, a strong cord, and heavy lead sinker, let down to the bottom, every now and then twitch to the right, then to the left, then upward, and inwise, and outward. Fifty of the silvery villains fell victims to my industry, till the proprietor of the fall came personally to pay me a visit, and had the audacity to question both my right to fish and the fairness of the style of it. As to the fairness of it, said I, all is fair in love, war, and fishing; and as to the right, you'll particularly honor me by the acceptance of this card, where my name and rank are neatly engraved for the satisfaction of all gentlemen who may render themselves worthy of my notice. Will you believe that the spalpeen refused to fight, and talked something about the law? I wished him good day—regretted I had mistaken his calling—the mistake being exactly the converse of Hamlet's, as I had conceived *a fishmonger was a gentleman.* I gave him no chance for his law, as I pushed on beyond his district before he had obtained the summons. But the fifty salmon were capital. I distributed them among all the poor cottagers as I passed along. Faith, it was many a day since any of them had seen such a meal, although living on the very banks of the river.—Did you see that rise?"

The intimation was enough. The fish had begun to stir, and the water was now clearing. We were within four miles of the town, which the major represented as bad enough at all times, but worse without notice. It was arranged, therefore, that Owen should push forward to apprise the landlord of our coming, and give the necessary orders. He was especially enjoined, if possible, to take with him a salmon, which was to be ready on our arrival. Owen pocketed his black pipe, and, charged by so important a mission, in which his skill as an angler was to be put to the test, with an air of offended dignity at the doubt implied, strutted over the bog, while the major and myself prepared our tackle.

The major's first throw instantly rose a fish, but he rose short. The same fish rose again at my fly, still short. Down went the major's rod, and, regardless of the recent rains, he proceeded to seat himself on the grass.

"Now, what fly do the willful vermin want? A flood, and a light yellow golden pheasant not do for the epicurean villains?"

We produced the books, and, after a long examination and due balancing of probabilities, we selected a light-blue hackle and gray wing. We were right; the first cast produced a salmon firmly hooked; he was my prize. In a minute, the major was fast linked to another. In the hilarity of the moment, the major hurled up his hat, as his fish steadily pushed up the stream.

I was not less exulting; but the moment of conflict I knew had not yet arrived. In due course, my fish conceived it more agreeable to travel downward—a disposition I had no means of restraining—and, favored by the strong current, had thought proper to adopt the railroad rate of traveling; I mean that rate expressed in the splendid schedules, about arriving here and there at such particular hours, but which schedules, and the columns they contain, have no further effect than that of disappointing elderly gentlemen who look for a hot dinner at 3:30, and get it cold at 5:20. My salmon had none of this irregularity; he pushed downward in earnest, and not according to any schedule. In doing so—I could not help it, whatever my gallant colleague may say when he reads these pages—he crossed the major's line, whose fish was traveling upward at the slow coach pace, checked the lines, and, I grieve to say, with such violence as to smash both. The remnants came up without trouble. The major looked at me, and I looked at the major.

$$* \quad * \quad * \quad * \quad * \quad * \quad *$$

These asterisks express a pause—it was a long one. It is altogether wrong, and very wicked, to ejaculate,—and so it is to write down apostrophes that have immediate reference to a state of misfortune not quite applicable to sublunary matters, but which exclusively belong to a particular extent of heat hereafter, and, therefore, I refrain. But I must record the fact that my gallant companion in arms did throw down his white hat—that he did stamp upon it, notwithstanding its intrinsic value as a hat—that he did commit devastation on the very small proportion of hair which remained at the back of his head, regardless of its inestimable beauty—and that he did then and there declare that I had no right—that it was wholly against the common law of angling, and, as he believed on his soul, against a particular act of parliament—to allow my fish to run down while his was taking the opposite direction!

There was nothing to be said; I had no excuse to offer; the fish was pertinacious, and the act of parliament referred to did not extend to him, however applicable to me. That was all I could urge; but if it had not happened that the major had some respect for me on other accounts, I verily believe our friendship had been from that moment at an end.

"That was the right color," I observed, after some time, and looking cautiously at the major as he gazed on the stream in a certain inert state of intellect and bodily function. He looked toward me peeringly, as though he was examining the extent of my grief, expecting, doubtlessly, to observe a height of mental anguish which equaled or exceeded his own.

"It was a tolerable color, by St. Patrick!" and he began to mend the disposition of his hat, by thrusting his hand rather energetically into the crown, and using other persuasives to a resumption of its original form. "You may say that; it was a tolerable color."

I like to see a man recovering from a violent passion, the cause of which is irremediable. The indignation evaporates, but a strong pride remains, which will not allow the possessor to acknowledge that the cause was irremediable. The major had been unhappy but for the opportunity of casting all blame on me; and I ventured, therefore, to hint that the statute to which he had so learnedly referred really applied to himself, as it strictly forbade any person or persons whatever, under a penalty thereinafter named, holding, playing, drowning, or following any fish, whensoever it shall or may happen that another person, &c. The recitation of this act did not convince him; but it sufficiently soothed him to endure the renovation of the tackle with some coolness, although the knots were completed with some jerks, each being accompanied by a consignment direct to inferior regions.

We were presently surprised by a succession of leaps; four or five salmon at once cleared the surface. Our surprise and curiosity were soon satisfied; the nose of an otter was elevated, then another, and another. We were up in a moment; the rifle had been left with Owen. It was a brood.

"Pelt them with stones!" cried the major.

This I did with all imaginable industry, and succeeded in separating the young ones from the parents. The latter had gone down the stream, while the three whelps, unable to sustain themselves under water for so great a length of time, popped up their heads in exactly the most inconvenient places. The chase now began; as the young ones had started up the stream, we had no difficulty in keeping them in that direction. At length the three perched on a rock, and began to cry with the small voice of a cat; they were obviously in the wrong, and had missed the old ones, who were doubtless not far off.

The skill of the major was now in requisition; he had hastily tied to his line all the large salmon flies he could find, and, at the distance of twenty yards, ere I was informed of his intention, covered the three whelps by a foot; they immediately started, and the major as immediately drew.

"Here's one at least," exclaimed he.

It was true; he had one of the otters fast; but the difficulty of holding him was not trifling. The fight was exactly in the style of a large and heavy fish; first he was down to the bottom of the pool, then, with the rapidity of lightning, he rose at another part where he was least expected. The contest was one of most singular dexterity on one part, and of strength and agility on the other. At length, the smaller of the two fishermen began to yield, and, in a few minutes, he was dragged by main force to the shore. I now assisted in the fight, but warily, as the little animal bit ferociously at everything that was put toward him. He died the death of honor; he was stoned to death, and crammed into the creel as the most remarkable trophy of expert angling.

It was hopeless to expect any success, at least within a considerable range of the river, the otters having taken down the stream; and I was by no means unwilling to dismount the flies, and go in search of comfort, a very attenuated portion of which had, for the last twenty-four hours, been our lot. In the triumph of his skill, my companion had forgotten the contretemps in which he affected to believe me so deeply implicated, and we improved in good humor and courtesy as we shortened the distance to Castlebar.

The road was indeed a rough and boggy one; but, after the difficulties we had encountered by the riverside, even this seemed tolerably direct; every second step did not, as before, give us one foot in the bog.

At length the turfy smoke of Castlebar met our view, and the exhilaration I immediately felt at the near prospect of food, raiment, and lodging, would not be repressed; strength returned to my previously tottering limbs, and my companion's heavy stump became more energetic.

On our entrance into Castlebar, and on inquiring for the inn, we found that the town was really in a hubbub. It happened to be market-day, and groups of persons surrounded us. At last we were accosted by one of the country people, who seemed more capable of addressing the strangers than the rest, who informed us that our attendant, Owen, was in trouble—in truth, at that moment, in durance—for an offense of rather an extraordinary character. The landlord, who was of the roughest order, received us at the door.

"If it's your honor's man that's taken up, he has sent a dozen times to inquire for you, to clear him before the magistrate."

The major, who had contracted a real friendship for our humble attendant, was on fire.

"Who is the magistrate that dares to take up my man, without first informing myself? Oh, it's myself will settle the matter without the law at all at all."

I could perceive, without much difficulty, that my friend was in an unlikely mood to become just then a very successful advocate. Leaving him, therefore, to the pocketbook from which he was selecting a card, with no very friendly intention toward the magistrate, I proceeded to make further inquiries, and learned that our Achates had been exhibiting himself in a state that would have even offended the ladies of the Connemara wilds—in fact, that he had been stopped in a state of entire nudity, running like a madman among all the people coming to market—that he had been seized, covered, and brought before the magistrate, to whom he gave so lame an account of our honors, that he had been consigned to durance till our arrival.

Our astonishment was immeasurable, and could only be appeased by the supposition that Owen's peculiarity of character had at length subsided into absolute madness. We forthwith proceeded to the rescue, the major burning with indignation, and determined to get up a fight with someone on this score. I succeeded, however, in prevailing on him to allow me to be the manager of the business; and, having sent up my name to the magistrate, we were immediately admitted. His account was that our companion had really been taken as described in the road; and that the people were fully impressed with the notion that he was deranged—a conviction to which he himself had arrived upon hearing the facts. For our satisfaction, he would send again for him, to enable him to give what explanation he pleased of the matter.

Owen was soon produced. At sight of us he forthwith brightened up.

"Och, and it's all right now, anyway! Your honors have got the salmon; I left him to be dressed; and is it myself would go to disappoint your honors of a breakfast along with a few spalpeen market people! I wonder what divil of a country this, that a man mayn't catch a salmon, because the river runs by the side of the road. But your honors will spake for me, and explain it, anyhow, to his nobleness the justice."

I requested permission to ask Owen for his own version, which being readily granted, the prisoner began:—

"It's clear, your honors will remember ordering me to catch a salmon, and go on before to the inn. Well, burn the rise I'd get, your honor, till I came within half a mile of the town; there I sees as fair a rise at the nathural as ever my eyes was blest with. Oh! be aisy, sis I —is it there you are, and I wanting ye for my master's breakfast? With that, I makes a clane cast, and covered the beauty to an inch. Up he came—away went my winch, and I thought of my sowl he'd niver done running till my line was smashed. Into the river I pitches my rod—away run the fish, and away run I—and, faith, I'd enough to do to keep up, anyway, for the stones and the bogs bothered my speed intirely. At last he stops; oh! sis I, it's my turn now, and with that I goes up toward my rod; off boults the fish to the other side the stream. There was nothing but a swimming or a ducking for it, and, to keep all clane and go dacent into the town like, I pulls off my bits of things, and swims over the river to the place where the wild brute had carried my rod. The divil a bit he stand a minute. Off went the salmon again; and it was then I had a run for it after the river, so, seeing my rod going doubts tide, and, finding the road alongside the river far best for running, to the road I went; and it's a pity your honors weren't there to see the sport—run salmon, run I, for a good half mile—there I caught my rod; and it's a good to the heart to see the way he played. But I soon landed my fish, and what do your honors think? In a fine country like this, a lot of spalpeens, without with your leave, or by your leave, or any politeness at all, seizes hould of me, crams an ould frieze or two over me, and brings me to be put to prison. 'Oh!' sis I, 'but I'm a freeborn Irishman,' sis I; 'and there are two rale gintlemen that'll see me righted,' sis I. 'And what have I done?' sis I.—'Done?' sis they. 'Haven't ye been running stark naked among the people, and them women?' sis they.—'The divil a woman or man,' sis I, 'did I see at all at all'; and if your nobleness and honor will give me the book, I'll swear the same on my Bible oath this moment. What do they tell his honor, but that there were lots of women coming to market, and his honor believes 'em, maybe because I am a Catholic. I saw nobody all the time but the rod, and that was running swately."

I assured the magistrate of my entire conviction that Owen was innocent of any intentional wrong; and such was, I believe, the ardor with which he pursued the sport, that I did not doubt his declaration that he had seen nobody.

The magistrate was pleased to find that the affair was of no further consequence, and ordered Owen to be discharged, assuring him, however, that his being a Catholic had had nothing whatever to do with his detention or discharge, and in this declaration I joined; but the major, seizing the hand of Owen, and in the presence of the magistrate, declared his entire approval of the fisherman's whole course of conduct. "And, for myself, I'd follow a salmon into the very palace rather than lose him, anyway. So, say nothing of being a trifle deficient in the cut of your surtout."

The major was now about to wax wroth in approval of Owen's conduct; and just as he was fumbling about for the card, on which was neatly engraved "Major ———, —th Regiment," I thrust my arm within his, bowed to the man of authority, and we were at our inn before the gallant officer could determine in what way the proper insult ought to be conveyed to a magistrate. Owen was admitted to dine with us off the salmon which had been the cause of all his distress and degradation.

We were indeed weary, but had acquired in our peregrinations a perfect knowledge of what will be reasonably expected in a night up the mountains by the sportsman in Ireland.

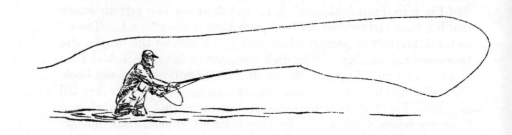

In the Rainbow Kingdom

RUSSELL ANNABEL

Although many angling writers returned from our new state to rave of the angling opportunities it provided, Alaska has few native writers on the subject. None has a broader knowledge of Alaskan angling than Russell Annabel, who fortunately has the gift of taking a reader with him on his fishing trips. In "In the Rainbow Kingdom," from Hunting and Fishing in Alaska, *Annabel proves his point.*

G O AHEAD and cast out there," Doc told Tex, looking up from the job of repairing his tackle with a wildish gleam in his eye. "G'wan try it and find out something. In just about three seconds you'll be patching up your gear too."

Doc was sitting on the grassy bank of the pool bending on a new 2-X leader. Doc is a guy who makes a cult of using cobweb gut and tiny flies, no matter what size trout he is going up against. He thinks there ought to be a law against heavier stuff. A competent angler, he says, doesn't need a hawser and a swamp hook with a feather duster tied onto it to hold his own with big fish. On this trip he had even succeeded in persuading Tex to fish with a five-ounce rod, No. 14 flies, and a nine-foot leader tapered to 4-X, something nobody had ever done before. There were in the waters hereabouts, however, such trout as Doc never in his life had hooked into. Having started with a 4-X leader, he was now going to the heaviest gear he ever used. There were monsters here, the mightiest strain of fighting rainbows in the world, and they were plentiful and usually in the mood to assault any likely lure you cast over them.

"Person'ly, I think he's jest makin' conversation to keep us out'n his fishin' hole until he gits ready to operate ag'in," Tex said. "But since he did say go ahead an' try hit, why, let's accept his invite."

Neither Tex nor I had wet a line yet, as we had been busy helping to moor the plane where it would be safe from wind and waves. So now we moved downstream a few yards and cast out into the foot of the pool. A rising trout made a ring on the quiet water thirty feet out, and Tex promptly dropped a silver doctor on that spot. Nothing happened. He cast again over the place, letting the fly float down with the slow current. Something that looked like a chunk of dark driftwood slanted up from the bottom behind the fly. There was a dimple on the water; then the silver doctor vanished, and Tex's reel purred as several yards of line ran off. Tex hit the fish, and abruptly the pool exploded. The fish was a rainbow and there were about three feet of it. That's merely an estimate, though, for we never laid hands on the noble creature. He blasted himself high out of the water, and when he came down he fell on the leader and smacked it with his great fluke. That was that. Tex reeled in and gazed thoughtfully at the broken gut. After a moment he got out his kit and took from it his favorite combination of fresh-water tackle—a length of ten-pound-test leader and a nameless oversize fly of his own manufacture that resembles nothing so much as a full-fed Malay fruit bat.

"You didn't stay in business as long as I thought you would," Doc said without looking up. "About two seconds, wasn't it?"

"He took me by su'prise," Tex explained. "I was jest warmin' up, sorta. But if I git another crack at him hit'll be his turn to be su'prised, dang his hide. I'm reely gonna pop his tail fer him."

"That's exactly what happened to me," Doc said. "I was just warming up, sorta."

We were on the bank of Tularik Creek, a tributary to Lake Iliamna, two hundred and fifty miles southwest of Anchorage. Iliamna, which drains into Bristol Bay, is one hundred miles long and thirty-five miles wide and lies in the heart of what certainly is one of the finest of all rainbow-fishing regions. Nobody knows how large the rainbows grow there. Anglers discovered the race of giants only about ten years ago and were just beginning to explore the many creeks, rivers, and lakes on the watershed when the late war interrupted them. It is an established fact, however, that thirty-inchers are common, and that a number of thirty-six-inchers have been taken. The Indians and white trappers state, moreover, that rainbows measuring forty inches have been taken here in salmon nets. I have never seen one of these forty-inch trout, but I once did see, on the beach near an Indian fish camp, a rainbow tail that measured eleven inches across. Tex and I have spent a good deal of time arguing about the probable length and weight of that trout, and our estimates always scare us. It simply isn't possible that a rainbow could be so large.

Doc had never fished the Iliamna country, and the yarns he kept hearing about the place fired his angler's soul. He said they interfered with his business and prevented him from getting the proper amount of sleep. So at last he turned his practice over to a sympathetic rival, prescribed a week of Iliamna fishing for himself, tracked down Tex and me, and informed us we had twenty-four hours to prepare for what he termed Operation Rainbow. We knew from experience that a stand-by airplane is a wonderful aid in fishing the Iliamna area, so we went immediately to our friend Keith Capper. Keith owns an athletic club and sportsman's headquarters at Anchorage, has a pilot's license and a float-equipped airplane, and is a sucker for such propositions as we dropped into his lap.

"I will be ready," Keith said, "as soon as I count the cash in the safe, feed my dog, have a brief argument with the cook, and find my boots."

We chose Tularik for our first evening's fishing because it is ideal for fly-casting and is one of the most beautiful stretches of water in Alaska. In the June dusk the glassy pools were ringed and dimpled by feeding fish as far as we could see. A slow wind moaned through the grass and the dark spruces, and all about us the huge snow-crowned peaks loomed, bright with the last of the day's sunlight. The creek chuckled and purled musically over its rocky bed. *Tularik* is the Tena word for rainbow, and it is a most appropriate name for this lovely creek. Anglers who have fished from the Maori Pool to Oregon's Rogue River and northward to Alaska's trout waters will tell you that for its size Tularik probably is unequaled anywhere as a rainbow stream. I don't, myself, see how it could be improved.

"I think I am now ready for the second round," Doc said. "I just hope that big rainbow is."

I was trying to interest a fish that had been rising below a cutbank. I had seen him twice and he was a fish to write home about, but thus far he had ignored the royal coachman I was offering him. I waded deeper into the stream and tried again. This time I caught another glimpse of him. He edged out into the current and let the fly drift within six inches of his head. The only encouraging thing was that he didn't go away; he stayed right where he was, finning easily, about a foot below the surface. I decided to try the coachman once more, then change to a brighter fly. I dropped the coachman ten feet above the cutbank and let the current have it. At the instant the fly settled softly to the water, Doc let out one of the ear-shattering yells he employs to announce the fact that he has hooked a fish. I didn't look around. I was watching Grampa, and it was a good thing, because Grampa had made up his mind. He didn't even wait for the fly to float down to him. He met it halfway and socked it, whereupon I socked him. The result was as lively a bit of action as I ever took part in on a trout stream.

Grampa surged out to midstream, jumping toward me as fast as he could throw himself out of the water. At the same time Doc's fish came tearing down with the current. Not only did the two lines cross, but Doc's line caught me under the chin. I batted the line down to prevent it from sawing through my windpipe, and in some diabolical fashion it got caught under the sheath of my belt knife. Doc, appalled by this, came charging down toward me, slipping and stumbling over the moss-grown rocks. He looked so worried that I made the supreme sacrifice. I tried to hold Grampa with one hand while I reached down with the other and fumbled the line from under the knife sheath. While I was doing this, Grampa got some slack from me. I tried to check him, but as I did so, he suddenly bulled against the tackle. There was the rubbery snap of the leader parting, and Grampa went away from there with my coachman in his face.

Doc's fish had gone out of the pool and down a riffle and now was jumping in the next pool below. It was so far away it looked to be only the size of an average rainbow. Doc floundered after it like an amphibious tank, reeling in desperately and yelling for assistance.

"Get down here and help me, somebody," he bawled. "This is the biggest trout I ever hooked in my life, and I got no gaff, no landing net, no nothing. You know I'd help you guys in a case like this."

Keith had come up from the plane, and now he joined us on the bank of the lower pool, where we watched Doc fight down his Tularik rainbow. When the fish was ready, Keith waded in behind it. Keith has had much experience with large trout, as his chief hobby is discovering wilderness lakes from the air and making a thorough survey of their fishing possibilities. He carefully slipped a hand under Doc's fish, and, when it was quiet, heaved it out on the shingle, brown-bear fashion. Doc fell on the fish, clutched it to his bosom, and ran back into the grass with it. It was a twenty-nine-incher, weighing ten and a half pounds. Its coloring was brilliant, the deep rose stripe running from head to tail, the black spots showing clear and bold against its green back and silvery sides. The fish was winter-lean, as many Iliamna trout are during the spring months. If it had been plump it probably would have weighed close to twelve pounds. Doc carried it down to the water, held it upright until it had taken in some oxygen, then pushed it out into the current. It swam slowly into the dusky water, flirted its tail once, and disappeared.

"I'm glad you feel the same way I do about putting the little ones back," Keith told Doc, deadpan. "It'd be a shame to kill one of them. They haven't lived long enough to know what it's all about."

Doc opened his mouth to reply to this, but thought better of it and remained silent. I appreciated his feelings. After your first half hour of fishing in Tularik, you are ready to believe just about anything you are told about the rainbows there. You are so dazzled by yarns of forty-inchers and giants with eleven-inch tails that what you normally would consider an impossibly tall tale suddenly seems quite plausible. So Doc didn't say a word when Keith told him his twenty-nine-incher was practically a fingerling. He just grinned in a dazed fashion, put on a new leader, and began casting for bigger fish.

The rainbows are the glamour fish of this watershed, but there are other species present. There are lake trout, grayling, northern pike, Dolly Varden, and, in season, the five species of Pacific salmon. The lake-trout fishing alone would be worth a trip to Iliamna. You don't take them here as they usually are taken in the States. You fish for them in the cold, shallow, sparkling water of streams flowing out of the lakes, using spinners or large wet flies. Thus the fish aren't stupefied by change of pressure, as they are when you bring them up from a deep lake bottom. They hit like demons on artificials, and will outjump any fish we have except the rainbows and the silver salmon. I have fished here with anglers from the States who at first wouldn't believe that the leaping, rampaging fish they had on were lake trout. I especially like these big lakers because they are more vividly colored than the deep-water specimens I have seen. They have bright sides, red fins, and a jade-green mottling on their backs. Sometimes they have orange bellies and a golden edging on their red fins. They are something to look at, all right. No record has been kept of their size, but I believe, judging from the fish I have seen, that when experienced lake-trout fishermen start working these waters, they probably will take some that will go fifty pounds or more.

The northern pike are plentiful, but they have few if any fans in this region. In lakes where the species is dominant the pike prey on young ducks, muskrats, kit beaver and any fish they can capture. I have seen so many of them swarming at a favorite feeding ground that acres of the surface churned like a tide rip. You could hook one at every cast, and when you brought it in, a shoal of other pike would follow it. I don't know what their maximum size is either, but I will tell you something: a pike was caught a few years ago in Tutna Lake, a short flight northwest from Iliamna, that was at least five feet long. The six-foot trapper who caught this pike had his photograph taken with the great fish over his shoulder, and its tail reached the ground. The photograph is in the files of the Fish and Wildlife Service at Anchorage. Others who have seen it were convinced, as I am, that Tutna Lake would be no place to go swimming. I would just as soon take a chance with crocodiles.

Then, of course, there is the Dolly Varden, the frightfully abused Cinderella fish of the north. It has been stated often before, but it can't be repeated too often, that the dolly is nothing more or less than the Western form of the Eastern brook trout. The only difference ichthyologists and sportsmen have found between the two fish is that the dolly grows much larger—up to twenty-five pounds—jumps oftener when hooked, and has a fork to its tail. These differences hardly would seem to justify a government-sponsored campaign to exterminate the species, yet such a campaign, paid for with taxpayers' money, was waged in Alaska for eleven years. This began in 1929 when the Bureau of Fisheries, at the insistence of cannery owners, placed a bounty of two and a half cents per tail on the dolly. As a result, *in one year,* in the Bristol Bay district alone, twenty thousand dollars was paid out for trout tails.

This part of the matter is history; the bounty no longer is being paid. But the whole thing needs bringing up again because the Dolly Varden is not yet out of trouble. The wording of the Alaska fish-and-game regulations at first glance seems to show that the dolly has adequate protection, but more careful reading reveals the fact that the fish still is virtually outlawed.

The avowed reason for the attempt to wipe out the dolly was that it eats salmon eggs (as all Pacific trout do in some degree), but the real reason was that bounty-seining for the fish provided remunerative off-season employment for resident commercial salmon fishermen. So many fish were killed that for years dried trout tails were used as currency all along the western Alaska coast. It was well known that you could collect on any kind of sport-fish tail. Village postmasters, trading-post proprietors, and local petty officials entrusted with the job of accepting the tails weren't at all particular what kind of tails you turned in. They took the tails of rainbows, grayling, and steelhead as readily as dolly tails. Time and again I watched the bounty fishermen seine the Iliamna creek mouths. I watched them pull the nets and chop the tails from thousands of living trout, and wondered how it was that a nation of sportsmen would tolerate such a crime.

Well, they didn't tolerate it after they found out what was going on. They turned on a lot of heat then, and some of our legislators and bureaucrats became very busy denying they'd ever had anything to do with the sorry business.

But, as I said, the dolly still needs help. In the fish-and-game regulations it is stated in bold black type that the dolly now is classed as a game fish. It states this right in the same paragraph that gives the seasons and limits on the rainbow, the grayling, and the cutthroat. A little above this, however, and a little farther down, in less striking type, you find it stated that dollies may be taken in any number by the use of trap, net, or seine in salt water and in any of the lakes and streams west of Cook Inlet, except only the Snake and Nome rivers on the Seward Peninsula, and sold or shipped from the territory for any use whatsoever. I don't know why the region west of Cook Inlet was singled out, because it is further stated in the law that dollies may also be taken east of Cook Inlet by any of the abovementioned means in the glacial waters of Trail, Kenai, Skilak, and Tustymena lakes—in short, in the principal fishing waters of the Kenai Peninsula.

All that has been changed is that the government no longer is paying the boys to destroy game fish. They can go ahead on their own if they want to, but Uncle Sam won't foot the bill. As before, the law threatens all sport fish, because no way has ever been found to operate a trap, net, or seine in these waters so that only one species of fish will get in. Every kind of game fish present is going to get caught, and die or be injured by the meshes, or hauled away to share the ultimate destiny of the luckless dolly. When you ask the fish protectors about this, they shake their heads sadly and say it is too bad, but that, after all, some one else makes the laws. And if you ask the lawmakers about it, they change the subject. They aren't as hard-boiled as the cannery people. The cannery people I've talked with about it asked me why the hell I didn't mind my own business.

Doc reluctantly reeled in when it was time to go down to camp for supper. "Any time now," he said, "I'm going to wake up and find out this is just a fisherman's dream. In technicolor and with sound effects."

In one hour and twenty minutes the four of us had beached twelve rainbows, few smaller than Doc's twenty-nine-incher. All were taken with wet flies, the royal coachman and the parma belle drawing the most strikes. We killed one beautifully colored giant and turned him over to Keith, whom we had selected, as a restaurateur, as the logical one to take charge of our mess. Keith filleted and boned the fish and broiled it over wood coals, then served it with a sauce made of butter, lemon juice and herbs. The result was fish as it seldom is served in camp. It was pleasant to behold, fascinating to smell, and doggoned good to eat. We finished the nine-pound trout so handily that we wished we had saved two of them.

From Tularik we flew next morning to the outlet of Lake Clark. This lake lies twenty miles north of Iliamna, to which it is joined by the Newhalen River. Clark is sixty miles long and averages seven miles wide, and it is full of fish. Our purpose in going there was to introduce Doc to our gem-bright shallow-water lake trout. There were plenty of them in the outlet. You could see them lying in the clear water like salmon, and some of them were tremendous. We tried them first with flies, but failed to get any good strikes. They would come up behind your fly and look at it, then go back to the bottom. I decided that what they wanted was a spinner, fished deep. So Doc bent on a copper 1/0 Colorado with a bucktail streamer, and cast this out and let it sink before he began bringing it in. When he had stripped in about a third of the line, he got action. I was watching the fish nearest his lure, when all at once it vanished. It just wasn't there any more. The next time I saw the fish it was shooting to the surface with Doc's spinner in its mouth.

Now, these big shallow-water lakers are the only fish we have except the Arctic grayling that, when hooked, will come out and turn a half somersault in the air and re-enter the water head first. This one did it twice in two seconds. When he made his third jump he outdid himself. He executed three quarters of a turn and came down on his side with a splash that threw water clear out on the bank. Then he headed downstream, banging out into the heaviest current. Doc was using thirty yards of fly line and seventy-five yards of nylon backing on a single-action reel, and was down to a few turns of nylon when he succeeded in turning the fish. The big fellow immediately made a run upstream, passing Doc and ripping off another forty yards of line. It made two more jumps, shaking its head savagely and thrashing on the surface, before Doc was able to lead it in to the beach.

Doc wanted to weigh the fish, but it wouldn't stay quiet when he lifted it out, and he didn't want to kill it. So Tex and I showed him a trick that will work with any of our northern fish except salmon. When you tell people about this trick, they think you are kidding them, but once they have tried it themselves they make a habit of going around telling their fishing pals about it. We waited until the laker was motionless in the water, then slipped the hook of the spring scales under his gill covers at the V of the maxillary and very carefully lifted him out. It was a fifteen pounder, and it didn't move a fin. The trick is to lift your fish straight up, taking care not to swing it or let it touch anything. If it so much as brushes against a spear of grass it will at once begin struggling. I nearly always take rainbows and cutthroats out this way, provided their weight isn't greater than the test of my leader. They behave exactly as if they are hypnotized. Not even a tremor runs through them until they touch the ground. Then they throw themselves about wildly, as if angry with themselves for having been so easily beached. Don't ask me why you can do this with trout. I only know that it works.

After agreeing that they would meet us a quarter of a mile downstream, Tex and Keith prepared to move on down the Newhalen. Before they left, however, Tex announced that he had a theory about the lake trout here.

"The big'uns ain't hittin'," he said, "an hit's because they ain't interested in spinners, flies, an' sech. If we slung some bait out to 'em, betcha we'd catch some gollywhoppers." For the past hour Tex had been pretending to grumble about the artificial lures Doc had missionaried him into using. Tex insists he is a practical frontier angler, and the devil with store-boughten tackle.

"I wouldn't put it past you to use bait," Doc snorted. "But I wanta remind you that we agreed to stick to artificials, to find out what can be done with them here. No worms, salmon eggs, bacon rinds, or porcupine livers."

"All right," Tex said with an exaggerated sigh of regret, "but I shore have caught some fine fish on porky livers—usin' a birch pole and a chalk line, o' course."

An hour later, working down through some cottonwoods, Doc and I found Tex and Keith beside a campfire on a bar point. They had the lunch gear laid out and were frying lake-trout steaks. The fish from which they were slicing the steaks was a big one. It would have weighed right around thirty pounds, a third heavier than the best fish Doc had beached. Doc stood looking at it, appreciatively sniffing the aroma of the browning steaks. Suddenly he started as if he had been stabbed with a needle. Following the direction of his gaze, I saw a pint jar of salmon eggs on a rock beside Tex's fishing tackle.

"So that's how you got that big one!" he said accusingly. "Salmon eggs, huh?"

"Shucks, them ain't bait eggs," Tex protested. "Keith and I brung 'em along to eat." As if to prove this, he picked up the jar and a spoon, scooped out a generous helping, and ate it, smacking his lips with apparent relish.

Doc smiled wickedly. "Brought 'em along to eat, did you? That's the damnedest alibi I ever heard in my life. A half-wit could have thought of a better one. Well, let's see you eat some more. Go ahead."

It was a gag. Tex finished the jar of eggs, then showed Doc the label —golden caviar. The method of making caviar with salmon eggs was discovered by the Russian fishermen in Alaska, who, hungry for their national appetizer but finding no sturgeon in these waters, did the best they could with salmon eggs. They did all right. Connoisseurs tell you that salmon caviar is the equal of all but the very best imported sturgeon caviar. To prepare it, you make a strong brine, add one teaspoonful of sodium salicylate to the gallon, bring the brine to a boil, and pour it over the skein eggs. The hot brine turns the eggs white and hardens them, so that they can easily be removed from the membrane enclosing them. Leave the eggs in the brine about three minutes, then place them in a hot jar and seal them. After a day or two they will soften and regain their original color. If stored in a cool place they will keep indefinitely.

Tex got out another jar, and when Doc had eaten some of the caviar mixed with chopped onion and spread on bread, he declared that when he got home his long-suffering wife was going to have to put up about five gallons of it. "But before I apologize to you," he said, pointing a spoon at Tex, "I want to know one thing. Did you or did you not use some of this stuff for bait when you caught that lake trout?"

"Shore I did," Tex said, looking at me and lowering an eyelid. "Ever since I was a little boy I allus wanted to ketch a fish with caviar, an' now, by gosh, I've done hit. Betcha I'm the only feller in the world that has, too."

We flew to Tanalion Point, on the east side of Clark, and fished for grayling. These handsome fish, all purplish and green, with lavender spots, average about fourteen inches here, and hit so eagerly that if you dangle your fly a few inches above the water they will leap out for it. They wanted brown, black or gray flies, fished dry, and when they took one and the hook was set, they fought on the surface, cutting big circles and figure eights, but not jumping so often as the rainbows and lake trout. I have taken them in the tributaries of the Kobuk River, in the Arctic, that were around twenty-three inches long and weighed up to four pounds. They don't reach that size here, but they are plentiful, and are a delight to dry-fly fishermen. Because of their tall blue-green dorsal fin the Indians call them *staydenna,* or wing-finned, and it is a grand name for them.

"Now that we've taken the glamour fish," Keith said, "let's go back to the mouth of the Newhalen and pay our respects to that persecuted but very swell citizen the Dolly Varden."

At a fish camp near the river mouth we met a Russian-Tena breed named Paul Kashevnikoff, who had an outboard-powered dory and who agreed to take us up into the river to a hole where there were large dollies. Doc took three small fish and then hooked into a big one. He had cast out into the pool a No. 2 copper Colorado with a polar-bear streamer attached and was twitching it in when the big dolly came up from the bottom after it, its mouth open like the top of a white china water pitcher. It inhaled the spinner and about three inches of the leader, snapped its mouth shut, and turned leisurely downstream. Doc belted him as hard as he dared, but it didn't feaze the big trout. It swam on several feet before it gave any indication that it realized it was hooked. It then slanted down into the green water, opening and shutting its mouth and shaking its head. Then, abruptly, it was gone. A half second later it shot up almost in our faces, its heavy length bent in an arc the way a big bass bends sometimes when it is trying to throw a plug. Doc fought it for twenty minutes before he managed to bring it alongside. I hoisted it aboard and killed it because I wanted to prove to Doc that a large dolly is a better table fish than a large rainbow.

This dolly weighed thirteen pounds and was thirty-two inches long. When I dressed the fish it proved to be one of the rare red-fleshed dollies. Most of the species have pink flesh, and a few have flesh as white as a halibut's, but occasionally you take one with bright-red flesh like this one. Paul said it was a big dolly, all right, but that we ought to see some of those that got caught with his salmon nets. He said he thought some of them would weigh around twenty-five pounds. Maybe thirty pounds. Doc was satisfied with his thirteen-pounder. It was gaudily colored, stippled with red spots, its fins edged with white, its back light green, and its belly washed with golden orange.

"If you released that fish in one of the streams back East," Keith said, "and an angler caught it, he would go around the rest of his life describing how he took the monarch of brook trout. But too many of the characters up here kill 'em and throw 'em into the brush for the bears and sea gulls—just because commercial fishermen gave the fish a publicity smear. It's a hell of a note."

I would have liked to take Doc over to Kalgin Island, in Cook Inlet, for sea-run dollies. There is a creek mouth at the southern tip of Kalgin where these fish gather in fantastic numbers in the spring and summer months. They run in schools like salmon and will hit anything. I discovered this amazing place one July evening when Tex and I landed there in a dory and I waded out into the water to dress a salmon we had taken trolling. It was a female salmon, and when I split it open and tossed the skeins of roe into the water, I felt something bumping against my boots. The water was alive with dollies competing for the eggs. Next morning we took a number of them with flies—one of the few times I ever successfully fished with flies in salt water. They were very bright, a metallic sheen almost blanking out their characteristic red spots, and in this icy water they were as firm as any fish I had ever taken. I would have enjoyed seeing Doc get in among some of these fish, but Keith didn't want to risk a landing in the Kalgin rips, so we had to scratch that fishing spot.

There were plenty of other places to go. Within a couple of hours we could reach the Naknek lakes, the Wood River lakes, Kukaklek Lake, Becharof Lake, or the spread of fish-filled lakes on the Mulchatna watershed. We got out the map and held a conference, and decided that since we had taken rainbows, lake trout, grayling, and dollies, we ought to go where we could take some steelhead. The best steelhead streams are the Karluk and the Buskin on Kodiak Island, but Doc said he wanted to stay on Bristol Bay drainage, so we agreed that Naknek was our best bet. There is an early run of steelhead in the Naknek River, and we thought that if we were lucky we might catch the first of the upstream migration.

Naknek is a rough, hustling cannery town in which oilskins and sea boots are formal attire, everything smells like fish, and nobody seems to talk about anything but fish. Tex met an old acquaintance, a Scandinavian giant named Bjorklund, who informed us there were steelheads in the bay, but that he didn't know whether or not they had entered the river. Nobody here, he said, bothered to fish with hook and line. When you were making one hundred dollars a day netting salmon, he said, why would you fool around trying to take fish one at a time on a hook? Tex didn't reply. Sometimes Tex seems afraid he will be mistaken for a dude. Usually at such times he just drifts away and forgathers with the local folk until he has the situation properly explained. He insists on maintaining his status as a professional. He doesn't want anybody to mistake him for a pilgrim.

Doc, Keith, and I set up our gear and went down to the river. I presently hung into a dog salmon, landed it after a fifteen minute struggle, cast again and hooked another dog salmon, and chased it down the stream two hundred yards before I could salvage my tackle. Doc was some distance above us, casting into an eddy below a point. As I was wondering where I could fish without hooking another dog, he let out a war whoop that must have startled villagers for hundreds of yards around. Keith and I reeled in and went up to him. His fish was jumping. It was a steelhead.

"Lookit that sweetheart go!" he yelled delightedly.

Well, there were some steelheads in. Before long Keith and I were each fast to one. It was a wonderful place. Even Bjorklund, the blasé commercial fisherman, got excited when the big silvery fish began jumping high, wide, and handsome.

"You wanta take my rod an' try hit?" Tex asked him. "All you gotta do is throw the fly out there an' then be keerful, when one hits, not to bust nothin'. We use them little spiderweb leaders on account o' hit ain't sportin', they tell me, to use heavy ones. The idee is to ketch 'em the hard way—the harder the better. Anybody, they tell me, could do hit the easy way."

"Damn right I wanta try it," Bjorklund boomed. "Gimme that rod and gimme room."

We took our steelheads, and next morning, we started home. Everywhere we looked under the plane's wings there were lakes and streams, and as you watched them slide past, you wanted to land and try them out. This is some of the greatest fish country we have left. It is vacation country. It is country every fresh-water angler should visit.

BARKER'S DELIGHT

OR,

THE ART OF

ANGLING

*Wherein are discovered many rare
secrets very necessary to be
known by all that delight in that
Recreation, both for catching
the Fish, and dressing thereof.*

The Second EDITION *much enlarged.*

By THOMAS BARKER, *an ancient
practitioner in the said Art.*

ECCLES. 3.1.11.
*There is a time and season to every purpose under
heaven: Every thing is beautifull in his time.*

LONDON,

Printed by F. G. *for* Richard Marriot, *and
are to be sold at his shop in S.* Dunstans
Church-yard Fleetstreet. 1657.

*Thomas Barker, unlike Messrs. Walton and Cotton,
did not believe in beating about the bush when he
discussed angling methods and practices, and many
find this rather refreshing. As one of our early
angling writers, he made a heavy mark on the sport.*

On the choyce Treatise called
Barker's Delight.

*Come come, ye bunglers, learn the skill
The greedy nimble trout to kill.
For twelve pence (now) thou maist learn more
Than in an age was known before;
All baits to know, tackle to fit,
Brave* Barker *I commend thy wit.
What, catch the Prey, and cook the Fish?
And more than this, Sir, can you wish?*
Radulphus Hoptonus
Gen. Wigorniens.

In Barkeri librum de arte piscandi
Encomium.

*Barkeri in laudem, lector, latrare nolito,
  Nam mordere queat dentibus absq, suis.
Vincere si pisces cupias, documenta memento
  Aurea, scripta libro commoditate tuâ.*

Bark not at Barker, *lest he bite;
  But if in angling thou delight,
To kill the Trout, and cook the Fish,
  Follow his rules and have thy wish.*
Per Morganum Hoptonum
Armig.

The Art of Angling.

Noble Lord,

Under favour I will complement and put a case to your Honour.
I met with a man, and upon our discourse he fell out with me, having
a good weapon, but neither stomach nor skil; I say this man may
come home by Weeping cross, I will cause the Clerk to toll his knell.

It is the very like case to the gentleman Angler that goeth to the River for his pleasure: this Angler hath neither judgement nor experience, he may come home light laden at his leisure.

A man that goeth to the River for his pleasure, must understand when he cometh there to set forth his tackle: The first thing he must do, is to observe the Sun and the Wind for day, the Moon, the Stars, and the wanes of the Aire for night, to set forth his tackles for day or night, and accordingly to go for his pleasure and some profit.

For example. The Sun proves cloudy, then must you set forth either your ground-bait tackles, or of the brighest of your flyes. If the Sun prove bright and clear, then must you put on the darkest of your flyes; thus must you to work with your flyes, light for darkness, and dark for lightness, with the wind in the South, which blowes the fly in the Trouts mouth. Though I set down the wind in the South, I am indifferent where the wind standeth, either with ground-bait or menow, so that I can cast my bait into the River. The very same observation is for night as for day; for, if the Moon prove clear, or the Stars glitter in the sky, it is as ill angling that night as if it were at high noon in the midst of the summer, when the Sun shineth at the brightest, wherein there is no hopes of pleasure.

I will begin to angle for the Trout, and discourse his qualitie.

The first thing you must gain must be a neat taper rod light before, with a tender hasel top which is very gentle, with a single hair of five lengths long, one tyed to another, for the bottom of my line, and a line of three haired links for the uppermost part, and so you may kill the greatest Trout that swims, with sea room.

Now I say he that angles with a line made of three haired links for the bottom, and more at the top, may kill fish, but he that angles with a line made of one haired link, shall kill five to the others one; for, the Trout is very quick-sighted, therefore the best way either for night or day is to keep out of sight.

You must angle always with the point of the rod down the stream, for trouts have not quickness of sight so perfect up the stream as they have opposite against them.

But observe the seasonable times. For example, we begin to angle in *March:* if it prove cloudy, you may angle with the ground baits all day long: but if it prove bright and clear, you must take evening and morning, or else you are not like to do good: so times must be observed and truly understood; for when an angler cometh to the River for his pleasure, and doth not understand to set forth his tackles fit for the time, it is as good keep them in the bag as to set them forth.

Now I am determined to angle with the ground baits, and set my tackles to my rod, and go to my pleasure. I begin at the uppermost part of the stream, carrying my line with an upright hand, feeling my plummet running truly on the ground some ten inches from the hook, plumming my line according to the swiftness of the stream I angle in, for one plummet will not serve for all streams; for the true angling is that the plummet run truly on the ground.

For the bait, the red knotted worm is very good, where Brandlins are not to be had; but Brandlins are better.

Now I will shew you how to make these Brandlins fit to angle with, and to make them lusty and fat, that they may live long on the hook, which causeth the best sport; for that is a chief point, and causeth the best sport.

You must take the yolk of an egg, and some eight or ten spoonfulls of the top of new milk, beaten well together in a porringer, warm it a little untill you see it curdle, then take it off the fire and set it to cool; when it is cold, take a spoonfull and drop it on the moss in an earthen pot, every drop about the bigness of a green pease, shifting your moss twice in the summer, and once a week in the winter. Thus doing, you shall feed your worms and make them fat and lusty, that they will live long and be lusty and lively on your hook. And thus you may keep them all the year long. This is my true experiment for the ground baits, with the running line for the trout.

My Lord, I will now shew the angling with a Menow (called in some places Pincks) for the Trout, which is a pleasant sport, and killeth the greatest fish: The Trout cometh boldly at the bait, as if it were a Mastiffe dog at a Beare; you may angle with greater Tackles and stronger, and be no prejudice in your Angling. A line made of three silks and three hairs twisted for the uppermost part of your line, and a line made of two silks and two hairs twisted for the bottome next your hook, with a swivel nigh the middle of your line, and an indifferent long hook. But if you can attain to angle with a line of foure haired links for the uppermost part, and a line of three haired links for the bottom, for the finer you angle with, it is the better.

Now I must shew you how to bait the menow on your hook: You must put your hook through the lowermost part of the menow's mouth, so draw your hook through; then put the hook in at the mouth again, let the point of the hook come out at the hindmost fin; then draw your line and the menow's mouth will close, that no water get into its belly; you must be alwayes angling with the point of your rod down the stream, drawing your menow up the side of the stream by little & little, nigh the top of the water; the trout seeing the bait, cometh at it most fiercely; give a little time before you strike. This is the true way without lead, for many times I have had them come at the lead and forsake the menow. He that trieth shall prove it in time.

My Lord, I will shew you the way to angle with a flye, which is a delightfull sport.

The rod must be light and tender, if you can fit your self with a hasel of one piece, or of two pieces set together in the most convenient manner, light and gentle. Set your line to your rod, for the uppermost part you may use your own discretion, for the lowermost part next your flye it must be of three or four haired links. If you can attain to angle with a line made of one hair, two or three links one tyed to another next your hook, you shall have more rises and kill more fish. Be sure you do not overload your self with lengths of your line. Before you begin to angle make a triall, having the wind on your back, to see at what length you can cast your flye, that the flye light first into the water, and no longer, for if any of the line fall into the water before the flye, it is better uncast than thrown. Be sure you be casting alwayes down the stream with the wind behind you, and the Sun before you. It is a speciall point to have the Sun and Moon before you, for the very motion of the rod drives all the pleasure from you, either by day or by night in all your anglings, both with worms and flyes, there must be a great care of that.

Let us begin to angle in March with the flye. If the weather prove windy or cloudy, there are severall kinds of Palmers that are good for that time.

First, a black Palmer, ribbed with silver. Secondly, a black Palmer ribbed with an orenge-tawny body. Thirdly, a black Palmer made all of black. Fourthly, a red Palmer ribbed with gold. Fifthly, a red Palmer mixed with an orenge-tawny body of cruell. All these flyes must be made with hackles, and they will serve all the year long morning and evening, windy or cloudy. Without these flyes you cannot make a dayes angling good. I have heard say that there is for every moneth in the year a flye for that moneth; but that is but talk, for there is but one monethly flye in the yeare, that is the May-flye. Then if the aire prove clear you must imitate the Hawthorn flye, which is all black and very small, the smaller the better. In May take the May flye, imitate that. Some make it with a shammy body, and ribbed with a black hair. Another way it is made with sandy hogs hair ribbed with black silk, and winged with Mallards feathers, according to the fancy of the angler, if he hath judgement. For first, when it comes out of the shell, the flye is somewhat whiter, then afterwards it grows browner, so there is judgement in that. There is another fly called the Oak-flye that is a very good flye, which is made of orenge colour cruell and black, with a brown wing, imitate that. There is another flye made with the strain of a Peacocks feather, imitating the Flesh-flye, which is very good in a bright day. The Grasse-hopper which is green, imitate that. The smaller these flyes be made, and of indifferent small hooks, they are the better. These sorts which I have set down will serve all the year long, observing the times and seasons, if the angler have any judgement. Note the lightest of your flies for cloudy and dark, and the darkest of your flyes for the brightest dayes, and the rest for indifferent times; a mans own judgement with some experience must guide him: If he mean to kill fish he must alter his flyes according to these directions. Now of late I have found that hogs wooll of several colours makes good bodies, & the wooll of a red heifer makes a good body, and beares wooll makes a good body: there are many good furres that make good bodies: and now I work much of hogs wooll, for I finde it floateth best and procureth the best sport.

The naturall flye is sure angling, and will kill great store of trouts with much pleasure. As for the May-flie you shall have him playing alwayes at the rivers side, especially against rain: the Oak-flie is to be had on the but of an oak or an ash, from the beginning of May to the end of August; it is a brownish flie, and standeth alwaies with his head towards the root of the tree, very easie to be found: the small black fly is to be had on every hathorn tree after the buds be come forth: your grasse-hopper which is green is to be had in any medow of grass in June or July. With these flies you must angle with such a rod as you angle with the ground bait: the line must not be so long as the rod, drawing your flye as you finde convenient in your angling: When you come to the deep waters that stand somewhat still, make your line two yards long or thereabouts, and dop or drop your flye behind a bush, which angling I have had good sport at; we call it *dopping*.

My Lord sent to me at Sun going down to provide him a good dish of Trouts against the next morning by six of the clock, I went to the door to see how the wanes of the aire were like to prove. I returned answer, that I doubted not, God willing, but to be provided at his time appointed. I went presently to the river, and it proved very dark, I drew out a line of three silks and three hairs twisted for the uppermost part, and a line of two hairs and two silks twisted for the lower part, with a good large hook: I baited my hook with two lob-worms, the four ends hanging as meet as I could guess them in the dark, I fell to angle. It proved very dark, so that I had good sport angling with the lob-worms as I do with the flye on the top of the water; you shall hear the fish rise at the top of the water, then you must loose a slack line down to the bottom as nigh as you can guess, then hold your line strait, feeling the fish bite, give time, there is no doubt of losing the fish, for there is not one among twenty but doth gorge the bait; the least stroke you can strike fastens the hook and makes the fish sure; letting the fish take a turn or two you may take the fish up with your hands. The night began to alter and grow somewhat lighter, I took off the lob-worms and set to my rod a white Palmer-flye, made of a large hook; I had sport for the time untill it grew lighter; so I took off the white Palmer and set to a red Palmer made of a large hook; I had good sport untill it grew very light: then I took off the red Palmer and set to a black Palmer; I had good sport, made up the dish of fish. So I put up my tackles and was with my Lord at his time appointed for the service.

These three flyes with the help of the lob-worms serve to angle all the year for the night, observing the times as I have shewed you in this night-work, the white flye for darknesse, the red flye in *medio,* and the black flye for lightnesse. This is the true experience for angling in the night, which is the surest angling of all, and killeth the greatest Trouts. Your lines may be strong, but must not be longer then your rod.

> *The rod light and taper, thy tackle fine,*
> *Thy lead ten inches upon the line;*
> *Bigger or lesse, according to the stream,*
> *Angle in the dark, when others dream:*
> *Or in a cloudy day with a lively worm,*
> *The Brandlin is best; but give him a turn*
> *Before thou do land a large wel grown Trout.*
> *And if with a flye thou wilt have a bout,*
> *Overload not with links, that the flye may fall*
> *First on the stream, for that's all in all.*
> *The line shorter than the rod, with a naturall flye:*
> *But the chief point of all is the cookery.*

Now having taken a good dish of Trouts I presented them to my Lord. He having provided good company, commanded me to turn Cook and dress them for dinner. Whereupon I gave my Lord this bill of fare, which did furnish his table as it was furnished with flesh.

Trouts in broth, which is restorative, which must be boyled in milk, putting to it some large mace, letting it boyle up. Before you put the trouts into the Kettle, the trouts must be drawn and clean washed before you put them in. So keep them with high boyling, untill you think them boyled sufficient. Then you must take a slice or two of good sweet butter and put into your dish, so pour on the broth, having provided the yolks of half a dozen eggs, being very well beaten in a dish or porringer, pour it into your broth, so stir it well; I make no doubt but it will be good broth.

The broth eaten, provide for the sauce some butter, the inner part of a lemmon, the yolk of an egge well beaten together, so pour it into the dish, I make no doubt but it will be well liked of. If they doe not like of this broth, when you boyle other trouts for the service, let the trouts be boyled sufficiently in such liquor as I will shew you now following. You may take the quantity of a quart of the top of the liquor with half a pint of Sack, boyle it together, then provide the yolks of half a dozen eggs well beaten together; beat all this together with a slice or two of good sweet butter; no doubt but this will be very good.

Now we must have two dishes of calvored Trouts hot. For the first course the sauce shall be butter and vinegar, 2 or 3 Anchoves, the bones taken out, beaten together with the yolk of one egge for one of the dishes, with a lemmon squeezed on them. For the other dish the sauce and purtenances shall be a quart of Oysters stewed in half a pint of Whitewine, so put on the fish, then butter and vinegar being well beaten, with the yolk of an egge poured on that, squeezing a lemmon on the fish, there is no question but they will be eaten with delight.

Out of this Kettle we must have two dishes to eat cold for the latter course.

Fishing

Reverend Thomas Bastard, 1498

Fishing, if I, a fisher, may protest
Of pleasures is the sweet'st, of sports the best,
Of exercises the most excellent,
Of Recreations the most innocent.
But now the sport is marred, and wot ye why?
Fishes decrease, and fishers multiply.

Daniel Webster
and the Sea Serpent

STEPHEN VINCENT BENÉT

This is not an angling story, but although the sea serpent has not been accurately classified, those who have reported the creature insist that it has gills, which should put it in the fish family. No angler, regardless of his single dedication to the sport, can afford to miss this great tale by Stephen Vincent Benét.

IT HAPPENED, one summer's day, that Dan'l Webster and some of his friends were out fishing. That was in the high days of his power and his fame, when the question wasn't if he was going to be President but when he was going to be President, and everybody at Kingston depot stood up when Dan'l Webster arrived to take the cars.

But in spite of being Secretary of State and the biggest man in New England, he was just the same Dan'l Webster. He bought his Jamaica personal and in the jug at Colonel Sever's store in Kingston, right under a sign saying ENGLISH AND WEST INDIA GOODS, and he never was too busy to do a hand's turn for a friend. And, as for his big farm at Marshfield, that was just the apple of his eye. He buried his favorite horses with their shoes on, standing up, in a private graveyard, and wrote Latin epitaphs for them, and he often was heard to say that his big Hungarian bull, Saint Stephen, had more sense in his rear off hoof than most politicians. But, if there was one thing he loved better than Marshfield itself, it was the sea and the waters around it, for he was a fisherman born.

This time, he was salt-water fishing in the *Comet,* well out of sight of land. It was a good day for fishing, not too hazy, but not too clear, and Dan'l Webster enjoyed it, as he enjoyed everything in life, except maybe listening to the speeches of Henry Clay. He'd stolen a half-dozen days to come up to Marshfield, and well he needed the rest, for we'd nearly gone to war with England the year before, and now he was trying to fix up a real copper-riveted treaty that would iron out all the old differences that still kept the two countries unfriendly. And that was a job, even for Dan'l Webster. But as soon as he stepped aboard the *Comet,* he was carefree and heartwhole. He had his real friends around him and he wouldn't allow a word of politics talked on the boat—though that rule got broken this time, and for a good reason, as you'll see. And when he struck his first cod, and felt the fish take the hook, a kind of big slow smile went over his features, and he said, "Gentlemen, this is solid comfort." That was the kind of man he was.

I don't know how many there were of them aboard—half a dozen or so—just enough for good company. We'll say there were George Blake and Rufus Choate and young Peter Harvey and a boy named Jim Billings. And, of course, there was Seth Peterson, Dan'l's boat captain, in his red flannel shirt, New England as cod and beach plums, and Dan'l Webster's fast friend. Dan'l happened to be Secretary of State, and Seth Peterson happened to be a boat captain, but that didn't make any difference between them. And, once the *Comet* left dock, Seth Peterson ran the show, as it's right that a captain should.

Well, they'd fished all morning and knocked off for a bite of lunch, and some had had segars and snoozes afterward, and some hadn't, but in any case, it was around midafternoon, and everybody was kind of comfortable and contented. They still fished, and they fished well, but they knew in an hour or so they'd be heading back for home with a fine catch on board. So maybe there was more conversation than Seth Peterson would have approved of earlier, and maybe some jokes were passed and some stories told. I don't know, but you know how it is when men get together at the end of a good day. All the same, they were still paying attention to their business—and I guess it was George Blake that noticed it first.

"Dan'l," he said, breathing hard, "I've got something on my line that pulls like a Morgan horse."

"Well, yank him in!" sang out Dan'l, and then his face changed as his own line began to stiffen and twang. "George," he said, "I beat you! I got something on my line that pulls like a pair of steers!"

"Give 'em more line, Mr. Webster!" yells Seth Peterson, and Dan'l did. But at that, the line ran out so fast it smoked when it hit the water, and any hands but Dan'l Webster's would have been cut to the bone. Nor you couldn't see where it went to, except Something deep in the waters must be pulling it out as a cat pulls yarn from a ball. The veins in Dan'l Webster's arm stood out like cords. He played the fish and played the fish; he fought it with every trick he knew. And still the little waves danced and the other men gaped at the fight—and still he couldn't bring the Something to time.

"By the big elm at Marshfield!" he said at last, with his dark face glowing and a fisherman's pride in his eyes. "Have I hooked onto a frigate with all sails set? I've payed out a mile of my own particular line, and she still pulls like ten wild horses. Gentlemen, what's this?"

And even as he said it, the tough line broke in two with a crack like a musket shot, and out of the deep of ocean, a mile away, the creature rose, majestic. Neighbors, that was a sight! Shaking the hook from its jaw, it rose, the sea serpent of the Scriptures, exact and to specifications as laid down in the Good Book, with its hairy face and its furlong on furlong of body, wallowing and thrashing in the troubled sea. As it rose, it gave a long low melancholy hoot, like a kind of forsaken steamboat; and when it gave out that hoot, young Jim Billings, the boy, fainted dead away on the deck. But nobody even noticed him —they were all staring at the sea serpent with bulging eyes.

Even Dan'l Webster was shaken. He passed his hand for a moment across his brow and gave a sort of inquiring look at the jug of Jamaica by the hatch.

"Gentlemen," he said in a low voice, "the evidence—the ocular evidence would seem to be conclusive. And yet, speaking as a lawyer—"

"Thar she blows! I never thought to see her again!" yells Seth Peterson, half driven out of his mind by the sight, as the sea serpent roiled the waters. "Thar she blows, by the Book of Genesis! Oh, why ain't I got a harpoon?"

"Quiet, Seth," said Dan'l Webster. "Let us rather give thanks for being permitted to witness this glorious and unbelievable sight." And then you could see the real majesty of the man, for no sooner were the words out of his mouth than the sea serpent started swimming straight toward the *Comet*. She came like a railway train and her wake boiled out behind her for an acre. And yet, there was something kind of skittish about her, too—you might say that she came kind of shaking her skirts and bridling. I don't know what there was about her that made you sure she was a female, but they were all sure.

She came, direct as a bullet, till you could count the white teeth shining in her jaws. I don't know what the rest of them did—though doubtless some prayers were put up in a hasty way—but Dan'l Webster stood there and faced her, with his brow dark and his eyes like a sleepy lion's, giving her glance for glance. Yes, there was a minute, there, when she lifted her head high out of water and they looked at each other eye to eye. They say hers were reddish but handsome. And then, just as it seemed she'd crash plump through the *Comet*, she made a wide wheel and turned. Three times she circled the boat, hooting lonesomely, while the *Comet* danced up and down like a cork on the waves. But Dan'l Webster kept his footing, one hand grasping the mast, and whenever he got a chance, he fixed her with his eye. Till finally, on the third circuit, she gave one last long hoot—like twenty foghorns at once, it was, and nearly deafened them all—and plunged back whence she'd come, to the bottomless depths of the sea.

But even after the waters were calm again, they didn't say anything for quite a while. Till, finally, Seth Peterson spoke.

"Well, Mr. Webster," he said, "that one got away"—and he grinned a dry grin.

"Leviathan of the Scriptures! Give me paper and pen," said Dan'l Webster. "We must write this down and attest it." And then they all began to talk.

Well, he wrote an account of just what they'd seen, very plain and honest. And everybody there signed his name to it. Then he read it over to them again aloud. And then there was another silence, while they looked at one another.

Finally, Seth Peterson shook his head, slow and thoughtful.

"It won't do, Dan'l," he said, in a deep voice.

"Won't do?" said Dan'l Webster, with his eyes blazing. "What do you mean, Seth?"

"I mean it just won't do, Dan'l," said Seth Peterson, perfectly respectful, but perfectly firm. "I put it up to you, gentlemen," he said, turning to the others. "I can go home and say I've seen the sea serpent. And everybody'll say, 'Oh, that's just that old liar, Seth Peterson.' But if it's Dan'l Webster says so—can't you see the difference?"

He paused for a minute, but nobody said a word.

"Well, I can," he said. He drawled out the words very slow. "Dan'l

Webster—Secretary of State—sees and talks to a sea serpent—off Plymouth Bay. Why, it would plumb ruin him! And I don't mind being ruint, but it's different with Dan'l Webster. Would you vote for a man for President who claimed he'd saw the sea serpent? Well, would you? Would anybody?"

There was another little silence, and then George Blake spoke.

"He's right, Dan'l," he said, while the others nodded. "Give me that paper." He took it from Dan'l Webster's hand and threw it in the sea.

"And now," he said in a firm voice, "I saw cod. Nothing but cod. Except maybe a couple of halibut. Did any gentleman here see anything else?"

Well, at that, it turned out, of course, that nobody aboard had seen anything but cod all day. And with that, they put back for shore. All the same, they all looked over their shoulders a good deal till they got back to harbor.

And yet Dan'l Webster wasn't too contented that evening, in spite of his fine catch. For, after all, he had seen the sea serpent, and not only seen her but played her on the line for twenty-seven minutes by his gold repeater, and, being a fisherman, he'd like to have said so. And yet, if he did—Seth was right—folks would think him crazy or worse. It took his mind off Lord Ashburton and the treaty with England—till, finally, he pushed aside the papers on his desk.

"Oh, a plague on the beast!" he said, kind of crossly. "I'll leave it alone and hope it leaves me alone." So he took his candle and went up to bed. But just as he was dropping off to sleep, he thought he heard a long low hoot from the mouth of Green Harbor River, two miles away.

The next night the hooting continued, and the third day there was a piece in the Kingston paper about the new government foghorn at Rocky Ledge. Well, the thing began to get on Dan'l Webster's nerves, and when his temper was roused he wasn't a patient man. Moreover, the noises seemed to disturb the stock—at least his overseer said so—and the third night his favorite gray kicked half the door out of her stall. "That sea serpent's getting to be an infernal nuisance," thought Dan'l Webster. "I've got to protect my property." So, the fourth night he put on his old duck-shooting clothes and took his favorite shotgun, Learned Selden, and went down to a blind at the mouth of Green Harbor River, to see what he could see. He didn't tell anybody else about his intentions, because he still felt kind of sensitive about the whole affair.

Well, there was a fine moon that night, and sure enough, about eleven o'clock, the sea serpent showed up, steaming in from ocean, all one continuous wave length, like a giant garden hose. She was quite a handsome sight, all speckled with the moonlight, but Dan'l Webster couldn't rightly appreciate it. And just as she came to the blind, she lifted her head and looked sorrowfully in the direction of Marshfield and let out a long low soulful hoot like a homesick train.

Dan'l Webster hated to do it. But he couldn't have a sea serpent living in Green Harbor River and scaring the stock—not to speak of the universal consternation and panic there'd be in the countryside when such a thing was known. So he lifted Learned Selden and gave her both barrels for a starter, just a trifle over her head. And as soon as the gun exploded, the sea serpent let out a screech you could hear a mile and headed back for open sea. If she'd traveled fast before, she traveled like lightning now, and it wasn't any time before she was just a black streak on the waters.

Dan'l Webster stepped out of the blind and wiped his brow. He felt sorry, but he felt relieved. He didn't think she'd be back, after that sort of scare, and he wanted to leave everything shipshape before he went down to Washington, next morning. But next day, when he told Seth Peterson what he'd done, he didn't feel so chipper. For, "You shouldn't have done that, Mr. Webster," said Seth Peterson, shaking his head, and that was all he would say except a kind of mutter that sounded like "Samanthy was always particular set in her likes." But Dan'l didn't pay any attention to that, though he remembered it later, and he was quite short with Seth for the first time in their long relationship. So Seth shut up like a quahog, and Dan'l took the cars for Washington.

When he got there he was busy enough, for the British treaty was on the boil, and within twenty-four hours he'd forgot all about the sea serpent. Or thought he had. But three days later, as he was walking home to his house on Lafayette Square, with a Senator friend of his, in the cool of the evening, they heard a curious noise. It seemed to come from the direction of the Potomac River.

"Must have got a new whistle for the Baltimore night boat," said the Senator. "Noisy too."

"Oh, that's just the bullfrogs on the banks," said Dan'l Webster steadily. But he knew what it was, just the same, and his heart sank within him. But nobody ever called Dan'l Webster a coward. So, as soon as he'd got rid of the Senator, he went down to the banks of the Potomac. Well, it was the sea serpent, all right.

She looked a little tired, as well she might, having swum from Plymouth Bay. But as soon as she saw Dan'l Webster, she stretched out her neck and gave a long low loving hoot. Then Dan'l knew what the trouble was and, for once in his life, he didn't know what to do. But he'd brought along a couple of roe herring, in a paper, just in case; so he fed them to her and she hooted, affectionate and grateful.

Then he walked back to his house with his head bowed. And that very night he sent a special express letter to Seth Peterson at Marshfield, for, it seemed to him, Seth must know more about the business than he let on.

Well, Seth got to Washington as fast as the cars would bring him, and the very evening he arrived Dan'l sent him over to interview the serpent. But when Seth came back, Dan'l could see by his face that he hadn't made much progress.

"Could you talk to her, Seth?" he said, and his voice was eager. "Can she understand United States?"

"Oh, she can understand it all right," said Seth. "She's even picking up a few words. They was always a smart family, those Rock Ledge serpents, and she's the old maid of the lot, and the best educated. The only trouble with 'em is, they're so terrible sot in their ways."

"You might have warned me, Seth," said Dan'l Webster, kind of reproachful, and Seth looked uncomfortable.

"Well, to tell you the truth," he said, "I thought all of 'em was dead. Nor I never thought she'd act up like this—her father was as respectable a serpent as you'd see in a long summer's day. Her father—"

"Bother her father!" said Dan'l Webster and set his jaw. "Tell me what she says."

"Well, Mr. Webster," said Seth, and stared at his boots, "she says you're quite a handsome man. She says she never did see anybody quite like you," he went on. "I hate to tell you this, Mr. Webster, and I feel kind of responsible, but I think you ought to know. And I told you that you oughtn't to have shot at her—she's pretty proud of that. She says she knows just how you meant it. Well, I'm no great hand at being embarrassed, Mr. Webster, but, I tell you, she embarrassed me. You see, she's been an old maid for about a hundred and fifty years, I guess, and that's the worst of it. And being the last of her folks in those particular waters, there's just no way to restrain her—her father and mother was as sensible, hard-working serpents as ever gave a feller a tow through a fog, but you know how it is with those old families. Well, she says wherever you go, she'll follow you, and she claims she wants to hear you speak before the Supreme Court—"

"Did you tell her I'm a married man?" said Dan'l. "Did you tell her that?"

"Yes, I told her," said Seth, and you could see the perspiration on his forehead. "But she says that doesn't signify—her being a serpent and different—and she's fixing to move right in. She says Washington's got a lovely climate and she's heard all about the balls and the diplomatic receptions. I don't know how she's heard about them, but she has." He swallowed. "I got her to promise she'd kind of lie low for two weeks and not come up the Potomac by daylight—she was fixing to do that because she wants to meet the President. Well, I got her to promise that much. But she says, even so, if you don't come to see her once an evening, she'll hoot till you do, and she told me to tell you that you haven't heard hooting yet. And as soon as the fish market's open, I better run down and buy a barrel of flaked cod, Mr. Webster —she's partial to flaked cod and she usually takes it in the barrel. Well, I don't want to worry you, Mr. Webster, but I'm afraid that we're in a fix."

"A fix!" said Dan'l Webster. "It's the biggest fix I ever was in in my life!"

"Well, it's kind of complimentary, in a way, I guess," said Seth Peterson, "but—"

"Does she say anything else?" said Dan'l Webster, drawing a long breath.

"Yes, Mr. Webster," said Seth Peterson, his eyes on his boots. "She says you're a little shy. But she says she likes that in a man."

Dan'l Webster went to bed that night, but he didn't sleep. He worked and worked those great brains of his till he nearly wore out the wheels, but he still couldn't think of a way to get rid of the sea serpent. And just about the time dawn broke, he heard one long low hoot, faithful and reminiscent, from the direction of the Potomac.

Well, the next two weeks were certainly bad ones for him. For, as the days wore on, the sea serpent got more and more restive. She wanted him to call her Samanthy, which he wouldn't, and she kept asking him when he was going to introduce her into society, till he had to feed her Italian sardines in olive oil to keep her quiet. And that ran up a bill at the fish market that he hated to think of—besides, her continually threatening to come up the Potomac by day. Moreover, and to put the cap on things, the great Webster-Ashburton treaty that was to make his name as Secretary of State had struck a snag and England didn't seem at all partial to admitting the American claims. Oh, it was a weary fortnight and a troublesome one!

The last afternoon of the fortnight, he sat in his office and he didn't know where to turn. For Lord Ashburton was coming to see him for a secret conference that night at nine, and he had to see the sea serpent at ten, and how to satisfy either of them he didn't know. His eyes stared wearily at the papers on his desk. He rang the bell for his secretary.

"The corvette *Benjamin Franklin* reports—" he said. "This should have gone to the Navy Department, Mr. Jones." Then he glanced at the naval report again and his eyes began to glow like furnaces. "By the bones of Leviathan! I've got it!" he said, with a shout. "Where's my hat, Mr. Jones? I must see the President at once!"

There was a different feeling about the house on Lafayette Square that evening, for Dan'l Webster was himself again. He cracked a joke with Seth Peterson and took a glass of Madeira and turned it to the light. And when Lord Ashburton was announced—a nice, white-haired old gentleman, though a little stiff in his joints—he received him with all the courtesy of a king.

"I am glad to see you so much restored, Mr. Webster," said Lord Ashburton, when the greetings had been exchanged. "And yet I fear I bring you bad news. Concerning clauses six and seven of the proposed treaty between Her Majesty's Government and the United States of America, it is my duty to state—"

"My lord, let us drop the clauses for a moment and take the wider view," said Dan'l Webster, smiling. "This is a matter concerning the future welfare and peace of two great nations. Your government claims the right to search our ships; that right we deny. And our attitude seems to you preposterous. Is that not so?"

"I would hesitate to use the word 'preposterous,'" said Lord Ashburton cautiously. "Yet—"

"And yet," said Dan'l Webster, leaning forward, "there are things which may seem preposterous, and yet are not. Let me put a case. Let us say that Great Britain has the strongest navy afloat."

"Britannia rules the waves," said Lord Ashburton, with a noble smile.

"There were a couple she didn't rule in 1812," said Dan'l Webster, "but let that pass. Let me ask you, Lord Ashburton, and let me ask you solemnly, what could even the power and might of Britain's Navy avail against Leviathan?"

"Leviathan?" said Lord Ashburton, rather coldly. "Naturally, I understand the Biblical allusion. Yet—"

"The sea serpent," said Dan'l Webster, kind of impatient. "What could all Britain's Navy do against the sea serpent out of the Scriptures?"

Lord Ashburton stared at him as if he had gone mad. "God bless my soul, Mr. Secretary!" he said. "But I fail to see the point of your question. The sea serpent doesn't exist!"

"Doesn't he—I mean she?" said Dan'l Webster, calmly. "And suppose I should prove to you that it does exist?"

"Well, 'pon my word! God bless my soul!" said Lord Ashburton, kind of taken aback. "Naturally—in that case—however—but even so—"

Dan'l Webster touched a bell on his desk. "Lord Ashburton," he said, kind of solemn, "I am putting my life, and what is dearer to me, my honor and reputation, in your hands. Nevertheless, I feel it necessary, for a better understanding between our two countries."

Seth Peterson came into the room and Dan'l nodded at him.

"Seth," he said, "Lord Ashburton is coming with us to see Saman-thy."

"It's all right if you say so, Mr. Webster," said Seth Peterson, "but he'll have to help carry the sardines."

"Well, 'pon my word! Bless my soul! A very strange proceeding!" said Lord Ashburton, but he followed along.

Well, they got to the banks of the Potomac, the three of them, and when they were there, Seth whistled. Samanthy was lying mostly under water, behind a little brushy island, but when she heard the whistle, she began to heave up and uncoil, all shining in the moon-light. It was what you might call a kind of impressive sight. Dan'l Webster looked at Lord Ashburton, but Lord Ashburton's words seemed sort of stuck in his throat.

Finally he got them out. "Bless my soul!" he said. "You Americans are very extraordinary! Is it alive?"

But then all he could do was goggle, for Samanthy had lifted her head, and, giving a low friendly hoot, she commenced to swim around the island.

"Now, is that a sea serpent or isn't it?" said Dan'l Webster, with a kind of quiet pride.

"Indubitably," said Lord Ashburton, staring through his eyeglass. "Indubitably." And he kind of cleared his throat. "It is, indeed and in fact, a serpent of the sea. And I am asleep and in bed, in my room at the British Embassy." He pinched himself. "Ouch!" he said. "No, I am not."

"Would you call it sizable, for a sea serpent?" persisted Dan'l Webster.

Lord Ashburton stared again through his eyeglass. "Quite," he said. "Oh, yes, quite, quite!"

"And powerful?" asked Dan'l.

"I should judge so," said Lord Ashburton, faintly, as the sea serpent swam around and around the island and the waves of its wake broke crashing on the bank. "Yes, indeed, a very powerful engine of de-struction. May I ask what it feeds upon?"

"Italian sardines, for preference," said Dan'l. "But that's beside the point." He drew a long breath. "Well, my lord," he said, "we're intending to commission that sea serpent as a regular and acknowl-edged war vessel in the United States Navy. And then, where's your wooden walls?"

Lord Ashburton, he was a diplomat, and his face didn't change expression as he stared first at the sea serpent and then at the face of Dan'l Webster. But after a while, he nodded. "You need not labor the point, Mr. Secretary," he said. "My government, I am sure, will be glad to reconsider its position on the last two clauses and on the right of search."

"Then I'm sure we can reach an agreement," said Dan'l Webster, and wiped the sweat from his brow. "And now, let's feed Samanthy."

He whistled to her himself, a long musical whistle, and she came bounding and looping in toward shore. It took all three of them to heave her the barrel of sardines, and she swallowed it down in one gulp. After that, she gave a hoot of thanks and gratitude, and Lord Ashburton sat down on the bank for a minute and took snuff. He said that he needed something to clear his mind.

"Naturally," he said, after a while, "Her Majesty's Government must have adequate assurances as to the good conduct of this—this lady." He'd meant to say "creature" at first, but Samanthy rolled her eye at him just then, and he changed the word.

"You shall have them," said Dan'l Webster, and whistled Samanthy even closer. She came in kind of skittish, flirting her coils, and Lord Ashburton closed his eyes for a minute. But when Dan'l Webster spoke, it was in the voice that hushed the Senate whenever he rose.

"Samanthy," he said, "I speak to you now as Secretary of State of the United States of America." It was the great voice that had rung in the Supreme Court and replied to Hayne, and even a sea serpent had to listen respectful. For the voice was mellow and deep, and he pictured Samanthy's early years as a carefree young serpent, playing with her fellows, and then her hard life of toil and struggle when she was left lone and lorn, till even Seth Peterson and Lord Ashburton realized the sorrow and tragedy of her lonely lot. And then, in the gentlest and kindest way you could ask, he showed her where her duty lay.

"For, if you keep on hooting in the Potomac, Samanthy," he said, "you'll become a public menace to navigation and get sat upon by the Senate Committee for Rivers and Harbors. They'll drag you up on land, Samanthy, and put you in the Smithsonian Institution; they'll stick you in a stagnant little pool and children will come to throw you peanuts on Sundays, and their nurses will poke you with umbrellas if you don't act lively enough. The U. S. Navy will shoot at you for target practice, Samanthy, and the scientists will examine you, and the ladies of the Pure Conduct League will knit you a bathing suit, and you'll be bothered every minute by Congressmen and professors and visitors and foreign celebrities till you won't be able to call your scales your own. Oh, yes, it'll be fame, Samanthy, but it won't be good enough. Believe me, I know something about fame and it's begging letters from strangers and calls from people you don't know and don't want to know, and the burden and wear and tear of being a public character till it's enough to break your heart. It isn't good enough, Samanthy; it won't give you back your free waters and your sporting in the deep. Yes, Samanthy, it'd be a remarkable thing to have you here in Washington, but it isn't the life you were meant for and I can't take advantage of your trust. And now," he said to Seth Peterson, "just what does she say?"

Seth Peterson listened, attentive, to the hootings.

"She says the Washington climate isn't what she thought it was," he said. "And the Potomac River's too warm; it's bad for her sciatica. And she's plumb tired of sardines."

"Does she say anything about me?" asked Dan'l Webster, anxiously.

"Well," said Seth Peterson, listening, "she says—if you'll excuse me, Mr. Webster—that you may be a great man, but you wouldn't make much of a sea serpent. She says you haven't got enough coils. She says—well, she says no hard feelings, but she guesses it was a mistake on both sides."

He listened again. "But she says one thing," he said. "She says she's got to have recognition and a husband, if she has to take this Lord Ashburton. She says he doesn't look like much, but he might get her introduced at court."

A great light broke over Dan'l's face and his voice rang out like thunder. "She shall have them both," he said. "Come here, Samanthy. By virtue of the authority vested in me as Secretary of State, and by special order of the President of the United States and the Secretary of the Navy, as witness the attached commission in blank which I now fill in with your name, I hereby attach you to the United States Navy, to rank as a forty-four-gun frigate on special duty, rating a rear admiral's flag and a salute of the appropriate number of guns, wherever encountered in American waters. And, by virtue of the following special order, I hereby order you to the South Seas, there to cruise until further orders for the purpose of seeking a suitable and proper husband, with all the rights, privileges, duties and appurtenances pertaining to said search and said American citizenship, as aforesaid and Hail Columbia. Signed John Tyler, President. With which is subjoined a passport signed by Daniel Webster, Secretary of State, bidding all foreign nations let pass without hindrance the American citizen, Samanthy Doe, on her lawful journeys and errands." He dropped his voice for a moment and added reflectively, "The American corvette, *Benjamin Franklin,* reports sighting a handsome young male sea serpent on February third of the present year, just off the coast of the Sandwich Islands. Said serpent had forty-two coils by actual count, and when last sighted was swimming SSW at full speed."

But hardly had he spoken when Samanthy, for the last time, lifted her head and gave out a last long hoot. She looked upon Dan'l Webster as she did so, and there was regret in her eye. But the regret was tinctured with eagerness and hope.

Then she beat the water to a froth, and, before they really saw her go, she was gone, leaving only her wake on the moonlit Potomac.

"Well," said Dan'l Webster, yawning a little, "there we are. And now, Lord Ashburton, if you'll come home with me, we can draw up that treaty."

"Gladly," said Lord Ashburton, brushing his coat with his handkerchief. "Is it really gone? 'Pon my soul! You know, for a moment, I imagined that I actually saw a sea serpent. You have a very vivid way of putting things, Mr. Webster. But I think I understand the American attitude now, from the—er—analogy you were pleased to draw between such a—er—fabulous animal and the young strength of your growing country."

"I was confident that you would appreciate it, once it was brought to your attention," said Dan'l Webster. But he winked one eye at Seth Peterson, and Seth Peterson winked back.

And I'll say this for Dan'l Webster, too—he kept his promises. All through the time he was Secretary of State, he saw to it that the forty-four-gun frigate *Samanthy Doe* was carried on a special account on the books of the Navy. In fact, there's some people say that she's still so carried, and that it was her give Ericsson the idea for building the *Monitor* in the Civil War—if she wasn't the *Monitor* herself. And when the White Fleet went around the world in Teddy Roosevelt's time—well, there was a lookout in the crow's nest of the flagship, one still calm night, as they passed by the palmy isles of the South Seas. And all of a sudden, the water boiled, tremendous and phosphorescent, and there was a pair of sea serpents and seven young ones, circling, calm and majestic, three times around the fleet. He rubbed his eyes and he stared, but there they were. Well, he was the only one that saw it, and they put him in the brig for it next morning. But he swore, till the day he died, they were flying the Stars and Stripes.

Some Field Problems
and Their Solutions

RAY BERGMAN

Few individuals have devoted as much time to fresh-water fishing—either fishing or writing about fishing—as Ray Bergman. His books, unquestionably, have converted more trout fishermen from worms to flies than have any other single cause. Bergman not only writes easily and well, he writes convincingly, and although his points are not as emphatic as Aesop's, they are there. Just Fishing was one of his earliest and best books, and for the angler who wants to get something from his reading, this chapter should prove very satisfactory.

THIS IS a chapter of trout-fishing experiences. The incidents narrated are some that have been carefully selected from my notes covering many years of angling and most of them illustrate conditions in which it was necessary to use certain tactics or a specific fly, lure or bait in order to achieve best results at the time.

45

It is also a chapter which deals with the trials and tribulations of an angler who gets his greatest thrill from the game of angling by outwitting the wary trout of the hard-fished streams, where, besides the natural wiliness of the fish, one must contend with trout which have become angler-wise and also with an army of fishermen who continuously keep the streams in a state of agitation quite out of keeping with their natural condition.

I have chosen my first incident from field notes of July 4, 1926. It is mostly about a fly, the Brown Bivisible Spider tied "dry" on a number sixteen hook.

It is quite a creation, this Brown Spider, although it is really nothing more than an improved edition of the old-time Pool Hackle which I have fished wet for a good many years. But the Brown Spider is different. It is made with the same abnormally long hackles but instead of being soft they are quite stiff and bristly. Besides this it has a stiff tail and a top hackle of white for visibility to the angler. This construction, together with the tiny hook, unites in making a fluffy bit of a fly which one cannot help but drop softly on the water. And it rides high with the hook usually in the air above the water. Therein lies its singular effectiveness in bringing forth a rise. Its ethereal lightness is so apparent that it simulates insect life of certain sorts to perfection and in addition it is very likely to be lifted lightly from the water by a sudden gust of wind to be deposited softly in some other part of the water being fished. If this happens in the vicinity of a trout results are sure to prove interesting to the angler.

I carried the Spider two years without using it, without even considering its possibilities. I never could tell you why I bought it but it was probably because of the sales talk of some super tackle salesman enthused with his product. But anyway it found its way into my box to lie there forgotten and neglected until that day in July when adverse conditions started me experimenting with odd patterns of flies in hope of finding something that might tempt the trout.

I discovered it buried under an assortment of fan wings. I disengaged it from the rest of the flies and decided to try it.

Some thirty feet above me two large rocks breasted the rather swift current. Between them the water glided smooth and dark. Ordinarily such a place would have brought a rise but today it had failed. I had floated various flies over the place at least fifty times without interesting a fish.

I cast the fly to the upper end of the glide tentatively but without hope. I really expected nothing more than a repetition of failure. A sudden gust of wind took the Spider just before it alighted on the water and deposited it some four feet farther upstream than where I had intended to place it.

"What a fly," I grumbled. "It won't even go where you cast it."

And then it happened! Of course the current brought the fly downstream very quickly indeed and as it reached the upper end of the smooth glide I heard a sucking noise and my Spider disappeared. Luck hooked that trout. I was so surprised that whatever I did to hook the fish was done entirely subconsciously. The result was extremely gratifying. It was a two-pound-four-ounce brown trout, a nice plump fellow about eighteen inches long.

"It might have been a freak rise," I soliloquized, "or perhaps the trout are just starting to feed. Well, anyway, I'll give this fly another try."

This time I dropped the Spider so that it would float down to a rock which barely showed its top above the water. It was a likely-looking place and I had fished it faithfully with my other flies.

The Spider never reached the rock. A trout darted from his position by it and took the fly with such speed that he came out of the water in a splendid leap. But I missed him, either because I was too quick in striking or because I was too excited to strike at all. My mind was too confused to analyze just what the trouble was.

This was all quite thrilling. To rise two fish on two successive floats after eight hours of inaction was very exciting. I began to feel a positive affection for the fluffy Brown Spider and I dried it out very carefully, and I must admit reverently, before making another cast.

A small eddy between a triangle of three rocks next claimed my attention. As the Spider danced over the surface of this water a brown trout weighing a good pound leaped clear of the water. He came down within an inch of the fly and drowned it but he did not touch it, of that I am sure.

Then on six successive casts this trout either jumped over the Spider or slapped at it with his tail. Not once did he rise for it as if he meant business. This incident intrigued me. I had floated many other flies over this place innumerable times without getting a strike or even the slightest indication of interest. What was there about this Spider which aroused the trout's interest enough to have him rise and why did he refuse it even though he was interested?

"Perhaps," I thought, "now that his interest is aroused enough to investigate the Spider he might actually take another fly if I cast it over him."

Figuring that a large, attractive-looking morsel might prove more tempting under such conditions, I tied a number ten fan wing Royal Coachman to my leader. To my great delight the ruse worked. The trout took the fan wing with a sureness and a deliberateness which seemed to denote real desire and positive satisfaction.

As the day went on I found out many things about the queer-looking Spider and its effect on different trout. Some took it readily, even savagely and without any preliminary maneuvers. Others would rise to it a number of times with a great deal of fuss and splashing but without actually taking it. Then finally they would suck it in very calmly. Still others would jump over it or slap it with their tails for a few floats and then ignore it entirely. This last class, with a few exceptions, I either hooked or rose fairly by floating a fan wing over them after they had discontinued rising to the Spider.

Since that time I have found many uses for the Brown Spider. It has proved invaluable in arousing the interest of trout on those days when they are inclined to be inactive, that is on some streams. Often it will rise a particularly wary specimen who has refused countless other artificials.

I must admit that at times it is a very exasperating fly to use. I have experienced days with it when I have missed every trout that rose and others when I have lost every good trout hooked by the tiny hook pulling out. But on the other hand I have had days when I have hooked and landed every fish that took it. On some streams it is consistently effective. On others it will not interest a trout. I have no explanation to offer for these peculiarities. The reader may arrive at his own conclusions regarding them.

Since the arrival of the bivisibles in the angling world I have come to consider them quite essential and necessary to my assortment. Without them I could not get the most out of my fishing.

The following incident is taken from an article of mine in *Field and Stream Magazine*.

An interesting old character whose name I neglected to get and whom I have never seen since gave me some bivisibles on a day when I was having abominable luck and was absolutely discouraged and downhearted over my inability to get a single rise from the many trout I knew lived in the stream I was fishing.

This interesting and quite fascinating gentleman had a quaint name for trout that were indisposed. "'Crastinatin' trout" he called them. His explanation of the term was just as quaint. "Don't feel a hull lot like feedin' an' are puttin' it off, but they'll start if food comes 'long as looks good 'nough or temptin' 'nough to 'cite their appetites."

This old fellow tied his own flies and was quite prodigal in his disposal of them. Bringing me to an advantageous position where we could look down into a deep pool and see the trout, he deliberately opened his box and dropped a fly on the water. He kept doing this until a couple of the fish began to show signs of interest. Then he went below the pool and started casting over the trout. On the eighth cast he took a twelve-inch fish. Then he gave me a handful of the bivisibles and left.

But I did not benefit from the old man's lesson until some weeks later. A hatch of Iron Blues appeared immediately after he had left me and the trout began rising to them with great gusto. I promptly forgot about bivisibles and " 'crastinatin' " trout and took a limit catch on a winged imitation of the Iron Blue. From that day until the last day of the season not a single thought of the old man or his bivisibles entered my mind. Then, at the very last moment of the last day, the entire incident came back to me very opportunely.

It had been an intolerable day. The water was low, quite warm and extremely clear. I had fished hard for the entire day without stirring anything but a few fingerlings. Even the hoped-for and expected evening rise did not materialize. I was disgruntled, upset, and ready to quit, when I chanced to notice the long-neglected bivisibles in my fly box, and started casting one over a large pocket hole that I had been fishing halfheartedly with a Cahill.

It floated so well and looked so good that I soon forgot my day of failure in the keen joy of watching it ride the rough water. I really had no thought of rising a trout; in fact I was positive that such an event was impossible, so that I was utterly unprepared when I saw the fly suddenly disappear in a swirl. In my confusion and anxiety to be quick enough I struck entirely too hard. For an instant I felt a great weight and then came a sickening slack as my line went flying in the air minus the fly.

Feverishly, in the waning daylight, I dug into my fly box and extracted a Gray Bivisible. I tied it on hurriedly, carelessly, too excited to see if the knot was safe. I cast the fly over the hole quickly, many times. Advancing night was rapidly obscuring my vision. Then, when I could just make out its outline at intervals, I suddenly sensed that a trout had taken it and I struck to find that I was fast to a heavy fish.

For a moment I was supremely happy. The fight of the trout made me tingle. And then he was gone. Not a bit of commotion, no undue strain, no splashing or jumping—just gone! Later when I examined my leader I found that a faulty knot had been the cause of my losing the fish. It had come untied.

All that winter the loss of those two trout and the circumstances which had led up to their striking the bivisible occupied my thoughts to a great extent. Having carefully recorded my experience with the old man, the notes now took on a new interest, really occupied the prominent place in my thoughts to which they were entitled. I determined that the following year I would go thoroughly into the matter of fishing for " 'crastinatin' " trout.

I did, and I've been doing it ever since. I have come to the conclusion that many times trout may be taken when they appear to be inactive by the persistent cast in one spot system with suitable fly. The bivisibles are ideal for this purpose because of their buoyancy and the fact that it does not matter, as far as the trout are concerned, in what position they alight on the water. And besides, they have other advantages. With them one may fish fast water on which it is impossible to float an ordinary dry fly. This alone is enough to recommend their place in any angler's fly box.

The following episodes in which bivisibles take a leading part were selected from my field notes between the years of 1920 and 1930. I am not narrating them from any desire to prove anything. They are merely unbiased accounts of fishing adventures in which I have seemingly won success by the use of the bivisible flies.

For instance there was that day on the Neversink River—in the big water below Bridgeville where the trout average large size and are very vigorous and strong.

It was a day of heavy winds, bright sun and rather low temperature for dry-fly fishing. The time was May 15 and at noon the air in the shady places registered forty degrees Fahrenheit. The water varied between forty-six and forty-eight degrees.

During every lull in the wind clouds of gray flies swarmed over the stream where they danced just above the surface, occasionally alighting on the water to float with the current a foot or two and then rising in the air again. During these periods the trout rose in great numbers.

I started fishing with the Light Hendrickson because its color resembled the natural. It brought a response all right but the trout would not take it. They would just rise to the surface, look at it and then go down again. I fussed with this fly for at least an hour without getting a rise. After that I tried in succession the Blue Dun, Blue Quill, Gray Drake and Winged Willow. Not one of these provoked the least bit of interest.

It was quite exasperating. I sat down on the shore after a while to think it over. Without doubt the Light Hendrickson was nearly right but it lacked something. Perhaps it was because the natural insects were high riders, while the Hendrickson, due to its construction, floated low. Acting on this theory I tied a Badger Bivisible on the leader. The very trout who could only be induced to look at the Hendrickson took this fly without hesitation.

The next incident is taken verbatim from my notes.

August, 1922—The water has been so low in most parts of the trout country that the fishing has been rather poor. But I found a stream last year which holds a good head of water even under drought conditions and thought this would be an opportune time to fish it.

It is a narrow brook with a very fast flow and quick precipitation. It rushes wildly through a densely wooded ravine where it is almost impossible to walk because of the tangled underbrush. Very little sunlight strikes the stream; even the brightest days seem gloomy when one leaves behind the few open fields at its mouth and gets up into the forested valley.

Of the three times I have fished this brook this is the only time that I have succeeded in making a catch, and I think I owe it all to the "persistent-cast-in-one-spot" system and the Brown Bivisible fly. Of course I realize that one wastes considerable time fishing in this manner; the majority of places one tries will not yield a trout. But when the fish are not rising to natural flies and seem to be indisposed generally I do think it is the best way to take them.

On this stream the most effective places to cast to seemed to be where the swift water pulsated close against the wooded bank. The larger pools, the shallow riffles and the exposed pockets did not yield any strikes. The only exception to this was one pool which was partially cluttered up with a fallen spruce tree. Here I rose six trout, after having cast for a least twenty minutes to interest the first one. Owing to the hazards presented by the entanglements of the tree I lost five of these trout. The main current passed directly through the branches of the tree, and as the trout took the fly while it floated in close proximity to these branches, most of them broke away before I could lead them away from the hazard. Lost five flies and one entire leader in these encounters.

Altogether I was well satisfied with the day's results. Eleven trout weighing ten pounds looked good to me in these days of hard fishing. Used two patterns of flies, the Brown Bivisible and the Royal Coachman (not fan wing). Of the eleven fish the Royal accounted for only four. As each fly was given an equal chance, I am satisfied in my own mind that the bivisible is the best for this stream.

Since the above episode I have fished this brook twenty-nine times and have hooked a total of three hundred and fifty trout over ten inches in length. Two hundred of these fish were accounted for by the Brown Bivisible, with equal honors going to the eight and ten sizes. Ninety rose to the fan wing Royal Coachman size ten and the balance took the Gray Bivisible or the fan wing Whirling Dun. On every one of these trips equal chance was given to the regulation patterns of flies in order to find out if they would take the fish. Except for small trout they did not bring results.

During this time I have taken five other anglers, all good dry-fly men, with me so that they could try their luck. Every one of these fellows had an aversion to bivisibles and fan wings but they could not take any worth-while specimens until they used them. One of these anglers I took along three or four times. He refused to use anything but his pet flies and he always finished the day without any trout in his creel.

On the last trip he came in with two beautiful specimens. He was very enthusiastic over his catch but said nothing about the fly he took them with. This made me suspicious.

"Well, old man," I remarked, "I suppose you'll think that our theory about this stream is all wrong, now that you've taken those good trout on the Cahill."

He looked at me queerly.

"I did not say I got them on the Cahill," he protested. Then he laughed. "The smokes are on me, boys," he admitted. "I took those two beauties on the Brown Bivisible. I had been fishing all day with every fly I owned and never got a rise from anything bigger than eight inches. Well, this evening I got disgusted. 'What's the use,' I asked myself, 'of being so infernally stubborn about the flies I use?' Well, I wasn't very far from the car when I got to thinking this way, and knowing that you always carry an extra box of bivisibles in it I rushed to it, got a couple of brown ones and went back to the stream, to the big meadow pool. Believe it or not I took that seventeen-incher on the first cast and then just before it got too dark to see my fly I took the other fellow. So you win—hands down! From now on I'm going to carry both bivisibles and fan wing Royal Coachmen in my fly box and, what is more to the point, I'm going to use them."

One of the reasons for this preference of bivisibles and fan wings by the trout of this stream may be a matter of buoyancy. Rarely will one find the larger trout in water where the ordinary dry fly would stay afloat, even for a few seconds. Another reason may be that inasmuch as the trout in this stream do not seem to be regular surface feeders, except on those rare occasions when large natural flies are in evidence, they are not interested in any artificial which does not look like a good mouthful. Of course one might argue in this instance that if the trout are not natural surface feeders they would be more interested in the flies which did not float so well; which sank slightly under the surface when one cast them on the broken, fast water. This would be a point well taken except for the fact that on every occasion where I used wet flies on this water it was necessary to sink them deep in order to get a strike. It would seem that these fish were partial to having their surface food served dry, that they did not care about it if it was drowned. On the other hand, they did like and accept artificials which in some measure resembled the nymphs and other aquatic life with which the stream swarmed.

In my twenty-nine visits to this brook I have seen only one real rise. This occurred in late May when a scattered hatch of May Flies brought the big fellows to the surface for two hours during the day. Aside from this I have observed only ten individual trout rise. All of these fish rose to large flies and in two of the instances the rise was to a butterfly.

Of course this does not mean that these were the only rises which occurred. Twenty-nine days is only a small percentage of the fishing days during ten years. Besides, my personal observance covered only a very small portion of the stream at a time. But it does show the character of the stream and it seems reasonable to suppose that my experiences were typically characteristic.

As a direct contrast to these accounts of bivisible effectiveness the following observations show that at times small flies or those lightly tied, such as the divided wing type, are the most effective.

There are two stretches of the Neversink River in New York State which I fish quite extensively, stretches where I have never had any degree of success with either bivisibles or fan wings except one day when the trout went crazy and rose to any fly I wanted to give them.

Generally these stretches are tough problems. Usually the Light Hendrickson or Light Cahill, tied with a lightweight hook and stiff, sparse hackles, will bring the best results. Many times I have cast over a pool for an hour or more with bivisibles, fan wings and double-winged dry flies without getting a strike, only to take a trout the instant that I changed to a Light Cahill tied in the manner I have described. It is hard to give a logical reason for this peculiarity. It may be that these trout like a fly which rides low in the water. Something which bears out this theory is the fact that if one will take a bivisible and flatten the hackles out on the bottom so that they do not bristle out as they are intended to they will often catch the trout, that is if the fly alights on the water so that it floats with the flattened hackles lying on the water. If they are not full, bushy hackles they will work even better. But even at that they do not begin to bring the rises that the divided-wing flies do.

It was for this type of stream that I designed my special patterns of divided-wing flies, the Basherkill, Bataviakill, Paulinskill and Wallkill. Often during May I have been on a stream during a hatch of greenish-yellow flies. The Basherkill serves me well under this condition. The Bataviakill as a dark olive cannot be beaten and the Paulinskill will take care of a variety of hatches where the naturals run to light shades of sulphur and tan. The Wallkill has also served me in good stead, but I consider it to be a special fly for only certain conditions and without general merit. While I use it frequently with quite satisfactory results, I do not feel that it is at all a necessary pattern.

Of course these are all conclusions based on actual experiences and should be taken for what they are worth as such. There can be no hard and fast rule covering the flies used in trout fishing. One can only experiment and then apply the results of such experiences to his fishing.

I have been very enthusiastic over the fan wing type of dry fly during the past nine years. In my story "Conquest of the Fan Wing," which appeared in the March, 1930, issue of *The National Sportsman* I gave an account of my introduction to this fly and as it is pertinent to this chapter I think it worth while quoting.

When I saw the fan wing flies for the first time I looked upon them with ill-concealed disgust.

"What are we coming to?" I exclaimed to the salesman who had displayed them to me with very evident pride. "Do you mean to tell me that these flies are used by expert dry-fly anglers? That they really catch trout on them?"

"Very few fellows have used them as yet," he admitted, "but that does not prove anything. They have only been on the market for a month or two and most anglers do not know about them. When they do I predict a great sale."

"If they haven't used them how do you know they're any good?" I questioned.

"Oh, of course we have given them a fairly extensive tryout. You know Mr. Blank?"

I nodded. He was the best angler in the establishment.

"Well," the salesman resumed, "Mr. Blank tried them out all last season and he claims that they are positively wonderful, that they will often rise trout when nothing else will. Besides, he says that they can be floated over the roughest sort of water and that you can see them far better than the regular type of dry flies. He also told us that he thought they would be of great benefit to the novice; would make it easier for him to catch trout."

"Humph," I ejaculated. "Well, I suppose I'll have to buy some just to keep in style. But it is foolish just the same and I know that I'll never use them, not as long as I can get the Cahill, Royal Coachman and some of my other favorites."

"Believe me, you'll never regret buying some, that is if you'll give them a try," insisted the salesman. "Don't forget that they come tied in your favorite Cahill and Royal Coachman patterns as well as some others."

Thus I became the owner of some three dozen fan wing flies. After showing them to several unappreciative anglers I put a couple in my pocket fly box and the rest in storage. Then I promptly forgot all about them.

Two months later I stopped in the store where I had purchased the flies.

"How did you make out with those fan wings?" asked the courteous salesman.

"What? Oh, you mean those sailboats that you stuck me with this spring. Well, to tell the truth I never used any of them. But that's all right. I know that you've got to sell new goods and I'm willing to be the goat once in a while."

The salesman smiled.

"Mr. Somebody made a record catch with them on the Esopus last Sunday," he said.

"What? Why, I was on the Esopus Sunday and didn't do a thing. Just took a couple of small trout, and what's more—*the trout weren't rising!* What are you trying to do, string me?"

"Not a bit, sir. Everyone here saw the catch. Mr. Somebody brought them here and laid them out on the counter. Said he wanted us to know what wonderful flies the fan wings were."

I gasped.

"Probably caught them on bait," I said meanly and I knew that it wasn't so—that the extreme low water precluded this possibility.

"Mr. Somebody never uses bait," protested the salesman rather haughtily. "Besides, I happened to be fishing with him and caught almost as many as he—and on the fan wing too!"

I went away from the store in a confused state of mind. The truth was that my antipathy to the fan wing flies had started to waver. Still, I wasn't convinced absolutely. Not so easily could I accept them or assign them a place alongside the old tried and trusted favorites. I had been using small and delicately tied creations too many years to have my pet theories exploded without argument. Large, unwieldy-looking flies for low clear water? Impossible, I thought and yet . . . well, I had just heard the proof from a reliable source!

A week later we were fishing the Beaverkill. It was very unfriendly and quite disappointing. It was low and crystal-clear; most of the riffles had disappeared and on all the water my eyes gazed upon not a trout rose to break the extreme monotony of hot sun, barren rocks and glaring reflection. My partner made a dozen casts and quit.

"Not for me, Bergie," he said. "I'm going up to the clubhouse and take a nap. Maybe we might get a short rise just before dark but

I'll be darned if I can see the use of fishing through the middle of the day under these conditions."

"But it isn't the middle of the day," I protested. "It's only eight o'clock and the trout should rise for at least an hour yet."

"Oh yes . . . look at them rise! The water is boiling with hungry trout." He gave a dirty sort of laugh and continued. "Sometimes you make me sick with your notions. The trout should rise! Well, perhaps they should—but they're not! Oh, go ahead and make a fool of yourself if you wish. You'll be tired, not to mention disgusted, by night and then you won't be able to fish the evening rise properly when it comes—if it does!"

"Guess he's right," I admitted dolefully to myself. "Suppose I am a nut to think I can take trout under these conditions."

I looked over my fly assortment. There were those two fan wings. Could it be possible that they would take trout on this low water? I could not believe it. And yet the Esopus was every bit as low and clear as this last week and that tackle salesman had taken trout there when I hadn't done a thing. I took one of them out of the box and examined it. Then I looked at the stream, sighed and put it back in the box.

"The Dark Hendrickson number sixteen will be best," I said aloud to the Beaverkill. You see, I could not bring myself to believe that the fan wings were really any good.

The hot and stifling morning dragged along. Not a trout rose to my fly or to any natural insect. I scared a few from under the rocks as I went along and these fish just wriggled away for a few feet and then hid under other rocks. And the sun got hotter and the water seemed to get lower.

I came to a series of rock pocket holes. The stream narrowed here and the water was fast and quite deep. Besides, it was partially shaded by some huge trees which arched overhead. It was the most enticing spot I had seen during the morning and I began to feel more hopeful. "Surely," I murmured, "a trout will rise here." But I was mistaken.

After fishing ten of the pockets very carefully I decided to try another fly. As I opened the box the fan wings seemed to overshadow the rest of the flies. "Try us," they seemed to say. "We'll show you something interesting."

"They do look as if they might be attractive," I soliloquized as I picked one up to examine it. "But," I continued, "it doesn't seem possible that they can be any good, at least under these conditions." Then I put it back in the box and took out a number-fifteen Queen of the Waters. With this fly I fished over the ten pocket holes again and after that with three other patterns. Not a fish stirred.

"Good or no good," I said disgustedly, "I'm going to try one of those fan wings. They can't possibly be any worse than those I have been using." So I put one on. It was the Royal Coachman pattern, tied on a number ten hook.

I cast it tentatively over the first of the pocket holes. It whirled and gyrated through the air and fluttered down to alight on the water upside down. "What a fly," I snorted. I was quite disgusted.

Ten times I cast it and each time it fell wrong side up. On the eleventh cast it did the same thing, but the leader, having been twisted considerably from the previous cast, suddenly started to untwist and the fly after fluttering on the surface a moment came to rest right side up. At the same instant a flash appeared under it and I heard an audible smack. Excited, unprepared, I struck too hard and left the fly in the mouth of the trout!

I was dumfounded. What had caused this trout to rise? The fly itself or the peculiar action of it on that particular cast? Or was it the repeated casting over the one spot? It might have been any one of these reasons or even a combination of them. At any rate the atrocious-looking fly had brought a rise and that was something.

I put on the other fan wing I had with me. It was of the same size and pattern. This one acted even worse than the first. I thought that I would never get a decent upright float with it and became quite interested in the task of trying to make it alight on the water in the way it should. Then it studdenly started to ride the water with the wings cocked nicely. It certainly was easy to see and it rode the rough spots like a buoyant ship. Between two of the rocks was a short and deep run. I let the fly float over this place a dozen times. On the last float I noticed a flash just above the lower rock. Was it a trout becoming interested? I believed so.

I cast again. The fly floated over the run and passed the lower rock. I was just about to lift it from the water when I saw a good trout dart downstream after it. He took it solidly and I connected. It began to look as if the fan wing was some fly after all. Too bad I had left the rest of them at home. I would need to be careful with this one.

I took two more trout from the pocket hole stretch, both after a session of repeated casts over the same spot. That seemed to exhaust the possibilities of the section, so I moved upstream until I came to a long, deep pool, the deepest part of which was in dense shade and also protected by a steep bank.

Casting as long a line as possible I dropped the fly on the water at the very head of the pool. It floated with the current for a dozen feet and then came to rest well under the sheltering brush of the steep bank. I thought it best to let it float there for a few minutes, as I knew that the lifting of it on the glassy surface would cause a disturbance which would ruin any possible chance I might have of rising a trout. I am not sure how long I let the fly lie there silently. Probably it was about three minutes. Then suddenly it disappeared in a dimple that barely disturbed the surface of the water. With all the slack line out I misgauged the strike and set too hard! I felt a heavy weight for a fraction of an instant and then my last fan wing was gone and another Beaverkill trout had an unusual and colorful appendage attached to his mouth.

And that ended the sport for the day. Not another fly I possessed produced a rise. In the evening my partner came out and we both fished until dark without catching a trout, without even seeing one rise.

What was there about these fan wing flies which caused apparently unwilling fish to rise? Was it because they excited the trout's appetite? Or was it because the flies were so unusual that the trout became angry and struck from a desire to find out what they were?

From that day I used these flies frequently. They were not always successful, but often they brought results when other flies failed. Many times they have served to put interest in an otherwise dull day by bringing forth unexpected rises.

I was on the Mongaup once during a rise of trout when they were taking a natural which I could barely see, even when they floated near me. The smallest flies I had with me were sixteens and they looked like sailboats alongside the tiny naturals. But I kept one of them on and cast until my wrist ached and my rod seemed to lose its backbone, without getting a single rise. I finally gave it up and sat down on the shore fully convinced that the trout could not be taken.

While I sat there another angler appeared. He worked upstream to the pool I had been fishing and started casting over it. From where I sat I could see his fly floating on the water perfectly. It was very large and looked like a fan wing Royal Coachman. I chuckled to myself and wondered at the dumbness of some fishermen. "Just imagine," I murmured, "anyone thinking that he can take fish with a large fly like that when the trout are feeding on midges."

Even as I mumbled this I got a shock. The angler's fly had suddenly disappeared and in its place I saw a large swirl. He had hooked into one of those rising trout!

And that isn't all. In the next thirty minutes I saw that fellow take eight good trout and calmly put each one of them back into the stream after he had netted them. Think of it! Catching and putting back the very trout I had been vainly trying to catch for hours! It was very humiliating. But I bravely swallowed my discomfiture and greeted the angler with a smile when he came in from the pool.

"Well, you surely had some rare sport out there," I said.

"I'll say I did," he replied. "But it is getting tiresome and I think I'll call it a day. Did you ever see the trout so eager as they are today? I've put back more fish than I'd ordinarily catch in a month and I've got a creelful here that I'm positively ashamed of. I see you've started to dismantle. Suppose that you've got your limit too and have grown tired of it."

I know that my face got as red as a beet.

"Well . . . ah . . . you see," I stammered. "No . . . I . . . well . . . you see . . . to tell the truth I haven't caught a trout."

"What!" he exclaimed. "Haven't caught a trout? What in the world has been the matter with you?"

"A matter of fly, I think," I answered. "At least that is the conclusion I've reached since watching you take those fish from that pool yonder. Whatever made you try that fan wing Royal Coachman anyway? The trout are rising to midges. I was using the smallest thing I had trying to imitate them but I couldn't do a thing with them."

"That's just why I used the fan wing," explained the angler. "You see, I knew that I couldn't possibly imitate those midges so I never tried to. I always figure that when a fellow is in this sort of a fix it is a good plan to try a fly which is radically different, both in size and color, from the natural insect on the stream. I figure that the trout seeing this atrocity coming down in the midst of so many tiny flies will be quite likely to consider it a tidbit worth picking up. I admit that this theory doesn't always work but it does often enough to try it on every occasion the trout happen to be midge-feeding. And today it couldn't possibly have worked any better. The trout fairly broke their necks trying to beat each other getting at my fly."

"Well, now that you've blazed the way I hope to have a bit of your luck," I said laughingly. "It is certainly lucky for me that you came along. Usually I have enough sense to try out different things but today I simply could not get the idea out of my head that it would be necessary to imitate those midge flies in order to take any trout. I was going to quit in disgust."

The angler smiled. "The very last thing I ever do," he confided, "is to try and imitate natural flies of any kind. I always figure that when thousands of flies are continuously floating over the trout only a few of them are taken. If one does have an imitation of the natural it is only one fly among many and its chances of being taken are very slight indeed, of course the percentage depending upon the number of flies that happen to be floating over the fish. On the other hand if I use a fly radically different from the natural, something large and conspicuous like the fan wing Royal, it is bound to be noticed by the fish and he is quite likely to take it. If the trick works then I get my trout without going to the sometimes exasperating trouble of imitating the natural. If my method does not work I am only out a little time. Candidly I think that most of this close-imitation business is all the bunk anyway." He paused and looked at me. From the feeling of my face I knew that I had reddened again. "No offense meant, old man," he apologized. "That's only my own fool idea."

This was a bit of dry fly lore new to me at the time but it brought me success on that day and I have often used the method since with excellent results. Sometimes I wonder if this angler's ideas on the subject of imitating naturals aren't the soundest after all. Certainly through many periods of my own fishing experiences it would appear that his theory was the right one.

But always when I get to the point where I feel positive that I could get along with one fly a condition arises where a specific pattern is needed to rise the trout on a certain day and I immediately fall back on the old ideas. But I have adopted the practice of ignoring the imitation question to the following extent. No matter what the trout are rising to or if they are not rising at all I frequently start fishing with either the Brown Bivisible or the fan wing Royal Coachman. Then if neither of these works I start experimenting with different patterns. I find this is an excellent rule to follow. The two mentioned flies are effective so many times that the practice of using them first often saves one a lot of bother and fussing. Then if they do not bring results one can use flies which might imitate the naturals on the water.

Contrary to custom I highly recommend the frequent use of the fan wing Royal Coachman during the usual low-water conditions of July and August. To some it may seem quite ridiculous to use a large fly such as a number ten or twelve fan wing when the water is low and clear, but the practice of doing so has often brought me a great measure of success at times when other flies are ineffective. I could give many incidents to illustrate this.

But there are other sides of trout angling I wish to talk about; matters of approach, of lures which work when the trout would not look at a dry fly and of weather conditions. For the moment we shall put aside the matter of lures and consider an incident concerning approach.

Location: On one of Jersey's best streams.

There is a slow-moving and deep run in this charming Jersey brook which has been a bugbear to me ever since my first attempts to fish it failed miserably. The first time I came to it I thought that I was in for a very wonderful experience. At least two dozen really large trout were rising with a deliberateness which denoted serious feeding.

The logical way to fish this water was without question from the opposite side of the run from where the fish were feeding. The water where they were rising was deep and the bank an impenetrable mass of alders. On the opposite side the water was shallow and the bank free of trees and brush.

But when I attempted to fish from the shallow side the trout stopped rising, even before I cast a fly over them. The strangest thing of all was the fact that even when I waited until the disturbance attendant on my getting in position had been forgotten by the trout and they had started to rise again the first wave of my rod put them all down in the twinkling of an eye. During a period of two years I fished this place six times and never took a fish except from the very head, where the water was broken by the rapid leading into it. When I experienced the same disappointment on the first visit of the third year I began to think that perhaps I was trying to fish from a position where my presence was clearly perceived by the trout and that this was the reason for my failure to take them.

Acting on this thought, I took a position directly below the run. It was an extremely hard place from which to fish, the water being very deep and quite swift, but I managed to hold my balance and made a slack line cast to the tail of the run. I had only a five-inch float at the most from this position and it was necessary to hold the rod high to get that, but it was enough. A pound brown trout took solidly before the fly floated three inches.

I took one more fish from this position and then, not getting any more rises, I worked up slowly to the very lip of the run, where I could easily cast well up to the head. On attaining this position I refrained from casting for fifteen minutes. Then I saw a trout rise fifteen feet above me and close in to the bank. He took my fly the first time I floated it over him, and the instant I set the hook I rushed him down to the lip of the run to keep the fight from disturbing the other occupants of the place. Luckily the trout darted past me without getting tangled in my legs and I followed him down to the next pool, where I played him to a finish.

During the next hour I took two more good trout from the run by following this procedure. The last fish, however, was a fighting fool and I could not force the fight. With a rush against which my light tackle was unavailing he darted directly upstream and into the rapid above. When the pressure I exerted against him finally took effect it seemed to infuriate him and he darted back into the run, where he gave vent to his spleen by executing a series of acrobatic aerials. He tired quickly after this spectacular display, but the damage was done as far as getting any more rises was concerned.

This incident taught me a lesson which has since netted me many trout. That is never to give up trying to rise trout in a particular location until it has been approached from all possible angles. It is surprising how many times I find there is a more suitable position than the obvious one.

Often we chance upon a stream with the water and weather conditions apparently ideal for dry-fly fishing, with a fair hatch of natural flies in evidence, and yet find it impossible to rise a fish with the dry fly.

Usually this condition is due to the fact that the trout are feeding on some form of aquatic life. This may be the pupa of the very flies that are hatching and which are being taken as they rise to hatch on the surface of the stream, or it may be some form of bottom life which is prevalent at the time and of which the trout are very fond. Then too, sometimes the natural flies which one sees on the surface may be of a variety which the trout do not relish. (Apropos of this I have often seen trout consistently refusing a certain variety of bright-yellow flies.)

But whatever the reason may be, it is true that this condition frequently exists, and if one wishes to make the most of his fishing he should, under such circumstances, change from dry-fly to wet-fly fishing or even to lure fishing if it is necessary. One might contend that if the water is clear and not too high trout may be enticed to the surface even if they are feeding on nymphs. Sometimes this is very true and it is always worth trying by the persistent cast-in-one-spot system, but there are times when one cannot interest them in surface flies no matter how often one casts or what fly he uses.

A very graphic illustration of this condition is the following taken from my notes of a fishing trip in Pennsylvania during 1919.

The weather has been glorious in the mountains the past few days. A shower on Sunday cleared the rather humid air and since then a prevailing west wind has been rustling through the trees.

Monday and Tuesday the fishing was positively wonderful. I started out with the Light Cahill number twelve and took so many fish in the course of the morning that I got tired of it and began experimenting with other flies. From the results it would seem that any fly at all would take fish on these two days. I tried over two dozen patterns and every one brought rises without end. But size did make a difference. Twelves and fourteens brought the best results. Tens were out of the question and flies smaller than fourteens brought but few rises. During this period there were very few naturals on the stream. The ones that were about resembled a Light Cahill in coloration and were taken readily by the trout.

But today (Wednesday) something happened. The same weather

conditions prevailed and the water seemed to be holding its height. If anything there were more natural flies in evidence than on the other two days, but the trout were not taking them.

For the first three hours of the morning I did not pay much attention to the fact that I was not getting any rises. Fishing had been so good that the temporary absence of strikes seemed a relief. But after that I began to look for rises and when they were not forthcoming began to wonder what the trouble was.

Noon arrived. I had been fishing for six hours. During that time I had had rises from only three fish and they had been very small, barely seven inches in length. I grew a little tired of the inaction, so I selected a comfortable seat where I could observe a large pool and started eating my lunch.

As I sat there another angler appeared on the stream below me. To all appearances he was fishing with a dry fly. Even as I watched he took what appeared from the distance to be a good trout. Immediately my interest was aroused. I had fished that very water not twenty minutes previously and I had not received a single strike. I watched him closely.

He worked upstream rapidly. He skipped a stretch of forty feet and then concentrated on a small run which I had fished very carefully and persistently just before stopping to eat lunch. Again he hooked a good trout.

"If he is using a dry fly," I muttered, "he must be a wizard, or else he's got a fly that will do more than any of mine."

He skipped the water between the small run and the pool by which I was sitting and then spied me just as he started to cast. With an apologetic look he reeled in his line and came over to me.

"Any objection to my fishing here?" he asked. "Or perhaps you are resting the water. If you are I shall leave the stream and enter it some distance above."

"You go right ahead and fish," I said. "I haven't fished the pool at all yet and did not intend to for some time. Besides, you've got me interested. I saw you take some fish just now from water where I failed, and I'd like to get in on the way you did it. You see, I haven't taken a trout today and I'm a bit curious about your method, which seems to work so well."

He smiled. "There's really nothing to it," he protested. "I'm just fishing with small wet flies, letting them drift naturally slightly under the water. It's just like fishing the dry fly except that my flies are under the surface instead of on it."

"Do you mean to tell me that the trout will take a fly just under the surface and refuse a fly floating on the surface?" I asked a bit skeptically.

"Well, it does seem a bit farfetched," he admitted, "and often this slight difference in the location of the fly in the water does not matter, but it does today. I started out this morning with the dry fly because it has been the only thing to use for the last two days, but when I found that I wasn't getting any rises I spent a little time investigating the water in a comparatively slow-moving stretch and finally obtained a tiny dark-blue nymph from it. The nearest thing I had to imitate the thing was an Iron Blue Dun number fifteen so I put it on and started fishing downstream. This didn't work, so I turned around and started upstream again. Didn't have any luck for a while but suddenly started getting strikes and have been getting them ever since.

"But it's been very spotty fishing. At first I fished all the water one usually fishes when he is using dry flies and had many barren stretches. The places where I got the strikes were in the small runs where the water was under three feet deep and in the tails of the larger pools. As soon as I found out that this condition was quite consistent I simply fished such places and skipped the rest.

"So far the method has brought me very good results. I've taken over twenty trout and have kept eight of them that must weigh at least a total of five pounds."

This was very interesting information and in keeping with my own ideas concerning the day with the exception that I still persisted in the belief that these nymph-feeding trout could be induced to take a dry fly.

"Well, you go ahead and fish the tail of this pool," I suggested. "I'd just like to see you work. Then after you've tried I'll fish over the same water with a dry fly. I'd like to prove conclusively that these trout will not take a dry fly under these conditions."

He was a canny angler. Before casting he looked the water over very carefully. The tail of the pool flattened out considerably and was very shallow, but over on the opposite side from us it deepened close against a slightly overhanging bank. It was to this spot that he directed his attention.

He made the cast so that the flies alighted on the water some distance above the run. I noted that they sank instantly. After they sank he took up all slack line, and as the flies floated down with the current he gave them a slight motion with an almost imperceptible movement of his rod tip. As the flies reached the shelter of the overhanging bank I saw a flash and then came a splash as he hooked the trout and brought it away from the bank to play it out in water where the disturbance would not bother any other fish that might be in the run.

"Nicely done," I commented, "but you made one misstatement in the description of your method. You said that you let the flies float naturally with the current and I presumed from that you meant without any movement except that supplied by the water. Well, you didn't do that. You gave them a slight movement by raising and lowering your rod tip. I admit that one would not notice this unless he looked closely but it is true. I wonder if that little trick is the secret of your success?"

"By George, you're a keen one!" he exclaimed. "I *have* been fishing my flies that way but I didn't think you'd notice it. When I first started fishing wet this morning I did so with an absolute slack line. As I did not have any success while using that method I changed to this and immediately took trout."

"Before you try again let me float a dry fly over that place a few times," I suggested.

"Fine," he responded. "It will be an interesting test."

I floated my dry fly over the place not only once but a dozen times. I even tried an Iron Blue Dun the same size as the other fellow's wet Iron Blue. But I did not get a rise.

Then my acquaintance fished over the place again with his wet flies. Before they even reached the deep part of the run a trout took with a rush.

"That certainly seems conclusive enough," I laughed. "I'm telling you that I wouldn't have believed it if I hadn't been here to see with my own eyes. And now why not try the slack float over the place? Just to see if it really does make a difference." He did this, not just once but a dozen times. I watched the water closely and did not see any movement or flash which would have denoted interest on the part of the trout.

Then he returned to the taut-line-and-slight-movement method. A moment later he was fast to a twelve-inch brown. Needless to say I spent the rest of that day fishing wet and otherwise following closely the tactics of this new angling acquaintance.

Now, I do not mean to have the reader infer that the method of fishing wet flies mentioned in this incident is the best and only way to fish them. It is only one of the many ways in which they should be manipulated, depending on the mood of the trout. Nor is it always necessary to be so much concerned over a point as finely drawn as this. But one should always be on the lookout for such occurrences and be prepared for them when ordinary methods do not work. My notebooks are full of experiences where apparently insignificant differences in the way one handled his flies had everything to do with success. That angler who is known as a fish catcher may not be conscious of the little tricks he uses in the manipulation of his fly or bait but you may be sure that he does use them. It is those insignificant trifles which make the difference between the really successful angler and the fellow who gets them only when everyone else does.

And do not get the idea that trout may not be taken if your wet or dry flies do not bring rises. I remember one day on the Ausable when this was called to my attention quite forcibly.

The fly fishing had been abominable for days and on this day it was positively dead. My partner and I had fished for seven straight hours without getting a rise. It was so bad that I became quite indifferent as to whether I fished or not.

At noon I gathered some grasshoppers from a small clearing where our car was parked. I thought that they might prove useful before the day was over.

After lunch we went back to the stream and fished a gorgeous-looking pool. Partner whipped it carefully from one side while I took care of the other. We never got a rise, even from a minnow. When we reached the head of the pool I quit and sat on a rock while I watched Partner fish a pocket stretch above.

Then it occurred to me that I might as well drown a few wet flies while I sat there resting. I flipped these around for a half hour or so, trying various methods, but nothing happened. I was just about to give up the fishing entirely when I thought of the grasshoppers. It was certainly a good time to try bait! I dismantled a fly and stuck a hopper on the bare hook thus obtained. I cast it out on the water indifferently and let it float down with the current. The hopper stayed on the surface for only a moment and then the undertow sucked it below. About thirty feet from the rock I saw a swirl of a fish and felt a tug. I struck and felt nothing. But my hopper was gone!

In the next half hour I had twenty strikes on those hoppers. Of these strikes I missed all but three. I examined the entrails of the trout I caught and they were absolutely empty.

I then tried an imitation grasshopper, sinking it as I had the live ones. This did not work at all. I had four dead hoppers left and decided to use them. Every one brought a strike and I hooked two of the trout.

Consider this carefully. The water had been thoroughly fished with both wet and dry flies before the hoppers were used. The trout I had caught were empty. What made them take these hoppers so readily? It must have been because they wanted food of this type in preference to anything else. The odd part of the whole affair is the fact that there were no grasshoppers in the immediate vicinity of the stream at this point. The ones I had used came from a place at least a quarter of a mile from the river.

Such things as this always make me wonder. The moods and habits of trout are often so puzzling that they baffle me. On this same pool the very next day I could not get a strike with grasshoppers. This was after I had fished the stream below the pool without getting a rise on a dry fly for a period of six hours.

But while I sat on the rock vainly trying to provoke a strike with a hopper a scattered hatch of blue duns appeared. Immediately my spirits rose, and, changing back to the dry fly, I returned to the tail of the pool so that I would be ready when the rise started.

I waited twenty minutes or so but not a trout rose. I did not have a Blue Dun with me but I did have a Blue Spider, so I started casting it over the tail of the pool although I had no hopes of getting a rise. "If they won't take the natural," I soliloquized, "there's not much chance of their taking my artificial."

But they did. Before an hour passed I had four beautiful trout, three browns and one rainbow. By the time the next hour had passed I had all the trout I cared about keeping. And all during this time I never saw a trout rise to the natural fly.

This is not an uncommon experience. Often one will see many natural insects on the stream with not a trout rising to them and yet get rise after rise on an artificial which does not in any way look like the natural.

Such incidents make me wonder at times how much our theories concerning trout and flies amount to. It is all so confusing and inconsistent. Sometimes the fish rise wildly to naturals and refuse our offerings, no matter what flies we use. Often they will take our artificial in preference to the natural, even when they are feeding on such naturals steadily. At other times they will refuse our offerings until we get a fly over them which has the appearance of the natural, at least to us. Often we will make wonderful catches on the dry fly when not a natural is on the water. At other times we must resort to wet flies when natural flies are floating on the surface of the water. It fairly makes one's head whirl. And yet I feel that there is a logical reason for it all even if my conclusions so often prove erroneous and the complete truth continually evades me.

There isn't any doubt that bucktails often solve the problem of catching large trout which have become minnow feeders. I fondly believe that my effective bucktail is imitating a minnow when I am using it. But does it look like one to the trout? During certain periods when I have been enjoying exceptional fishing with a bucktail I have tried live minnows with very poor results. At other times when I have been having exceeding good fortune with minnows I have failed to take a trout with bucktails. And then again I have experienced many times when the trout will take either a bucktail or a minnow with equal avidity. It is all quite confusing and if it were not for the many times my theories work out consistently I would feel that in all my years of angling I have been but groping blindly, always on the verge of but not quite grasping the elusive answer.

There are those large brutes of the lower Oswegatchie. One of their favorite tricks is to take a dry fly which is being floated downstream to them just as the limit of the float is reached and the fly starts dragging across the current to straighten out taut against the rod. I have never observed a natural fly doing this. I can readily understand how these trout could appreciate this action if it were imparted to a minnow, because a minnow might dart through the water in this manner. But a dry fly dragging on the surface! I cannot figure it out.

This is all honest confession and has nothing to do with the fundamental principles of angling. There are many incidents in every angler's experiences which cannot be explained in a logical manner and I sometimes wonder, after I have brought a certain problem to a successful conclusion, whether I am really getting anywhere or just fooling myself.

Mrs. F. W. Morrell, a friend of mine who possesses a stretch of an exceedingly charming native trout stream, always amused me when she insisted that small flies were needed to bring about any degree of success when fishing her water. It seemed preposterous to me that such a condition could exist consistently. But eventually I fished her stream and found out, after an unsuccessful day of fishing with large flies, that she was perfectly right about it. But why? Four miles below her, on the same stream and under the same conditions, I have had wonderful success with a number ten bivisible.

It is such things that make me wonder if I really do know anything about this trout-fishing game or whether I just think I do. I must admit that it all keeps me quite subdued. The chastening effects of an absolute failure after a period of exhilarating success is a wonderful mold of character. Years of such experiences are bound to mellow the heart and temper the judgment.

The weather and our fishing! There is a subject for you. Show me the angler who does not have his favorite weather conditions if you can. In some the preference may be more pronounced than in others, but all have it in greater or less degree.

My own favorite weather for dry-fly fishing is quite different from that preferred by most anglers I have ever known. It *is* a rather queer choice when one considers it from the surface only, but it comes from the result of experience and is really quite logical.

I like cold, windy weather, provided the sun is shining. And by windy weather I mean wind which blows a veritable gale, wind which buffets the stream unmercifully, which prevents you from casting your fly except during the temporary lulls which occur between gusts.

I admit that fishing under such conditions is far from pleasant from a physical standpoint, but the glorious rise of trout which usually occurs at such times makes up for the discomfort. I think that the chief reason for the effectiveness of the dry fly during these cold, early-season windstorms is the fact that the wind displaces many flies from the foliage of the surrounding trees and bushes and batters them down on the stream. The trout evidently know this and come to the surface prepared to glut themselves with luscious morsels.

In checking over my field notes I find a preponderance of exceptional dry-fly days during cold windstorms in May, especially during the period between May fifteenth and June fifth. This is probably because a number of fly hatches occur during this time, including the famed May fly. But even at that the windy days during such periods seem to have been most lucrative, according to my notes, which have been faithfully kept. It seems to me that some of our most choice stream flies hatch under conditions which would seem prohibitive. Looking back over ten years I find that never once during this period have I failed to find quantities of flies on the water and make a good catch on the dry fly if the temperature was low and the wind high and blustery. That is, of course, if the stream itself was not discolored. On the other hand, the records of those same ten years disclose many failures of the dry fly when the day was still and perhaps warm for the time of year.

This certainly seems quite inconsistent as we humans figure things out. 'Most everyone is prone to think of muggy, still weather as conducive to flies hatching and trout rising, but it doesn't always work out that way. While I do find records of good dry-fly fishing under such conditions, I find that I have had more success during the periods when the air is free from humidity.

I must admit that even during the summer I prefer those cheerful days when the sky is azure blue and the air cool, with a fresh wind blowing. Such days are a great tonic to the angler and they seem to have a like effect on the fish, at least in my experience. But sometimes rain promotes good dry-fly fishing, and I never rush for cover when a summer shower makes its appearance, even if it does mean a drenching.

Although many anglers prefer cloudy days for their fishing, I cannot say that I have ever found them superior to those when the sun is bright; in fact I prefer a cool, sunshiny day to all others except when fishing spring holes, when a cloudy day does make a great difference. Still waters of any kind are best fished during cloudy weather, or during that part of the day when the sun does not shine on them.

I do not mind thunder in the least except when the bolts of lightning come too close for comfort. Then it makes me nervous. But in spite of the statements of many anglers I cannot believe that it frightens the trout or keeps them from rising. Both by day and by night I have fly-fished through heavy thunderstorms and have made good catches. Often during such storms at night I have hooked a fish at the very moment that a flash of lightning has illuminated the water, so that I could actually see the trout take my fly. And often while the peals of a terrific crash of thunder still rang in my ears I have had a trout take my fly with a vim which certainly did not show any fear of the elements.

There is also much difference of opinion as to the best time of day to fish. Many anglers insist that there is no time like the early morning, others say that if they can have the evening fishing the rest of the day can go hang. Well, I also like the early-morning fishing. It is charming. Invariably I start as soon as I can see my fly on the water. And I thoroughly enjoy the evening fishing. Without doubt it is the pleasantest time of the entire day. But that does not mean that I get my best fishing then. Of course at times I have, but when I really start a systematic tabulation of my fishing trips I find that I have taken more trout between the hours of eight and ten and from four to six than at any other time. The early-morning fishing shows up best during those times when the water is too warm for good fishing and the evening fishing shows a great percentage of extraordinary rises of trout to natural flies with the catch of the angler small in comparison. I even find that the hours between eleven and three have been exceedingly productive in certain streams and ponds.

But there is nothing sure about it all. One day the best fishing may come at daylight and become very poor after that. Another day it may start early, hold good all day and last until after dark. At other times it may be spotty, occurring off and on throughout the day. It may be best at noon or in the evening. A lot depends on the fly hatches, the water temperature, the type of stream and the mood of the trout.

The thing I go by most is temperature. When the water of any stream gets warmer than sixty-eight I have no faith in my ability to take trout, no matter what the weather conditions are. This is despite the fact that I have, in a few instances, taken some good trout with the temperature of the water as high as seventy-four degrees. For this reason I always carry a thermometer with me. If the temperature of the streams we happen to visit is unfavorable we pass it up and go to some other stream where it is favorable. We have found this a worth-while rule to follow and it certainly saves a lot of fruitless fishing.

On the Loch

WILLIAM BLACK

William Black, although something of a tradi-
tionalist, added real color to his angling writings.
"On the Loch" is, unquestionably, one of his best
stories.

A CONSIDERABLE wind arose during the night; Mr. Hodson did not sleep very well; and, lying awake toward morning, he came to the conclusion that he had been befooled, or rather that he had befooled himself, with regard to that prodigy of a gamekeeper. He argued with himself that his mental faculties must have been dulled by the long day's travel; he had come into the inn jaded and tired; and then, finding himself face to face with an ordinarily alert and intrepid intellect, he had no doubt exaggerated the young man's abilities, and made a wonder of him where no wonder was needed. That he was a person of considerable information and showed common sense was likely enough. Mr. Hodson, in his studies of men and things, had heard something of the intelligence and education to be found among the working classes in Scotland. He had heard of the hand-loom weavers who were learned botanists; of the stonemasons who were great geologists; of the village poets who, if most of their efforts were but imitations of Ferguson and Burns and Tannahill, would here and there, in some chance moment of inspiration, sing out some true and pathetic song, to be taken to the hearts of their countrymen, and added to a treasure store of rustic minstrelsy such as no other nation in the world has ever produced. At the same time he was rather anxious to meet Strang again, the better to get the measure of him. And as he was also curious to see what this neighborhood into which he had penetrated looked like, he rose betimes in the morning—indeed, before the day was fully declared.

The wind still moaned about the house, but outside there was no sign of any storm; on the contrary, everything was strangely calm. The lake lay a dark lurid purple in the hollow of the encircling hills; and these, along the eastern heavens, were of the deepest and softest olive green; just over them was a line of gleaming salmon red, keen and resplendent as if molten from a furnace; and over that again soft saffron-dusky clouds, deepening in tone the higher they hung in the clear pale steel hues of the overhead sky. There was no sign of life anywhere—nothing but the birch woods sloping down to the shore; the moorland wastes of the lower hills; and above these the giant bulk and solemn shadows of Ben Clebrig,* dark against the dawn. It was a lovely sight; he began to think he had never before in his life felt himself so much alone. But whence came the sound of the wind that seemed to go moaning down the strath toward the purple lake?

Well, he made no doubt that it was up toward the north and west that the storm was brewing; and he remembered that a window in the sitting room below looked in that direction; there he would be able to ascertain whether any fishing was practicable. He finished his dressing and went down. The breakfast table was laid; a mighty mass of peats was blazing cheerfully in the spacious fireplace. And the storm? Why, all the wide strath on this northern side of the house was one glow of yellow light in the now spreading sunrise; and still farther away in the north the great shoulders of Ben Loyal † had caught a faint roseate tinge; and the same pale and beautiful color seemed to transfuse a large and fleecy cloud that clung around the snow-scarred peak. So he came to the conclusion that in this corner of the glen the wind said more than it meant; and that they might adventure on the loch without risk of being swamped or blown ashore.

* That is, the Hill of the Playing Trout.
† More properly Ben Laoghal, the Hill of the Calves.

The slim tall Highland lass made her appearance with further plenishings for the table, and "Good moarning!" she said, in her pretty way, in answer to his greeting.

"Say, now, has that man come down from Tongue yet?"

"No, sir," said Nelly, "he wass no come down yet." And then she looked up with a demure smile. "They would be keeping the New Year at Tongue last night."

"Keeping the New Year on the fourteenth of January?"

"It's the twelfth is the usual day, sir," she explained, "but that was Saturday, and they do not like a Saturday night, for they have to stop at twelve o'clock, and so most of them were keeping it last night."

"Oh, indeed. Then the festive gentleman won't show up today?"

"But it is of no matter whateffer whether he comes or no; for I am sure that Ronald will be willing to lend a hand. Oh, I am sure of it. I will ask him myself."

"*You* will ask him?" was Mr. Hodson's internal soliloquy. "It is to *you* he will grant a favor. Indeed!"

He fixed his eyes on her.

"He is a good-looking young fellow, that Ronald."

She did not answer that; she was putting the marmalade, and the honey, and the cream on the table.

"He is not married?"

"No, sir."

"Well, now, when he thinks about getting married, I suppose he'll pretty well have his choice about here?"

"Indeed there iss others besides him," said Nelly rather proudly, but her face was red as she opened the door.

Well, whether it was owing to the intervention of Nelly or not, as soon as Mr. Hodson was ready to start he found Ronald waiting for him without; and not only that, but he had already assumed command of the expedition, having sent the one gillie who had arrived down to bale the boat. And then he would overhaul Mr. Hodson's fishing gear —examining the rods, testing the lines and traces, and rejecting all the spoon baits, angels, sand eels, and what not, that had been supplied by the London tackle maker, for two or three of the familiar phantom minnows. Mr. Hodson could scarcely believe that this was the same man who last night had been discussing the disestablishment of state churches and the policy of protecting native industries. He had not a word for anything but the business before him; and the bold fashion in which he handled those minnows, all bristling with hooks, or drew the catgut traces through his fingers (Mr. Hodson shivered and seemed to feel his own fingers being cut to the bone), showed that he was as familiar with the loch as with the hillside or the kennel.

"I'm not much on salmon-fishing myself," the American remarked modestly.

"It's rather early in the season, sir, I'm afraid," was the answer. "But we might get a fish after all; and if we do it'll be the first caught in Scotland this year, I warrant."

They set out and walked down to the shore of the loch, and there Mr. Hodson seated himself on the gunwale of the flat-bottomed coble and watched the two men putting the rods together and fixing the traces. The day had now declared itself; wild and stormy in appearance, but fair on the whole; great floods of sunshine falling suddenly on the yellow slopes and the russet birch woods; and shadows coming as rapidly across the far heights of Clebrig, steeping the mountains in gloom. As for the gillie who had been proof against the seductions of keeping the New Year, and who was now down on one knee, biting catgut with his teeth, he was a man as tall and as sallow as Mr. Hodson himself, but with an added expression of intense melancholy and hopelessness. Or was that but temporary?

"Duncan doesna like that boat," Ronald said, glancing at Mr. Hodson.

The melancholy man did not speak, but shook his head gloomily.

"Why?"

As the gillie did not answer, Ronald said, "He thinks there is no luck with that boat."

"That boat?" the gillie said, with an angry look toward the hapless coble. "She has the worst luck of any boat in Sutherland—*tam her!*" he added, under his breath.

"In my country," the American said, in his slow way, "we don't mind luck much; we find perseverance about as good a horse to win with in the end."

He was soon to have his perseverance tried. Everything being ready, they pushed off from the shore, Ronald taking stroke oar, the gillie at the bow, Mr. Hodson left to pay out the lines of the two rods, and fix these in the stern, when about five-and-thirty yards had gone forth. At first, it is true, he waited and watched with a trifle of anxiety. He wanted to catch a salmon; it would be something to write about to his daughter; it would be a new experience for himself. But when time passed and the boat was slowly rowed along the loch at a measured distance from the shore, without any touch of anything coming to make the point of either rod tremble, he rather gave up his hope in that direction, and took to talking with Ronald. After all, it was not salmon fishing alone that had brought him into these wilds.

"I suppose it is really too early in the season," he observed, without much chagrin.

"Rayther," said Ronald.

"Rawther," said the melancholy gillie.

But at that instant something happened that startled every one of them out of their apathy. The top of one of the rods was violently pulled at, and then there was a long shrill yell of the reel.

"There he is, sir! there he is, sir!" Ronald called.

Mr. Hodson made a grab blindly—for he had been looking at the scenery around—at one of the rods. It was the wrong one. But before he knew where he was, Ronald had got hold of the other and raised the top so as to keep a strain on the fish. The exchange of the rods was effected in a moment. Then when Ronald had wound in the other line and put the rod at the bow, he took to his oar again, leaving Mr. Hodson to fight his unknown enemy as best he might, but giving him a few words of direction from time to time, quietly, as if it were all a matter of course.

"Reel in, sir, reel in—keep an even strain on him—let him go—let him go if he wants—"

Well, the fish was not a fierce fighter; after the first long rush he scarcely did anything; he kept boring downward, with a dull, heavy weight. It seemed easy work; and Mr. Hodson—triumphant in the hope of catching his first salmon—was tempted to call aloud to the melancholy gillie, "Well, Duncan, how about luck now?"

"I think it's a kelt," the man answered morosely.

But the sinister meaning of this reply was not understood.

"I don't know what you call him," said Mr. Hodson, holding on with both hands to the long, lithe grilse rod that was bent almost double. "Celt or Saxon, I don't know; but I seem to have got a good grip of him."

Then he heard Ronald say, in an undertone, to the gillie, "A kelt? No fears. The first rush was too heavy for that."

And the gillie responded sullenly, "He's following the boat like a cow."

"What is a kelt, anyway?" the American called out. "Something that swims, I suppose? It ain't a man?"

"I hope it's no a kelt, sir," said Ronald—but doubtfully.

"But what is a kelt, then, when he's at home?"

"A salmon, sir, that hasna been down to the sea; we'll have to put him back if he is."

Whirr! went the reel again; the fish, kelt or clean salmon, had struck deep down. But the melancholy creature at the bow was taking no further interest in the fight. He was sure it was a kelt. Most likely the minnow would be destroyed. Maybe he would break the trace. But a kelt it was. He knew the luck of this "tammed" boat.

The struggle was a tedious one. The beast kept boring down with the mere force of its weight, but following the coble steadily; and even

Ronald, who had been combating his own doubts, at length gave in: he was afraid it was a kelt. Presently the last suspicion of hope was banished. With a tight strain on him, the now exhausted animal began to show near the surface of the water—his long eel-like shape and black back revealing too obviously what manner of creature he was. But this revelation had no effect on the amateur fisherman, who at last beheld the enemy he had been fighting with so long. He grew quite excited. A kelt?—he was a beautiful fine fish! If he could not be eaten he could be stuffed! Twenty pounds he was, if an ounce!—would he throw back such a trophy into the loch?

Ronald was crouching in the stern of the boat, the big landing net in his hand, watching the slow circling of the kelt as it was being hauled nearer and nearer. His sentiments were of a different kind.

"Ah, you ugly brute!—ah, you rascal—ah—ah!"—and then there was a deep scoop of the landing net; and the next minute the huge eel-like beast was in the bottom of the boat, Duncan holding on to its tail, and Ronald gripping it by the gills, while he set to work to get the minnow out of its jaws. And then without further ado—and without stopping to discuss the question of stuffing—the creature was heaved into the water again, with a parting benediction of "Bah, you brute!" It took its leave rapidly.

"Well, it's a pity, sir," Ronald said; "that would have been a twenty-four-pound salmon if he had been down to the sea."

"It's the luck of this tammed boat," Duncan said gloomily.

But Mr. Hodson could not confess to any such keen sense of disappointment. He had never played so big a fish before, and was rather proud that so slight a grilse rod and so slender a line should (of course, with some discretion and careful nursing on his part) have overmastered so big a beast. Then, he did not eat salmon; there was no loss in that direction. And as he had not injured the kelt in any way, he reflected that he had enjoyed half an hour's excitement without doing harm to anything or anybody, and he was well content. So he paid out the two lines again, and set the rods, and began to renew his talk with Ronald touching the customs connected with the keeping of the New Year.

After all, it was a picturesque kind of occupation, kelts or no kelts. Look at the scene around them—the lapping waters of the loch, a vivid and brilliant blue when the skies were shining fair, or black and stormy again when the clouds were heavy in the heavens; and always the permanent features of the landscape—the soft yellows of the lower straths, where the withered grass was mixed with the orange bracken; the soft russet of the leafless birch woods fringing the shores of the lake; the deep-violet shadows of Ben Clebrig stretching up into the long swaths of mist; and then the fair amphitheater of hills—Ben Hee, and

Ben Hope, and Ben Loyal—with sunlight and shade intermingling their ethereal tints, but leaving the snow streaks always sparkling and clear. He got used to the monotony of the slow circling of the upper waters of the lake. He forgot to watch the points of the rods. He was asking all kinds of questions about the stags and the hinds, about ptarmigan, and white hares, and roe, about the price of sheep, the rents of crofts, the comparative wages of gillies, and shepherds, and foresters, and keepers, and stalkers, and the habits and customs of land agents and factors. And at length, when it came to lunchtime, and when they landed and found for him a sheltered place under the lee of a big rock, and when Ronald pointed out to him a grassy bank, and said rather ruefully—

"I dinna like to see that place empty, sir. That's where the gentlemen have the salmon laid out, that they may look at them at lunchtime—"

Mr. Hodson, as he opened the little basket that had been provided for him, answered cheerfully enough—

"My good friend, don't you imagine that I feel like giving it up yet. I'm not finished with this lake, and I'll back perseverance against luck any day. Seems to me we've done very well so far; I'm content."

By and by they went back into the coble again and resumed their patient pursuit; and there is little doubt that by this time Ronald had come to the conclusion that this stranger who had come among them was a singularly odd and whimsical person. It was remarkable enough that he should have undertaken this long and solitary journey in order to fish for salmon, and then show himself quite indifferent as to whether he got any or not; and it was scarcely human for anyone to betray no disappointment whatever when the first fish caught proved to be a kelt; but it was still stranger than man rich enough to talk about renting a deer forest should busy himself with the petty affairs of the very poorest people around. Why, he wanted to know how much Nelly the housemaid could possibly save on her year's wages; whether she was supposed to lay by something as against her wedding day; or whether any of the lads about would marry her for her pretty face alone. And when he discovered that Mr. Murray, the innkeeper, was about to give a New Year supper and dance to the lads and lasses of the neighborhood, he made no scruple about hinting plainly that he would be glad of an invitation to join that festive party.

"Not if I'm going to be anything of a wet blanket," he said candidly. "My dancing days are over, and I'm not much in the way of singing; but I'll tell them an American story; or I'll present them with a barrel of whisky—if that will keep the fun going."

"I'm sure they'll be very glad, sir," Ronald said, "if ye just come and look on. When there's gentlemen at the Lodge, they generally come down to hear the pipes, and the young gentlemen have a dance too."

"What night did you say?"

"Monday next, sir."

Well, he had only intended remaining here for a day or two, to see what the place was like; but this temptation was too great. Here was a famous opportunity for the pursuit of his favorite study—the study of life and manners. This, had Ronald but known it, was the constant and engrossing occupation that enabled this contented traveler to accept with equanimity the ill luck of kelt catching; it was a hobby he could carry about with him everywhere; it gave a continuous interest to every hour of his life. He cared little for the analyses of science; he cared less for philosophical systems; metaphysics he laughed at; but men and women—the problems of their lives and surroundings, their diverse fortunes and aspirations and dealings with each other— that was the one and constant subject that engrossed his interest. No doubt there was a little more than this; it was not merely as an abtract study that he was so fond of getting to know how people lived. The fact was that, even after having made ample provision for his family, he still remained possessed of a large fortune; his own expenditure was moderate; and he liked to go about with the consciousness that here or there, as occasion served, he could play the part of a little Providence. It was a harmless vanity; moreover, he was a shrewd man, not likely to be deceived by spurious appeals for charity. Many was the young artist whom he had introduced to buyers; many the young clerk whom he had helped to a better situation; more than one young woman in the humblest of circumstances had suddenly found herself enabled to purchase her wedding outfit (with a trifle over, toward the giving her greater value in her lover's eyes), through the mysterious benevolence of some unknown benefactor. This man had been brought up in a country where everyone is restlessly pushing forward; and being possessed of abundant means, and a friendly disposition, it seemed the most natural thing in the world that here or there, at a fitting opportunity, he should lend a helping hand. And there was always this possibility present to him—this sense of power—as he made those minute inquiries of his into the conditions of the lives of those among whom he chanced to be living.

The short winter day was drawing to a close; the brilliant steely blue of the driven water had given place to a livid gray; and the faint gleams of saffron yellow were dying out in the western skies.

"Suppose we'd better be going home now," Mr. Hodson remarked at a venture, and with no great disappointment in his tone.

"I'm afraid, sir, there's no much chance now," Ronald said.

"We must call again; they're not at home today," the other remarked, and began with much complacency to reel in one of the lines.

He was doing so slowly, and the men were as slowly pulling in for the shore in the gathering dusk, when *whirr!* went the other reel. The loud and sudden shriek in this silence was a startling thing; and no less so was the springing into the air—at apparently an immense distance away—of some creature, kelt or salmon, that fell into the water again with a mighty splash. Instinctively Mr. Hodson had gripped this rod and passed the other one he had been reeling in to Strang. It was an anxious moment. *Whirr!* went another dozen yards of line; and again the fish sprang into the air—this time plainly visible.

"A clean fish, sir! a clean fish!" was the welcome cry.

But there was no time to hazard doubts or ask questions; this sudden visitor at the end of the line had not at all made up his mind to be easily captured. First of all he came sailing in quietly toward the boat, giving the fisherman all he could do to reel in and keep a strain on him; then he whirled out the line so suddenly that the rod was nearly bent double; and then, in deep water, he kept persistently sulking and boring, refusing to yield an inch. This was a temporary respite.

"Well, now, is this one all right?" Mr. Hodson called out—but he was rather bewildered, for he knew not what this violent beast might not be after next, and the gathering darkness looked strange, the shadows of Clebrig overhead seeming to blot out the sky.

"A clean fish, sir," was the confident answer.

"No doubt o' that, sir," even the melancholy Duncan admitted; for he foresaw a dram now, if not a tip in actual money.

Then slowly and slowly the salmon began to yield to the strain on him—which was considerable, for this was the heavier of the two rods —and quickly the line was got in, the pliant curve of the rod remaining always the same; while Mr. Hodson flattered himself that he was doing very well now, and that he was surely becoming the master of the situation. But the next instant something happened that his mind was not rapid enough to comprehend: something dreadful and horrible and sudden: there was a whirring out of the reel so rapid that he had to lower the point of the rod almost to the water; then the fish made one flashing spring along the surface—and this time he saw the creature, a gleam of silver in the dusk—and then, to his unspeakable dismay and mortification, he felt the line quite slack. He did utter a little monosyllable.

"He's off, sir," the melancholy gillie said in a tone of sad resignation.

"Not a bit, sir, not a bit! Reel in, quick!" Ronald called to him; and the fisherman had sense enough to throw the rod as far back as he could to see if there was yet some strain on it. Undoubtedly the fish was still there. Moreover, this last cantrip seemed to have taken the spirit out of him. By and by, with a strong, steady strain on him, he suffered himself to be guided more and more toward the boat, until, now and again, they could see a faint gleam in the dark water; and

now Ronald had relinquished his oar and was crouching down in the
stern—this time not with the landing net in his hand, but with the
bright steel clip just resting on the gunwale.

"He's showing the white feather now, sir; give him a little more of
the butt."

However, he had not quite given in yet; each time he came in sight
of the boat he would make another ineffectual rush, but rarely getting
down deeper than three or four yards. And then, with a short line and
the butt well toward him, he began to make slow semicircles this way
and that; and always he was being steadily hauled nearer the coble;
until with one quick dip and powerful upward pull Ronald had got
him transfixed on the gaff and landed—the huge, gleaming, beautiful
silver creature!—in the bottom of the boat.

"Well done, sir!—a clean fish—a beauty—the first caught in Scotland this year, I know!"—these were the exclamations he heard now;
but he scarcely knew how it had all happened, for he had been more
excited than he was aware of. He felt a vague and general sense of
satisfaction; wanted to give the men a glass of whisky, and had none
to give them; thought that the capture of a salmon was a noble thing;
would have liked his daughter Carry to hear the tidings at once; and
had a kind of general purpose to devote the rest of that year to salmon
fishing in the Highlands. From this entrancement he was awakened by
a dispute between the two men as to the size of the fish.

"He's twelve pounds, and no more," the melancholy Duncan said,
eying him all over.

"Look at his shoulders, man," Ronald rejoined. "Fourteen pounds
if he's an ounce. Duncan, lad, ye've been put off your guessing by the
sight of the kelt."

"He's a good fish whateffer," Duncan was constrained to admit—
for he still foresaw that prospect of a dram when they returned to the
inn, with perhaps a more substantial handseling of good luck.

Of course, they could do no more fishing that afternoon, for it was
nearly dark; but it was wonderful how the capture of this single salmon
seemed to raise the spirits of the little party as they got ashore and
walked home. There was a kind of excitement in the evening air.
They talked in a rapid and eager way—about what the fish had done,
what were the chances of such and such a rush, the probable length
of time it had been up from the sea, the beauty of its shape, the
smallness of its head, the freshness of its color, and so forth—and
there was a kind of jubilation abroad. The first fish caught in Scotland
that year!—of course, it must be packed forthwith and sent south to
his daughter Carry and her friends. And Mr. Hodson was quite
facetious with the pretty Nelly when she came in to lay the table for
dinner, and would have her say whether she had not yet fixed her

mind on one or other of these young fellows around. As for the small hamlet of Inver-Mudal, it was about as solitary and forlorn a habitation as any to be found in the wilds of northern Scotland; and he was there all by himself; but with the blazing peat fire, and the brilliant white cloth on the dinner table, and the consciousness that the firm, stout-shouldered, clean-run fourteen-pounder was lying in the dairy on a slab of cold stone, he considered that Inver-Mudal was a most enjoyable and sociable and comfortable place, and that he had not felt himself so snug and so much at home for many and many a day.

Crocker's Hole

R. D. BLACKMORE

Those who were forced to read Lorna Doone *will find it difficult to accept the fact that R. D. Blackmore was an accomplished angling writer. He was. "Crocker's Hole" has been dubbed a masterpiece by writers as well as anglers.*

PART I

THE CULM, which rises in Somersetshire, and hastening into a fairer land (as the border waters wisely do) falls into the Exe near Killerton, formerly was a lovely trout stream, such as perverts the Devonshire angler from due respect toward Father Thames and the other canals round London. In the Devonshire valleys it is sweet to see how soon a spring becomes a rill, and a rill runs on into a rivulet, and a rivulet swells into a brook; and before one has time to say, "What are you at?"—before the first tree it ever spoke to is a dummy, or the first hill it ever ran down has turned blue, here we have all the airs and graces, demands and assertions of a full-grown river.

But what is the test of a river? Who shall say? "The power to drown a man," replies the river darkly. But rudeness is not argument. Rather shall we say that the power to work a good undershot wheel, without being dammed up all night in a pond, and leaving a tidy back stream to spare at the bottom of the orchard, is a fair certificate of riverhood. If so, many Devonshire streams attain that rank within five miles of their spring; aye, and rapidly add to it. At every turn they gather aid, from ash-clad dingle and aldered meadow, mossy rock and ferny wall, hedge-trough-roofed with bramble netting, where the baby water lurks, and lanes that coming down to ford bring suicidal tribute. Arrogant, all-engrossing river, now it has claimed a great valley of its own; and whatever falls within the hill scoop sooner or later belongs to itself. Even the crystal "shutt" that crosses the farmyard by the woodrick, and glides down an aqueduct of last year's bark for Mary to fill the kettle from; and even the tricklets that have no organs for telling or knowing their business, but only get into unwary oozings in and among the water grass, and there make moss and forget themselves among it—one and all, they come to the same thing at last, and that is the river.

The Culm used to be a good river at Culmstock, tormented already by a factory, but not strangled as yet by a railroad. How it is now the present writer does not know, and is afraid to ask, having heard of a vile "Culm Valley Line." But Culmstock bridge was a very pretty place to stand and contemplate the ways of trout; which is easier work than to catch them. When I was just big enough to peep above the rim, or to lie upon it with one leg inside for fear of tumbling over, what a mighty river it used to seem, for it takes a treat there and spreads itself. Above the bridge the factory stream falls in again, having done its business, and washing its hands in the innocent half that has strayed down the meadows. Then under the arches they both rejoice and come to a slide of about two feet, and make a short, wide pool below, and indulge themselves in perhaps two islands, through which a little river always magnifies itself and maintains a mysterious middle. But after that, all of it used to come together, and make off in one body for the meadows, intent upon nurturing trout with rapid stickles, and butter-cuppy corners where fat flies may tumble in. And here you may find in the very first meadow, or at any rate you might have found, forty years ago, the celebrated "Crocker's Hole."

The story of Crocker is unknown to me, and interesting as it doubt-less was, I do not deal with him, but with his Hole. Tradition said that he was a baker's boy who, during his basket rounds, fell in love with a maiden who received the cottage loaf, or perhaps good "House-holds," for her master's use. No doubt she was charming, as a girl should be, but whether she encouraged the youthful baker and then betrayed him with false role, or whether she "consisted" throughout—as our cousins across the water express it—is known to their *manes* only. Enough that she would not have the floury lad; and that he, after giving in his books and money, sought an untimely grave among the trout. And this was the first pool below the bread walk deep enough to drown a five-foot baker boy. Sad it was; but such things must be, and bread must still be delivered daily.

A truce to such reflections—as our foremost writers always say, when they do not see how to go on with them—but it is a serious thing to know what Crocker's Hole was like; because at a time when (if he had only persevered, and married the maid, and succeeded to the oven, and reared a large family of short-weight bakers) he might have been leaning on his crutch beside the pool, and teaching his grandson to swim by precept (that beautiful proxy for practice)—at such a time, I say, there lived a remarkably fine trout in that hole. Anglers are notoriously truthful, especially as to what they catch, or even more frequently have not caught. Though I may have written fiction, among many other sins—as a nice old lady told me once— now I have to deal with facts; and foul scorn would I count it ever to make believe that I caught that fish. My length at that time was not more than the butt of a four-jointed rod, and all I could catch was a minnow with a pin, which our cook Lydia would not cook, but used to say, "Oh, what a shame, Master Richard! They would have been trout in the summer, please God! if you would only a' let 'em grow on." She is living now and will bear me out in this.

But upon every great occasion there arises a great man; or to put it more accurately, in the present instance, a mighty and distinguished boy. My father, being the parson of the parish, and getting, need it be said, small pay, took sundry pupils, very pleasant fellows, about to adorn the universities. Among them was the original "Bude Light," as he was satirically called at Cambridge, for he came from Bude, and there was no light in him. Among them also was John Pike, a born Zebedee if ever there was one.

John Pike was a thickset younker, with a large and bushy head, keen blue eyes that could see through water, and the proper slouch of shoulder into which great anglers ripen; but greater still are born with it; and of these was Master John. It mattered little what the weather was, and scarcely more as to the time of year, John Pike must have his fishing every day, and on Sundays he read about it, and made flies. All the rest of the time he was thinking about it.

My father was coaching him in the fourth book of *The Aeneid* and all those wonderful speeches of Dido, where passion disdains construction; but the only line Pike cared for was of horsehair. "I fear, Mr. Pike, that you are not giving me your entire attention," my father used to say in his mild dry way; and once when Pike was more than usually abroad, his tutor begged to share his meditations. "Well, sir," said Pike, who was very truthful, "I can see a green drake by the strawberry tree, the first of the season, and your derivation of 'barbarous' put me in mind of my barberry dye." In those days it was a very nice point to get the right tint for the mallard's feather.

No sooner was lesson done than Pike, whose rod was ready upon the lawn, dashed away always for the river, rushing headlong down the hill, and away to the left through a private yard, where "No Thoroughfare" was put up and a big dog stationed to enforce it. But Cerberus himself could not have stopped John Pike; his conscience backed him up in trespass the most sinful when his heart was inditing of a trout upon the rise.

All this, however, is preliminary, as the boy said when he put his father's coat upon his grandfather's tenterhooks, with felonious intent upon his grandmother's apples; the main point to be understood is this, that nothing—neither brazen tower, hundred-eyed Argus, nor Cretan Minotaur—could stop John Pike from getting at a good stickle. But, even as the world knows nothing of its greatest men, its greatest men know nothing of the world beneath their very nose, till fortune sneezes dexter. For two years John Pike must have been whipping the water as hard as Xerxes, without having ever once dreamed of the glorious trout that lived in Crocker's Hole. But why, when he ought to have been at least on bowing terms with every fish as long as his middle finger, why had he failed to know this champion? The answer is simple—because of his short cuts. Flying as he did like an arrow from a bow, Pike used to hit his beloved river at an elbow, some furlong below Crocker's Hole, where a sweet little stickle sailed away downstream, whereas for the length of a meadow upward the water lay smooth, clear, and shallow; therefore the youth, with so little time to spare, rushed into the downward joy.

And here it may be noted that the leading maxim of the present period, that man can discharge his duty only by going counter to the stream, was scarcely mooted in those days. My grandfather (who was a wonderful man, if he was accustomed to fill a cart in two days of fly fishing on the Barle) regularly fished downstream; and what more than a cartload need anyone put into his basket?

And surely it is more genial and pleasant to behold our friend the river growing and thriving as we go on, strengthening its voice and enlarging its bosom, and sparkling through each successive meadow with richer plenitude of silver, than to trace it against its own grain and good will toward weakness, and littleness, and immature conceptions.

However, you will say that if John Pike had fished upstream, he would have found this trout much sooner. And that is true; but still, as it was, the trout had more time to grow into such a prize. And the way in which John found him out was this. For some days he had been tormented with a very painful tooth, which even poisoned all the joys of fishing. Therefore he resolved to have it out and sturdily entered the shop of John Sweetland, the village blacksmith, and there paid his sixpence. Sweetland extracted the teeth of the village, whenever they required it, in the simplest and most effectual way. A piece of fine wire was fastened round the tooth, and the other end round the anvil's nose, then the sturdy blacksmith shut the lower half of his shop door, which was about breast-high, with the patient outside and the anvil within; a strong push of the foot upset the anvil, and the tooth flew out like a well-thrown fly.

When John Pike had suffered this very bravely, "Ah, Master Pike," said the blacksmith, with a grin, "I reckon you won't pull out thic there big vish"—the smithy commanded a view of the river—"clever as you be, quite so peart as thiccy."

"What big fish?" asked the boy, with deepest interest, though his mouth was bleeding fearfully.

"Why, that girt mortial of a vish as hath his hover in Crocker's Hole. Zum on 'em saith as a' must be a zammon."

Off went Pike with his handkerchief to his mouth, and after him ran Alec Bolt, one of his fellow pupils, who had come to the shop to enjoy the extraction.

"Oh, my!" was all that Pike could utter, when by craftily posting himself he had obtained a good view of this grand fish.

"I'll lay you a crown you don't catch him!" cried Bolt, an impatient youth, who scorned angling.

"How long will you give me?" asked the wary Pike, who never made rash wagers.

"Oh! till the holidays if you like; or, if that won't do, till Michaelmas."

Now the midsummer holidays were six weeks off—boys used not to talk of "vacations" then, still less of "recesses."

"I think I'll bet you," said Pike, in his slow way, bending forward carefully, with his keen eyes on this monster; "but it would not be fair to take till Michaelmas. I'll bet you a crown that I catch him before the holidays—at least, unless some other fellow does."

Part II

The day of that most momentous interview must have been the 14th day of May. Of the year I will not be so sure; for children take more note of days than of years, for which the latter have their full revenge thereafter. It must have been the 14th, because the morrow was our holiday, given upon the 15th of May, in honor of a birthday.

Now, John Pike was beyond his years wary as well as enterprising, calm as well are ardent, quite as rich in patience as in promptitude and vigor. But Alec Bolt was a headlong youth, volatile, hot, and hasty, fit only to fish the Maelstrom, or a torrent of new lava. And the moment he had laid that wager he expected his crown piece; though time, as the lawyers phrase it, was "expressly of the essence of the contract." And now he demanded that Pike should spend the holiday in trying to catch that trout.

"I shall not go near him," that lad replied, "until I have got a new collar." No piece of personal adornment was it, without which he would not act, but rather that which now is called the fly cast, or the gut cast, or the trace, or what it may be. "And another thing," continued Pike; "the bet is off if you go near him, either now or at any other time, without asking my leave first, and then only going as I tell you."

"What do I want with the great slimy beggar?" the arrogant Bolt made answer. "A good rat is worth fifty of him. No fear of my going near him, Pike. You shan't get out of it that way."

Pike showed his remarkable qualities that day, by fishing exactly as he would have fished without having heard of the great Crockerite. He was up and away upon the millstream before breakfast; and the forenoon he devoted to his favorite course—first down the Craddock stream, a very pretty confluent of the Culm, and from its junction, down the pleasant hams, where the river winds toward Uffculme. It was my privilege to accompany this hero, as his humble Sancho; while Bolt and the faster race went up the river ratting. We were back in time to have Pike's trout (which ranged between two ounces and one half pound) fried for the early dinner; and here it may be lawful to remark that the trout of the Culm are of the very purest excellence, by reason of the flinty bottom, at any rate in these the upper regions. For the valley is the western outlet of the Black Down range, with the Beacon hill upon the north, and Hackpen long ridge to the south; and beyond that again the Whetstone hill, upon whose western end dark portholes scarped with white grit mark the pits. But flint is the staple of the broad Culm Valley, under good, well-pastured loam; and here are chalcedonies and agate stones.

At dinner everybody had a brace of trout—large for the larger folk, little for the little ones, with coughing and some patting on the back for bones. What of equal purport could the fierce rat hunter show? Pike explained many points in the history of each fish, seeming to know them none the worse, and love them all the better, for being fried. We banqueted, neither a whit did soul get stinted of banquet impartial. Then the wielder of the magic rod very modestly sought leave of absence at the teatime.

"Fishing again, Mr. Pike, I suppose," my father answered pleasantly; "I used to be fond of it at your age; but never so entirely wrapped up in it as you are."

"No, sir; I am not going fishing again. I want to walk to Wellington, to get some things at Cherry's."

"Books, Mr. Pike? Ah! I am very glad of that. But I fear it can only be fly books."

"I want a little Horace for eighteenpence—the Cambridge one just published, to carry in my pocket—and a new hank of gut."

"Which of the two is more important? Put that into Latin, and answer it."

"*Utrum pluris facio? Flaccum flocci. Viscera magni.*" With this vast effort Pike turned as red as any trout spot.

"After that who could refuse you?" said my father. "You always tell the truth, my boy, in Latin or in English."

Although it was a long walk, some fourteen miles to Wellington and back, I got permission to go with Pike; and as we crossed the bridge and saw the tree that overhung Crocker's Hole, I begged him to show me that mighty fish.

"Not a bit of it," he replied. "It would bring the blackguards. If the blackguards once find him out, it is all over with him."

"The blackguards are all in factory now, and I am sure they cannot see us from the windows. They won't be out till five o'clock."

With the true liberality of young England, which abides even now as large and glorious as ever, we always called the free and enlightened operatives of the period by the courteous name above set down, and it must be acknowledged that some of them deserved it, although perhaps they poached with less of science than their sons. But the cowardly murder of fish by liming the water was already prevalent.

Yielding to my request and perhaps his own desire—manfully kept in check that morning—Pike very carefully approached that pool, commanding me to sit down while he reconnoitered from the meadow upon the right bank of the stream. And the place which had so sadly quenched the fire of the poor baker's love filled my childish heart with dread and deep wonder at the cruelty of women. But as for John Pike, all he thought of was the fish and the best way to get at him.

Very likely that hole is "holed out" now, as the Yankees well express it, or at any rate changed out of knowledge. Even in my time a very heavy flood entirely altered its character; but to the eager eye of Pike it seemed pretty much as follows, and possibly it may have come to such a form again:

The river, after passing through a hurdle fence at the head of the meadow, takes a little turn or two of bright and shallow indifference, then gathers itself into a good strong slide, as if going down a slope instead of steps. The right bank is high and beetles over with yellow loam and grassy fringe; but the other side is of flinty shingle, low and bare and washed by floods. At the end of this rapid, the stream turns sharply under an ancient alder tree into a large, deep, calm repose, cool, unruffled, and sheltered from the sun by branch and leaf—and that is the hole of poor Crocker.

At the head of the pool (where the hasty current rushes in so eagerly, with noisy excitement and much ado) the quieter waters from below, having rested and enlarged themselves, come lapping up round either curve, with some recollection of their past career, the hoary experience of foam. And sidling toward the new arrival of the impulsive column, where they meet it, things go on which no man can describe without his mouth being full of water. A V is formed, a fancy letter V, beyond any designer's tracery, and even beyond his imagination, a perpetually fluctuating limpid wedge, perpetually creneled and rippled into by little ups and downs that try to make an impress but can only glide away upon either side or sink in dimples under it. And here a gray bough of the ancient alder stretches across, like a thirsty giant's arm, and makes it a very ticklish place to throw a fly. Yet this was the very spot our John Pike must put his fly into, or lose his crown.

Because the great tenant of Crocker's Hole, who allowed no other fish to wag a fin there, and from strict monopoly had grown so fat, kept his victualing yard—if so low an expression can be used concerning him—within above a square yard of this spot. He had a sweet hover, both for rest and recreation, under the bank, in a placid antre, where the water made no noise, but tickled his belly in digestive ease. The loftier the character is of any being, the slower and more dignified his movements are. No true psychologist could have believed—as Sweetland the blacksmith did, and Mr. Pook the tinman—that this trout could ever be the embodiment of Crocker. For this was the last trout in the universal world to drown himself for love; if truly any trout has done so.

"You may come now, and try to look along my back," John Pike, with a reverential whisper, said to me. "Now, don't be in a hurry, young stupid; kneel down. He is not to be disturbed at his dinner, mind. You keep behind me, and look along my back; I never clapped eyes on such a whopper."

I had to kneel down in a tender reminiscence of pastureland and gaze carefully; and not having eyes like those of our Zebedee (who offered his spine for a camera, as he crawled on all fours in front of me), it took me a long time to descry an object most distinct to all who have that special gift of piercing with their eyes the water. See what is said upon this subject in that delicious book, *The Gamekeeper at Home*.

"You are no better than a muff," said Pike, and it was not in my power to deny it.

"If the sun would only leave off," I said. But the sun, who was having a very pleasant play with the sparkle of the water and the twinkle of the leaves, had no inclination to leave off yet, but kept the rippling crystal in a dance of flashing facets, and the quivering verdure in a steady flush of gold.

But suddenly a May fly, a luscious gray drake, richer and more delicate than canvasback or woodcock, with a dart and a leap and a merry zigzag, began to enjoy a little game above the stream. Rising and falling like a gnat, thrilling her gauzy wings, and arching her elegant pellucid frame, every now and then she almost dipped her three long tapering whisks into the dimples of the water.

"He sees her! He'll have her as sure as a gun!" cried Pike, with a gulp, as if he himself were "rising." "Now can you see him, stupid?"

"Crikey, crokums!" I exclaimed, with classic elegance; "I have seen that long thing for five minutes; but I took it for a tree."

"You little"—animal quite early in the alphabet—"now don't you stir a peg, or I'll dig my elbow into you."

The great trout was stationary almost as a stone, in the middle of the V above described. He was gently fanning with his large clear fins, but holding his own against the current mainly by the wagging of his broad-fluked tail. As soon as my slow eyes had once defined him, he grew upon them mightily, molding himself in the matrix of the water, as a thing put into jelly does. And I doubt whether even John Pike saw him more accurately than I did. His size was such, or seemed to be such, that I fear to say a word about it; not because language does not contain the word, but from dread of exaggeration. But his shape and color may be reasonably told without wounding the feeling of an age whose incredulity springs from self-knowledge.

His head was truly small, his shoulders vast; the spring of his back was like a rainbow when the sun is southing; the generous sweep of his deep elastic belly, nobly pulped out with rich nurture, showed what the power of his brain must be, and seemed to undulate, time for time, with the vibrant vigilance of his large wise eyes. His latter end was consistent also. An elegant taper run of counter, coming almost to a cylinder, as a mackerel does, boldly developed with a hugeous spread to a glorious amplitude of swallowtail. His color was all that can well be desired, but ill described by any poor word palette. Enough that he seemed to tone away from olive and umber, with carmine stars, to glowing gold and soft pure silver, mantled with a subtle flush of rose and fawn and opal.

Swoop came a swallow, as we gazed, and was gone with a flick, having missed the May fly. But the wind of his passage, or the skir of wing, struck the merry dancer down, so that he fluttered for one instant on the wave, and that instant was enough. Swift as the swallow, and more true of aim, the great trout made one dart, and a sound, deeper than a tinkle, but as silvery as a bell, rang the poor ephemerid's knell. The rapid water scarcely showed a break; but a bubble sailed down the pool, and the dark hollow echoed with the music of a rise.

"He knows how to take a fly," said Pike; "he has had too many to be tricked with mine. Have him I must; but how ever shall I do it?"

All the way to Wellington he uttered not a word, but shambled along with a mind full of care. When I ventured to look up now and then, to surmise what was going on beneath his hat, deeply set eyes and a wrinkled forehead, relieved at long intervals by a solid shake, proved that there are meditations deeper than those of philosopher or statesman.

PART III

Surely no trout could have been misled by the artificial May fly of that time, unless he were either a very young fish, quite new to ento-mology, or else one afflicted with a combination of myopy and bulimy. Even now there is room for plenty of improvement in our counterfeit presentment; but in those days the body was made with yellow mo-hair, ribbed with red silk and gold twist, and as thick as a fertile bum-blebee. John Pike perceived that to offer such a thing to Crocker's trout would probably consign him—even if his great stamina should overget the horror—to an uneatable death, through just and natural indignation. On the other hand, while the May fly lasted, a trout so cultured, so highly refined, so full of light and sweetness, would never demean himself to low bait, or any coarse son of a maggot.

Meanwhile Alec Bolt allowed poor Pike no peaceful thought, no calm absorption of high mind into the world of flies, no placid period of cobbler's wax, floss silk, turned hackles, and dubbing. For in making of flies John Pike had his special moments of inspiration, times of clearer insight into the everlasting verities, times of brighter concep-tion and more subtle execution, tails of more elastic grace and heads of a neater and nattier expression. As a poet labors at one immortal line, compressing worlds of wisdom into the music of ten syllables, so toiled the patient Pike about the fabric of a fly comprising all the excellence that ever sprang from maggot. Yet Bolt rejoiced to jerk his elbow at the moment of sublimest art. And a swarm of flies was blighted thus.

Peaceful, therefore, and long-suffering, and full of resignation as he was, John Pike came slowly to the sad perception that arts avail not without arms. The elbow, so often jerked, at last took a voluntary jerk from the shoulder, and Alex Bolt lay prostrate, with his right eye full of cobbler's wax. This put a desirable check upon his energies for a week or more, and by that time Pike had flown his fly.

When the honeymoon of spring and summer (which they are now too fashionable to celebrate in this country), the heyday of the whole year marked by the budding of the wild rose, the start of the wheat ear from its sheath, the feathering of the lesser plantain, and flowering of the meadowsweet, and, foremost for the angler's joy, the caracole of May flies—when these things are to be seen and felt (which has not happened at all this year), then rivers should be mild and bright, skies blue and white with fleecy cloud, the west wind blowing softly, and the trout in charming appetite.

On such a day came Pike to the bank of Culm, with a loudly beating heart. A fly there is, not ignominious, or of cowdab origin, neither gross and heavy-bodied, from cradlehood of slimy stones, nor yet of menacing aspect and suggesting deeds of poison, but elegant, bland, and of sunny nature, and obviously good to eat. Him or her—why quest we which?—the shepherd of the dale, contemptuous of gender, except in his own species, has called, and as long as they two coexist will call, the Yellow Sally. A fly that does not waste the day in giddy dances and the fervid waltz, but undergoes family incidents with decorum and discretion. He or she, as the case may be—for the natural history of the riverbank is a book to come hereafter, and of fifty men who make flies not one knows the name of the fly he is making—in the early morning of June, or else in the second quarter of the afternoon, this Yellow Sally fares abroad, with a nice well-ordered flutter.

Despairing of the May fly, as it still may be despaired of, Pike came down to the river with his masterpiece of portraiture. The artificial Yellow Sally is generally always—as they say in Cheshire—a mile or more too yellow. On the other hand, the Yellow Dun conveys no idea of any Sally. But Pike had made a very decent Sally, not perfect (for he was young as well as wise), but far above any counterfeit to be had in fishing-tackle shops. How he made it, he told nobody. But if he lives now, as I hope he does, any of my readers may ask him through the G. P. O. and hope to get an answer.

It fluttered beautifully on the breeze, and in such living form that a brother or sister Sally came up to see it, and went away sadder and wiser. Then Pike said: "Get away, you young wretch," to your humble servant who tells this tale; yet, being better than his words, allowed that pious follower to lie down upon his digestive organs and with deep attention watch. There must have been great things to see, but to see them so was difficult. And if I huddle up what happened, excitement also shares the blame.

Pike had fashioned well the time and manner of this overture. He knew that the giant Crockerite was satiate now with May flies, or began to find their flavor failing, as happens to us with asparagus, marrow-fat peas, or strawberries, when we have had a month of them. And he thought that the first Yellow Sally of the season, inferior though it were, might have the special charm of novelty. With the skill of a Zulu, he stole up through the branches over the lower pool till he came to a spot where a yard-wide opening gave just space for spring of rod. Then he saw his desirable friend at dinner, wagging his tail, as a hungry gentleman dining with the Lord Mayor agitates his coat. With one dexterous whirl, untaught by any of the many books upon the subject, John Pike laid his Yellow Sally (for he cast with one fly only) as lightly as gossamer upon the rapid, about a yard in front of the big trout's head. A moment's pause, and then too quick for words was the thing that happened.

A heavy plunge was followed by a fearful rush. Forgetful of current the river was ridged, as if with a plow driven under it; the strong line, though given out as fast as might be, twanged like a harp string as it cut the wave, and then Pike stood up, like a ship dismasted, with the butt of his rod snapped below the ferrule. He had one of those foolish things, just invented, a hollow butt of hickory; and the finial ring of his spare top looked out, to ask what had happened to the rest of it. "Bad luck!" cried the fisherman; "but never mind, I shall have him next time, to a certainty."

When this great issue came to be considered, the cause of it was sadly obvious. The fish, being hooked, had made off with the rush of a shark for the bottom of the pool. A thicket of saplings below the alder tree had stopped the judicious hooker from all possibility of following; and when he strove to turn him by elastic pliance, his rod broke at the breach of pliability. "I have learned a sad lesson," said John Pike, looking sadly.

How many fellows would have given up this matter, and glorified themselves for having hooked so grand a fish, while explaining that they must have caught him, if they could have done it! But Pike only told me not to say a word about it, and began to make ready for another tug of war. He made himself a splice rod, short and handy, of well-seasoned ash, with a stout top of bamboo, tapered so discreetly, and so balanced in its spring, that verily it formed an arc, with any pressure on it, as perfect as a leafy poplar in a stormy summer. "Now break it if you can," he said, "by any amount of rushes; I'll hook you by your jacket collar; you cut away now, and I'll land you."

This was highly skillful, and he did it many times; and whenever

I was landed well, I got a lollipop, so that I was careful not to break his tackle. Moreover he made him a landing net, with a kidney-bean stick, a ring of wire, and his own best nightcap of strong cotton net. Then he got the farmer's leave, and lopped obnoxious bushes; and now the chiefest question was: What bait, and when to offer it? In spite of his sad rebuff, the spirit of John Pike had been equable. The genuine angling mind is steadfast, large, and self-supported, and to the vapid, ignominious chaff, tossed by swine upon the idle wind, it pays as much heed as a big trout does to a dance of midges. People put their fingers to their noses and said: "Master Pike, have you caught him yet?" and Pike only answered: "Wait a bit." If ever this forti-tude and perseverance is to be recovered as the English Brand (the one thing that has made us what we are, and may yet redeem us from niddering shame), a degenerate age should encourage the habit of fish-ing and never despairing. And the brightest sign yet for our future is the increasing demand for hooks and gut.

Pike fished in a manlier age, when nobody would dream of cower-ing from a savage because he was clever at skulking; and when, if a big fish broke the rod, a stronger rod was made for him, according to the usage of Great Britain. And though the young angler had been defeated, he did not sit down and have a good cry over it.

About the second week in June, when the May fly had danced its day and died—for the season was an early one—and Crocker's trout had recovered from the wound to his feelings and philanthropy, there came a night of gentle rain, of pleasant tinkling upon window ledges, and a soothing patter among young leaves, and the Culm was yellow in the morning. "I mean to do it this afternoon," Pike whispered to me, as he came back panting. "When the water clears there will be a splendid time."

The lover of the rose knows well a gay voluptuous beetle, whose pleasure is to lie embedded in a fount of beauty. Deep among the in-curving petals of the blushing fragrance, he loses himself in his joys sometimes, till a breezy waft reveals him. And when the sunlight breaks upon his luscious dissipation, few would have the heart to oust him, such a gem from such a setting. All his back is emerald sparkles, all his front red Indian gold, and here and there he grows white spots to save the eye from aching. Pike put his finger in and fetched him out, and offered him a little change of joys, by putting a Limerick hook through his thorax, and bringing it out between his elytra. Cetonia aurata liked it not, but pawed the air very naturally, and fluttered with his wings attractively.

"I meant to have tried with a fern web," said the angler; "until I saw one of these beggars this morning. If he works like that upon the water, he will do. It was hopeless to try artificials again. What a lovely color the water is! Only three days now to the holidays. I have run it very close. You be ready, younker."

With these words he stepped upon a branch of the alder, for the tone of the waters allowed approach, being soft and sublustrous, without any mud. Also Master Pike's own tone was such as becomes the fisherman, calm, deliberate, free from nerve, but full of eye and muscle. He stepped upon the alder bough to get as near as might be to the fish, for he could not cast this beetle like a fly; it must be dropped gently and allowed to play. "You may come and look," he said to me; "when the water is so, they have no eyes in their tails."

The rose beetle trod upon the water prettily, under a lively vibration, and he looked quite as happy, and considerably more active, than when he had been cradled in the anthers of the rose. To the eye of a fish he was a strong individual, fighting courageously with the current, but sure to be beaten through lack of fins; and mercy suggested, as well as appetite, that the proper solution was to gulp him.

"Hooked him in the gullet. He can't get off!" cried John Pike, laboring to keep his nerves under. "Every inch of tackle is as strong as a bell pull. Now, if I don't land him, I will never fish again!"

Providence, which had constructed Pike, foremost of all things, for lofty angling—disdainful of worm and even minnow—Providence, I say, at this adjuration, pronounced that Pike must catch that trout. Not many anglers are heaven-born; and for one to drop off the hook halfway through his teens would be infinitely worse than to slay the champion trout. Pike felt the force of this, and rushing through the rushes, shouted: "I am sure to have him, Dick! Be ready with my nightcap."

Rod in a bow, like a springle riser; line on the hum, like the string of Paganini; winch on the gallop, like a harpoon wheel, Pike, the head-center of everything, dashing through thick and thin, and once taken overhead—for he jumped into the hole, when he must have lost him else, but the fish too impetuously towed him out, and made off in passion for another pool, when, if he had only retired to his hover, the angler might have shared the baker's fate—all these things (I tell you, for they all come up again, as if the day were yesterday) so scared me of my never very steadfast wits, that I could only holloa! But one thing I did, I kept the nightcap ready.

The Rajah's Rock

PAUL HYDE BONNER

A fishing story with a twist is a rare thing, and with the exception of the angler's somewhat fantastic tendency for exaggeration, fantasy has little place in angling. This, of course, is not a statement which would be confirmed by a nonangler. Paul Hyde Bonner is a versatile sportsman as well as writer, and I have always thought "The Rajah's Rock" topped all of his sporting stories.

THE FINAL beat of the Owenmore before it flows into the tidewater is as delightfully varied as a fisherman's dream. It starts with a pool so broad and calm and edged with reeds and lily pads that one might call it a small lake, or lough, as they spell it in Ireland. Salmon do not lie there as a rule, though cruising ones that show occasionally on the edge of the reeds often tempt a fisherman to take a boat out and try for them, without success, as fish on the move are rarely, if ever, interested in a fly or a spinner. The shores of this lake are rough, heathery hillocks, devoid of trees or shrubs and inhabited by scraggy blackface highland sheep. Two streams flow out of this large pool, forming an island in the river, a fat, egg-shaped island of about five acres which is remarkable for three features: It is an oasis of verdant grass and shrubs and stunted oak and beech in a landscape of rocks and heather; it has on its near shore one solitary boulder, round, smooth, about ten feet high, and looking like the egg of some giant prehistoric bird; and it is inhabited throughout the summer by a lone donkey. This great boulder, like a bastion, surveys the left-hand (looking downstream) branch of the river and is known locally as the Rajah's Rock. Just why it is so called you will learn in due time. It is enough for the moment to remark that this portion of the left-hand branch which rounds the island is a favorite holding ground for salmon. Here they are apt to lie in numbers, not in company front as they do in some pools, but in file along the deep, narrow channel between the waving rows of weed.

Below the island, from the point where the two streams meet until one reaches the long rapid that descends to tidewater, the whole character of the water and the landscape changes. Instead of the gentle flow and the peaceful upland country, there is a noisy, foam-lashed torrent that dashes over rocks, forms black, slick pools in a wild and jagged canyon from which the fair landscape of Connemara is hidden. But it is no place for a fisherman who is not sure-footed, with a steady head and an ability to Spey or loop-cast. One has to have the agility of a mountain goat and an expert's control of the line to stand on a slippery rock at the base of the canyon cliff and get a fly over a fish in such a way that he might be tempted.

It was certainly nothing for Mrs. Evans, and she knew it and so did her husband and Tom Walsh, the gillie. When they had parked the car and walked down the hill to the little stone bridge by the luncheon hut, which is at the dividing line between the gentle and wild halves of the beat, Mrs. Evans had said, after one glance, "If you expect me to fish down there, you're mistaken."

" 'Twould be better that you fished the Rajah's Rock, madam," Tom Walsh said.

"Where is that?" Jim Evans asked.

It was their first day on the Owenmore and everything was a little strange and unreal. Only two days before Jim and Gertrude Evans had left their home in Greenwich, Connecticut, and, via Idlewild and Gander, had reached Shannon Airport, where a drive-yourself car had met them, and they had motored the hundred miles north to the Cashel Hotel in Connemara. For years they had fished together in New Brunswick and Nova Scotia, but this was different. There were no deep forests, no cabins in a birch grove, no red-shirted, leather-booted guides, no long boats in which to be paddled or rowed to a pool. It seemed unlikely to them that the same variety of Atlantic salmon which they had stalked and fought for years in somber woodland rivers could inhabit this picture-book stream in an open, rolling country with neat white cottages behind towering hedges of fuchsia. The layout was quaint but improbable, they had thought, when they had entered the hotel on the previous evening and found it comfortable to the point of luxury, with its broad lounge full of deep chairs and couches, its billiard-room bar, its bright dining room with a bouquet of flowers on each table, and the water running piping hot in their own bathroom. Then there had been the park about the hotel with its great old beeches and its garden bordered with rhododendron and the river flowing quietly at the foot of a flower-bordered terrace. The sole encouragement had been the long rack in the stair hall, half filled with salmon rods, not little ten-foot rods like their own, but great two-handed poles, twelve to sixteen feet in length. Surely, they had thought, guests would not bring those cumbersome weapons here unless there were salmon to be caught. Then, before dinner, when they had gone to the billiard-room bar for a cocktail, they had seen the evidence. On a marble-top table against the oak paneling of the wall lay seven fine salmon, each one with a card placed on its broad side on which was written the name of the fisherman, the beat where it was killed, and the variety of lure used.

Tom Walsh unlocked the door of the hut and put the picnic basket on the table inside. When he came out again, he pointed upstream in the direction of the island. "It'll be up there a piece," he said. "No more'n a short walk."

"Do you wish us to start there?" Jim Evans asked. He believed in following a guide's advice on water with which he was unfamiliar.

"You can do as you're mind," the gillie said. He was a tall, lanky man in a threadbare jacket of Connemara tweed and patched trousers that were stuck into a pair of short waders which were covered with vulcanized patches of red rubber. "There's plenty of fish from the bridge down, but the goin' will be rough for the lady."

"Now, Tom," Evans said to the gillie pleasantly but firmly. "We are going to put ourselves in your hands. We've never fished this river and we know nothing about it. You're the guide on this reach and you tell us what to do." Jim Evans was a lawyer with a precise, orderly mind. He liked things planned, and once the plans were laid, he liked to stick to them.

Tom Walsh eyed him skeptically. "Is it that you'll both be wanting to fish at the same time?" he asked.

"That's up to you," Jim said firmly. "You tell us who is to fish where and when."

"What fly have you on?" the gillie asked, looking at Gertrude Evans.

"I have a Mar Lodge," Mrs. Evans answered. Most fishermen have superstitions about patterns and Gertrude Evans was no exception. Ever since she had killed an eighteen-pound salmon on the Miramichi with a Mar Lodge, she was convinced that it was a fly of deadly virtuosity.

"A good fly it is—at times," Tom Walsh said, picking up her rod, which was leaning against the side of the hut, and examining the fly. "I'm thinkin' that with the brightness the way it is, mebbe they'll fancy a bit of blue. Have you your fly box, sir?"

Jim Evans fished in the sack that was hanging from his shoulder and brought out an aluminum box which he handed to the gillie. Tom fingered them over thoughtfully, then picked out a low-water Teal and Silver and, without saying a word, took out a pair of scissors, nipped off the Mar Lodge and bent on the new fly. He had barely finished tying the knot when the air was shattered by a hoarse, panting scream.

Gertrude Evans jumped. "Good God! What's that?" she exclaimed.

"Joe, the donkey, it is," Tom Walsh said, a faint smile wrinkling the corners of his beady blue eyes. He gave the fly a strong tug against the nylon leader to make sure that the knot was strong. "Come, madam," he said, putting the barb of the fly into the cork of the handle and picking up his gaff. "We might be risin' a fish at the Rajah's Rock."

"A donkey?" Gertrude said, incredulous. "Can a donkey make a noise like that?"

Jim Evans laughed. "You gave yourself away that time, you little city urchin," he said to his wife. "Have you never heard a donkey bray?"

"Never. I've only read about it," Gertrude said, starting after the gillie.

"Am I to fish here, or go with you?" Jim called to Tom, who was walking rapidly on up the path.

Tom turned his head without slowing his pace. "Better you be comin' with us," he said. "There's likely a fish for the two of ye."

When they had gone about two hundred yards, the path brought them to the rise of a hillock from which they could see the island. It came suddenly into view without warning, a luxuriant oasis, framed by the two streams, and on its edge, like the stone of a ring, the great round rock.

Gertrude stopped to admire. "Oh, Jim, isn't it lovely? But look, there's someone there ahead of us."

Jim had already seen the figure standing on the top of the round boulder. It took him a few seconds to make out that it was a puce-colored donkey, faced directly toward them so that its body and hind-quarters were hidden by its thick neck and chest. Then its ears, which had been attentively, inquisitively erect, started to flap back and forth.

"Whoever it is, he's waving to us," Gertrude said.

Jim laughed. "You need glasses, honey. That's the donkey."

His wife shaded her eyes from the glare as she looked again carefully. She laughed, too. "Of course it is. How funny. It looked just like a little man in tweeds standing there."

"Dr. Melrose," Jim said, laughing. "Wait till I tell him you mistook him for a donkey." Dr. Melrose was a short, stocky Englishman they had met in the bar the evening before. He had come in from fishing wearing tan corduroys and a Harris tweed jacket.

They hurried up the path now to catch up with Tom, who was almost at the stream by the rock. Jim was carrying his own rod and the canvas sack with his flies and leaders and the other bits of equipment which a practiced fisherman always has with him. He was a pleasant, clean-cut-looking man of fifty-five, getting a little round in the belly, as sedentary American businessmen are apt to. The skin of his smooth-shaven face was still the opaque of the commuting lawyer. It would be a week before the wind and the sun would give it a pink tone, but it would never achieve that ruddy glow which the sportsmen of the British Isles seem to maintain the year round, even though their holidays are no more protracted than his. His clothes, too, tagged him unquestionably. The canvas jacket, the red flannel lumberman's shirt, the khaki breeches with elastic knitted cuffs which he wore inside his laced rubber boots, and his tight-fitting cap with its stiff, outsize peak were clearly out of the Northeast woodlands and the catalogue of Mr. L. L. Bean. They were as strange to County Galway as the dhoti of a Hindu.

With Gertrude dressed identically in every detail—they always bought their fishing clothes at the same time and to match—they looked like twins, or rather like members of the same outing club, for Gertrude, who was only forty-eight, was thin and wiry, with a parchmentlike outdoor complexion that came from constant and passionate gardening. They had wondered why everyone in the dining room that morning at breakfast had stared at them so intently, and they had put it down to new faces, and not their outfits, as they should have.

When they caught up with Tom Walsh, he was standing by the bank at the point where the left-hand stream flows out of the little lake. The great round rock was opposite them a bit downstream, with the donkey still standing on its pinnacle, switching his scrawny tail against the flies and watching them intently, his ears forward stiffly, emphasizing his concentration.

"Why, the donkey is on the island!" Gertrude said, suddenly realizing that the rock was not accessible to their shore except by boat.

"Does he swim across?" Jim Evans asked the gillie.

"No sir, he don't," Tom replied.

"Then how did he get there?" Jim asked.

"I ferry him across in the boat," Tom answered.

"And just leave him there?" Gertrude exclaimed, shocked by the poor beast's enforced exile.

"That I do, for the summer indeed," Tom said. "He's plenty of grass to feed on over there, and he don't be gettin' into any mischief."

"He's your donkey?" Jim asked.

"That he is," Tom answered. "And a sinful one at that." He handed Gertrude her rod. "Now, madam, will you be fishin' that bit of water right out there. You mark where the waves is heaviest from the wind. That'll be the channel down the middle where the fish lie. 'Twould be best to put your fly on the far side of it and let the current be takin' it down. And mind the weeds when it swings too near this bank."

Tom watched her appraisingly as she stripped line from her reel and false-cast until her fly could reach the center of the stream. He could see at once that she knew what she was doing, and he was pleased. The costumes of the couple and the little ten-foot rods had filled him with misgivings. He had a deep-seated distrust of tyros, even though they be Americans, for he had a special sympathy for the United States what with so many of the family there.

"Another foot or two will do it," he said to Mrs. Evans, eager to assist now that he saw that she could drift a salmon fly on a greased line.

Gertrude stripped more line and cast again. As the fly hit the water the donkey let out another ear-splitting bray. The noise was so great, with the donkey not more than a hundred yards from them, and so unexpected that Gertrude almost dropped her rod. "Good God!" she said, her hand shaking so that the rod quivered. "He frightened me to death. I could feel my heart stop."

"He be tellin' us that the salmon is further downstream," Tom said. "Keep fishing along—one step to each cast."

Gertrude Evans laughed as she cast again. "That's wonderful!

Did you hear that, Jim? Tom says that the donkey was trying to tell us that the salmon are further down."

Jim, who was sitting on a hummock of heather below them, grinned. "He's right, too. I saw one roll right out here in front of me. Only I wish he'd whisper his messages instead of splitting my eardrums. Tom, I didn't know that your Irish leprechauns were that noisy."

"They told you, did they, sir?" Tom said, not taking his eyes from the fly and the water.

"Told me what?" Jim asked.

"That Joe was a leprechaun," Tom replied, pronouncing it "leprehawn." "That he is, as sure as he's standin' there watchin' the fish."

The donkey uttered a couple of short, tentative grunts as if he were getting up steam for another bray.

"Easy now, madam," Tom cautioned. "You be over a fish as will be takin'."

"Did you see him?" Gertrude asked, casting again skillfully, gently, over the same spot.

"I did not, but Joe did," Tom said almost in a whisper.

A salmon boiled at the fly, erupting the surface of the stream, and Gertrude, reacting too quickly, as one is apt to do on the first day out each season, jerked her rod tip and the fly swung high in the air and landed in the heather behind her.

"What a pity!" Jim called. "That was a nice fish."

"Did you prick him, madam?" Tom asked.

Gertrude was about to answer when she saw the donkey stamping his right front foot on the rock as if he were thoroughly disgusted with her. She shook her rod at the beast angrily. "No comments from you, please," she yelled, then started to reel in her line. "No, I didn't prick him," she said to Tom with a sigh of disappointment. "I never gave him a chance to get it in his mouth. I jerked it right away from him."

"We'll give him a bit of a rest," Tom said consolingly. "Like as not he'll be comin' again."

Gertrude sat down on the grass and lit a cigarette. "You come up here and have a try at him," she called to her husband.

"Nothing doing," Jim said. "He's your fish. He likes your fly."

"Is that what they call the Rajah's Rock?" Gertrude asked the gillie, pointing to the great boulder on which the donkey stood.

"It is," Tom replied.

"How did it get that name?"

Tom Walsh's beady eyes that were watching the water crinkled into a smile. "An old story it is. I was only a bit of a lad at the time and me father was then the gillie on this beat. One of them Indian princes let the river for a season. The Rajah of Baypoor they used to call him. A heathen he was, but not a bad man. One day he was fishin' right where you raised your salmon—there, facin' the big rock —when he gets his fly into a giant of a big spring fish. He was an impatient sort of a man, likin' to do things in a hurry. When he'd seen what he had on his line, he started bearin' hard on the fish to keep him from headin' into the lough. Oh, many's the time I've heard me father tell the story. How he kept sayin' to the Rajah, 'Easy now, your Highness. Be lettin' him have line, your Excellency. Keep his head outa the weeds, sir. Don't be pullin' him so strong! Ach, you've lost him, you black bastard!' "

Gertrude laughed heartily. "What a marvelous story! So the rock is a monument to the Rajah's lost fish. I think that's wonderful. He was a really big salmon, was he?"

"Thirty-seven pounds four ounces when he was sold in the market at Clifden," Tom said.

"But you said the Rajah lost him."

"That he did, but me uncle, Joe Walsh—may his soul rest in peace —caught him the following night."

The donkey started again to grunt the preliminary bars of his song.

"Come on, madam," Tom said. "Joe says that salmon is ready to have another go at your Teal and Silver."

Gertrude threw away her cigarette and stood up. She picked up her rod and started casting upstream, as far away as possible from the spot where she had had the rise, until she had out the right amount of line. Then precisely, holding her rod at the top of the swing long enough to let the line change its arc behind her, she cast so that her fly would travel the same route as before. When the salmon came, she was prepared. She let him take it and turn before she came up with a smart twitch of the rod tip.

The battle was a good one, though she could have done with slightly less advice. Tom Walsh confined his brief remarks to warnings about weed and the danger of letting him get into the lake where he might take all of the line and backing. Her husband, whose steady, thoughtful character had a way of changing, of becoming emotional and excited whenever she had a salmon on, dashed up to stand near her, telling her to reel in, to hold her rod tip up, to let the fish go, to mind her footing, in a voice so loud anyone might have thought she was deaf. And Joe, the donkey, made his own comments with sighs, grunts and violent flapping of his ears.

In the end Tom Walsh stepped down into the shallow edge of the stream and gaffed the salmon skillfully, swinging its wriggling body over onto the grass of the bank, where he held it securely while he gave the *coup de grâce* with the blackthorn handle of the gaff. It was a well-formed hen fish with good depth in the belly and weighed, on Jim's hand scales, just under nine pounds.

"My first Irish salmon," Gertrude said proudly as the three of them stood looking down at the beautiful silver fish which lay at their feet in the grass.

Jim Evans was about to remark that the sea lice were still on it when he was interrupted by another rending bray from Joe.

"Is he congratulating me?" Gertrude asked the gillie when the horrifying noise had subsided into a series of short, squeaking gasps.

"Might be he is," Tom said, glancing at the donkey on the opposite shore. "He's an eye for the ladies." The donkey shifted his position, pricking up his ears and looking at a spot downstream of them. " 'Tis likely, too, that he sees another takin' fish."

Jim walked back into the heather and picked up his rod. He tried to move calmly, with measured tread, but the anticipation forced him to hurry. "Damn it, Tom," he said, annoyed with himself for succumbing to the excitement, which a sober lawyer should never do—that is, not where he can be observed by other eyes—"you've got me believing that Joe is really trying to give us a tip. Where does he want me to fish?"

Tom Walsh smiled. "Pity he ain't a man. He'd be a powerful poacher. As it is, I have to be puttin' him on the island all summer to keep him from stealin'."

"Can't you tie him up?" Gertrude asked, still feeling sorry for the exile.

"There ain't a knot known to man he can't untie with the teeth of him," the gillie answered. "And once he's loose he'll be stealin' corn and sugar and apples and pears from every byre and cottage within a mile of Cushatrower. Oh, a wicked, cute beast he is."

"What do you do with him in winter?" Gertrude asked.

The donkey brayed again, ruling out talk.

"I had better get going," Jim Evans said, believing now that the donkey was urging him, though cross with himself for believing.

"Pay no mind to him, sir," Tom said. "Like all thieves, 'tis impatient he is. 'Twill do no harm to let the pool quiet down a bit after the last fish." He turned to Gertrude. "In winter, madam, he's plenty of work to do, haulin' turf and takin' the car to Roundstone. He's kept tight in a box in me byre, which no man can get out of from the inside, let alone a schemin' donkey."

"Can't you keep him there in summer, too?" Gertrude asked.

"And let him be eatin' his head off of corn and turnips? No, madam, only a rich man, like Mr. Evans now, or me brother Paddy who owns a pub in New York, could afford that. He's fine where he is, with plenty of grass to eat and the salmon to watch."

"Okey. Let's go. Where do I start fishing?" Jim said impatiently.

"You might be startin' right there where the missus left off," Tom said. "Fish it along as she did, sir, a step to each cast."

It was a repetition of the first performance. When Jim had progressed about four yards downstream, covering the water expertly, Joe had uttered his three or four grunting coughs and on the next cast Jim was fast to a salmon. He fought it well, though he had a tendency to horse it. Gertrude noted this and worried that the leader might part at the hook, but she said nothing. She was a wise woman who realized that husbands dislike wifely advice in the heat of a contest, or in the presence of others. He brought it to gaff finally, after fifteen minutes of struggle. It was not as big a fish as Gertrude's, weighing only about seven and a half pounds, but it had been a strong, dashing fighter and Jim was proud and happy as he surveyed it on the grass.

Dr. Melrose was in the billiard-room bar when they came in at six that evening, followed by Tom and the two salmon. They had not touched a fish after Jim had killed his before lunch. The wind had dropped entirely and the sun had made the still water too bright. But they were happy with their brace, and not ashamed to have them placed on the official scales and ticketed by Tom as he laid them on the marble slab. They read the legends with pride: "The Island Beat. 8 lbs 14 ozs. Teal & Silver. Mrs. James Evans." "The Island Beat. 7 lbs 6 ozs. Silver Doctor. Mr. James Evans."

"Jolly good!" Dr. Melrose said, peering between them at the salmon. "Where were they taken, Tom?" he asked the gillie.

"At the Rajah's Rock, sir," Tom replied.

"Ah! Fine spot that when the water's right," the doctor said. "Needs a breeze of wind, though."

"We had it, sir, for the morning only," Tom said, then touched his forelock to Jim and Gertrude. "Well, sir, good night, sir. Good night, madam. It'll be time for me to be pedalin' home."

"Can't I buy you a drink, Tom?" Jim asked.

"Thank you, sir, but I'd best be on my way. 'Tis a good ride I have on my bicycle back to the Island Beat."

"Do you live there?" Gertrude asked.

"I do. Over the hill beyond the hut."

Jim took two pound notes out of his pocket and folded them up. "Thanks for a splendid day, Tom," he said, shaking hands with the gillie and giving him the money at the same time.

"And thank Joe for me, Tom," Gertrude said. "The next time we fish your beat, which will be a week from Friday, I'm going to bring him some sugar and a carrot."

Tom shook his hand. "Mind you don't be too good to him. He's easy spoilt, that rogue of a Joe is."

When Tom left, Jim rang for the barman and asked Dr. Melrose to join them in a drink. The three of them drew up chairs around a little table in the corner of the room.

Jim started laughing softly to himself.

"What's so funny?" Gertrude asked.

"That story of Tom's about the donkey," Jim answered. "Of all the Irish malarky I ever heard that beats anything. And to think that I fell for it, believed that Joe was actually telling me where the salmon were lying."

"So Joe performed for you, did he?" the doctor said. "Jolly lucky you are. He won't do it for everyone."

"It's a good show, anyway," Jim said, still laughing. "The trick is, of course, that the keen fisherman is usually tensed with excitement when he's on the river. This tends to give him an emotional lift which clouds his ability to reason. The donkey brays, a salmon takes his fly, and he is in a frame of euphoria to believe that the beast has supernatural powers."

"I don't care what you say, Jim," his wife stated firmly, "that donkey guided me to my salmon. Do you remember when he brayed while I was fishing up at the top? Remember that Tom said to me, 'He's saying the fish is further down, so walk along, a cast at each step'?"

"Sure. It was Tom who knew where the fish was," Jim said. "He'd probably seen a flash with those keen eyes of his. The donkey on the rock is just part of the act, the leprechaun touch to give the visiting firemen a taste of Irish folklore, and to get a bigger tip for Tom Walsh."

"How about those little snorts he gave just before my salmon rose?" Gertrude persisted. "He did it again before you hooked yours."

Jim winked at the doctor, as if to say, We hard-headed males are not taken in by such fairy tales. "Tom probably waved his gaff, gave him some sort of a signal to sound off." He turned to Dr. Melrose. "Has Tom ever put on this show for you?"

"Oh yes, two or three times in past years," the doctor replied. "But you know, I should hardly call it Tom's show, unless, of course, you mean that Tom puts Joe on the island to help him make a good job of the fishing."

"Just as I say—for added interest, to keep the customers happy," Jim said.

"No, I don't mean that," Dr. Melrose said quietly, weighing his words. "I mean that he uses Joe as an actual aid, as an indicator of fish in the Rajah's Rock pool."

The barman brought the drinks, a gin-and-tonic for Gertrude and whisky-and-sodas for the men.

The doctor lifted his glass to the two Americans. "Congratulations!" he said.

"And thanks to Joe," Gertrude said.

"You don't mean to tell me, Doctor, that you think Joe actually sees the fish and notifies Tom," Jim said, finding it hard to believe that any sober physician could be taken in by a gillie's little joke.

Dr. Melrose sipped his drink and put it down on the table before answering. "Oh, I'm convinced that he does. But that is not all of it, for as you have seen and I have experienced, he does not indicate just any salmon lying in the channel, and, with the water as it is now, there might well be twenty there. By some means which I will not attempt to explain he gives notice only when a salmon is ready and eager to take. It may be that a taking fish is more restless than the others and flashes about 'way down there where Joe from his high perch can see him. That is one theory, but I do not altogether fancy it. It has been my experience over many years of fishing that the restless fish is the least inclined to take. If that is true, then one must assume that Joe can detect the inner impulse of a given salmon by some supersensory perception. That animals have such gifts, far beyond anything of which man is capable, is well known to science."

"Granted," Jim Evans said, "but why should a donkey have instincts related to fish? He doesn't eat them. He doesn't fear them. They live in a water world totally unrelated to his life and habits."

"Righto," Dr. Melrose said with a smile. "As you say, the whole performance is so illogical as to appear to a practical American to be a hoax. And that brings us to another realm, a realm that is uniquely Irish. I might even say, uniquely Connemara. Tell me, just what did Tom tell you about Joe and the Rajah's Rock?"

"He told us—" Jim began.

"He told me," Gertrude interrupted. "I don't think you heard it all, Jim. He told me that Joe was a thief who had to be exiled to the island during the summer to keep him from stealing from other people's barns and cottages. He said that Joe could untie with his teeth any knot one could put on his halter rope."

"Did he tell you how the rock got its name?" the doctor asked her.

Gertrude laughed. "Indeed he did. The story about the Indian prince and the big salmon he lost. Very funny, I thought. 'You've lost him, you black bastard!'"

Dr. Melrose chuckled. "Yes, it is a good story, though it loses somewhat from repetition. It is the most popular anecdote in this part of the country. They never seem to tire of telling it. Naturally, old Mike Walsh, Tom's father, never said those words, but I'm quite prepared

to believe that he thought them and much worse ones. Did he tell
you how the salmon was finally caught?"

"I believe he said his uncle caught it the next night," Gertrude
answered. "It seems it weighed over thirty-seven pounds."

"And did he tell you the sequel?" Melrose asked.

"What sequel?"

"What happened to the late Joe Walsh as a result of that bit of
poaching," the doctor replied.

"No, he didn't tell me that."

Dr. Melrose took a long drink, then put his glass down on the table
while his hazel-brown eyes behind his spectacles flicked back and
forth from Jim to Gertrude.

"Aren't we getting away from the donkey?" Jim asked, believing
that the doctor had got himself out on an untenable limb and was
trying to lead them off on a new branch.

"Quite the contrary," Melrose said, his eyes twinkling, sensing Jim's
suspicion. "The fate of Joe Walsh is the nub of the story. It explains
everything, even that brace of fine, fresh-run salmon on the marble
over there."

"Oh, do tell us. I'm fascinated," Gertrude exclaimed impatiently.

The doctor's audience was now where he wanted it, the one half
skeptical, yet curious, the other brimming with anticipation and
willing to believe. He lit a cigarette and leaned back in his chair.
"First, I must warn you," he said, "that things can happen in Ireland
which could not occur in England or the United States. Just why this
is I do not know, nor would I hazard a guess. Some people claim that
it is atmospheric, that it has to do with the juxtaposition of the Gulf
Stream and the arctic winds. Others believe that it is an ancient hyper-
physical inheritance from the earliest Celtic tribes. Be that as it may,
we doctors know that belief can produce fact. A psychosomatic illness,
for example, can be as real and as fatal as any strictly pathological
one. You are Americans. In America, as your Miss Gertrude Stein
has said, a rose is a rose is a rose. Donkeys and fish do not commu-
nicate there except through the medium of Mr. Walt Disney. You
told me last evening that this was your first visit to Ireland. If you will
pardon my saying so, you are both still wrapped in sterilized cellophane. In a matter of hours you were whisked from New York to
the highlands of Connemara. Then, in a few more hours you were
subjected to an occurrence which, as seen through your American in-
sulation, seems improbable and fantastic. So I must suggest to you
that you rip off the cellophane and listen to this story through Irish
ears.

"In 1923 this hotel, which was then a country house, and the
river belonged to Lord Balater. As he was then in India on a special

mission for the Viceroy, he let this place for the summer to the Maharajah of Baipur, a keen sportsman and, from all accounts, a very genial, attractive chap. I believe it was more or less of a swap—Baipur was to have the Owenmore fishing and Cashel House, and Balater was to have one of the Prince's minor palaces, together with the tiger and sand grouse shooting. At that time Michael Walsh of storied fame was the gillie on the Island Beat, as his son, Tom, is today. Mike was a good and faithful gillie who bore on his shoulders a very heavy burden. He was the brother of Joseph Walsh, who was known from Clifden to Galway as the greatest and most cunning poacher in Connemara. To say that Mike disapproved of his brother's profession would be an understatement. It shocked and horrified him that any man, let alone his brother, would stoop to thieving salmon from private water. Curse him and berate him he did, but he could hardly call the constable against his own flesh and blood. However, it was well understood between them that the Island Beat was strictly off limits for Joe's pursuits. Mike had made it quite clear that if he ever caught Joe on his territory, he would turn him in to the police.

"Of course the story of Baipur's lost fish was all over the countryside within an hour. Even those famous injunctions which Mike is supposed to have given to the Maharajah were thought up by some wit in the Cushatrower pub that very day. And as the story spread, it was natural that the size of the fish grew until it became as big as anything ever seen in Norway. Well, this was too much for the artful Joe. When he heard the stories of a salmon that weighed in the neighborhood of fifty or sixty pounds, he quickly calculated that at six shillings a pound a veritable fortune was lying in wait in the cool waters off the island. Yes, it was the very size of the fish that did him in. Had it been of normal size for these waters, say even twenty pounds, he might well have got away with it. As it was, the minute he showed the fish to the fishmonger in Clifden the jig was up. Like lightning, word came back to Cushatrower that Joe had snagged Baipur's salmon. When Mike heard it, he boiled over. Without saying a word to his wife or his children he got on his bike and pedaled to the house of Father O'Malley, the parish priest of Balinafad. With a face so drawn with anger that it would have frightened the Pope, he called upon the good priest to accompany him to Cushatrower pub, where he knew his brother would be standing drinks to all on the proceeds of his sale. Father O'Malley wanted to know what the trouble was, thinking it might be a drunken brawl, which was more rightly a matter for the constable. When Mike said that it had to do with his brother Joe, the priest guessed at once that it was an affair of poaching.

"You see, good old Mike, in spite of his threats, could still not bring himself to put his brother into the hands of the law. He first had to try the Church, and then the salmon's owner. What he really wanted, I feel sure, was Father O'Malley's moral support while he denounced his brother to the Maharajah. Well, they found Joe right enough, and the two of them took him, much against his wish, as you may surmise, straight here to Cashel House.

"The scene that took place here has been described many times. One has to make allowances for the native proclivities of Irish story-tellers to embellish and ornament. From a distillation of the various versions, the facts would appear to be more or less as follows:

"Baipur, quite alone and not encumbered by secretaries and re-tainers, as Indian princes are apt to be, brought the three Irishmen into this billiard room and bade them sit down—probably right here where we are sitting this minute. Mike, who still was boiling with anger, at once accused his brother of having poached the very salmon which Baipur had lost on the previous day. He gave the weight of the fish and said that it had been sold to Mr. Joyce, the fishmonger in Clifden, who could confirm the weight and the fact that a small, number ten Silver Doctor had been found embedded in the fish's lower jaw. The Prince then asked Joe if the accusation was true. Had Father O'Malley not been there, the chances are that Joe would have hotly denied it. The presence of the priest was too much for him. He knew that he would have to confess his guilt anyway the coming Sunday, so the words of denial stuck in his throat. He merely lowered his head and said nothing.

"Baipur then assumed his most princely manner and proceeded to pronounce judgment. It was true, he said, that he had hooked an exceptionally large salmon in the pool beneath the rock on a small Silver Doctor, and that the fish had broken the cast. It had been a noble salmon, worthy of a fine sportsman, a better one than he, who in his eagerness had put too great a strain on the tackle. It made him sad, he said, to think of that splendid fish being wrenched from the stream in the night by a miserable poacher and sold in the market for anyone to eat. Such things were against the laws of God and man, and the thief would receive his just punishment.

"Here he turned to Father O'Malley and said, 'You are a Christian, Father, whereas I am a Hindu, or to be exact, a Brahmin. You teach, I believe, that the soul of man, when it passes from this earth, goes to a purgatory where it is purified or punished in accordance with its mortal behavior, and thence to an eventual heaven or hell. The Vedic abode of temporary sojourn is indeed similar to your purgatory. There, also, the departed spirit is blessed or punished. But from this point our beliefs take different roads—yours to heaven and hell, and mine to another chance on earth to atone and struggle up the long road to Brahma. Our teachings tell us that the soul of a poacher would be directed by Yama into the body of a humble beast, probably a poor beast of burden, and as such he would have to atone for the sin of stealing the fish of others.

"'But this is a matter for the all-powerful Deity,' he went on as Father O'Malley crossed himself against any heathen taint. 'I may do no more,' he said, 'than pronounce an earthly punishment for one who has illegally taken my salmon. So, Joseph Walsh, I order you to give to Father O'Malley, for the use of his Church, all the money which you received from the sale of that fish, and to obtain from Mr. Joyce, the fishmonger, that Silver Doctor, and to wear it in your hat as long as you shall live.'

"With that, he arose and walked with dignity out of the room, looking every inch the potentate in his well-cut Harris tweeds and his turban of baby-blue silk."

Dr. Melrose reached for his glass and poured the last of the whisky down his throat.

"Did Joe Walsh do as he was told?" Gertrude asked.

"Indeed he did," the doctor replied. "Father O'Malley saw to that. But the damage to his pride was too much for him. The taunts and jibes that were piled on him when he went to the Cushatrower pub with that fly in his cap were more than he could take. He soon ceased to be seen about, staying at home in his cottage and never appearing beyond his hedge before he had made sure there was no one on the road. Then the chagrin made him sickly and rheumatic, and the next winter he caught pneumonia and died in the night before Father O'Malley could reach his bedside for a final absolution."

Dr. Melrose stopped to light a fresh cigarette, but it was clear from the smile on his face that he had not finished.

"It was on his way home from the funeral and wake that Mike heard strange noises in his barn and went in to investigate," he went on. "He found that his jenny had given birth to a fine male foal. Being very full of whisky and sentiment at the time, he named the little donkey Joe."

"The same Joe we met today?" Gertrude asked.

"The very same," the doctor answered. "Though now he is a middle-aged fellow of twenty-nine, who is working his way back to grace by aiding you in your sport."

Gertrude raised her glass. "God rest his soul!" she murmured before drinking.

Jim Evans motioned to the barman. "Another round. Make them doubles." He turned to Dr. Melrose. "Maybe that's the way to imbibe the spirit of this country," he said.

"As good a way as any," the doctor answered, grinning.

The Shining Tides

WIN BROOKS

What Haig-Brown and Williamson did for the salmons—Atlantic and Pacific—Win Brooks has done for one of the great game fish of salt water, the striped bass. The Shining Tides can be compared with no other modern book on salt-water fishing, for it can best be described as a novel with angling undertones, or perhaps an angling book with novel undertones. Had space permitted, the editor would have included the entire volume and had no fear that any angling reader would have been bored. Instead it was necessary to select, with one brief side excursion, the portions dealing with the major character—Roccus, the striped bass. Brooks is not only a fine writer, he is an experienced angler and something of an amateur marine biologist.

SUN AND a wafer edge of dissolving moon rose a few minutes apart. From a late roost in a scrub oak on Blake Point, Nycti the Quawk, the black-crowned night heron, resented them hoarsely.

Roccus, a great striped bass, swinging a four-fathom curve and following a tide press, passed south of Centerboard Shoal and turned north. From deeper water she moved into nine feet off Bird Island. Spiny and soft dorsal fins slashed a V-ream in the stipple made by the breeze. Against a submerged granite boulder cored with magnetite, lightning-split from the ledge five hundred years before, she came to rest, tail and pectorals fanning gently, at a meeting of tide and currents.

More than a quarter century had passed since Roccus first rested beside this boulder during her original migration as a three-year-old in the company of a hungry thousand of her age and sex. To it she annually returned, sometimes with small pods of big fish, more recently as a solitary, in late May or June, when the spawning season of Roccus saxatilis was ended and the eggs were spilled in the milt-chalked Roanoke above Albemarle Sound or, on occasion, in the region of Chesapeake Bay.

This resting place off the southern coast of Massachusetts was her domain until October's northeasters sent her coursing southward. The boulder lie she had found good, and she returned to it as the experienced traveler returns time and again to tavern or hotel where he has found comfort and safety and food to his taste.

This year Roccus was making her earliest journey. For the sixth spring since she had attained a length of sixteen inches, no urge within her belly set her coursing up the Roanoke or the Chesapeake feeders, past the thin tides to the gravel bars where, in other ecstatic Mays, she had reproduced. Instead, on a spangled night when the moon had waned, a counterurge had drawn her into the open Atlantic; and, passing migrating schoolfish too young to spawn, she had turned north and east along a thoroughfare as plainly marked for striped bass by current and tide and pressure, by food and temperature, by the instinct to avoid danger, as any broad, paved highway is posted for the guidance of man. The migrating shoals of small stripers, or rockfish, or rock, had remained in the Barnegat surf when Roccus passed between Sakonnet and Cuttyhunk into Buzzards Bay and into the tides of the Narrow Land where Maushop, giant of Cape Cod legend, still blew the smoke of his pipe down a southwest wind to make the fog.

Now the thirty-six foot beacon on Bird Island caught the first rays of sun and splintered the dazzling light of new day. The moon paled and Mars and Venus and Jupiter were snuffed out in a sky of azure. Gong buoy 9, better than a mile to the south, winked green at five-second intervals. East, against the sun, the old Wings Neck Light lost color. Roccus grooved her lie. She had come alone, too early, to a latitude of disquiet, troubled strangely, strangely drawn, and here in the merging, changing weights of waters familiar to the nerve ends along her laterals—in the surge of the sucking, thickening tide—she held her place while the light of the dying May moon transfused the direct stream of brilliance of which it was only a reflection.

In an overhang of the same boulder, behind a curtain of rockweed and moss and bladder wrack, on a scour of sand ground from granite by the tides of thousands of years, Homarus the lobster lay partially embedded and concealed, expelling water through twenty pairs of gills, her stalked, compound eyes fixed on the fringe of weed shielding her cave. Her two pairs of antennae rippled with the flow of the weed in the sun's first strike.

Homarus weighed nineteen pounds and was nearly as old as Roccus. Since her final molt as a free-swimming surface larva she had shed shell, esophagus, stomach and intestine seventeen times as her body became too large for the armor encasing it. During her years she had carried more than a million eggs glued to the flexed pocket of her abdomen. She was almost uniformly black, with tinges of green at her knuckles and streaks of chitin at the edge of her back shell. She was a cannibal and a glutton, vicious and ugly. In her youth she had made an annual crawl to deep water. During recent years she had strayed little from Bird Island ledge. For her, as for Roccus, the boulder was a familiar lie, the lobster in the hole made by tide scour through the overhang, the bass above the overhang near the holdfast of the weed. Homarus was secure in her knowledge that anything small enough to enter the cavern was prey for her appetite. The aperture was too small for the green snout and jaws of the bass.

Each was aware of the other for hours.

Tide ebbed its extreme. In changing pressure, in degrees of salinity, in varying temperatures, there was conveyed to Roccus the memory of many feeding grounds. Around the boulder's westerly side in slow pouring came drained warmth from shallows over lutaceous bottoms, a peculiar freshness tasting of algae, alewives, larvae and shellfish. This current was the confluence of drainage from Sippican Harbor, the Weweantic and Wareham rivers, from Beaverdam Creek, Agawam River and Hammett Cove and a score of lesser waters into which anadromous fishes made their way. Around the boulder's easterly side swept an icy current from Cape Cod Bay which plunged with the west-flowing current through Cape Cod Canal. This was underlay for a streak of warmer, less saline water which, on the flood, covered Big Bay and Buttermilk Flats and the Onset mudbanks and had been freshened slightly by Red Brook's discharge.

The separate currents ran and slowed, stirred and stilled, and there was a semblance of complete slack, a hushed suspension of motion.

Roccus turned outward from the boulder, and the broad fan of her tail made a roil of water and sand which parted the weed curtain of the overhang and caused Homarus to back deeper into her lodge, waving antennae in anger and spanning her crusher claw. Roccus resumed her lie.

The still of the sea was only an illusion; there was no dead calm. End of one tide was but the beginning of a new, and birth of the new tide aroused activity in the sea. Life about the ledge responded. Clams extended their siphons, clearing holes. Crabs settled carapaces deeper. Scallops thrust upward, dropped back like leaves falling through dead air. Sea robins changed lairs, crawling on the first three rays of their pectoral fins, and sculpins settled in the weed on the rocks, awaiting questing green crabs. Soft-finned rock cod moved lazily through caverns; and from countless hiding places the sharp-toothed cunners emerged in schools, nibbling at barnacles and the sand tubes of annelids. The cunners were the bait-stealing curse of bottom fishermen.

New tide awakened hunger in the lobster. Before Roccus' arrival Homarus had dined on a two-pound male of her own kind. Later she had killed a flounder, which, by treading her legs, she had buried beneath her as a dog buries a bone for future reference.

Tide also awakened hunger in Roccus. She made a three-quarter leaping turn, a sprung bow of steel, and her tail drove into the overhang. Homarus, nearly dislodged, backed farther into her cave, gripping deeper. The disturbance of Roccus' thrust caused a surface commotion which excited seven herring gulls.

As the tide turned, Anguilla the eel swam to the ledge, surfaced, sucking larvae of a kind she had not tasted for seven years. Anguilla was a thirty-two-inch ripple of macrurous grace, blue-black but showing yellowish-white on her underside in a transformation which would make her a silver eel returned from fresh water to the sea for completion of her catadromous life. She carried within her ovaries, moving down from fresh water, more than ten million eggs which would ripen swiftly when she reached the Sargasso deep. The urge to procreate swept her more relentlessly than any current.

As Anguilla approached Roccus' lie and Homarus' lodge, she deflated her air bladder and sank close to the bottom, moving with slow undulation like a weed torn from anchorage. At the base of the boulder she came to rest, arrowed head near the weed curtain, a third of her elongated body curled beneath her.

Homarus tasted oil from the eel. She withdrew her legs from the sand and buoyed her body and waved her antennae in excitement. She was fond of eels. Stealthily she extended her sharp cutter claw along the sand into the weed fringe.

Roccus saw the eel in the cone of vision of her gold-rimmed black left eye. She also tasted the eel's oil.

Anguilla moved an inch nearer the hole, though appearing not to move. Behind the weed Homarus moved an inch nearer Anguilla. Roccus saw the lobster's claw.

Though her superior nostrils sensed danger, Anguilla had no experience with lobsters or striped bass. She moved another inch, questing, tasting, testing. Her head, weaving, swung between the open jaws of Homarus' cutting claw, which snapped like a trap. The cutter slashed embedded linear scales, flesh and bone, its blades meeting between the severed head and body of the eel.

As Anguilla's body reacted in a hoop, Roccus made a violent tail smash against the weed curtain, and the compression dislodged the lobster, overturning her outside the hole. Before Homarus could right herself, Roccus overleaped and bit through her tail, crushing shell and flesh between double-toothed tongue and vomer plate.

In the strengthening of tide, Roccus lay content. She had eaten the tail of Homarus and all of Anguilla. The claws and body of Homarus bumped along the bottom in the quickening pulse of the sea, all but concealed by a cloud of cunners, some already inside the body.

Three days later her body shell, first crimsoned, then paled pink by the sun, was found on Indian Neck by a boy who showed it at home to the amazement of his parents. They had never seen one so large. The boy saved it a few days, but it grew rank and his mother made him bury it in their garden, where, in August, it fed a clump of coral phlox envied by all their neighbors.

Out of the southern sky, against the afterglow of sun when flashes of the Wings Neck Light grew bolder, a wedge of birds came driving beneath the first sprinkling of stars. They flew in wavering formation, eighteen on the right flank, twenty on the left: Canada geese seeking rest. They were in flight from Texas to Crane Lake in Saskatchewan and since daybreak they had been on the wing. Cutting across Cape Cod, they flew at two thousand feet with a following breeze. As they passed over Bird Island the gander leader sighted the distant sheen of Big Bay and Little Bay, Buttermilk and Great Herring, and the mirrored, shadowed surfaces of Sandy and Long Pond and Gallows and Bloody and Boot, and a score of others. He honked and towered, circling, climbing. Then all the flock began to honk and gabble, their voices like those of beagles chasing rabbits among the constellations.

Nine miles away, coursing a meadow where quail had roaded, a dog fox heard the geese and cocked mangy ears. Saliva drooled from his mouth because once he had tasted gosling in the yard of a farmer. Fear rose in his heart because he had met ganders, to his sorrow. He stood silent, listening, pretending not to listen.

The geese reached peak of tower and the old bird made his choice, which was Little Bay where the eelgrass was thick. Honking ceased, the wedge drove north in silence, losing altitude. The fox did not hear the geese again and was relieved that his appetite would not place a strain upon his fortitude. He wet where the quail had been and went off to hunt a mole.

Until the tide turned, Roccus occupied her boulder lie, at times suspended in the current, at times on the scour outside the empty lodge of Homarus.

Saturn was the evening star. The moon had crossed the meridian with the sun and was invisible from earth; it was dark o' the moon. When the blanket of stars lay close and heavy on the water, shimmering and opalescent, Roccus broke through it with a roll and tail-slap and fell back on her side. The stars scattered, danced, reformed in wavering pattern. The bass slashed the surface, sinuating on her right side, then on her left, leaped half clear. Three yellowish-brown sea lice fell from her shoulder and were promptly devoured by a cunner which an hour later was eaten by a crab which before morning, was swallowed by a master sculpin.

Nycti the Quawk, belly yearning, flapped from the filth of his roost for a night of hunting in Planting Island Cove. His flight voice was harsh: *quuaawwk, quuaawwk!* Roccus leaped once more in the brief sustention of the tide.

From Dry Ledge, Roccus drove northwest again seeking warmth. Alewives were in abundance but their appetite was held in check by enervating cold. In the rivers a few bass which had wintered over began to lose sluggishness.

On a morning ebb there was a definite change of pressure and the wind backed into the northeast. Roccus swam to the sandy shoal between Warren Point and Long Beach Point, lay finning in three feet of water. Even the hermit crabs had moved off the shoal in advance of the storm. The wind made up and the surface ran angrily in lifts, sulkily in hollows, and Roccus gave herself to the conflicting movement of the water, warmed by water thinned by rain. Half buoyant, she was vibrant with storm, knowing it with all her body, comforted by its warmth; she was of the storm as well as of the sea. Wind pushed against the tide, tide pushed the surface; the surface waters ran counter to the movement of the tide. Roccus lent herself to the opposing actions and in the turbulence maintained her lie without effort, now feeling the scrape of sand against belly and anal fins and tail, now delighting in the lash of raindrops along her dorsal.

By slack of ebb the wind was a half-gale and seas ran more regularly and higher over milky sands. Roccus dropped back into deeper water. The first northeaster of the reluctant spring gathered force from a thick, gray ceiling of clouds.

So the May was gone. The backward spring leaped to keep abreast of the sun's orbit. Anglers sandpapered rods, wound guides and tips, varnished with their fingers, cut sticks of glass, Burma, Calcutta cane; cleaned reels, tested old lines of nylon and linen and discarded them; applied emery to dulled metal squids; replaced rusted hooks in favorite plugs; built herring cars; wired squid rigs for bottom fishing; cast lead for surf weights; filed gaff hooks; counted eelskin rigs; stood hypnotized before tackle displays, mobbed tackle counters; made phone calls to charter boatmen.

The bass were in!

Gilligan wrote in the New York *Herald Tribune* that a few were being taken in the New Jersey surf. Ray Camp in the New York *Times* said they were off Shinnecock Inlet. Trullinger and Hurley and Brawley sent word to the *World-Telegram,* the *Mirror* and the *Journal* that they were knee-deep in them in the Sound. In the Boston *Herald* Henry Moore wrote that there were bright fish in Buzzards Bay. Earl Banner in the Boston *Globe* said he had reports they were in the Weweantic River but he wanted to be shown. Dark Montreal in the Boston *Advertiser* outlined the Cape Cod Canal Derby, and Cliff Davis in the *Post* wrote of the Martha's Vineyard striped-bass tournament.

The bass were in and it was time for fishing!

There were at least four good months ahead. The sea, which gave earth life and might some day reclaim it, traced pattern and plot in the shining tides. The net was of greater strength and wider sweep than any Roccus had avoided. Roccus and the shining tides were one. She cleaved upriver.

Bobby Meade steered a twenty-five-degree course through the platinum haze, holding the bow of *Carey's Chicken* in line with the first left-hand buoy marking the Hog Island channel approach to Cape Cod Canal. Both engines were revved to twenty-one hundred and the slipstream was wet, pouring past the spray shield. He and Cal were taking her over from the Vineyard to the base on the river for the first of the fishing.

Cal Knight lay on his back, an ear close to the panel opening of the port engine housing; his eyes were closed under a frown of concentrated listening. If there was a fault in the engine the skipper'd find it, Bobby thought.

Hooking on as Cal's mate had taken a deal of doing. Not that Cal, who was his second cousin, didn't want him, knowing him able, but his ma, and Cal too, had needed convincing that three years of high school were enough for a boy not planning college, and that this particular boy could quit before the end of his third year as well off as ever he'd be.

"Your pa always said you can't learn navigation without you know your arithmetic," his ma had warned, using the strongest argument she could muster.

But he had the need to earn some money. "Pa would figure I should. I'll make more working for Cal than I can off the Vineyard on somebody else's boat."

"You'll spend, boarding places and suchlike."

"I'll sleep aboard and mostly eat aboard. And Cal will pay me ten dollars every day he has a charter."

"On days he doesn't you won't earn."

"He will 'most every day 'cept in foul weather. All the best fishermen want Cal. We'll maybe go for tuna and make a lot of money."

"I don't care; you're too young."

"I'm seventeen!" He'd sounded as if seventeen were mighty close to man's expectancy. "Besides, I'm big enough."

He was, too—tall enough, at any rate, tall like his pa had been but skinny as the pole of a boathook. He had a knowledge of boats and fishing gained from his pa, who had always been a good earner, though with him it was easy come, easy go. It was Cal, in the conclusive argument, who'd won his ma over. "I'll look after him and Father O'Meara'll see that he gets to mass. Holds an early mass for the boatmen and anglers." It was Cal who'd . . .

"Mind your helm!" Cal said.

Bobby started from daydreaming and noticed he was three points off course. Cal still lay with eyes closed, listening. The boy turned the wheel gently.

"Hey, Cal."

"Yuh?"

"How'd you know I was off course?"

"Wave slap changed on the bow."

"How can you hear the slap above the motor?"

"Pick a fiddle out of an orchestra, can't you?"

"You find the trouble?"

"Carburetor adjustment. Doesn't amount to anything." Cal slammed the panel back into the housing box and secured it and came standing without touching his hands to the deck. "I'll take her now. Bad water here for you to learn." He took the wheel.

"You sore, Cal?"

"Nope."

"I shouldn't have let her fall off like that."

"You shouldn't have."

"Nothing happened that time, but next time it could."

"That's right. Now you've said it all yourself without my having to say it. No next times. We set a course, we hold it. Right?"

"Right, Cal."

"Fetch one of the glass rods and rig a plug. Get that big hooper-dooper I made. Might's well wet a line."

Bobby fetched a rod from the cabin ceiling and snapped the big teak plug to the leader. Cal throttled down to four hundred, to three hundred, to two-fifty, and Bobby let the plug go astern, thumbing a free spool. "Boy, what action!" the boy said.

"Let out a couple hundred feet, get it deep. Any fish around here, they'll be deep. Tell you something."

"Yuh?"

"Throw your reel in gear and loosen the star drag. Strip your line off against the drag. Know why?"

"Guess so. Fish hits when I'm free spooling I maybe get a back-lash or a burned thumb."

"And if you don't and you throw into gear with the drag set up, you break off. So you knew half it anyway." He grinned. "Guess I can't teach you much, mate."

Cal swung right rudder to a forty-degree course, leaving Abiel's close to port for the run along Stony Point Dike toward the canal proper. They bucked an outgoing tide with the rips strongly made. Revved down, they had barely steerage way. There was little traffic. A tanker was standing down past Mashnee, riding light, and a dragger, loaded to the gunwales, passed them with her diesels pounding, Boston-bound. There were a few small craft distant and one closing rapidly on their starboard bow.

Cal said, "That's a fast job, Bobby. Coming up."

The approaching cruiser's bow was a brown dot in a ten-foot V-fountain of spray. She passed a hundred feet distant at not less than thirty knots, a low, three-quarter-decked mahogany hull built for speed and some weather. The big man at her wheel kept his eyes ahead, but the girl beside him, her hair streaming, waved. Cal waved back and Bobby pumped the rod and cranked the reel to give an imitation of handling a fish. The sucked-down stern of the boat showed the bronze letters, *Tiderunner,* and, beneath them, *Marble-head.*

Bobby stripped line, and the action of the plug was in every fiber of the line and rod and in the nerves of his hands. Then he felt shock up his arms to his shoulders.

"Cal!"

When the tide ebbed with the west flow of colder water through the canal, Roccus in mid-channel dropped back with it under the railroad bridge, past State Pier, through the straits between Hog Neck and Hog Island into the warmer waters of Buzzards Bay. She swam onto the shoal at Cedar Island Point and in three fathoms there hunted food, finding little except a few of the first of the humpbacked scup. These, in the adult growth, had dorsal fins too sharp to be relished. Some of the smaller ones she swallowed. She pursued and lost a small school of sand launce. She rooted for them but could not find where they had buried themselves.

With the wash of *Tiderunner's* wake over the shoal she swam into deeper water, not alarmed but wary, and within the cone of vision of her right eye detected an active, elongated shadow, something like a whiting, swimming in jerks as if wounded, and fluttering from one side to the other. She closed on its strangeness and followed leisurely until the object leaped away from her. She accelerated and swam abreast of it, but it jerked away swiftly. She swam beneath it and bunted it gently with her head. In her years Roccus had encountered many kinds of artificial lures, and a few, when they had proved sufficiently tantalizing in action and the conditions of light or approach were such as to obscure leader and line, she had struck. Decision and action in this case were simultaneous. She swirled and took the hooper-dooper head on just as it jerked again. Two of the gang of head hooks embedded themselves in her upper lip.

"Cal!"

Cal heeded. "You hung on bottom, Bobby?"

"On fish!" Bobby grunted. The rod arced and the line hissed against the light drag, and hissed cutting the surface.

"Good boy!" He revved the port motor, turned right rudder to keep the line from the hull. "Take him easy. Bass?"

"Yuh. Big one, Cal."

"They all feel big first-out in the spring."

Bobby held the rod tip fairly high and kept the reel cranking, but the line still payed out.

"You best tighten up a little on that drag."

"That's what I was going to tell you," Bobby grunted. "I'm buttoned down tight already."

"Oh." Could be a big fish at that, Cal thought, though it was awful early. He gunned the motors and began to follow the fish across channel. Bobby picked up some line. The fish dogged deep and the rod butt, jumping alive, bruised his groin. "Get me a belt, Cal."

Cal reached into the cabin for a leather bib and buckled it on the boy and helped set the butt in the pocket, feeling as he did so the springy surge of power away out at the end of the line. The fish *was* big. Twenty minutes passed. The battle had taken them across the channel to the south end of Mashnee, a boulder-strewn bottom.

"That rod'll stand all you can give it and the line is new. Your fish is well hooked or you'd have lost him long ago. Better go to work, son."

The young mate lowered the rod tip, reeling; pumped, lowered reeling; pumped again, repeated.

"Gets in those boulders, he'll cut off, Bobby."

"Know it. Moved him some. This can't be no bass."

"It's bass," Cal said. "Nothing else acts like that. Give it to him."

Bobby gained fifty feet, lost it; gained sixty, lost fifty. Ten minutes later after a series of short runs the fish had only a hundred feet of line.

"Coming up!" Bobby yelled in triumph.

Off the stern Roccus surfaced in a great shower of foam and Bobby called on the Mother of God to witness the sight. Cal kicked into slow reverse and said quietly, "Don't give him slack. Ease off a little on your drag and watch out. He just came up to look around; he's going to move sudden."

Roccus sinuated, swirled and sounded, and all the line so laboriously won was lost before the boat could be brought on a following course.

"He ain't even winded," Cal said.

"Cal."

"Yuh."

"You take him."

"If you don't want him I'll cut him off."

"But you saw him."

"Yuh, and how!"

"How big, Cal?"

"Oh, maybe thirty, forty pounds." He knew it was wiser not to say how big.

The fish lunged and the line sang.

"I saw him, too."

"How big you think?"

"Bigger than any bass I ever saw."

"That so? Well, watch your rod tip."

No kidding him, Cal thought. *He saw as well as I. He knows he's hung to a record.*

The rod was a glass half-circle.

"Not much line left."

"We'll run up on him again. Take in steadily, keep the pressure on him."

They'd worked back to the channel edge, and Cal noticed with apprehension that the mahogany speed cruiser which had passed them outbound was headed in again at high speed, bearing directly across their course. He sounded a sharp warning on his horn and saw the bow wave diminish sharply. They hadn't seen him before. He gave his attention to the fish.

With the help of the boat, Bobby had the fish within a hundred feet again, and surfacing. Cal kicked into neutral.

"You tired him some; don't let him rest now." He went below for the big gaff. When he came topside with it, he saw with consternation that *Tiderunner* was laying to, not a hundred feet beyond the surfaced, thrashing bass. He cupped his hands and shouted, "Ahoy, *Tiderunner!* Move off, please! This fish will run again!"

The man and the girl had taken seats on the cabin to watch the fight. The man gave no sign he heard; Cal saw the girl turn to speak to her companion, probably repeating the message. The man pointed at the fish and said something. Cal shouted a warning again but it was ignored.

"He's going to move again, Cal, I can tell. He's getting ready! There he goes!"

The surface leaped and boiled. The bass took line once more and the tip of Bobby's rod was pointed directly at the other boat.

"I can't turn him, Cal," he called.

"He'll pass under that lardhead. I'll swing in an arc around him. Don't pressure him enough to keep him up."

He gunned both motors. He saw the man on *Tiderunner* leap for the wheel and shouted, "Don't start up! Lay where you are!"

The girl waved, but *Tiderunner's* motors came alive with a roar and the mahogany leaped, crossing *Carey's Chicken's* bow.

"He's going right over my line!" Bobby shouted.

Cal kicked into neutral, slammed into reverse. *Tiderunner* jumped clear, the man at her wheel shaking a fist.

"He cut me off!" Bobby's cry was anguish. Life had gone from the rod, line drooped from its tip. The mahogany cruiser, her damage done, lay to, motors idling again, and the boy called to her skipper in Cal's own phrase, "You big lardhead!"

Cal said, "Easy. I can do better than that. Reel in your line." He ran over alongside *Tiderunner,* and the man emerged from her wheelhouse. He was younger than Cal had thought, and the girl was better-looking. But even so . . .

He said, deliberately, easily, "You're a no-good son of a bitch. At first I wasn't going to say it in the presence of the lady, but then I figured anyone who'd be palling around with you wouldn't mind an understatement like that. . . . You don't, do you?" he asked, his eyes on the girl.

Her companion had a bull of a voice. "You wouldn't say that ashore, you clam mucker! You haven't got the guts!"

"I'd say it ashore, afloat, or flying. And with ditto marks. I base on the river at Farrell's Wharf and I'll be there in less than an hour. I'll be glad to say it then and there or any time later, anywhere."

He moved out and headed upchannel. *Tiderunner* passed him, heading in.

"Maybe he'll be waiting, Cal," Bobby said.

"Good. I need it."

"Looks pretty big. In good shape."

"I need a licking. Do me good. Shouldn't have said it—not in front of her."

"She didn't look the kind would be with him."

"Doesn't make any difference. Shouldn't have said it. Don't you ever."

"I won't. . . . Cal?"

"Yuh?"

"How big was that bass?"

"Really want to know? Make you feel bad."

"I want to know."

"Not less than one hundred pounds. Not less than five and a half feet long. Now you can cry in your pillow tonight."

"Maybe I'll get a bigger one."

Cal grinned. "I got me a good mate," he said. He put an arm around the boy's shoulder. "Listen, kid. No sense to tell a man not to feel bad when he loses a record fish. But if you'd caught it you wouldn't have had any fun bass fishing the rest of your life. Imagine that!"

They both laughed. . . .

Tiderunner wasn't in sight when they tied up at Farrell's Wharf.

"Wash down and make up the bunks," Cal said. "I'm going up to see Tom Salter and tell him about that fish, and I'm going to call New Haven and tell Dan Merriman, who's doing striped-bass research at Yale. No sense telling anyone else; they'll just figure we're dreaming. If I'm not back in fifteen minutes get some chow cooking; anything suits me."

"Okay, skipper." Bobby grinned.

Cal found Tom Salter at his boat station and told him of the fish. Tom told of the fish he and Father O'Meara had seen.

"Could be the same," Tom said. "Fish we saw wouldn't stay in the river long."

"How is the father?"

"No younger. But well enough. And asking for you recently."

"I'll drop by the rectory and say hello. Someone I want him to keep an eye on."

"You won't find him this afternoon. Manuel Riba is giving him some worry and he went up to Manuel's place. That damn-fool chief down at the Coast Guard Station, Maddox—you know him—he's got

Father in a frame of mind to believe that all his works are in vain if he can't save Manuel from the devil."

"By the way, you know a sport cruiser, *Tiderunner?*"

"I've seen it lately. Seems to belong up the river. Saw it moored off a new house up there where some professor and his daughter come to live. Why?"

"Quite a craft."

The soft, warm light was going. Cal paid his respects to Mrs. Salter and decided to go back to the boat without telephoning Merriman. He saw the riding and cabin lights were already turned on; Bobby would have something cooking. Maybe later they'd go uptown to the movies. Right now he was hungry.

He called when he walked out on the apron of the wharf, but Bobby didn't answer. The new tide hadn't raised *Carey's Chicken* much. He swung down four rungs of the ladder and jumped abroad. Bobby lay sprawled on the deck between the engine housings, his head on his hands, sobbing. Cal knelt swiftly.

"Hey, kid, what gives?"

The boy half turned his head. It was a bloody mess, mouth and cheeks cut, both eyes swollen, nose torn at one nostril.

"What happened?"

"That guy came looking for you. Said you'd run out on him. Called you a yellow bastard. I told him everything you'd said went for me, too. That's all. Except he's awful fast and awful good."

Cal got him sitting up and washed out the cuts. The nose wasn't broken. Nor the spirit.

"I wasn't crying because I took a licking."

"I know."

"It was because I'd lost the fish. Cal, you'd have had him if you'd been handling him. Would have meant a lot for the reputation of the boat."

So that was it.

"Listen, Bobby. I couldn't have done any better than you. Nobody could. You made no mistakes. That rod was too light to kill that fish in anything under an hour. Hadn't have been for that son of a bitch you'd have had him."

"Maybe."

"Come on, let's chow. You want to go to the movies later?"

"Sure, anything you say."

"I say the movies for you. I got an errand to do."

Roccus sank to the bouldered deeps off Mashnee. The hooks of the plug were merely an annoyance, the weight of it a nuisance which did not greatly alarm her. She had rid herself of similar lures before. Behind her, as she swam, trailed one hundred and twenty feet of forty-five-pound-test nylon line and three feet of nylon leader. Before dusk all except a foot of the line had been cut off by the sharp edges of barnacles, mussels and rocks. She expelled with an exertion that tired her and somehow caused her to be tense. Awkwardly, she fed through squid though she was not hungry. She sought the reassurance of normality.

Roccus jaw healed swiftly, causing her no pain. As June waned she joined first one and then another of the many schools of striped bass which remained in the area of Cape Cod Canal. Some of these fish were from the Chesapeake region and more were native to the Hudson and its tributaries. There were few from the Roanoke; most of the migrating Roanoke fish had come no farther north than the Jersey coast.

All these fish in the canal area moved back and forth with the tides through the big ditch, driving whiting from the bottom to the surface, where, in the rips, they skitted furiously, heads out of water, terrorized. The bass rose beneath them in pursuit, tail-smashing to stun them.

Day and night the anglers lined the canal riprap to cast for the bass, using eelskins on weighted rigs during the darkness and plugs in daylight hours. Favorite spots were crowded. These were adjacent to the swiftest rips and had been given names common among the angling fraternity. Some of the names were Halfway Gate, Split Rock, The Mussel Bed, the Cradle, Lobster Pound, Lumber Yard, Paddy's Rock, The Beacon, The Herring Run, The High Tension, Portugee Hole and The Basin. There were a score more. Some men fished all night and slept in the daytime in cars parked in a wooded section under the Bourne highway bridge. Some fished for market, some only for sport; others fished for sport, yet marketed their catch so they could meet expenses and continue to fish for fun. When the bass were choosy, or chasing whiting far out in the middle of the canal, hard to reach, many of the fishermen lived for days on nothing more substantial than coffee and doughnuts. Restaurants stayed open all night to cater to them, and these, on the slack tides, were crowded with anglers who were waiting for the rips to make up. They had only one subject of conversation—striped bass. There was none but dreamed of catching a record fish. None really expected to. They were a red-eyed, bewhiskered, somewhat odoriferous congregation of zealots.

Roccus scattered the stars and seized a compressed slab of moonlight, swallowing it.

The July moon beamed on waters slapped by the tails of late-arriving menhaden moving inshore along both sides of the Cape. There were many thousands in each school and there were countless thousands of schools. Into one dimpling over three fathoms Roccus drove again.

Other fish were feeding on the pogy—many other bass, squeteague, late pollock, the first of the bluefish, blue and hammerhead sharks, bonito, dolphin and, in deeper waters, broadbill swordfish and whales. Nearly all life of the ocean fed on the menhaden. Lobstermen seined them for bait. Fleets of white vessels seined them by the millions for oil and fertilizer. They swam fin to fin, tiers deep, the most abundant species in the Atlantic fishery. They were late arriving because the sea on the shoals had been late to warm. Now they would summer in the bays and harbors, the inlets and surf, waxing fatter and oilier on algae, sediment of organic decay and minute crustacean life, and their enemies from the land and of the sea would deplete their numbers by millions, yet fail appreciably to deplete their population. For each mature menhaden moving inshore had spawned more than one hundred thousand eggs. They were a countless streaming under the stars of the tide, showering as Roccus drove again.

When the July moon filled, Roccus returned to the lie by the Bird Island boulder, gorged with pogy, and at two o'clock of a morning, when the light on the water was one six-hundred-thousandth of the brilliance of the midday sun, she moved into the circle of a seine. She felt it against her tail before she saw it; she felt it against her side. Lesser bass, also trapped, began in excitement to mill about her. She surfaced and found no escape; she sounded and encountered wide-mesh twine. She swam the closing circle of the seine, brushing against it. Some of the smaller bass were gilled, thrashing, floundering. But she was not greatly alarmed. In the Roanoke, in an arm of the Chesapeake, once in the Hudson, she had been in nets before. From traps, like most bass, she always found her way; these were the offshore weirs with openings never closed except on low water. This trap was different; its opening already had closed, its diameter was closing.

Roccus moved slowly in a half-circle, well inside the closing wall of mesh. Then, with a rush and thrust that scattered the smaller bass, she surged to the surface, flashed like a bright spearhead in the July moonlight, and re-entered the protecting water a fathom clear of the net floats. The thrust of the broad tail carried her to the channel past Bird Island and the safety of the flowing depths. She passed a pod of pogy, scattering them in a frenzy of flashing silver, then slowing to alert movement along the margin of the channel.

In the moon's last quarter Roccus re-entered the canal, following schools of spike and tinker mackerel, feeding only at night, lying on the bottom with lesser fish during the hours of sun. Her appetite diminished and she was easily satisfied. She no longer pursued the darting whiting to the surface to whack them and gorge them. She moved lazily after eels, not eager for their taste. As the water warmed her stripes darkened from brown to deep blue, and a reddish hue appeared on the edge of her gill covers. Sea lice left her for fish traveling to the surf. A benign lassitude of old age crept upon her.

Lovely and peaceful beat the sea of summer, cruel with death. Schools of small tuna were annihilating squid. Giant bluefins were decimating the mackerel shoals. Stalking the big tuna came the killers.

Through the canal with the tide east-flowing Roccus moved under Sagamore Highway Bridge, past Paddys Reef, past the dolphins in the mooring basin across from The Blinker, past breakwater and sandcatcher and into the surge of Cape Cod Bay, where the half-flood kicked a chop of seventy-one-degree surface water against the current disgorging between the riprap. A light easterly behind the fetch of sea added to surface commotion at the canal's east entrance. Roccus felt an uneasiness. She moved across the Sagamore bar where sand eels and sperling silvered the surf.

The school tuna harassing the summer squid were between twenty and forty pounds in weight, fish which in the larval stage three and four years before had measured only a quarter inch in length. Several hundred of these in two or three distinct schools had moved higher along the bay arm from the Barnstable traps where they had gorged on herring. Now they moved through and under acres of the small red squid, gorging again.

It was not coincidence that the adult members of their family were in the same area. Departing from the fathom curve of their migration highway between the tip of Cape Cod and Nova Scotia, they had moved in from Wood End to intercept the mackerel which swam with the east wind. They raced at great speed effortlessly. Between their bullet-shaped heads and their tails of tremendous power there was no line of water resistance; their giant fins fitted into grooves in their bodies. Sun rainbowed the spray above them when they surfaced, sporting; they made a slick caused by the slimy substance adhering to their tiny scales. The slick made a pattern of betrayal on the water.

Orcinus, the killer whale, was leader of a pack which had sped south with the Labrador Current, then followed a bent course inside the Gulf Stream to a point three miles off The Race. There they had been sighted, an even dozen of them, and reported by two draggers inbound from the Georges Bank. They had been seen in combat with a finback whale of sixty feet which they had mortally wounded but upon which they had not fed. They had come south to feed on the tuna.

Orcinus was twenty-nine feet long, with huge rounded flippers, great tail flukes and a dorsal fin, curved with age, more than five feet in length. About three quarters of his scaleless skin was black, but his chin and belly were white and there were white oval patches above each eye. In his pack were six males only slightly smaller. The five females were less than half as large, and their flippers, flukes and fins were disproportionately smaller, perhaps a quarter of the size of the males'. These were the gangsters of the Atlantic and their molls, unmatched in ruthlessness, working with a mob instinct that struck terror to the hearts of the largest whales and sharks.

Off Barnstable the killers had intercepted the trail of the tuna and soon began to take toll of them in all sizes. A forty-pound schoolfish was a half-bite appetizer for Orcinus, a five-hundred-pound bluefin a two-bite hors d'oeuvre. Despite the speed of the tuna the killers overtook them at will. Yet they did not harry them ceaselessly. They withdrew as their appetites were satisfied, so that the bluefins were not completely stampeded.

Now, having swum outside the tuna for several miles during half a day while the bluefins, their alarm diminishing, resumed feeding, the killers drove toward the land again and the giant tuna fled before them among the schoolfish. The schoolfish turned over the shoals in terror.

Inside Roccus there was no hunger except a yearning which had no significance for her senses. She moved leisurely across the Sagamore bar and onto the shoals off Scorton Harbor Creek in Sandwich. There, encountering extreme shoaling, she finned farther off the land. And farther off the land, where the water deepened to eight fathoms, Orcinus hit her.

The bass had brief warning. A tuna of about twenty pounds arced into her vision, leaped and twisted and turned offshore again. Roccus followed from curiosity and met, nearly head on, a giant tuna in a glide of frenzy, in flight before the closely following killer.

Orcinus saw Roccus only as a blurred shadow suspended where no shadow should be. He chopped at her with one side of his jaw in the flash of his passing. His twenty-two conically pointed teeth on that side sliced into the caudal peduncle of the bass—nearly to the backbone—just failing to sever.

Tuna and killer whale vanished as quickly as they had appeared. Roccus, seeking shallower water, swam slowly and with great exertion. Her broad tail, the propeller of her normal action, was fouled and its driving force drastically reduced. She was severely injured.

On the second night after being wounded by Orcinus, Roccus swam

awkwardly with the tide in the starry shallows past Sandwich Harbor
Creek to the deep of the canal's east end; and as the west tide began to
flow, she gave her hurt self to the pull of it and, dropping deep, moved
through. The wound on both sides of the wrist of her tail attracted two
lampreys, which she brushed off on a mussel bed, but cunners followed
her, as did dogfish, drawn by the flow of her life in the tide's life.

Her life was a life of great tides and currents but this life of the
moon's tide was small; the moon was in quarter stage, and the rips
were slow to make. This was a windless night when the eel-rig bouncers
got much distance in their casts but took few bass. Roccus saw a
dozen slow-moving, blue-backed, white-bellied skins, inflated with
water, move within her striking distance and withdraw with tantalizing tail action. Hungry, she might have struck. She did not hunger.

Before the new day crept under the span of the railroad bridge she
had reversed her journey through the canal and was again in Buzzards
Bay.

The wound confused her, rather than pained. The alarm building
within her was the result of confusion.

Sterna, the roseate tern, was fishing. From her lookout on the high
bank of the point near where Roccus rested, the bird watched the
schools of bait fish congregating near shore. The sun lay slightly behind her, past its zenith.

When there was a sufficient concentration of the small prey milling
about, Sterna performed the Trick of the Menacing Shadow, launching herself and swooping to within a few feet of the water. Her shadow
panicked the bait, which showered ahead of it, and the tern of greatest
symmetry dipped to scoop baby herring and sand eels, some of which
she took from the air.

Lying under four feet of water on the warm silt bottom, Roccus
watched this performance for an hour, at the end of which Sterna
had her fill. The bass moved slowly to feed on wounded, fluttering
bait.

Sun beat down on the surface of the river. No wind moved that surface, no fish, no bird. The tide had reached the peak of the salt mark
on the marsh grass. Bait fish kept to the cooler depths over sand, worrying shell lately turned by the quahoggers. Plankton clouded the iris-
blue water. A kingfisher swooped but held its dive over a cloud of minnows too deep to reach and returned with a cry of angry frustration
to its lookout at the brittle tip of a dead cedar.

Blue crabs crawled the bottom and in the weed crept up on partially
opened seed scallops, and on the bars snuggled with their hinges
against small rocks, waiting for clam snouts to show. They could move
fast and in any direction. A late-spawning horseshoe crab pushed sand

like a bulldozer. Fiddlers, their homes flooded, crept along cautiously, hunting shrimps and sand fleas and the broken clams gulls had dropped for cracking when the tide was down.

In a hole fourteen feet deep, off an old windwheel once used to make electricity for a pump, Roccus rested with her chin in mud, expelling water at an accelerated count, turning on one side, then the other, to present the healing wound at the base of her caudal to the black ooze, the warm and salving ooze. So she had rested for days moving into weeks since Orcinus had struck her, feeding lightly and not more than twice a week. She wasted away. She was still a great fish, but her depth and thickness had diminished, the deep bulge of her belly had vanished; she was flabby in her underside, there was an unhealthy sheen on her gill covers and no sea lice sought her as host.

August waned. Days of intense heat were followed by brief tempests that failed to clear the air. The dawns were red beyond the eye of the sun. Chain lightning, distant, licked the evening sky. There was no thunder. A season was approaching its end and the approach communicated itself to all life.

Man witnessed the quick ripening of his tomatoes, the sudden, overnight toughening of his corn, the withering of his potato vines, the indefinable feeling that a chore so long delayed as tacking a new tin blade on his snow shovel had better be attended to. There were days and weeks and possibly months before a sterner season claimed the earth, yet the grasp of change was on it.

The terns, their young flown, were hungrier for themselves; the mackerel gulls were less lazy; the fierce-winged gannet dived from greater height. The curlew cried above the moor at night and the plovers called at daybreak. The young of the native black ducks tested their strengthening wings above the guzzles. Sandpipers and swallows flew in clouds, and in the marsh the red-winged blackbird tucked her song beneath her wing.

In the dunes the hares developed a scent the gray fox could follow, and in the marsh the muskrat made a tentative selection of winter quarters. The otter ranged far, and in the night his whistle was a distant locomotive.

The life of the sea also felt change. Tuna coursed east, the killers in their wake. Cod and haddock began an inshore movement and the whiting went into the surf's first roller. Bluefish followed the whiting into the surf and the scup turned south. Off the beaches the young of the menhaden were nearly four inches long and the adult fish had disappeared; some said the pogy fleet had taken all of them, but they had merely moved into deeper water, a movement which was scarcely more than a drift accomplished on the ebb of a high-course tide.

Off Plum Island and Parker River, off the estuary of North and South rivers, off the Gurnet, outside Saquish and Clarks Island, off the Cape Cod Canal and Sandwich Harbor Creek and Scorton Harbor Creek, on shoals, the young striped bass began to school, school joining school, for southward migration, a movement wholly depending upon the movement of bait fish, which, in turn, depended completely upon the development of weather.

Roccus, mending slowly, felt a similar urge, though the schooling fish were mostly between five and fifteen pounds. Pods of the larger migrating fish usually formed later. She began to feed on the fugitive small bait, on a few late soft-shelled crabs. She mended slowly.

On the last night of the August moon, while a tempest cloud covered the crescent, Roccus dropped back through the narrows down, down the river and into the pulsing sea. Her wound had not healed completely and never would; she swam with half the strength of her usual tail thrust and only half her eagerness of questing. Otherwise she had the fair health of old age and a sudden desire to be gone to the far waters of her birth. With the tide she dropped back, until she reached the Mashnee Shoals at the western approach of the canal.

To the submerged granite boulder on the Bird Island ledge, where she had paused in her migrations of many years, Roccus made her way, driven by the urge to begin her southward journey. For three days of early September she occupied this hold. She gained strength as the wound at the wrist of her caudal healed despite its fouling, and her appetite returned. Here in May she had fed upon Anguilla, and here now the eels dropping back from the rivers to spawn swam in abundance and were tasty and nourishing.

These were bright days of mistrals at dawn, warming surface water through the hours of sun, and cool nights when the pattern of the universe beyond earth was mirrored on the frosty tides.

No striped bass joined her on the Bird Island ledge and on the night of the third day of her lie there she returned to the Mashnee shore. The instinct of early migration remained strong within her, but she was possessed by a stronger urge to seek the company of her kind.

Off Mashnee smaller bass were beginning to school. Some had passed through the canal from Cape Cod Bay, others were from the rivers and harbors adjacent to the canal's west end. These fish were restless, undetermined in their movements, uncertain, wavering with the tidal changes, held in the gathering place by the flow of feed on the canal edge, waiting on the weather.

Roccus joined a school of bass in the fifteen- to twenty-pound class. She was neither welcomed nor made unwelcome. She swam in a flanking position like an outrider edging a herd of cattle.

Three pods of bull bass which had summered in Cape Cod Canal, one group of fish individually approaching half the size of Roccus, joined the school to which Roccus had attached herself. Two days later more than one hundred striped bass from six to twelve pounds each joined up. All acted in response to the same urging that moved the matriarch for company of her species in a journey of varying lengths, none short, to the warmer waters of early life.

In the rips and backwaters the young menhaden and herring and the silver eels were plentiful. The nights were noisy as the bass fed and fattened on them. Only Roccus fed and strengthened yet did not grow in size. Despite her healing, her feeding, her strengthening, she continued to waste away.

Now the nights were cold, and the surface water, from the night air, was sometimes colder than the depths, and in the limitless element above the sea migrating birds were a-wing to lesser latitudes, quiet in their passage.

Roccus felt the change of pressure on the weight of waters at the Mashnee gathering place of the tides. Of the great and growing school of bass she alone felt it, being wiser in age and experience. It was a subtle change, not marked, telling her that heavy weather was definitely approaching, though not yet close. Only five barometers hinted this change; most did not. Yet next day all the school felt it, the larger fish first.

It was a signal for application to appetite, for satiation beyond appetite, for gorging against the needs of a journey that would begin at the height of the storm and allow no interval for seeking food. With the storm the school might move along to Cuttyhunk or to Sakonnet area, or even as far as Montauk Point; it would positively move from Mashnee and during passage it would not feed.

Roccus fed almost exclusively on the migrating eels, whose oily flavor, more pronounced now than that of young menhaden, she somehow needed. These she pursued at leisurely pace, approaching them from behind, accelerating to seize them broadside at the head. Some she bit in two, others she swallowed whole. Her best hunting was at night, when the eels were most active, emerging from their hiding places.

Because a high-pressure area from Canada slowed the storm's progress up the coast from Hatteras, the weather held fair beyond the time Roccus' instinct told her it would foul. The barometer even showed a slightly upward trend.

So came a cloudless night of thin moon, nearly dark o' the moon, a windless night, the sea flat, cold flat except for a distinguishable offshore ground swell. In the marshes, gathering black ducks were raucous. A flight of geese went over.

Hunger blinded caution, or Roccus would not have struck at the false Anguilla that darted past in a haze of phosphorescence. The very force of her strike, while it set the sharp hook, snapped the line with a vicious jerk that amazed the trolling, half-dozing angler.

Downtide, sounding, Roccus fought her doom with the utmost of her half-mended strength. Her savage strike had driven the head hook of the rigged eel through the roof of her mouth, and the barb of the middle hook had pierced her tongue and lower jaw. As pain stabbed her and she swirled, the tail hook of the false Anguilla slapped under her open gill cover and secured itself in her rakers.

A resistance which sought to turn her course, a sensation she had experienced in other misadventures, quickly ended. But one hook bled her gills, and the others, like a chain bolt on a door, secured her jaws, nearly locking them. Her breathing became labored. She was in a state of slow suffocation.

She surfaced in a flurry of panic, violently shaking her head, circling, creating a disturbance which in decent weather would have attracted the gulls from afar. This day the gulls were on the beaches or the pierheads or the rocks, or riding the updrafts of the wind above the faces of the dunes. None observed her.

She drove for bottom again, but not to rest. Although the pain of the hooks, a sudden reflex of her nervous system, subsided, there grew within her a feeling of bursting and a terror of the unknown that gripped her jaws. Without sense of direction or purpose, regardless of changing pressures, she swam swiftly about, often striking the rocks.

This phase of her struggle lasted for hours, but her strength waned as the day waned and the storm gathered itself for night assault. Finally her terror vanished and her aimless movements ceased; and in the late afternoon, the ebb tide nearly spent, herself spent, she gave herself to the tide, unconscious, drifting with it, her fins moving only from the turbulence of the water, and an uncontrolled trembling in all her muscles. Her tail was completely paralyzed.

Through the quickfall of night, into the first of the tide's resurgence, life clung to Roccus rather than she to life.

Then it was full dark and, though the heavy clouds completely obscured the new moon and the constellations, there came a moment when it seemed as if Roccus had entered again the spangled shallows of her youth. The golden burst of Capella in Auriga fired the sea. Bright were Deneb and Altair and Algol, and bright was Jupiter below the Great Square of Pegasus. And suddenly all of the planets and their moons, every one of the myriad stars, were pouring down the tide, streaming down the tide that had turned for home.

Dirty Work at the Covered Bridge

PAUL BROWN

Just as there are other ways of killing a cat, other than choking it to death on butter, there are devious ways of tricking a fish. In "Dirty Work at the Covered Bridge" Paul Brown shows the depth of trickery to which an angler will descend.

I T BEGAN to look as though we had gone for bass on one of those days about which I had so often heard—a day when it is impossible to catch fish because of the simple and painfully evident fact that they will neither bite nor strike, no matter what bait or lure is offered them. We had been fishing the Manatawny, in southeastern Pennsylvania, casting plugs and spoons, flies and spinners over all the likely-looking places in the stream as we waded from Pine Forge to Pleasantville, but with no success whatever.

"Doggone it! It's just one of those days!" my companion insisted for the tenth time, with infinite disgust. "They won't take anything to-day!"

Our experience certainly substantiated his opinion. My only difficulty in accepting it was that I had never believed that there ever was or could be such a day. Fish could always be caught, I maintained, if the effort were properly made. No situation or combination of circumstances could possibly occur during the open season for bass that would keep them from eating—and the fact that fish eat is, after all, the basis of angling. If fish did not eat, they could never be caught with hooks.

The solution of the problem of catching fish on "one of those days" accordingly becomes very plain. Give the fish what they want to eat, present it irresistibly with cunning naturalness—no matter how unique and unorthodox the means—and they will take it. Catching them depends upon the skill and ability of the angler.

Tired after our morning's fruitless effort and a little disgruntled at the result, we decided to resort to still fishing. Under a covered bridge just below Mahlon Weidner's gristmill there was a deep, cold pool where bass always could be found, and it was here we stopped to rest on the grassy bank.

We changed our rigging and gathered some live bait from the creek. A few minnows were netted. Several crawfish and hellgrammites and waterworms were caught; a few mussels were collected from the shallow, gravelly bed of the stream over which the water rushed before it eddied about the pool where the bass lay in the shadow of the overhanging bridge. We even caught a few small leopard frogs along the bank where the lush grass rose luxuriantly from the water, and scooped up a couple of fat, seductive tadpoles.

In the course of the next hour or so we had baited with every one of those things. We had fished with loose lines, with floats and on the bottom—yet we had no bites whatever. Surely it looked like one of those days when the fish simply would not bite.

That stock opinion had become a most attractive alibi, especially since we knew there were bass in that pool. We had peered from the bridge and seen them gently swaying just over the rocky bottom. We had actually watched while they disdainfully moved away from our proffered bait with contemptuous flirts of their tails.

It was most disconcerting. It cannot be denied that there are times when fish will refuse to take the usual bait extended to them in the usual manner, but that there are days when they will not take anything is absurd. Even so, there was nothing that we could think of doing which we had not already done. So we stretched out on the sunny bank and soaked up our share of the joy of living. As we lay there, watching our lines only halfheartedly, a heavy farm wagon came lumbering and groaning down the dirt road leading over the bridge. As it clattered and rumbled over the floor boards of the ancient structure a veritable shower of small litter and trash cascaded onto the surface of the pool.

Suddenly my companion jumped to his feet and stared intently at the pool.

"Well I'll be ding-donged!" he exclaimed, with delighted amazement.

"No doubt," I agreed cheerfully, "but why?"

"Because I'm dumb!" he admitted. "By golly, I'm the dumbest man I know! Just you watch me snake a bass out of that pool!"

He reeled in his line and replaced his baited hook with a tiny one which had been saved after the feathers were worn off by a trout. "Yes, sir!" he grinned. "It won't be long now!"

Then he began searching intently at the bottom of a rotting beech stump along the bank and returned presently with a huge black wood ant. I watched him curiously but without much interest. Our positions had been reversed. He had, incredibly enough, made me the skeptic, while he had become the enthusiast. "Even Ike Walton never thought of this!" he crowed. "Just watch me catch a bass!"

A moment later he gently cast the ant into the middle of the patch of dust and litter which was still slowly circling the surface of the pool. The little creature promptly kicked and struggled, creating a small tempest in the center of the dusty film—and almost immediately I could see a big bass rising from the cool depths of the hole. That ant was taken without the slightest hesitancy! My chum struck, and the placid waters of the pool were lashed into a turbulent fury as the little hook was imbedded in the jaws of the fish.

Minutes later the tired and exhausted fish was maneuvered along the bank and skillfully netted. It wasn't so large as it seemed to be when it first rose, but it had provided as much sport and even more thrill than had many a larger bass. The tiny hook made careful and skillful angling a strict necessity.

My friend was successful because he had seen what I had failed to observe—that the passage of wagons and cars over the bridge shook down ants and small insects and possibly grubs from the floor of the structure, and that the bass rose to take them from the patch of dust and litter. I had always believed that the noise and commotion caused by the passage of a vehicle over a wooden bridge close to the surface of a stream created a positive deterrent to good fishing. I felt that it was necessary to wait a while before a bite or strike could reasonably be expected. It never occurred to me that this might actually cause some good fishing until I saw it demonstrated.

For the rest of the afternoon my companion and I alternated casting ants and stamping on the floor boards of that old bridge. We got bass, and lots of them, and it was the only method we tried that day which was at all successful. Happily so, too, for our fishing was then considerably more than a mere matter of chucking a baited hook into the water and patiently waiting for possible results; it had become a matter of skill and intelligence, and was consequently much more satisfying.

Years later I was fishing a famous bass stream and had a tremendous bass strike under a bridge which spanned the creek between two fields, just below an overhanging clump of alders. I missed the fish, but the strike was so impressive that I talked about it at dinner that evening. The water I had covered that day was strange to me, but the others in our party had all fished it before. They listened to my comment with polite courtesy, and then they unanimously and promptly handed me a totally unexpected "royal razzberry"!

Eventually, when the hilarity had run its course, I learned that I had touched a topic which was generally regarded as taboo. Everyone in the party knew of that fish, and every one of those able and experienced fishermen had, at one time or another, felt it on the end of his line.

"There really is a monstrous bass under that bridge," I was told, "but it can't be caught. None of us has failed to try it, but we never even get a rise, much less a serious and determined strike. When we have tied onto the gentleman, it has been an accident and has invariably happened when we were not expecting it."

"And now everyone thinks he can't be caught?" I asked, with the gentle incredulity that shouts a private belief contrary to the general opinion.

"Well, it hasn't been done yet!" I was told.

Naturally, this increased my desire to catch that fish. I have often heard of the finny monsters that cannot be caught, and when it has been possible I have tried to get them. Usually I am no more successful than any of the other anglers who have attempted it, but I felt that I knew a stunt or two that might be new to that bass, as well as to the skeptical companions who enthusiastically showered me with ridiculous advice.

Possibly I did know a stunt or two that the bass had never encountered before; but when I tried them the following morning, they proved no more valuable than any of the old ones. I worked the hole under that bridge, with all the skill and knowledge I possessed. To induce the bass to strike I used small frogs, wriggling red worms, the pupae of a big butterfly, a crawfish, and even an artificial mouse. I caught small moths and grasshoppers and cast them on the surface and sank them slightly, without creating the slightest interest on the part of the fish.

Then I changed to flies. I used small ones and large ones, bright and dull ones, wet and dry. I permitted them to drift aimlessly on the surface of the pool and caused them to dart enticingly along the bank, but I had no more luck with them than I had had with bait.

Feeling that all those unsuccessful efforts had been little more than a preliminary after all, I went up on the bridge and stamped about until there was a considerable patch of dust and litter on the surface of the pool. I was sure that the huge uncatchable bass would do what those other bass had done years before. Before I went onto the bridge I had changed to a fly similar in appearance to the indigenous hatch, intending to cast it among the small debris as soon as possible—but I never did.

Suddenly I saw the bass through one of the wide cracks in the floor. It was incredibly large, a noble quarry that would make the painstaking efforts to catch it seem trivial. Evidently it was endowed with the wisdom of both years and experience, for it did not rise to any of the little insects visible in the dusty area on the roof of its aquatic home. Indeed, it seemed to me that the fish actually cocked one eye upward and leered at me—at least I had received a challenge.

I determined to abandon my efforts temporarily and watch that bass until it started to feed. It was, I reasoned apologetically, too late in the day to go elsewhere and expect good fishing, anyhow. I was sure that if I knew a little about that monster's habits of feeding I would be able to land it.

While I was lying flat on the bridge, staring steadily into the stream, I heard bare feet approaching. I looked up and saw a country lad coming to fish that pool. He had the usual equipment which barefoot boys are traditionally supposed to have—a long bamboo pole with a short length of line, no reel and a single, eyed hook. He looked at me as though he regretted—almost resented—my presence.

"Do you think there might be any big fish in this pool?" I asked him.

He looked at me scornfully before he replied, as though he recognized my transparent attempt at deception. "Pop just told me the Big One is back," he informed me briefly.

There was no need to elaborate. That designation, "the Big One," was respectful and positive identification. Quite evidently he and his father and all of his other relatives, not to mention the neighbors, knew all about that bass which I had been watching.

"Think you can catch him?" I asked curiously.

"Well," he began hesitantly, "I might get him this time. I've thought of something new that might fool him."

The boy continued over the bridge and a little later was searching in one of the fields beside the stream. Presidently he returned to the bank with a small stack of hard and partially dried cattle chips! The boy had actually thought of something that was new. At least, it was new to me.

I noticed that the bottoms of those chips were not dry and hard, as the tops were. They had remained moist, and there were small white maggots visible in the sodden mass.

The lad began tossing fragments of the chips into the stream. They bobbed merrily down into the quiet waters of the small pool in the shadow of the bridge, where they slowly revolved in the eddying current. I saw the Big One rise slowly and take the squirming white maggots!

"He's taking them, kid!" I nodded, elated at the boy's ingenuity.

The youngster grinned back. Then he thrust his hook through the last chip and baited it with one of those peculiar, brittle odoriferous worms which are known to youngsters as "stinkies." Carefully he drew the squirming worm up to the bottom of the chip, which he gently launched after the others. It was a splendid-looking arrangement. The worm, to all intents and purposes, was struggling to detach itself from the sticky substance in which it had been living. It was as natural a presentation of bait as I had ever seen.

I almost held my breath as the chip approached the lurking, watchful bass. The slow swirls swept the chip toward it. The fish started to rise almost insolently, so casual and disinterested did it appear. But I had noticed that same apparent lack of interest before.

Slowly the bass approached the chip, scrutinized it for a second and then, with a contemptuous wriggle of all its fins, sank to the bottom.

I almost groaned with disappointment. "He didn't take it, kid!" I called regretfully.

"Well, maybe he won't take anything. He never does, seems like."

The boy was near to tears, for he had banked heavily, with all the supreme confidence of youth, on his self-evolved stratagem. He came up on the bridge and lay down beside me.

"What was on the bottom of those chips?" I asked him.

"Grubs," he answered.

"White ones?"

"Yeah," he rejoined. "They're fly maggots."

"Then why did you try the Big One with a stinkie?" I complained.

"Oh, that worm was there just when I wanted to bait the hook. What's the difference? There's lots of stinkies in those chips."

"But maybe the bass doesn't like them. He actually touched the chips when he rose the first time. I believe he was taking only the white grubs."

The lad considered for a moment and then admitted that it might be so. "Think it might be any good to try again?" he asked, again hopeful.

"Sure! Hunt another chip," I suggested. "I have some big white June bug larvae in my bait can, and we can make one more effort."

He looked at me with sudden suspicion. "We?" he asked, with a trace of antagonism.

"You!" I corrected hastily. I had no desire to encroach on the youngster's plan.

"Wait right here!" He grinned, convinced of my total honesty of purpose.

Then he began a search of the adjoining pasture that was immediately fruitful. Again he slipped his hook through the center of the chip, the bottom of which was dotted with maggots. Then he baited with a large white grub and drew the worm up to the sticky bottom of the chip so that it seemed to be imbedded naturally. From his position above the pool he floated his lure into the quiet waters, while I waited and watched. The huge bass rose instantly and struck.

"Sock him, kid!" I yelled as I leaped to my feet. "He got it!"

And that's just what the kid did! He yanked mightily, no doubt expecting to horse that fish right onto the bank with one magnificent heave—but it couldn't be done. He was fast to the biggest bass of his experience.

When the lad struck, that fish turned into a fighting fury. It came to the surface like a streak of bronze light and broke water with a series of slashing, wrenching twists and contortions that should have sent any hook flying. Instead that two-for-a-penny hook held!

"Stop trying to horse him out!" I shouted, fearful that the boy's tackle would not stand the strain. "Play him!"

"Can't play him, mister!" the lad groaned. "What'll I play him with?"

It was unanswerable. How I wished that the youngster had my tackle, which had been so futile when I used it!

Then I realized that the excitement was too much for the lad's judgment. He was trying his best to hoist that noble bass onto the bank! His line would never have permitted it, even though his stalwart pole—under no circumstances could it have been called a rod—could have raised a river sturgeon.

The inevitable happened. Worried by the constant pull, the fish started for the bottom.

"Hold him!" I shouted encouragingly. "He's going for the bottom. If he gets among those big rocks, he'll get loose sure!"

"Can't hold him!" the youngster panted.

Suddenly the lad slacked away on his line by the simple expedient of lowering the tip of his pole almost to the surface of the stream. "He can't cut the line on the rocks if it's loose, can he?" he asked gleefully, feeling that he had frustrated the Big One for the moment.

"Not very well, but he might rub the hook out."

"That's right!" he agreed with alarm. "What'll I do now?"

What a time to give advice! If the fish were finally landed, the credit would be the kid's, and properly—but if he got away, the fault would be mine, no matter what I suggested.

"Nothing to do but wait, son."

I fervently hoped I was right, and it fortunately happened that I was. Presently the Big One got tired of sulking on the bottom and started upstream, fighting and twisting every foot of the way as the country lad pulled him toward a shallow bar by a frail line that incredibly held. At last he had dragged the fish onto the bar, where it appeared to be practically out of water because of its constant struggles to escape.

"Wade in and kick him out!" I ordered. "If you try to lift him, your line will never hold."

With a heave of his pole and a quick flip of his bare foot the boy spun that fish onto the bank. Whooping with wild delight, he dropped his pole and fell upon the flopping bass. The Big One was caught!

I was considerably more exercised and elated than the boy. To him that fish was just a big bass. It was practically a familiar acquaintance, somewhat of a local institution; but to me that catch was a symbol of accomplishment which falls to the fortunate lot of but a few men.

Cows served me well on another occasion when one of those unexpected and happy inspirations peculiar to fishermen came my way. I was after bass again and had been whipping a pool below a gravelly ripple, where I knew bass fed. None of the fish ever taken there had been unusually large, but they were completely satisfactory in every respect save one. They would not take my flies or bait.

I had tried everything I had, with a remarkably uniform lack of result, and finally quit in disgust. Before leaving for home I stood for a while on the bridge over the pool watching the stream below me speculatively. Just then some cows started crossing the shallow ripple above the pool on their way to the barnyard for the evening's milking. Most of them paused to drink.

Doubting that any self-respecting bass would remain in the presence of such tremendous disturbance, I glanced casually into the pool again. Instead of having darted away, a number of worth-while fish were all at the foot of the ripple, poised and alert!

The reason was instantly evident. Those cows had dislodged a lot of stones, with the invariable result. Small aquatic life had also been dislodged and was being carried to the waiting smallmouth beauties by the rushing water!

Chuckling delightedly, I stopped at the barnyard and asked when the cattle would be turned into the pasture. I determined to be there early the following morning, when they crossed the stream—and I was, equipped with every form of aquatic life I could get. I had waterworms, crawfish, hellgrammites, tadpoles and even salamanders.

I was waiting, rigged and baited, as the cows entered the creek, and I promptly cast a waterworm into the ripples and let it float down to the waiting fish. Instantly I had a strike! Before those cows left the stream I had landed four wholly satisfactory bass from that pool. They struck everything I offered but the salamanders, and I later discovered that there was none of those little reptiles in the stream naturally. It was a new form of food, or likely I would have been succeessful with them, too.

The various experiences I have had that centered about the use of such subterfuges were stimulating at the time, but since I have had ample time to think about them I have come to the conclusion that my elation was not entirely justified. Of course, I got fish, but I have never felt that merely getting fish is the purpose of angling. Catching game fish by exactly duplicating the most common conditions under which they feed could scarcely be called sporting. It largely destroys the elements of chance and skill, which yield the greatest comfort and satisfaction to a fisherman.

Of course, such deceptions prove to me once more that there are no days when fish cannot be induced to bite, but I have been positive of this for so long that there is no longer any particular satisfaction in providing it anew.

The Old Etonian Tramp

JOHN BUCHAN

In John Macnab, John Buchan made poaching a sporting proposition. Edward Leithan, having been advised by his physician that he might cure his ills by "stealing a horse in a country where horse thieves are hung," responded by making a trip to the Highlands. Here he assumed the name John Macnab and announced to neighboring landowners that, within a given period, he would take a salmon from the river and a stag from the hill. "The Old Etonian Tramp" deals with the salmon-poaching episode.

WHEN THE Hispaña crossed the Bridge of Larrig His Majesty's late Attorney-General was modestly concealed in a bush of broom on the Crask side, from which he could watch the sullen stretches of the Lang Whang. He was carefully dressed for the part in a pair of Wattie Lithgow's old trousers much too short for him, a waistcoat and jacket which belonged to Sime the butler and which had been made about the year 1890, and a vulgar flannel shirt borrowed from Shapp. He was innocent of a collar, he had not shaved for two days, and as he had forgotten to have his hair cut before leaving London his locks were of a disreputable length. Last, he had a shocking old hat of Sir Archie's from which the lining had long since gone. His hands were sunburned and grubby and he had removed his signet ring. A light ten-foot greenheart rod lay beside him, already put up, and to the tapered line was fixed a tapered cast ending in a strange little cocked fly. As he waited he was busy oiling fly and line.

His glass showed him an empty haugh, save for the figure of Jimsie, one of the gillies, at the far end close to the Wood of Larrigmore. The sun-warmed waters of the river drowsed in the long dead stretches, curled at rare intervals by the faintest western breeze. The banks were crisp green turf, scarcely broken by a boulder, but five yards from them the moss began—a wilderness of hags and tussocks. Somewhere in its depths he knew that Benjie lay coiled like an adder, waiting on events.

Leithan's plan, like all great strategy, was simple. Everything depended on having Jimsie out of sight of the Lang Whang for half an hour. Given that, he believed he might kill a salmon. He had marked out a pool where in the evening fish were usually stirring, one of those irrational haunts which no piscatorial psychologist has ever explained. If he could fish fine and far, he might cover it from a spot below a high bank where only the top of his rod would be visible to watchers at a distance. Unfortunately, that spot was on the other side of the stream. With such tackle, landing a salmon would be a critical business, but there was one chance in ten that it might be accomplished; Benjie would be at hand to conceal the fish, and he himself would disappear silently into the Crask thickets. But every step bristled with horrid dangers. Jimsie might be faithful to his post—in which case it was hopeless; he might find the salmon dour, or a fish might break him in the landing, or Jimsie might return to find him brazenly tethered to forbidden game. It was no good thinking about it. On one thing he was decided: If he were caught, he would not try to escape. That would mean retreat in the direction of Crask, and an exploration of the Crask covers would assuredly reveal what must at all costs be concealed. No. He would go quietly into captivity, and trust to his base appearance to be let off with a drubbing.

As he waited, watching the pools turn from gold to bronze, as the sun sank behind the Glenraden peaks, he suffered the inevitable reaction. The absurdities seemed huge as mountains, the difficulties innumerable as the waves of the sea. There remained less than an hour in which there would be sufficient light to fish—Jimsie was immovable (he had just lit his pipe and was sitting in meditation on a big stone)

—every moment the Larrig waters were cooling with the chill of evening. Leithen consulted his watch and found it half past eight. He had lost his wrist watch and had brought his hunter, attached to a thin gold chain. That was foolish, so he slipped the chain from his buttonhole and drew it through the armhole of his waistcoat.

Suddenly he rose to his feet, for things were happening at the far end of the haugh. Jimsie stood in an attitude of expectation—he seemed to be hearing something far upstream. Leithen heard it too, the cry of excited men. . . . Jimsie stood on one foot for a moment in doubt; then he turned and doubled toward the Wood of Larrigmore. . . . The gallant Crossby had got to business and was playing hare to the hounds inside the park wall. If human nature had not changed, Leithen thought, the whole force would presently join in the chase— Angus and Lennox and Jimsie and Davie and doubtless many volunteers. Heaven send fleetness and wind to the South London Harrier, for it was his duty to occupy the interest of every male in Strathlarrig till such time as he subsided with angry expostulation into captivity.

The road was empty, the valley was deserted, when Leithen raced across the bridge and up the south side of the river. It was not two hundred yards to his chosen stand, a spit of gravel below a high bank at the tail of a long pool. Close to the other bank, nearly thirty yards off, was the shelf where fish lay of an evening. He tested the water with his hand, and its temperature was at least sixty degrees. His theory, which he had learned long ago from the aged Bostonian, was that under such conditions some subconscious memory revived in salmon of their early days as parr when they fed on surface insects, and that they could be made to take a dry fly.

He got out his line to the required length with half a dozen casts in the air, and then put his fly three feet above the spot where a salmon was wont to lie. It was a curious type of cast, which he had been practicing lately in the early mornings, for by an adroit check he made the fly alight in a curl, so that it floated for a second or two with the leader in a straight line away from it. In this way he believed that the most suspicious fish would see nothing to alarm him, nothing but a hapless insect derelict on the water.

Sir Archie had spoken truth in describing Leithen to Wattie Lithgow as an artist. His long, straight, delicate casts were art indeed. Like thistledown the fly dropped, like thistledown it floated over the head of the salmon, but like thistledown it was disregarded. There was indeed a faint stirring of curiosity. From where he stood Leithen could see that slight ruffling of the surface which means an observant fish. . . .

Already ten minutes had been spent in this barren art. The crisis now craved other measures.

His new policy meant a short line, so with infinite stealth and care Leithen waded up the side of the water, sometimes treading precarious ledges of peat, sometimes waist-deep in mud and pondweed, 'til he was within twenty feet of the fishing ground. Here he had not the high bank for a shelter, and would have been sadly conspicuous to Jimsie, had that sentinel remained at his post. He crouched low and cast as before with the same curl just ahead of the chosen spot.

But now his tactics were different. So soon as the fly had floated past where he believed the fish to be, he sank it by a dexterous twist of the rod point, possible only with a short line. The fly was no longer a winged thing; drawn away under water, it roused in the salmon early memories of succulent nymphs. . . . At the first cast there was a slight swirl, which meant that a fish near the surface had turned to follow the lure. The second cast the line straightened and moved swiftly upstream.

Leithen had killed in his day many hundreds of salmon—once in Norway a notable beast of fifty-five pounds. But no salmon he had ever hooked had stirred in his breast such excitement as this modest fellow of eight pounds. " 'Tis not so wide as a church door,' " he reflected with Mercutio, " 'but 'twill suffice'—if I can only land him." But a dry-fly cast and a ten-foot rod are a frail wherewithal for killing a fish against time. With his ordinary fifteen-footer and gut of moderate strength he could have brought the little salmon to grass in five minutes, but now there was immense risk of a break, and a break would mean that the whole enterprise had failed. He dared not exert pressure; on the other hand, he could not follow the fish except by making himself conspicuous on the greensward. Worst of all, he had at the best ten minutes for the job.

Thirty yards off an otter slid into the water. Leithen wished he was King of the Otters, as in the Highland tale, to summon the brute to his aid.

The ten minutes had lengthened to fifteen—nine hundred seconds of heart disease—when, wet to the waist, he got his pocket gaff into the salmon's side and drew it onto the spit of gravel where he had started fishing. A dozen times he thought he had lost, and once when the fish ran straight up the pool his line was carried out to its last yard of backing. He gave thanks to high heaven, when, as he landed it, he observed that the fly had all but lost its hold and in another minute would have been free. By such narrow margins are great deeds accomplished.

He snapped the cast from the line and buried it in mud. Then cautiously he raised his head above the bank. The gloaming was gathering fast, and so far as he could see the haugh was still empty. Pushing his rod along the ground, he scrambled to the turf.

Then he had a grievous shock. Jimsie had reappeared, and he was in full view of him. Moreover, there were two men on bicycles coming up the road, who, with the deplorable instinct of human nature, would be certain to join in any pursuit. He was on turf as short as a lawn, cumbered with a telltale rod and a poached salmon. The friendly hags were a dozen yards off, and before he could reach them his damning baggage would be noted.

At this supreme moment he had an inspiration, derived from the memory of the otter. To get out his knife, cut a ragged wedge from the fish, and roll it in his handkerchief was the work of five seconds. To tilt the rod over the bank so that it lay in the deep shadow was the work of three more. . . . Jimsie had seen him, for a wild cry came down the stream, a cry which brought the cyclists off their machines and set them staring in his direction. Leithen dropped his gaff after the rod, and began running toward the Larrig bridge—slowly, limpingly, like a frightened man with no resolute purpose of escape. And as he ran he prayed that Benjie from the deeps of the moss had seen what had been done and drawn the proper inference.

It was a bold bluff, for he had decided to make the salmon evidence for, not against him. He hobbled down the bank, looking over his shoulder often as if in terror, and almost ran into the arms of the cyclists, who, warned by Jimsie's yells, were waiting to intercept him. He dodged them, however, and cut across to the road, for he had seen that Jimsie had paused and had noted the salmon lying blatantly on the sward, a silver splash in the twilight. Leithen doubled up the road as if going toward Strathlarrig, and Jimsie, the fleet of foot, did not catch up with him till almost on the edge of the Wood of Larrigmore. The cyclists, who had remounted, arrived at the same moment to find a wretched, muddy tramp in the grip of a stalwart but breathless gillie.

"I tell ye I was daein' nae harm," the tramp whined. "I was walkin' up the waterside—there's nae law to keep a body frae walkin' up a waterside when there's nae fence—and I seen an auld otter killin' a saumon. The fish is there still to prove I'm no leein'."

"There is a fush, but you wass thinkin' to steal the fush, and you would have had it in your breeks if I hadna seen you. That is poachin', ma man, and you will come up to Strathlarrig. The master said that anyone goin' near the watter was to be lockit up, and you will be lockit up. You can tell all the lees you like in the mornin'."

Then a thought struck Jimsie. He wanted the salmon, for the subject of otters in the Larrig had been a matter of dispute between him and Angus, and here was evidence for his own view.

"Would you two gentlemen oblige me by watchin' this man while I rin back and get the fush? Bash him on the head if he offers to rin."

The cyclists, who were journalists out to enjoy the evening air,

willingly agreed, but Leithen showed no wish to escape. He begged a
fag in a beggar's whine, and, since he seemed peaceable, the two kept
a good distance for fear of infection. He stood making damp streaks
in the dusty road, a pitiable specimen of humanity, for his original
getup was not improved by the liquefaction of his clothes and a
generous legacy of slimy peat. He seemed to be nervous, which indeed
he was, for if Benjie had not seized his chance he was utterly done,
and if Jimsie should light upon his rod he was gravely compromised.

But when Jimsie returned in a matter of ten minutes he was empty-
handed.

"I never kenned the like," he proclaimed. "That otter has come
back and gotten the fush. Ach, the maleecious brute!"

The rest of Leithen's progress was not triumphant. He was con-
ducted to Strathlarrig Lodge, where Angus, whose temper and wind
had alike been ruined by the pursuit of Crossby, laid savage hands
upon him and frog-marched him to the back premises. The head
keeper scarcely heeded Jimsie's tale.

"Ach, ye poachin' va-aga-bond. It is the jyle ye'll get," he roared,
for Angus was in a mood which could only be relieved by violence of
speech and action. Rumbling Gaelic imprecations, he hustled his
prisoner into an outhouse, which had once been a larder and was now
a supplementary garage, slammed and locked the door and, as a
final warning, kicked it viciously with his foot, as if to signify what
awaited the culprit when the time came to sit on his case.

. . . .

At Strathlarrig Junius Bandicott took Agatha aside.

"Look here, Miss Agatha, I want you to help me. The gillies have
been a little too active. They've gathered in some wretched hobo they
found looking at the river, and they've annexed a journalist who
stuck his nose inside the gates. It's the journalist that's worrying me.
From his card he seems to be rather a swell in his way—represents the
Monitor and writes for my father's New York paper. He gave the
gillies a fine race for their money, and now he's sitting cursing in the
garage and vowing every kind of revenge. It won't do to antagonize
the press, so we'd better let him out and grovel to him, if he wants
apologies. . . . The fact is, we're not in a very strong position, fend-
ing off the newspapers from Harold Blacktooth because of this ridiculous John Macnab. If you could let the fellow out it would be casting oil on troubled waters. You could smooth him down far better
than me."

"But what about the other? A hobo, you say! That's a tramp, isn't
it?"

"Oh, tell Angus to let him out too. Here are the keys of both garages. I don't want to turn this place into a lockup. Angus won't be pleased, but we have to keep a sharp watch for John Macnab tomorrow, and it's bad tactics in a campaign to cumber yourself with prisoners."

The two threaded mysterious passages and came out into a moonlit stable yard. Junius handed the girl a great electric torch. "Tell the fellow we eat dirt for our servant's officiousness. Offer him supper, and—I tell you what—ask him to lunch the day after tomorrow. No, that's the Muirtown day. Find out his address and say we'll write to him and give him first chop at the Viking. Blame it all on the gillies."

Agatha opened the door of the big garage and to her surprise found it brilliantly lit with electric light. Mr. Crossby was sitting in the driver's seat of a large motorcar, smoking a pipe and composing a story for his paper. At the sight of Agatha he descended hastily.

"We're so sorry," said the girl. "It's all been a stupid mistake. But, you know, you shouldn't have run away. Mr. Bandicott had to make rules to keep off poachers, and you ought to have stopped and explained who you were."

To this charming lady in the grass-green gown Mr. Crossby's manner was debonair and reassuring.

"No apology is needed. It wasn't in the least the gillie's blame. I wanted some exercise, and I had my fun with them. One of the young ones has a very pretty turn of speed. But I oughtn't to have done it— I quite see that—with everybody here on edge about this John Macnab. Have I your permission to go?"

"Indeed you have. Mr. Bandicott asked me to apologize most humbly. You're quite free unless—unless you'd like to have supper before you go."

Mr. Crossby excused himself and did not stay upon the order of his going. He knew nothing of the fate of his colleague, and hoped that he might pick up news from Benjie in the neighborhood of the Wood of Larrigmore.

The other garage stood retired in the lee of a clump of pines—a rude, old-fashioned place, which generally housed the station lorry. Agatha, rather than face the disappointed Angus, decided to complete the task of jail delivery herself. She had trouble with the lock, and when the door opened she looked into a pit of darkness scarcely lightened by the outer glow of moonshine. She flashed the torch into the interior and saw, seated on a stack of petrol tins, the figure of the tramp.

Leithen, who had been wondering how he was to find a bed in that stony place, beheld the apparition with amazement. He guessed that it was one of the Miss Radens, for he knew that they were dining at

Strathlarrig. As he stood sheepishly before her his wits suffered a dislocation which drove out of his head the remembrance of the part he had assumed.

"Mr. Bandicott sent me to tell you that you can go away," the girl said.

"Thank you very much," said Leithen in his ordinary voice.

Now in the scramble up the riverbank and in the rough handling of Angus, his garments had become disarranged, and his watch had swung out of his pocket. In adjusting it in the garage he had put it back in its normal place, so that the chain showed on Sime's ancient waistcoat. From it depended one of those squat little gold shields which are the badge of athletic prowess at a famous school. As he stood in the light of her torch Agatha noted this shield, and knew what it signified. Also his tone when he spoke had startled her.

"Oh," she cried, "you were at Eton?"

Leithen was for a moment nonplused. He thought of a dozen lies, then decided on qualified truth.

"Yes," he murmured shamefacedly. "Long ago I was at Eton."

The girl flushed with embarrassed sympathy.

"What—what brought you to this?" she murmured.

"Folly," said Leithen, recovering himself. "Drink and suchlike. I have had a lot of bad luck, but I've mostly myself to blame."

"You're only a tramp now?" Angels might have envied the melting sadness of her voice.

"At present. Sometimes I get a job, but I can't hold it down." Leithen was warming to his work, and his tones were a subtle study in dilapidated gentility.

"Can't anything be done?" Agatha asked, twining her pretty hands.

"Nothing," was the dismal answer. "I'm past helping. Let me go, please, and forget you ever saw me."

"But can't Papa . . . Won't you tell me your name or where we can find you?"

"My present name is not my own. Forget about me, my dear young lady. The life isn't so bad—I'm as happy as I deserve to be. I want to be off, for I don't like to stumble upon gentlefolk."

She stood aside to let him pass, noting the ruin of his clothes, his dirty unshaven face, the shameless old hat that he raised to her. Then, melancholy and reflective, she returned to Junius. She could not give away one of her own class, so, when Junius asked her about the tramp, she only shrugged her white shoulders. "A miserable creature. I hope Angus wasn't too rough with him. He looked as if a puff of wind would blow him to pieces."

. . . .

Early next morning, when the great door of Strathlarrig House was opened and the maids had begun their work, Oliphant, the butler—a stately man who had been trained in a ducal family—crossed the hall to reconnoiter the outer world. There he found an underhousemaid nursing a strange package which she averred she had found on the doorstep. It was some two feet long, swathed in brown paper, and attached to its string was a letter inscribed to Mr. Junius Bandicott.

The parcel was clammy and Oliphant handled it gingerly. He cut the cord, disentangled the letter, and revealed an oblong of green rushes bound with string. The wrapping must have been insecure, for something forthwith slipped from the rushes and flopped on the marble floor, revealing to Oliphant's disgusted eyes a small salmon, blue and stiff in death.

At that moment Junius, always an early bird, came whistling downstairs. So completely was he convinced of the inviolability of the Strathlarrig waters that the spectacle caused him no foreboding.

"What are you flinging fish about for, Oliphant?" he asked cheerfully.

The butler presented him with the envelope. He opened it and extracted a dirty half sheet of notepaper, on which was printed in capitals: with the compliments of John Macnab."

Amazement, chagrin, amusement followed each other on Junius' open countenance. Then he picked up the fish and marched out of doors shouting, "Angus!" at the top of a notably powerful voice. The sound brought the scared face of Professor Babwater to his bedroom window.

Angus, who had been up since four, appeared from Lady Maisie's Pool, where he had been contemplating the waters. His vigil had not improved his appearance or his temper, for his eye was red and choleric and his beard was wild as a mountain goat's. He cast one look at the salmon, surmised the truth, and held up imploring hands to heaven.

"John Macnab!" said Junius sternly. "What have you got to say to that?"

Angus had nothing audible to say. He was handling the fish with feverish hands and peering at its jaws, and presently under his fingers a segment fell out.

"That fush was cleekit," observed Lennox, who had come up. "It was never catched with a flee."

"You're a leear," Angus roared. "Just tak a look at the mouth of it. There's the mark of the huke, ye gommeril. The fush was took wi' a rod and line."

"You may reckon it was," observed Junius. "I trust John Macnab to abide by the rules of the game."

Suddenly light seemed to break in on Angus' soul. He bellowed for

Jimsie, who was placidly making his way toward the group at the door, lighting his pipe as he went.

"Look at that, James Mackenzie. Aye, look at it. Feast your een on it. You wass tellin' me there wass otters in the Larrig and I said there wass not. You wass tellin' me there wass an otter had a fush last night at the Lang Whang. There's your otter and be dammed to ye!"

Jimsie, slow of comprehension, rubbed his eyes. "Where wass you findin' the fush? Aye, it's the one I seen last night. The otter must be wrang in the heid."

"It is not wrang in the heid. It's you that are wrang in the heid, James Mackenzie. The otter is a verra clever man, and its name will be John Macnab."

Slowly enlightenment dawned on Jimsie's mind.

"He wass the tramp," he ingeminated. "He wass the tramp."

"And he's still lockit up," Angus cried joyfully. "Wait till I get my hands on him." He was striding off for the garage when a word from Junius held him back.

"You won't find him there. I gave orders last night to let him go. You know, Angus, you told me he was only a tramp that had been seen walking up the river."

"We'll catch him yet," cried the vindictive head keeper. "Get you on your bicycle, Jimsie, and away after him. He'll be on the Muirtown road. There's just the one road he can travel."

"No you don't," said Junius. "I don't want him here. He has beaten us fairly in a match of wits, and the business is finished."

"But the thing's no possible," Jimsie moaned. "The skeeliest fisher would not take a saumon in the Lang Whang with a flee. . . . And I wasn away many meenutes. . . . And the tramp was a poor shilpit body, not like a fisher or any kind of gentleman at all—at all. . . . And he hadna a rod. . . . The thing's no possible."

"Well, who else could it be?"

"I think it was the Deevil."

Jimsie, cross-examined, went over the details of the evening's experience.

"The journalist may have been in league with him—or he may not," Junius reflected. "Anyway, I'll tackle Mr. Crossby. I want to find out what I can about this remarkable sportsman."

"You will not find out anything at all, at all," said Angus morosely. "For I tell ye, sir, Jimsie is right in one thing. Macnab is not a man—he is the Deevil."

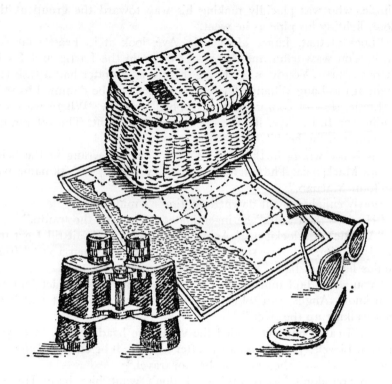

Stouthearted Men

RAYMOND R. CAMP

No angling writer could be expected to assemble an anthology without including at least one of his own efforts. The Shannon will always be a memorable river to me.

THE AVERAGE angler's inability to profit by experience—his own or another's—is legendary. Take me. As a young man making a summer tour in Europe I bore with me several letters of introduction from a relative. These epistles, I was assured, would open the doors of friends whose knowledge of local customs and scenes would make my travels more interesting and broadening.

After presenting two of these letters I concluded that my travels would be more interesting, if less broadening, if I lost the rest. I promptly did, and had no cause to regret it.

Even so, not long ago I sat in a glow of pleasant anticipation while a friend penned a letter to an old Irish fishing companion who had "the best stretch of water on the Shannon." A business trip (fishing) was taking me to Scandinavia and Scotland, and my friend was indignant that I'd even consider passing up the salmon opportunities of the ould sod.

"I realize you'll have only two days," he frowned, "and at this late date there's no hope of getting you on the Blackwater. The Shannon is the only answer. I'll just give you a note to Sean O'Gallaher, and I'll write him that you're coming. It will be an experience."

Had he added that it would be interesting and broadening I might have dug up an excuse. But I'm glad he didn't. It *was* an experience. The hotel he recommended at Limerick was another.

This hostelry is a hotbed of anglers, all local sportsmen, and most of them, I am certain, kill their salmon during the dark of the moon when the keeper's light warns of his approach. While I was signing the register the lone bellboy extracted two of my rods from their cases and exhibited them to an interested group in the bar. Now, the twenty-five-ounce, two-handed salmon rod has not lost its vogue in Ireland, so my six-ounce wands were discussed at some length. Two hours fled before I recalled there was a letter to present if I hoped to get any action with these rods during the next two days.

At that time I was convinced that Paris has the most interesting and unusual telephone system in the world. In less than an hour I realized this conviction was a hasty one. By the time I was connected with the "Sean" of my letter—he apparently was well known to every member of the Limerick exchange—I had attained almost ambassadorial status. All the local operators had relatives from Maine to Florida and points west. Considerable surprise was expressed at my extremely narrow circle of acquaintances, for I could not admit to knowing one of these emigrants. When it was learned that I resided only a few miles from Brooklyn and didn't even know Emmet Flynn, it became apparent that I was something of a recluse.

Sean was eventually run to earth at a local boating club, and got on the phone. "There's been a grand mistake," he said. "But you hurry right over here."

The "grand mistake" involved another American, a fellow passenger on my plane. Sean, having been notified of the time of my arrival, had sent a car to the airport to pick me up. Through an error that was never explained, the driver picked up the wrong American, who, by the time I got to the boating club, was in a stout-induced stupor. I never did get to meet him, for we left him sleeping peacefully in a large chair, and Sean did not think it politic to rouse him.

I was deposited at my hotel with a warning. "We take our saumon fishing seriously," Sean explained. "And with only two days to fish we'll want to be on the river early. I'll pick you up at the hotel tomorrow morning at seven. There's a good number of fish in the river, so we'll have a full day."

That parting comment still rings in my ears. A full day!

Promptly at the appointed hour, Sean and his good friend Peter, with whom he shared the Castle Connel water, drew up at my hotel in a gleaming new American sedan.

"This is Tim, my keeper." Sean nodded toward the driver, an elderly, weather-beaten individual who grasped the wheel like Barney Oldfield about to negotiate a bad curve. He and Oldfield, I discovered later, had much in common when it came to the matter of daring driving.

"Why he isn't on the river tending to his job I'll never know," Sean announced loudly. "And he'll never tell. I haven't had ten words from him in as many years. A hell of an Irishman." He paused to roar at Tim. "What is keeping us here?"

The car lurched into movement, and we roared down the narrow street, seriously threatening a score of bicyclists in the course of each block. I did not relax in my seat until we turned onto a quiet country road.

Castle Connel, I learned, is exactly twenty-two miles from Limerick. As we left the fringe of the city I glanced at my watch and at the speedometer, and made rapid calculations. We should arrive not later than eight o'clock. By eight-thirty, I told myself, I should be dropping a fly on the strange water.

We had stirred up the dust for less than half a mile when Sean leaned forward and smote Tim solidly on the back. "Are you daft?" he cried. "You'll be passing Pat's. A hundred miles' good travel you spurn from my tires every stop you make." He sat back and turned to me. "We always stop in Pat's for a glass of Guinness and to find what he's done with the pike. A coarse fisher, Pat, but goodhearted."

The "glass" stretched into two, then three, and as stout is both meat and drink, I began to regret my hearty breakfast. Pat's wife finally replaced him at the tiny bar, so we climbed back into the car and waited for Tim, who silently refused to gulp down his third glass.

At the next crossroad we came upon a large flock of sheep, apparently being herded by a man pushing a bicycle. Tim, by sheer legerdemain, coupled with astounding luck, managed to miss the bounding sheep, but one fender tore the bicycle from its owner's hands and sent him sprawling into the roadside grass. I'd been expecting a similar incident since we left the hotel, so I was concerned but not surprised.

No harm was done that a few glasses at the nearby pub could not cure, especially since the sheep's guardian proved to be Tim's cousin twice removed. However, upon emerging from the place of refreshment we found that the sheep had scattered, and it took our united efforts to round them up. After counting his flock three times, the herder reached the inescapable conclusion that one sheep was still missing. The lost one was eventually discovered, cropping the young garden of a widow who enjoyed local fame for her lively tongue. She screamed at us in what seemed gibberish as we drove the animal out of her garden.

"She's one o' thim Erse-fer-Erin biddies," the herder pointed out. "Won't speak a word but Gaelic, an' who'n hell knows what she might be sayin'? Nothin' the priest 'ud favor, most like."

At our next stop, a public house, a weathered stone marker pointed straight ahead for Castle Connel and bore the number 18.

"This lad runs a good pub," Sean whispered, although we were fully fifty feet from the door. "But he's a rotten poacher. With Tim in the town last night I'd put odds he has one of my saumon in his place." He turned to Tim. "While we're havin' a glass you nip around back to his outhouse and have a look for a fish." At his keeper's frown and incipient rebellion, Sean pushed him. "Get on. You can join us after you've looked."

At the bar I joined the rebellion. I could not face another pint of stout. I explained to my host that I was not accustomed to the drink, and he nodded.

"No doubt it's be a bit heavy for you. Just change to usquebaugh." He addressed the swarthy publican. "My friend here is from America, and he's strange to stout. Just you give him a glass of usquebaugh."

The small tumbler of colorless liquid that appeared before me was disarming in appearance and bouquet. So, I am informed, was the hemlock quaffed by Socrates. In toasting Sean's "Good fishing!" I gulped half the glsss. Had a timekeeper been present I might now possess the world record for breath holding. Sean swept my head between my knees while Peter smote me repeatedly on the back, and eventually I was able to breathe.

"What *do* you drink in America?" Sean demanded. "Never, never should you gulp usquebaugh. It has authority."

I peered at him mistily and nodded agreement. I had no control over my vocal cords.

A few moments later Tim appeared and shook his head vigorously at his employer. The publican—who could not have been deceived as to Tim's mission—coughed and concealed a smile behind his hand, on the hairy back of which was an unmistakable translucent chip. The scale of a large salmon.

I rested on my laurels and the bar until the others consumed two beakers of stout. It was almost noon when we departed, and as we left I saw Tim sweep up my glass and consume its fiery contents in one gulp. He did not even blink.

"We must remember to stop at the inn," Peter made his initial conversational gambit. "Four times now we've passed without picking up the lunch."

Sean nodded agreement. "It gets on the bill, never fear," he grumbled. "And Killian's brats eat it for their tea."

I wondered if my host was aware of the hour, but it did not seem politic to bring the matter to his attention. I wondered idly if Killian's "brats" would go hungry. At the inn the lunch was not ready, which brought a glint of dark suspicion to the eye of my host, who bestowed a meaningful glance on Peter.

"While they're putting it together," he suggested, "suppose we just step in the other room and have a glass. This driving puts a terrible thirst on me."

Tim nodded agreement.

I managed to stretch one glass to cover their three, and detected a shadow of disappointment in Tim's countenance when I waved aside an offer of another usquebaugh. He did, however, glean the last inch of my stout as he passed.

We paused at only three other places of refreshment before Tim swung the car in a rutted lane and skidded to a halt near the ivy-draped ruins of Castle Connel. The hands of my watch stood at four-thirty. Sean decanted himself from the car, graciously took my arm (for my support or his own), and led me to the rim of a steep, grassy bank overlooking the Shannon.

"There it flows." He swept an arm at the upstream expanse of the glittering river, tottered, grabbed wildly but vainly at Peter, and swooped down the bank. His friend, making a futile attempt at rescue, joined him at the bottom of the declivity. Both reclined peacefully on the bank, their legs in the water.

Tim, attracted by their shouts, advanced to the brink and peered over. Nodding silently in a manner that indicated the incident was mere routine, he returned to the car for the luncheon hamper, maneuvered a devious path to the brink of the river, and placed the hamper near the now-slumbering anglers.

While he sorted out my rod case and waders, I took the opportunity to study the Shannon. I had an unobstructed view of a mile of water, until the river turned at a narrow, brushy intervale. In width and character it resembled the Beaverkill at Cooks Falls, New York, and seemed as little likely to produce salmon. Then I recalled the scale on the publican's hand and took heart.

A loud snore from one of the sleepers woke me to a tardy concern for my host. "Don't you think we should haul them up the bank?" I suggested to Tim. "At least until their legs are out of the water?"

He shook his head, then nodded toward my waders.

While I rigged up a rod and climbed into the waders, he dressed half a dozen prawns on longshank hooks. My own preparations completed, I waited while he wrapped the joints of a fourteen-foot greenheart rod. After strapping his trousers at the knees, in the manner of a Dublin hostler, he stamped his boots firmly and with a beckoning nod led the way down the path. Still silent, he paused on the margin and glanced over the water for several minutes. Handing me three of the dressed prawns, he pointed to a long shelf of rock at the head of a broad, glassy pool.

Unconsciously I fell into pantomime too, returning the prawns and gesturing with my fly book. He frowned, paused a moment, then shrugged. Jerking a thumb at the allocated rock, he splashed downstream through the rocky shallows, bent on his own fishing.

The angle of the sun sent piercing beams through the deep pool, and I could make out every contour of the bottom for fifty or sixty feet. Then what I first took for a long strip of grass dissolved into a salmon. At this point I would not have been surprised had it proved to be a barracuda. Or a mahseer. (I have never fished in India, so this last statement is a sheer display of ichthyological braggadocio.)

What fly might interest a Shannon salmon? My letter-writing friend had suggested I take along "any standard pattern—Jock Scotts and Blue Charms ought to do well." Both patterns, from sizes 8 to 4, failed to coax a hint of interest from the salmon. Then, in the bright afterglow, a fish slashed the surface at the very tail of the pool. This evidence of activity gave renewed life to my weary arm, so I circled the rocky margin of the pool and paused within a few feet of my still-slumbering host.

The Shannon salmon, Sean had insisted the night before, would not give the "corner of a glance at a floating fly." This challenge, coupled with disgust at the wet fly's impotence, led me to thumb my nose at precedent. I tied on a No. 8 Gray Wulff, dressed to float high on a heavy mist, and made a short cast, letting the fly float aimlessly while I stripped out line for a longer one.

The inevitable happened while my tip was high and my left hand stripping line from the reel. For several seconds I did not know whether I had the salmon or the salmon had me. The line hissed through my fingers with uncontrollable speed. Why no loop fouled on a guide to snap the leader I'll never know. When the reel began to sing I took my first breath. Simultaneously the salmon broke water in a floundering leap, and his distance warned me I'd shortly be down to the backing unless I applied some restraint.

I began moving with the fish but failed to take the slimy rocks into account, and after several teetering lunges I fell headlong. The added weight of the water in my waders seemed to provide stability, and thereafter my progress was steadier.

A fast run at the head of the pool turned the fish, and I found myself muttering in what Sean, now awake and shouting directions from the bank, insisted was pure "Erse." My plunge had awakened him, and between his coaching screams he roared for the vanished Tim to hurry with the net, the gaff, or "bring a club or a great rock, you glittering bogtrotter!"

The afterglow was rapidly fading to dusk by the time I had even approximate control over the salmon, and Peter was now adding his appeals to the absent Tim.

"Sorry the day I ever let him fish," Sean moaned. "To leave my guest while he goes off to foul-hook saumon. And that he does, with a prawn for deceit. Fetch him, Peter. Fetch him while the saumon's still fast."

A few moments later the salmon, again above me, tried another leap, but a weaker one. I was hip-deep in the river, braced against the flow, when I heard a splash behind me. A hasty glance revealed Peter emerging from the water, a heavy wrench—known locally as a spanner—clutched in both hands.

"You might have directed the car lamps this way when you got that spanner," Sean complained. "Why, will someone tell me, am I surrounded by idiots?"

Inch by inch I was recovering line, and I began probing backward with my feet, remembering that a sloping shingle to my right rear would offer some hope of easing the fish to the shallows. When the water dropped to my ankles I paused and used the leverage of arm and elbow to work the fish closer. A moment later I caught the faint gleam of the salmon's side, just under the surface.

If I could just work it in close enough to tail it with one hand—before it could be knocked free or beaten to a pulp with the spanner—all would be well. But I reckoned without the gimlet night vision of Tim, who, having finally dashed up to find the cause of the excitement, threw himself bodily on the tired salmon. He emerged from the Shannon with the fish clutched firmly to his chest and a loop of my leader around one ear.

Half a dozen local citizens, attracted by the shouts and hoping it was a fight, set up a cheer at Tim's feet. In the faint light I could make out Peter, still knee-deep in the river, clutching the spanner like a cricket bat.

A procession moved up the path to the car, Tim leading with the salmon while I followed, still tethered by the leader, with Peter and his spanner and Sean with the hamper bringing up the rear. The "saumon," when hung from the scales, proved to weigh 22 pounds. The hamper, when opened, disclosed three thin sandwiches and twelve large bottles of Guinness.

"Not a big salmon for this water . . ." Sean blinked in the glare of the headlamps, then coughed at his keeper's piercing glance. "But a nice fish," he added hastily. "A nice fish. Tim must be getting better lately at dressing a prawn."

Tim grunted significantly, unwound the leader from his ear, and pried at the mouth of the salmon. When he held the bedraggled Gray Wulff up to the light his employer was so shocked he handed him the uncapped bottle of Guinness in exchange and did not recover it until almost too late. When I reeled in the leader to prevent further tangles, the fly was gone.

"This will go to the boating club tonight," Sean announced, "to bear out what I have always said—the Shannon is as good dry-fly water as you'll find in Ireland. What would you be callin' this fly now?" he demanded. "It's apparent it suits this water."

On being informed he shook his head. "Sad for us. All our wolves are in a benighted part of Ireland. Where would we get the hair to dress it?"

He brightened considerably when I gave him details on the dressing. And when Tim departed to recover his rod and gaff where he'd dropped them in the melee, he brought out a hidden bottle of usquebaugh.

"Don't be gulping it, now," he warned. "Let it slip down easy and it'll dry you out from heels to hair, and never a chill from your wetting. Let us all get a good sip before that keeper of mine lays his big nose to the air. The wind from this bottle is blowing his way."

When he dropped me at the hotel, four hours and several pubs later, Sean shook an admonitory finger. "We want to be on the river early, so I'll pick you up in the morning at seven. You'll be leaving in the night, so we'll want a full day on the river."

I watched the car until it turned the corner. Tim was more cautious at night. Only three bicyclists were endangered in the full block.

My letter-writing friend was right. Salmon on the Shannon was an experience. I even found myself looking forward to the morning's stout.

The Two Brothers

LEWIS CARROLL

Lewis Carroll was not an angling writer, but his
flights of fancy carried him far afield. This short
angling poem is a fair sample.

There were two brothers at Twyford school,
    And when they had left the place,
It was, "Will ye learn Greek and Latin?
    Or will ye run me a race?
Or will ye go up to yonder bridge,
    And there we will angle for dace?"

"I'm too stupid for Greek and for Latin,
    I'm too lazy by half for a race,
So I'll go up to yonder bridge,
    And there we will angle for dace."

He has fitted together two joints of his rod,
  And to them he has added another,
And then a great hook he took from his book,
  And ran it right into his brother.

Oh much is the noise that is made among boys
  When playfully pelting a pig,
But a far greater pother was made by his brother
  When flung from the top of the brigg.

The fish hurried up by the dozens,
  All ready and eager to bite,
For the lad that he flung was so tender and young,
  It quite gave them an appetite.

Said, "Thus shall he wallop about
  And the fish take him quite at their ease,
For me to annoy it was ever his joy,
  Now I'll teach him the meaning of 'Tees'!"

The wind to his ear brought a voice,
  "My brother, you didn't had ought ter!
And what have I done that you think it such fun
  To indulge in the pleasure of slaughter?

"A good nibble or bite is my chiefest delight,
  When I'm merely expected to see,
But a bite from a fish is not quite what I wish,
  When I get it performed upon me;
And just now here's a swarm of dace at my arm,
  And a perch has got hold of my knee.

"For water my thirst was not great at the first,
  And of fish I have quite sufficien—"
"Oh fear not!" he cried, "for whatever betide,
  We are both in the selfsame condition!

"I'm sure that our state's very nearly alike
  (Not considering the question of slaughter),
For I have my perch on top of the bridge,
  And you have your perch in the water.

"I stick to my perch and your perch sticks to you,
  We are really extremely alike!
I've a turnpike up here, and I very much fear
  You may soon have a turn with a pike."

"Oh grant but one wish! If I'm took by a fish
   (For your bait is your brother, good man!),
Pull him up if you like, but I hope you will strike
   As gently as ever you can."

"If the fish be a trout, I'm afraid there's no doubt
   I must strike him like lightning that's greased;
If the fish be a pike, I'll engage not to strike,
   Till I've waited ten minutes at least."

"But in those ten minutes to desolate Fate
   Your brother a victim may fall!"
"I'll reduce it to five, so perhaps you'll survive,
   But the chance is exceedingly small."

"Oh hard is your heart for to act such a part;
   Is it iron, or granite, or steel?"
"Why, I really can't say—it is many a day
   Since my heart was accustomed to feel.

" 'Twas my heart-cherished wish for to slay many fish,
   Each day did my malice grow worse,
For my heart didn't soften with doing it so often,
   But rather, I should say, the reverse."

"Oh would I were back at Twyford school,
   Learning lessons in fear of the birch!"
"Nay, brother!" he cried, "for whatever betide,
   You are better off here with your perch!

"I'm sure you'll allow you are happier now,
   With nothing to do but to play;
And this single line here, it is perfectly clear,
   Is much better than thirty a day!

"And as to the rod hanging over your head,
   And apparently ready to fall,
That, you know, was the case when you lived in that place,
   So it need not be reckoned at all.

"Do you see that old trout with a turn-up nose snout?
   (Just to speak on a pleasanter theme.)
Observe, my dear brother, our love for each other—
   He's the one I like best in the stream.

"*Tomorrow I mean to invite him to dine*
   (*We shall all of us think it a treat*),
If the day should be fine, I'll just drop him a line,
   And we'll settle what time we're to meet.

"*He hasn't been into society yet,*
   And his manners are not of the best,
So I think it quite fair that it should be my care,
   To see that he's properly dressed.

"*I know there are people who prate by the hour*
   Of the beauty of earth, sky, and ocean;
Of the birds as they fly, of the fish darting by,
   Rejoicing in Life and in Motion.

"*As to any delight to be got from the sight,*
   It is all very well for a flat,
But I think it gammon, for hooking a salmon
   Is better than twenty of that!

"*They say that a man of right-thinking mind*
   Will love the dumb creatures he sees—
What's the use of his mind, if he's never inclined
   To pull a fish out of the Tees?

"*Take my friends and my home—as an outcast I'll roam:*
   Take the money I have in the Bank:
It is just what I wish, but deprive me of fish,
   And my life would indeed be a blank!"

   .   .   .   .

Forth from the house his sister came,
   Her brothers for to see,
But when she saw the sight of awe,
   The tear stood in her e'e.

"*Oh what's that bait upon your hook,*
   My brother, tell to me?"
"*It is but the fan-tailed pigeon,*
   He would not sing for me."

"*Whoe'er would expect a pigeon to sing,*
   A simpleton he must be!
But a pigeon-cote is a different thing
   To the coat that there I see!

"*Oh what's that bait upon your hook,*
   Dear brother, tell to me?"
"*It is my younger brother,*" *he cried,*
   Oh woe and dole is me!

"*I's mighty wicked, that I is!*
   Oh how could such things be?
Farewell, farewell, sweet sister,
   I'm going o'er the sea."

"*And when will you come back again,*
   My brother, tell to me?"
"*When chub is good for human food,*
   And that will never be!"

She turned herself right round about,
   And her heart brake into three,
Said, "One of the two will be wet through and through,
   And t'other be late for his tea!"

The Hole

GUY DE MAUPASSANT

Guy de Maupassant is known for the situations in which he placed his characters, rather than for stories about fishing, but in "The Hole" he proved quite conclusively that angling was a topic well within his scope.

CUTS AND WOUNDS WHICH CAUSED DEATH"—That was the heading of the charge which brought Léopold Renard, upholsterer, before the Assize Court.

Round him were the principal witnesses, Mme. Flamèche, widow of the victim, Louis Ladureau, cabinetmaker, and Jean Durdent, plumber.

Near the criminal was his wife, dressed in black, a little ugly woman who looked like a monkey dressed as a lady.

This is how Renard described the drama:

"Good heavens, it is a misfortune of which I am the first and last victim and with which my will has nothing to do. The facts are their own commentary, Monsieur le Président. I am an honest man, a hard-working man, an upholsterer in the same street for the last sixteen years, known, liked, respected and esteemed by all, as my neighbors have testified, even the porter, who is not *folâtre* every day. I am fond of work, I am fond of saving, I like honest men and respectable pleasures. That is what has ruined me, so much the worse for me; but as my will had nothing to do with it, I continue to respect myself.

"Every Sunday for the last five years my wife and I have spent the day at Passy. We get fresh air, not to say that we are fond of fishing—as fond of it as we are of small onions. Mélie inspired me with that passion, the jade; she is more enthusiastic than I am, the scold, and all the mischief in this business is her fault, as you will see immediately.

"I am strong and mild-tempered, without a pennyworth of malice in me. But she, oh la la! She looks insignificant, she is short and thin, but she does more mischief than a weasel. I do not deny that she has some good qualities; she has some, and those very important to a man in business. But her character! Just ask about it in the neighborhood; even the porter's wife, who has just sent me about my business —she will tell you something about it.

"Every day she used to find fault with my mild temper: 'I would not put up with this! I would not put up with that.' If I had listened to her, Monsieur le Président, I should have had at least three bouts of fisticuffs a month."

Mme. Renard interrupted him: "And for good reasons too; they laugh best who laugh last."

He turned toward her frankly. "Oh! very well, I can blame you, since you were the cause of it."

Then, facing the president again, he said:

"I will continue. We used to go to Passy every Saturday evening, so as to be able to begin fishing at daybreak the next morning. It is a habit which has become second nature with us, as the saying it. Three years ago this summer I discovered a place, oh! such a spot! There, in the shade, were eight feet of water at least and perhaps ten, a hole with a *retour* under the bank, a regular retreat for fish and a paradise for any fisherman. I might look upon that hole as my property, Monsieur le Président, as I was its Christopher Columbus. Everybody in the neighborhood knew it, without making any opposition.

They used to say: 'That is Renard's place'; and nobody would have gone to it, not even Monsieur Plumsay, who is renowned, be it said without any offense, for appropriating other people's places.

"Well, I went as usual to that place, of which I felt as certain as if I had owned it. I had scarcely got there on Saturday when I got into *Delila,* with my wife. *Delila* is my Norwegian boat, which I had built by Fourmaise and which is light and safe. Well, as I said, we got into the boat and we were going to bait, and for baiting there is nobody to be compared with me, and they all know it. You want to know with what I bait? I cannot answer that question; it has nothing to do with the accident; I cannot answer, that is my secret. There are more than three hundred people who have asked me; I have been offered glasses of brandy and liquors, fried fish, matelote,* to make me tell! But just go and try whether the chub will come. Ah! they have patted my stomach to get at my secret, my recipe. Only my wife knows, and she will not tell it any more than I shall! Is not that so, Mélie?"

The president of the court interrupted him:

"Just get to the facts as soon as you can."

The accused continued: "I am getting to them; I am getting to them. Well, on Saturday, July eighth, we left by the five-twenty-five train, and before dinner we went to grind bait as usual. The weather promised to keep fine, and I said to Mélie: 'All right for tomorrow!' And she replied: 'It looks like it.' We never talk more than that together.

"And then we returned to dinner. I was happy and thirsty, and that was the cause of everything. I said to Mélie: 'Look here, Mélie, it is fine weather, so suppose I drink a bottle of *Casque à mèche.'* That is a little white wine which we have christened so because if you drink too much of it it prevents you from sleeping and is the opposite of a nightcap. Do you understand me?

"She replied: 'You can do as you please, but you will be ill again and will not be able to get up tomorrow.' That was true, sensible, prudent and clear-sighted, I must confess. Nevertheless, I could not withstand it, and I drank my bottle. It all comes from that.

"Well, I could not sleep. By Jove! It kept me awake till two o'clock in the morning, and then I went to sleep so soundly that I should not have heard the angel shouting at the Last Judgment.

"In short, my wife woke me at six o'clock and I jumped out of bed, hastily put on my trousers and jersey, washed my face and jumped on board *Delila.* But it was too late, for when I arrived at my hole it was already taken! Such a thing had never happened to me in three years, and it made me feel as if I were being robbed under my own eyes. I said to myself, 'Confound it all! Confound it!'

* A preparation of several kinds of fish with a sharp sauce.

And then my wife began to nag at me. 'Eh! What about your *Casque à mèche!* Get along, you drunkard! Are you satisfied, you great fool?' I could say nothing, because it was all quite true, and so I landed all the same near the spot and tried to profit by what was left. Perhaps, after all, the fellow might catch nothing and go away.

"He was a little thin man in white linen coat and waistcoat and with a large straw hat, and his wife, a fat woman who was doing embroidery, was behind him.

"When she saw us take up our position close to their place she murmured: 'I suppose there are no other places on the river!' And my wife, who was furious, replied: 'People who know how to behave make inquiries about the habits of the neighborhood before occupying reserved spots.'

"As I did not want a fuss I said to her: 'Hold your tongue, Mélie. Let them go on, let them go on; we shall see.'

"Well, we had fastened *Delila* under the willow trees and had landed and were fishing side by side, Mélie and I, close to the two others; but here, monsieur, I must enter into details.

"We had only been there about five minutes when our male neighbor's float began to go down two or three times, and then he pulled out a chub as thick as my thigh, rather less, perhaps, but nearly as big! My heart beat and the perspiration stood on my forehead, and Mélie said to me: 'Well, you sot, did you see that?'

"Just then Monsieur Bru, the grocer of Passy, who was fond of gudgeon fishing, passed in a boat and called out to me: 'So somebody has taken your usual place, Monsieur Renard?' And I replied: 'Yes, Monsieur Bru, there are some people in this world who do not know the usages of common politeness.'

"The little man in linen pretended not to hear, nor his fat lump of a wife, either."

Here the president interrupted him a second time: "Take care, you are insulting the widow, Madame Flamèche, who is present."

Renard made his excuses: "I beg your pardon, I beg your pardon; my anger carried me away. . . . Well, not a quarter of an hour had passed when the little man caught another chub and another almost immediately and another five minutes later.

"The tears were in my eyes, and then I knew that Madame Renard was boiling with rage, for she kept on nagging at me: 'Oh, how horrid! Don't you see that he is robbing you of your fish? Do you think that you will catch anything? Not even a frog, nothing whatever. Why, my hands are burning just to think of it.'

"But I said to myself: 'Let us wait until twelve o'clock. Then this poaching fellow will go to lunch, and I shall get my place again.' As for me, Monsieur le Président, I lunch on the spot every Sunday;

we bring our provisions in *Delila*. But there! At twelve o'clock the wretch produced a fowl out of a newspaper, and while he was eating, actually he caught another chub!

"Mélie and I had a morsel also, just a mouthful, a mere nothing, for our heart was not in it.

"Then I took up my newspaper, to aid my digestion. Every Sunday I read the *Gil Blas* in the shade like that, by the side of the water. It is Columbine's day, you know, Columbine who writes the articles in the *Gil Blas*. I generally put Madame Renard into a passion by pretending to know this Columbine. It is not true, for I do not know her and have never seen her, but that does not matter; she writes very well, and then she says things straight out for a woman. She suits me, and there are not many of her sort.

"Well, I began to tease my wife, but she got angry immediately and very angry, and so I held my tongue. At that moment our two witnesses, who are present here, Monsieur Ladureau and Monsieur Durdent, appeared on the other side of the river. We knew each other by sight. The little man began to fish again, and he caught so many that I trembled with vexation, and his wife said: 'It is an uncommonly good spot, and we will come here always, Desiré.' As for me, a cold shiver ran down my back, and Madame Renard kept repeating: 'You are not a man, you have the blood of a chicken in your veins'; and suddenly I said to her: 'Look here, I would rather go away, or I shall only be doing something foolish.'

"And she whispered to me as if she had put a red-hot iron under my nose: 'You are not a man. Now you are going to run away and surrender your place! Off you go, Bazaine!'

"Well, I felt that, but yet I did not move while the other fellow pulled out a bream. Oh! I never saw such a large one before, never! And then my wife began to talk aloud, as if she were thinking, and you can see her trickery. She said: 'That is what one might call stolen fish, seeing that we baited the place ourselves. At any rate they ought to give us back the money we have spent on bait.'

"Then the fat woman in the cottom dress said in turn: 'Do you mean to call us thieves, madame?' And they began to explain, and then they came to words. Oh Lord! those creatures know some good ones. They shouted so loud that our two witnesses, who were on the other bank, began to call out by way of a joke: 'Less noise over there; you will prevent your husbands from fishing.'

"The fact is that neither of us moved any more than if we had been two tree stumps. We remained there, with our noses over the water, as if we had heard nothing; but, by Jove, we heard all the same. 'You are a mere liar.'

" 'You are nothing better than a streetwalker.'

" 'You are only a trollop.'

" 'You are a regular strumpet.'

"And so on and so on; a sailor could not have said more.

"Suddenly I heard a noise behind me and turned round. It was the other one, the fat woman, who had fallen on to my wife with her parasol. *Whack! whack!* Mélie got two of them, but she was furious, and she hits hard when she is in a rage, so she caught the fat woman by the hair and then, *thump, thump.* Slaps in the face rained down like ripe plums. I should have let them go on—women among themselves, men among themselves—it does not do to mix the blows, but the little man in the linen jacket jumped up like a devil and was going to rush at my wife. Ah! no, no, not that, my friend! I caught the gentleman with the end of my fist, *crash, crash,* one on the nose, the other in the stomach. He threw up his arms and legs and fell on his back into the river, just into the hole.

"I should have fished him out most certainly, Monsieur le Président, if I had had the time. But unfortunately the fat woman got the better of it, and she was drubbing Mélie terribly. I know that I ought not to have assisted her while the man was drinking his fill, but I never thought that he would drown and said to myself: 'Bah, it will cool him.'

"I therefore ran up to the women to separate them, and all I received was scratches and bites. Good lord, what creatures! Well, it took me five minutes, and perhaps ten, to separate those two viragoes. When I turned around there was nothing to be seen, and the water was as smooth as a lake. The others yonder kept shouting: 'Fish him out!' It was all very well to say that, but I cannot swim and still less dive!

"At last the man from the dam came and two gentlemen with boat-hooks, but it had taken over a quarter of an hour. He was found at the bottom of the hole in eight feet of water, as I have said, but he was dead, the poor little man in his linen suit! There are the facts, such as I have sworn to. I am innocent, on my honor."

The witnesses having deposed to the same effect, the accused was acquitted.

The Devout Angler

COLIN D. B. ELLIS

The years will bring their anodyne
  But I shall never quite forget
The fish that I had counted mine
  And lost before they reached the net.

Last night I put my rod away
  Remorseful and disconsolate,
Yet I had suffered yesterday
  No more than I deserved from Fate.

And as I scored another trout
  Upon my list of fish uncaught,
I should have offered thanks, no doubt,
  For salutary lessons taught.

Alas! Philosophy avails
  As little as it used to do.
More comfort is there still in tales
  That may be, or may not, be true.

Is it not possible to pray
  That I may see those fish once more?—
I hear a voice that seems to say,
  "They are not lost but gone before."

When in my pilgrimage I reach
  The river that we all must cross,
And land upon that further beach
  Where earthly gains are counted loss,

May I not earthly loss repair?
  Well, if those fish should rise again,
There shall be no more parting there—
  Celestial gut will stand the strain.

And issuing from the portal, one
  Who was himself a fisherman
Will drop his keys and, shouting, run
  To help me land leviathan.

Peru

S. KIP FARRINGTON

S. Kip Farrington, through the medium of participation and exposition, has undoubtedly done more than any single individual to advance the pursuit of big-game angling. His personal pursuit of the giant game fish of salt water has led him to most, if not all, of the seven seas, and it would be impossible to find anyone more thoroughly saturated with his subject. Between the lines of "Peru," from Fishing the Pacific, *you will find something of the philosophy of big-game angling, along with the excitement that accompanies this form of fishing.*

THIS BOOK is the sixteenth I have written, and of all the chapters in these volumes this is the most difficult and at the same time the most exciting for me to write. By no stretch of the imagination could I get down on paper all the feelings that I have which would do justice to the grounds off Cabo Blanco, Peru, which is a salt-water fishing place every month in the year—the only one where you can fish twelve months and take fish; not only the largest fish in the world, but the greatest number of species.

Stop for a second and try to visualize what has happened off Cabo Blanco, and I can tell you that if the game of golf had five Bobby Joneses and five Ben Hogans playing today, that would be its equal.

If the U.S. Polo Association had ten ten-goal players ready to mount and ride they would have its equal. If tennis had Tilden, Johnston, Budge and Kramer ready to play with Tony Trabert and Dick Seixas on the present U.S. Davis Cup Team they would equal it.

Take all the good Yankee baseball teams, put them together, and you will have it. Put a hockey team on the ice composed of a line of Morenz, Milt Schmidt and Gordy Howe; a defense of Eddie Shore, and Red Kelly, and with Frank Brimsek playing goal, and you would have hockey's equal. How can I get so enthusiastic? How can I make such statements? Here are the figures.

Let us take the large fish first. Almost every variety caught in the Pacific Ocean has been taken here except Allison tuna, now called yellowfin by some, and wahoo. Large and small, and the finest surfcasting ever known. Some half a dozen species go along with it. For fifty-four years of salt-water fishing a 1,000-pound fish had never been caught legitimately by an angler. In one year and eight months on these grounds, with only three boats fishing spasmodically, fish weighing 1,025, 1,060, 1,090, 1,135, 1,352 and 1,560 pounds were caught.

The old New Zealand record on black marlin that had stood since 1926 was broken seven times the first year with only three boats fishing and has since been broken twice more as I write this in the second year. The first twenty-five black marlin averaged 817 pounds. Broadbill swordfish were taken weighing up to 687 pounds. Striped marlin were caught weighting up to 382 pounds.

This is the only place in the world where black marlin, striped marlin, broadbill swordfish and big-eye tuna abound in the same waters. All the records for men and women for big-eye tuna have been established here, fish weighing up to 368 pounds being caught—and the catch is constantly increasing in weight per fish. Pacific sailfish were practically ignored, as were striped marlin on many occasions. Few sportsmen bothered with mako sharks. Roosterfish by the dozens were picked up close to shore. One caught jacks, several varieties of grouper, two or three species native only to Peru. Dolphin fishing was the finest to be had anywhere—and the fish the biggest. Bonitos, blackfin tuna and large Sierra mackerel were reeled in like crazy—and this fabulous fishing went on at points from three hundred yards to eight miles offshore, in an area, running north and south, of twenty miles at most.

The Cabo Blanco Fishing Club had boats in operation by December 20, 1951. The first party to fare forth saw forty-four billfish in ten days. From that date to May 1, 1952, with three boats fishing from February 25 to April 11 and only two boats for the remainder of the time, nine black marlin were caught, some twenty others lost.

Alfred C. Glassell, Jr., caught the largest fish ever taken on rod and reel in all history, weighing 1,025 pounds, on April 7, 1952. He also took the smallest for that period, weighing 520. Glassell caught over twenty-odd striped marlin fishing there during March—also two big-eye tuna of 265 and 275 pounds respectively—a record at the time. He was primarily responsible for pioneering the place, and anglers throughout the world can never be sufficiently grateful to this noted angler for the time and energy he has devoted on their behalf.

On February 3, 4 and 6, Tony Hulman caught three black marlin weighing 918 pounds, 837 pounds, and 762 pounds respectively, and lost another. This was two months before that memorable April 7 when Glassell caught the big black. From February 6 until March 20 no more blacks were taken until Raymondo de Castro Maya took one weighing 625 pounds. The author then took three, weighing 725, 701 and 650 pounds respectively. Every fish brought into Cabo Blanco is used for food.

I sighted as many as sixteen striped marlin in one day and didn't even pause to bait them. During this time, over 150 striped marlin were caught weighing up to 310 pounds. Some forty of these grand fish were released. Two mako sharks were also picked up, the largest weighing 243 pounds, and Glassell took the first Pacific sailfish, at 123 pounds, since Michael Lerner's original one in 1940. In the club report it is stated that yellowfin tuna were taken weighing 275 pounds. The weight of this fish on the average probably soon will be exceeded. The bait is always extremely plentiful, the water excellent, the boats ideal, the crews efficient and new ones constantly being trained. Not a fish has been mutilated by a shark or other fish. These catches were made by some twenty-seven anglers. They are generally agreed that of the twelve-month season, August and September may prove to be the best black-marlin months. One party went into Cabo Blanco for a ten-day stay. They took six striped marlin and a broadbill swordfish in six days. Another party came in for a single day and the two men and their wives each took a striped marlin. In all, seventeen broadbill swordfish were caught, weighing up to 599 pounds.

From May 1, 1952, until July 22, no one wet a line on these grounds. A small clubhouse was being erected and the boats were taken out of service, but on July 22 Rod Rockefeller boated a 655-pound black marlin on a blind strike.

On August 2, Mrs. Tom Bates boated a 752-pound black marlin, to become the first Peruvian woman to catch a black marlin as well as the first woman to take one off Cabo Blanco. The following day her husband boated a 1,060-pounder, to break the record. The official report of the Cabo Blanco club relates: "From August 5 to August 22, Alfred C. Glassell, Jr., saw 12 black marlin, had 10 strikes, caught

5, weighing respectively 1,090, 985, 980, 855 and 720 pounds, with the phenomenal average of 926 pounds." The 985- and 855-pounders were caught in one day, making them by far the two largest fish ever taken in that length of time—and they still are. He also baited five broadbill swordfish during this trip. And this was the man who had broken the old New Zealand record three times!

The author fished nine days—from September 22 to October 1— sighted nine black marlin, had six strikes, hooked five, and caught three—weighing respectively 865, 555 and 1,135 pounds—the last two having been caught the same day and being the second two largest fish to be boated in that length of time, which they still are.

I also lost a broadbill swordfish, a species that was just coming in again in large numbers. Jamie Llavallol, member of the club from Buenos Aires, fished from October 1 to October 11 and caught black marlin weighing 777 pounds, 595 pounds and 820 pounds, and lost four others. A Dr. Hill from Buenos Aires fished for a single day. He boated a 991-pounder in the morning and on the way back to port passed up the chance of baiting another. He said he felt he had had enough sport for one day!

These fish that were taken were all headed north, were all sighted, no trolling being necessary. Sierra mackerel were used for bait with the three varieties of bonitos the second choice and they were always to be had in abundance. Some twenty-odd large black marlin were harpooned by commercial fishermen from July to September. Twelve excellent fishing guides were trained and broken in as well as three fine captains. Llavollol and I had no American guides with us. They were trained by Captain Red Stuart of Miami and Captains Bert Tuma and John Sweeting of Montauk, who had taken boats down there the previous winter. The three fishing boats installed by the club had proved themselves the finest ever built and able to take 1,000-pound fish in their stride. The surf casting had been opened up with lead jigs and plugs and phenomenal results were being obtained for big snook, corvina, jacks, etc., and the present hope is that rooster-fish will be taken eventually all along the beaches.

The next club report was issued May 1, 1953, for the period from November 1, 1952. In November and December the boats went out only from time to time. After January 1 reservations were taken by the club from friends and members for daily fishing. From February 1 on, conditions off Cabo Blanco were considerably disturbed when the warm equatorial current from the north forced the cold Humboldt, or Peru, Current some miles farther offshore than its usual course.

Naturally the broadbill swordfish were the most seriously affected, and only one was caught during this abnormal period. The water was unusually warm; a great deal of dirty water from swollen rivers was emptying into the waters off Cabo Blanco, discoloring them seriously.

But to make up for the lack of swordfish there was excellent fishing of the big-eye tuna. The world's record for this variety was 368 pounds, the fish caught by H. A. Woodward, and it was the third time the record had been broken in these waters in two months.

Mrs. Wendell Anderson, Jr., broke the women's record as well as the twenty-four-thread record with a 337-pounder, and Mrs. William Ford II took the ladies' thirty-nine-thread record with a 307-pounder. A total of fifteen fish were caught, the smallest weighing 274 pounds, and all were taken drifting.

Mrs. Maurice Meyer, Jr., one of America's greatest women fishermen, held the record for a couple of days, only to have it broken by Mrs. Anderson.

In the meantime, some terrific black marlin had been lost in November and December. Mrs. Alice Price of San Bernardino, California, broke the women's world record with a 920-pounder, the largest fish of any kind a woman has ever caught. Wendell Anderson, Sr., took one weighing 792 pounds; William K. Carpenter, two weighing 700 and 465 pounds respectively; Joe Peeler, a 685-pounder; Mrs. Jack Anderson, one that tipped the beam at 648. Then the low of 465 was broken by Arvid Carlander, great Swedish fisherman, who nailed a 385-pounder. One 800-pounder and a 700-pounder were also brought in but were disqualified, as the anglers had help in taking them. Four giant blacks were hooked and lost. And I almost forgot the case of J. C. Tippett of Lima, Peru, who came within one pound of equaling Woodward's record, with a 367-pound big-eye tuna. Sixty-two striped marlin were caught, along with seventeen Pacific sailfish and eight makos.

Fishing for the big dolphin proved the best ever experienced, roosterfishing was as good as ever, and bonitos, mackerel and other varieties were plentiful. The surf casting was as good as ever. Although this was a comparatively poor season for Cabo Blanco, this spot still was the leader for big fish caught in all-round angling in these months—ahead of any other place in the world—and it has now been demonstrated that this locale is unique in that one may enjoy prime sport the year round.

Conditions had returned to normal by the 15th of April and as many as twenty striped marlin were sighted from a single boat in a day's fishing.

The highlight of the year, of course, was the visit of the Yale University expedition headed by Wendell Anderson, a member of the club. The oceanographers aboard the laboratory boat studied the currents and took temperatures and were thankful for their good fortune in happening to be there during one of the few years when abnormal water conditions obtained. This phenomenon had not occurred since 1925.

In May, 1953, Raymondo de Castro Maya, club member from Rio de Janeiro, took a 721-pounder and lost a couple of other good ones, as well as a few striped marlin and Pacific sailfish. In June, Peter Carpenter, fifteen, youngest man ever to catch a black marlin, boated a 752-pound beauty and his father lost a fish which was reputed bigger than Glassell's 1,560-pounder, caught later. Enrique Cavaglia of Buenos Aires dropped in for four days and left with an 880-pounder and a 742-pounder.

During early July a good many big fish were seen that did not strike, and four or five were lost. Then on the 29th came Tom Bates's 1,352-pounder. Glassell started his fishing on July 15, and in eighteen days he had nine strikes and was to boat eight black marlin which weighed 878, 746, 911, 900, 755, 630, 532 and 1,560 pounds.

Glassell to date has taken seven black marlin weighing over 900 pounds and three over 1,000—an enviable record for any species. In all he has boated seventeen black marlin—fifteen off Cabo Blanco, two off New Zealand. He is indeed the black-marlin master of the world and has probably set a record for this species that may never be equaled. It takes guts and patience to go out day after day for any variety of fish, and Glassell does not miss when he gets the chance.

Cabo Blanco has nothing further to report at this writing except a 622-pound swordfish caught by the author and a 1,045-pound black marlin by B. W. Griffitts. It seems to me that the foregoing constitutes a sensational record, and imagine what it might have been if the nine boats of New Zealand or the twenty-odd boats that today fish at Bimini and Cat Cay had been working those waters.

The early development of Cabo Blanco is well worth a glance. In 1935 Thomas G. Stokes, a Canadian now retired and living at Vancouver Island, was in business in Lima, Peru, and resided there. He got hold of an old boat, put a Diesel engine in her and ran her up to Cabo Blanco to try the waters with rod and reel. A fine fresh-water fisherand all-round sportsman, Stokes had heard fabulous tales of the big fish the commercials had been taking, principally marlin. He soon proved that what he had heard was no fish tale when he boated a 601-pounder and returned the following year to take another of 712 pounds, and thus convinced the most particular of the angling fraternity that there was another superlative fishing ground off the west coast of South America. Cabo Blanco was not fished again until January, 1939, where G. P. Ted Seeley of New York, president of the Frederick Snare Corporation, who had been spending some months each year in Lima, went up to Cabo Blanco in a sixty-foot motor sailer. He brought with him four of his regular golf companions from Lima— H. S. Hunter, E. Roberts, C. F. Fritz and T. J. Kirkland, now operating vice-president of Pan American Grace Airways.

His craft was equipped with a heavy Diesel motor and was in no way adapted for big-game fishing. Mr. Seeley hired a commercial fisherman to go out with him and fished according to mood rather than schedule—and didn't expect too much. From a clumsy boat he was with nary a fighting chair, no tackle for hoisting the fish abroad—he was blithely going out for some of the biggest game fish in the world.

Using a piano stool as a fighting chair, with an unattached Gimbel rod socket between his legs, he took two black marlin of 718 and 704 pounds respectively. Some of the East Coast anglers who require the best of chairs and boats should think this one over. In seventeen days of actual fishing, Mr. Seeley reported more than fifty black marlin sighted from January 23 to February 14. Some of them may have been broadbill swordfish. There were only a couple of days when he didn't go out and he lost one that would have gone well over 1,000 pounds. At any rate he was there and had a good black-marlin run and it was due to his success in that period that I scheduled Tony Hulman for February, 1952, thirteen years later. Mr. Seeley never trolled a bait and had no outrigger—which goes to prove that they are dispensable in these waters.

Hearing about Mr. Seeley's success off Cabo Blanco, the late Daulton Mann, one of this country's leading steamship executives, a vice-president of the Grace Line, ordered for Cabo Blanco grounds two duplicates of the Elco Fishing Cruisers built for use off Tocopilla, Chile. They were delivered in April, 1940, and Michael Lerner, heading his first American Museum of Natural History expedition to Peru, made use of them.

Lerner had Captain Douglas Osborn and the late Captain Bill Hatch of Miami as guides—but in that month he saw very few black marlin and none of them would strike. He did see a great many broadbill swordfish, however, but they also refused to take the bait. Then, being his usual resourceful and courageous self, Mike began to make wide sweeps offshore, staying out three and four days at a time, sixty or seventy miles offshore in a thirty-foot boat. Not only did he find broadbill that would strike but he succeeded in catching the first and only ones caught off Peru—a 638- and a 384-pounder— until Enrique Pardo was to catch a couple in 1949.

Lerner's successful swordfish catch opened the eyes of the commercial fishermen to the broadbill fishing and today there are fleets of as many as twenty-five or thirty boats bringing in swordfish from Paita to Mancora, and Mancora has become the Gloucester of Peru through Lerner's efforts. All of which meant much to Peru.

These fish are not only chased with power boats but are sailed down, and it is some sight to see. They have no kegs and sometimes attempt to throw two harpoons into the fish. On two different occasions in the last three years off Cabo Blanco this little fleet of twenty-one sailing craft and some eight or nine power boats has harpooned over three hundred swordfish in a single day. They tend the fish from their balsa rafts.

They now get twenty dollars apiece for each swordfish or espada, no matter what the size, and some three hundred soles for every black marlin. A 1,500-pound broadbill swordfish was brought in to Paita in 1941 and the largest I know harpooned commercially at Cabo Blanco was a 1,040-pounder. Mike Lerner claims he saw the biggest swordfish he ever encountered off Cabo Blanco and he has fished for them more than any other man. He firmly believes that a broadbill weighing over 1,200 pounds will be brought in to this port.

The largest fish I ever heard of was harpooned off Cabo Blanco— a 2,250-pound black marlin—so it should not be too long before the record attains at least 1,800 pounds. I predicted 1,400 pounds for 1953 and it's already 1,560.

Swordfish were shipped to the States from these waters all through the war and still find a market there. Thus many of the inhabitants have been provided with a livelihood, thanks to Lerner.

During his visit to Cabo Blanco, Lerner was afforded considerable amusement by the unusually large squid off the Peruvian coast. He had fun fishing them at night, taking many weighing up to 150 pounds with clusters of eight gang hooks which were devised after some experimentation. He used 9-thread line. The fish showered the angler with so much black ink that he was forced to wear a mask to protect his eyes, and his guides did likewise.

In February, 1941, before going up to the magnificent new grounds off Salango, Ecuador, and north, Lerner led his second expedition to Peru and fished off Cabo Blanco for another ten days. All the black marlin sighted refused to strike but he did catch the first Pacific sailfish that was ever boated off Peru.

Lerner had used Hans Hinrichs' beautiful fishing cruiser *Alone*, which Hinrichs had shipped down, and Captain Osborn then left Mr. Lerner to fish Mr. Hinrichs. They succeeded in boating a 705-pound black marlin plus a pair of nice mako sharks, and Hinrichs became the first man to catch striped marlin on these bountiful Peruvian grounds.

He lost another black marlin that was estimated at more than 1,000 pounds. With the exception of his big black, all these fish were taken by the drifting method of fishing deep, with motors stopped, about five miles out of Cabo Blanco, and it is by this method that so many tuna have been caught.

Cabo Blanco was not seriously fished again until after the war. In 1948 Enrique Pardo, the great Peruvian sportsman and her leading angler, son of one of her ex-presidents and educated at Cambridge, bought Thorne Donnelly's *Mako II*, a twenty-eight-foot twin-screw fishing cruiser from Miami, renamed her the *Sansky* and shipped her to Cabo Blanco.

He fished this boat with some success, catching striped marlin and broadbill swordfish, and in 1950, when I was in Lima, cabled me an invitation to join him in an excursion. I didn't accept, but the day for which I'd been asked Pardo boated an 824-pound black marlin, the largest caught in the two Americas up to that time. He invited me again in April, 1951, and this time I was not slow in accepting.

I arrived in Talara, Peru, on April 6, hoping to fish for two weeks. I caught striped marlin the first day, passed up a few others, baited some broadbill swordfish—then, on that fateful Friday the 13th, hooked a black marlin that would have gone over a thousand pounds, only to lose it five hours later after breaking up the chair. Unfortunately, Pardo's boat was unable to go out again and therefore my fishing ended. But I was far from disappointed. In six days I had seen black marlin, striped marlin and swordfish aplenty and had the thrill of hooking and fighting a monstrous fish.

Meantime Alfred Glassell had been talking to some people he knew in the commercial tuna industry out of San Pedro. They were running freezer craft to Peru to freeze the tuna and allied species and offered to let him use *Oceanic V* as headquarters if he desired to fish off Peru, since he always wanted to try. Due to the facts that the International Petroleum Company and the Lobitos Oil Company own all the property on that coast, and Cabo Blanco belongs to Lobitos, none of them were interested in developing fishing and nothing had been done on that score.

International had put in a few boats for their resident employees and officials' friends to use out of Talara and these people enjoyed great success with the small fish. Glassell, accompanied by Red Stuart, went to Mancora, forty-four miles north of Talara, where he joined *Oceanic V*. He chartered a commercial fishing boat named *Don Freddie* and installed a fishing chair. In ten days' fishing in which the boat broke down some four or five times, once or twice when actually fighting fish, he boated eight striped marlin and two swordfish, one a 687-pounder, the largest ever taken off Peru.

Glassell did most of his fishing out of Mancora and a good portion of it on a bank some thirty-five miles offshore which was teeming with bait. He quit Mancora and Talara for Santiago, Chile, the day I arrived but left me a message saying that the place looked awfully good to him. When we met again in Santiago we decided that then and there was the place to found a club.

Enrique Pardo had already told me that he would erect a clubhouse and I said I'd provide a boat, while Glassell said he would furnish another. In the meantime, Pardo and I had gone to the Lobitos officials and sounded them out about letting us use the facilities at their mole and giving us a site on the beach for a clubhouse. This was arranged through C. N. Carroll, who had been in charge in Lima for many years; John Henry, resident manager in Peru; and Leonard Berry, the general manager in London—to all of whom we owe a debt of gratitude. Glassell and I went over to Buenos Aires to shoot with Jamie Llavallol and he eagerly wanted to join and contribute a boat. Thus the Cabo Blanco Club was born.

On my return to New York I immediately told Joe Gale that he had better join and he took my advice and we also asked Tony Hulman of Terre Haute. Tony, of course, said it sounded like the real thing to him and was glad to take Glassell's and my word on the matter. At that point we were not sure how many more members we would need. As the plans for the clubhouse became more pretentions, more people joined in and over a two-year period, from April, 1951, until as I write this in August, 1953, twenty-one men were invited to join, sixteen of whom accepted. One man offered me as much as $50,000 to get him in; another went into Talara and tried to buy his way in for $10,000; twice I was offered $10,000 at luncheon, on another occasion $10,000 before lunch, during the meal and afterward from an importunate aspirant. Many people naturally wanted to join but the aim was to restrict membership to a particularly fine crowd—above all, a congenial group. Following is a list of the members and the order in which they joined: Enrique Pardo of Lima, Peru, who is president; Alfred C. Glassell, Jr., of Houston, Texas; Jamie Llavallol of Buenos Aires, Argentina; M. C. Gale of New York City; Tony Hulman of Terre Haute, Indiana; Raymondo de Castro Maya of Rio de Janeiro, Brazil; S. Kip Farrington, Jr., of East Hampton, New York; Julian Crandall of Ashaway, Rhode Island; William K. Carpenter of Wilmington, Delaware; Wendell Anderson of Detroit, Michigan; Arvid Carlander of Stockholm, Sweden; James M. Hutton, Jr., of Cincinnati, Ohio; John M. Olin of East Alton, Illinois; Northrup R. Knox of Buffalo, New York; Douglas Huston of Buenos Aires; Chapin M. Kreck of East Hampton, New York. All save the president are vice-presidents, except for Gale, who also serves as treasurer.

I had the honor of personally picking all these men myself and we're fortunate to have two or three younger ones who will carry on after us. Additional members from the South American countries, who are so near the scene of operations, will be invited to join. Tom Bates was elected an honorary member, as were C. N. Carroll and John Henry of the Lobitos Oil Company, Max Crawford of International Petroleum, and J. C. Tippet of Lima. All of these gentlemen have done much for us and enough thanks and appreciation can hardly be given them. Max Crawford, manager of International Petroleum at Talara, his former assistant Jack Ashworth, as well as Hayden Hughes, former manager, Philo Maier, the president, and other officials provided us with sleeping accommodations and the use of their restaurant and clubs in Talara while we were waiting for the clubhouses at Cabo Blanco to be completed.

Richard Norris, chief engineer, acted as honorary secretary throughout the building and developing days and weighed in all of the records. Norris had been the I.G.F.A. representative for Peru since 1939 and Enrique Pardo has now been named to that post for southern Peru. Norris now is retired from the Lobitos Company and departed the scene, but his friendship, advice and hard work will not soon be forgotten.

The smaller clubhouse with five double rooms, bathroom and showers as well as the tackle room, dining room, living room and porch, was completed January 1, 1953, and a small attractive dwelling constructed for the manager. At first it was decided to have only this facility, which is actually adequate, but then Enrique Pardo and some of the members thought it would be nice to have the larger clubhouse, which is situated on a rise and commands one of the most magnificent vistas in the Pacific. The clubhouse has the finest tackle room ever built and tackle lockers for the members as well as guests—worktables, line driers and storage facilities; beautiful outside dining facilities and sleeping accommodations in ten double rooms with baths and showers. This commodious building will be ready for occupancy coincident with the publication of this book.

Cabo Blanco is 3.3° south of the equator. Talara is 953 airline miles from the Panama Canal and 596 miles north of Lima—a two-and-a-quarter-hour flight in a Panagra DC-6, and about 2,100 miles from Miami. You can leave Miami at eleven in the morning on Tuesdays and Thursdays, arriving Talara at nine that night, with a forty-five-minute stop at Panama and another twenty-five minutes at Guayaquil, and this flight on the tourist *El Pacifico* permits a ravishing view of the sunset as you cross the equator. The other flight leaves Miami at eight o'clock Sunday evening on Pan American's crack *Inter-Americano,* with its excellent dinner and good berths, and you arrive at Talara Monday morning about 4:45, with a stop at Panama. It is also possible to go to Panama any day and continue the flight down on Panagra 319, leaving Panama every morning except Sunday, and this alternative gives one a chance to see the beautiful Cordilleras and the great peaks of Chimborazo and Cotopaxi, as well as those near Quito.

The first problem we had was to select the type of boat that we wanted to use for fishing. We knew we had skillful commercial fishermen from among whom to choose our crews at Cabo Blanco. We picked nine and they have never let us down. Our first thought as to a boat was to have one about forty feet long, with a beam of twelve feet. All of us knew that it would be rough in the summer months and we wanted boats big enough to carry a couple of thousand-pound fish. Our first boat was constructed at Wedgeport with a Cape Island hull, flying bridge and enclosed deck cabin as well as a forward cabin. There was no stove and we had only one fighting chair along with a stout mast, up-top steering, roomy and airy toilet, and two gin poles fourteen feet in length. It was finally decided to build the other two boats thirty-eight feet long, with a beam of eleven feet. This model was molded more on Glassell's and my ideas, and as Glassell had much to do with the planning of the boat, he named her *Miss Texas.* Jamie Llavallol named the other boat *Petrel,* and Gale named the first one *Pescador Dos.* The two thirty-eight footers are my ideal of what fish boats should be. You can jump from any place aboard and land down with good footing; you can get around rapidly, weather cloths keep the spray off, you can boat bigger fish than can any other type of craft ever built. It was with great pride that I gave Joe Gale permission to call them the *Farrington Fishermen,* and now that they have taken seven fish weighing over a thousand pounds I am grateful that my name was used in this connection. This boat probably hasn't enough brassy glamour to catch on in the United States, but for a practical, rugged fish boat with a marvelous hull, a mast that will take two men in any kind of sea, fine up-top controls, no cleats, low stern—perfect in every respect for fighting big fish on light or heavy tackle—it's the finest I've ever fished from, by all odds.

I have taken black marlin out of all three of these boats, done a lot of light-tackle fishing from them and caught a 622-pound swordfish as well.

Many people wonder why development of Cabo Blanco wasn't begun the minute the war ended. Frankly, I was too busy playing hockey. I wanted to get more of that in before I was too old, and probably if the Korea situation hadn't arisen I might not have got there yet, because the St. Nicholas Hockey Club is not in operation on account of it. However, I left them to go to New Zealand. I always told friends in the States it would be 1952 before the fishing was reactivated in South America.

Why were we a little dubious about Cabo Blanco? Because almost everybody told us it would be too rough to fish there in the Peruvian winter months (North American summer) and I was at first afraid that it might prove an uncertain area. I knew black marlin would be caught, and very big ones—but I never realized that they would be so abundant and so near the coast. It was not until we got there that we found out that the best place for black marlin was in "black-marlin boulevard," from one to three or four miles offshore—practically never more than five.

The striped marlin were three to eight miles offshore and the majority of the broadbill from five to eight in the usual months, with the broadbill in closer during the Peruvian winter. We called these lanes Avenida Espada and Estación Pez Aguja respectively. My great good luck off Cabo Blanco followed a period of being in one of the worst slumps for blue and black marlin that had befallen me in all my fishing career. Baseball players good and bad have their batting slumps; the leading hockey players at times cannot find the net for game after game, or else keep hitting the post, and the goal tender barely deflects their finest, hardest shots aimed for the corners.

All good golfers have days when the putts, long or short, refuse to drop. Such runs of misfortune are not unusual with the fisherman angling salt water, but are particularly trying because he has had to devote so much time to the pursuit and frequently has had to travel long distances for the species he is after. There are days on end when the big-game fisherman fails to find and raise the fish he is after, other days when he may raise them yet cannot get the hook set properly in the enormous mouth. After having them on sometimes for hours at a time the hook will pull out or one of the many other disasters common to this game will overtake him.

I have had my share of this kind of luck, and after six years of endeavoring to catch my first swordfish off Montauk, Long Island, New York, before being successful, and having had other long waits after strenuous efforts, I thought I was practically immune to disappointment and could take anything.

It was in 1949, four years after the war ended, that I decided to tear myself away from ice hockey, go to New Zealand and Australia, sample their great black-marlin fishing as well as their fresh-water angling and try my luck for their lesser species. Naturally I wanted to meet their famed sportsmen. More than anything I was interested in seeing the wonderful country.

Black marlin is by far the most difficult of all the marlins to catch and the most coveted. It's the most difficult one to hook, has the most tremendous power and some of the fighting characteristics of the broadbill swordfish. He is, of course, the glamour boy of all fish since he runs the largest.

Leaving the United States, I was in the depths of a major slump on Atlantic blue marlin, which is the largest fish in that water. I had put in some forty-five days since the war without catching one and I was confident my luck would change Down Under. I fished off Havana, Walter Cay, Cat Cay and Bimini without boating a single blue—and in Australia my ill luck persisted, while my wife, on the other hand, picked up five black marlin.

I'd been at the game much too long to be much disturbed over my plight and I didn't worry unduly about not catching the small fish up to 300 pounds.

I'm not a particularly religious man, though I'm the grandson of an Episcopal minister. My only aunt is an Episcopal sister. I was sent to a couple of Episcopalian schools and I go to church once a month. I also say my prayers on occasion. I say them particularly when on fishing trips. But for some time I've been harboring the suspicion that the Episcopal Church is a very good tuna church but not a good marlin church.

In fact I'd even discussed this matter with my minister in my home village of East Hampton. I attended the Church of England services in Australia but it didn't improve my marlin luck. Now I was going to New Zealand—and was I confident of a break! I felt sure I'd emerge from my slump in those waters. I convinced myself I would because my grandfather named my father after Bishop Selwyn of Christ Church, Oxford, who'd founded the Church of England in New Zealand, and I, being Junior, was also named after him. Nobody visiting these islands and bearing the name of a great New Zealand bishop could possibly not enjoy tremendous luck with black marlin, I concluded. But when angling I am inclined to be superstitious in the matter of clothes, gloves, and sometimes rods and reels. Like many other fishermen, if given a good streak of luck I'll stick to the same clothes. To make a long story short, I had the honor of fishing the famous Bay of Islands grounds, New Zealand, for seventeen days before quitting to go after trout. In those seventeen days I didn't raise a single black marlin. But although I had no luck, a couple over 800 pounds were caught while I was on the grounds. A 654-pounder was taken from my boat the day after I left by a man to whom I had been giving striped marlin and who had been a guest on my boat for a couple of days.

As already mentioned, I arrived in Peru to begin my fishing in April, 1951, and Señor Pardo, having returned to Lima, very kindly loaned me his boat to fish for ten days. He had a good captain from Callao who was also skipper of his yacht—and a guide who had been trained by Michael Lerner and other Americans there prior to the war, and who was supposed to be the only Peruvian with a thorough knowledge of big-game fishing. The third member of my crew was a little fellow who had good eyes but not much strength and, as I was to find out soon, less guts. From April on it is pretty rough all the time and this particular day was no exception. There was a terrific current running from the north against the wind and at the time we knew little about it.

I was working about twenty miles north of Cabo Blanco, about twenty-five miles offshore, when at 2:35 in the afternoon we sighted a striped marlin. Here we do not do any trolling except to keep one short bait in the water. We look for the tails of the marlin, the dorsal fins and tails of the swordfish. Your eyes are better than your bait and you must cover ground to find the fish. Black marlin are all headed north and now we know they're inshore. We rarely find them more than five miles out and usually in the afternoon. The day was Friday, April 13, 1951, and I was never feeling less superstitious.

At any rate I gave no thought to the date as we worked around a striped marlin. We thought we would catch one and release him, as we needed the workout. This fish refused to strike and acted strangely. Most of them really like the bait in these waters, but he kept running away from us. After we had baited him four or five times he went down and I left my bait in the water without taking it in. About three minutes later we picked him up again. The crew told me in their Spanish that they thought it was the same fish. I was not too sure. For it is extremely difficult to tell the difference between the striped-marlin tail and the black-marlin tail when they are just protruding above the water. You have to get a good look at them to really distinguish them, although the black marlin usually do not stay up as long as the striped marlin—the tail goes up and down and under water much more often. However, some horrible mistakes have been made and some good anglers have hooked some big black marlin on light tackle. This particular fish came up behind the bait, followed it, then took it almost indolently. When I saw that dorsal fin I knew he was a black marlin and I could not believe my eyes or my luck. I gave him the usual treatment. As they take the bait they turn and you let the line run. In New Zealand you wait for the pause. Hooking black marlin off Peru has been patterned somewhat after New Zealand procedure, although I do not let them run as long after the pause as is customary Down Under.

You get a very slight pause, but you almost always get it. I hooked this fish, the boat was gunned, I struck him and I could feel that he weighed at least 500 or 600 pounds. For about seven minutes he did not show. Then he surfaced and the boys on top yelled, *"Grande!"*

At that distance he looked as if he might go 700 pounds. I fought him hard for about thirty-five or forty minutes and he did not jump. After thirty-five minutes they had the leader. The fish was over the stern and the little Peruvian held the gaff over him. I patted the boy on the back and told him to go ahead and gaff the fish, but he was scared by its size—so much so that he could not bring that gaff down. Juan held the leader, the boat had been handled perfectly and I was sure the fish was ready for gaffing. He was hurt. I should have jumped up and gaffed him myself but I could not see getting out of the chair after only a thirty-five-minute fight with a fish that might go 1,000 pounds. In a couple of minutes, of course, he broke loose and started to jump close around the stern. Just as the double line would run off he would greyhound, so I had a wonderful look at him and could see that my crew were greatly impressed.

In the next hour and a half Juan had the leader ten more times. The first three times the fish could easily have been gaffed but again I could not make the boy put the gaff to him and to this day I blame myself more and more for not having got up and done it myself. But I simply thought at the time that I'd wait until the fish died, when getting him aboard would be a simple matter even though the seas were becoming steadily rougher and the swells increasing all the time.

During this hour and a half he had taken us three or four miles to the southward with the current. He did all of his jumping with never more than 150 feet of line out, so we had look after look at him and if I had had a photographer the pictures would have been spectacular. All in all, the double line was on the reel twenty-five times and after that I stopped counting and got hold of the leader three more times, making a total of fourteen in all. At four-thirty or thereabouts the entire footrest of the chair came off and one arm went with it. With the terrific drag on the reel this catapulted me out of the chair across the counter in the stern. I took the full force of the blow on both hands and tried to protect the reel, which took a very hard rap. After loosening the drag I picked myself up. It is impossible to go overboard when fighting a big fish if the drag is loosened, regardless of what you may hear to the contrary. I got back into the chair but I had no more bracing. However, some cushions and life preservers aided me somewhat. My right hand was in bad shape but I didn't notice this, nor did I notice that the little finger on my left hand was pretty stiff. I was much more concerned about the reel, which fifteen minutes later began to act up. Between five and six o'clock I repaired the reel three times and again had the fish under pretty good control.

He started down once and I did not attempt to stop him too much until he got to about 250 feet, because I thought he was surely going to die. However, I brought him back up to the double line and he was still very much alive and made another little run. Finally he came to the surface and seemed to quiver as if he were in his death flurry, then sounded again. He had run off some 350 to 400 feet of line when the reel again went out of order. By this time it was getting dark and it was really blowing. The seas were very high and it was impossible to plane the fish. By "planing" we mean running away from him with as much drag on as can be given, then backing up fast and recovering line. This will often get a fish that is on a course off it and it is a good way to raise a dead fish.

Again the reel went out and he got down about 900 feet. With no foot-bracing and a faulty reel I was at a serious disadvantage. After having had him so near I was not in the best of humors. Around six-thirty I knew the fish was stone dead and I was having very little success in raising him, but I had him up to about 600 feet and things looked all right when the reel suddenly went out completely. The post had broken and I had no way of making repairs. The handle would turn around against me as the line ran out. I could only hold him on the top of certain swells. There are occasions when we can use the swells to help us get line back but this was now impossible. In all my big-game fishing this was my first experience with a broken reel and it is not one that I wish to repeat. Five different times in the next hour the line went out right down to the spool just as fast as I'm telling it. The simple little knot we use to tie the line onto the spool did not break. The line was thirty-nine-thread Ashaway, and on the 12/0 Vom Hofe reels I use we have 600 yards, or 1,800 feet. They are the same that are now made by Otto Swarg in St. Petersburg, Florida. At 7:44, or five hours and nine minutes after the fish had been hooked, with about 300 feet that I had recovered with no drag on the reel, all the line ran out again and it popped at the knot. How that handle can whirl around—and it can really crack you as it goes in reverse! This great fish, which I am still certain ranks among the largest I've ever seen, was stone dead in thousands of fathoms of water some twenty-five miles off Cabo Blanco. I pulled myself out of the chair, as one usually does, whether successful or not, put a couple of towels around my neck, dried myself off and sat down on deck to examine my hands as we headed back to port. We arrived at the mole around ten-thirty, and Dick Norris, God bless him, had waited up to see if I was all right. In fact he was just about ready to start out looking for me. However, from on top of the hill back of Cabo Blanco at El Alto he had been able to see our running lights as we came in. He examined my hands, gave me a bowl of soup at his house, then drove me to the hospital. I remember there was a very good-looking Peruvian nurse on hand and the doctor was excellent. He told me that my little finger was broken and he thought that my right hand was, too. At any rate, he bound it up so tightly that I could not move it and on the drive back to Talara, thirty-two miles, I cut the bandage off and left my little finger as it was. It had been broken before while I was playing hockey and I was not much concerned about it. My one thought was to get out fishing again on the morrow.

The next morning I drove back up to Cabo Blanco and much to my chagrin found that some of the struts in the boat had been severely strained and the motors were in very bad shape. Five hours of backing into these seas had been too much for the craft, which was a trifle small for such a big fish in the weather that we had battled. However, I thought that perhaps we could go the next day or the following one. After waiting around for six days we were afraid to use the boat any more for fear of damaging her further. Eventually she had to be pulled out so that the fractured struts could be replaced. Thus ended another six days of black-marlin fishing with no success.

My next big fishing adventure was over the Fourth of July, 1951, when I fished four days with Glassell at Bimini and promptly proceeded to pull the hook out of a blue marlin around 350 pounds at the boat when the guides had the leader, and it was a great sight to hook this boy, as he was pouncing on bonitos that were underneath the boat and he picked up five or six of them before taking my bait. But then to top it all off, two hours before my departure I pulled the hook out of a nice one around 650 pounds just over the stern while the fish was all in and coming easily. I took this loss so nonchalantly that the guide, Eddie Moore, and his crew thought I was crazy—but after the one I had lost at Cabo Blanco two months earlier I was now becoming reconciled to my bad fortune.

My next trip to Cabo Blanco lasted only five days in January, 1952, when I was going on down to Chile. After raising no black marlin during that time I was attempting to catch a striped marlin for Mrs. Tom Bates, wife of our great friend who was afterward to catch a 752-pounder. We were baiting the striped marlin when a black marlin around 700 pounds, maybe a trifle less, came up and took the bait. This fish was lost through no fault of Mrs. Bates's after a fight of over two hours.

After giving another black marlin away and seeing no more I wasn't in a very good frame of mind. I should have waked up to the fact that the black marlin was around from the way the striped marlin was acting. He rushed the bait, missed it, and the black marlin got in from underneath.

I returned again to Cabo Blanco in February for five days just after Tony Hulman had opened the fishing world's eyes with his great catches of three in four days—but again I failed to sight any black marlin.

Undaunted, I was back again on the 22nd of March for another go, fishing six days of that week—the 23rd, 24th, 25th, 26th, 27th and 28th—with no success. On Saturday afternoon, the 29th, around half past two, I remarked to Mrs. Bates's sister Inez Alvarez Calderon of Lima, that I would go to mass next morning. The question came back, "Six o'clock?" and I said: "No, I will go with you at eight. We'll be late starting out in the morning." The thought was still with me that I had put in fifty-four days of straight fishing for black marlin without having caught one since before the war and I also had forty days of blue-marlin fishing since the war without having one in the boat— a total of ninety-four days' fishing for the two big species in both oceans without success.

Within forty-five minutes after I had said that I'd go to church in the morning I got a blind strike on the bait that we keep very short, just off the double line in the wake. After about twenty minutes of the fish being under water, from which I knew it could be none other than a black, he emerged and started to jump. Forty-seven minutes later this fish was boated and my spell of ill luck had been broken. And this within two hours of the time I had announced I was going to the Catholic church with the señorita in the morning. It was fun to arrive at the dock that afternoon with a fish and all the little Peruvian boys and girls looking on from the mole. They clapped, cheered and yelled, "*Macanudo!*"—my favorite word in South America, meaning "You're the tops." These Peruvians from the smallest and poorest to the biggest and richest are courteous and kindly folk. This fish weighed 701 pounds and I went down to Talara feeling like a new man. The following morning I attended eight o'clock mass and came back up to fish, getting out around ten o'clock. We cruised around looking for that tail of all tails and around two o'clock sighted a fish and caught him. He weighed 650 pounds. Around four o'clock I sighted another but he wouldn't strike. At this point I would have gone to church on Monday if there had been a service.

I came back up again for my last day's fishing before leaving for the United States, and around three that afternoon hooked and boated another fish after forty-five minutes. This weighed 725 pounds. And then, believe it or not, I had another fish on for about a 100-yard dash shortly afterward.

Three black marlin and four strikes in three days. It was pretty good compensation for what I had had to suffer. A week later the finest news I ever received reached me in the form of a cable relating that Glassell had taken a 1,025-pound black marlin—the first fish ever caught to weigh over a thousand pounds.

Cabo Blanco was not fished again until late July, as I have already stated. On August 3 Tom Bates broke Glassell's record with a beautiful fish weighing 1,060 pounds, caught after a hard hour-and-fifty-five-minute fight in a rough sea. No one deserved the new record more than this fine sportsman. Bates has done a great deal of work in behalf of the club and is constantly concerned with its success and development. Glassell was on his way down to Peru the day Bates caught this fish and within seventeen days had regained his ascendancy with a 1,090-pounder. Thus, in a period of four months, three fish had been taken on these fabulous grounds weighing over a thousand pounds apiece. Glassell went back north to lead the American fishing team into second place in the international matches and knock off a 785-pound tuna at Wedgeport to wind up a noteworthy year. Probably no man ever had a greater one. In all, he had taken six broadbill swordfish, a half dozen huge tuna, seven black marlin, two big-eyes and twenty-odd striped marlin.

Glassell is the only man who has taken the four major species—black marlin, blue marlin, broadbill swordfish and tuna—weighing over 600 pounds apiece, and I hope to see him come through with a broadbill of over 800 as well as a tuna exceeding that weight, to equal my three prizes.

On Saturday, September 20, 1952, I left Miami for another ten days off Cabo Blanco. My object was primarily to see how construction work on the club was progressing, but I also wanted to sample the surf casting which had now been initiated with jigs and plugs. I arrived at Talara at nine o'clock Saturday night right on time on Panagra 333, the *El Pacifico,* and had a chat with Tom Bates that evening. The following morning I attended eight o'clock mass at the same church I had gone to before and decided afterward to do some surf casting instead of going offshore. I had marvelous luck, catching a seventeen-pound snook on my fourth cast with a lead jig. Later I took another, and was well satisfied with the day. The next day I had scarcely wet my lines when I saw a big fish only about 300 yards off the Cabo clubhouse, but he wouldn't strike.

At one o'clock that day, after an hour's battle, I boated an 865-pound black marlin. My lucky streak was still holding. I had taken four in four straight days. This fish pleased me particularly, because it gave me three different species weighing over 800 pounds each. My broadbill swordfish taken in Chile in June, 1941, my 830-pound tuna taken in Nova Scotia (Wedgeport) in September, 1945, and now this third specimen. I was the only man to have taken two species weighing over 800 pounds and I now had three—a sequence that pleased me enormously. My friends insisted on attributing my good fortune to my return visit to the church, and I must say that I was inclined to agree with them.

Next morning at ten o'clock I sighted a fine fish of about 900 pounds and got a good strike but did not hook it. This was the only black marlin strike I have had off Cabo Blanco that I have not hooked. This was the only fish I saw that day. The following two days I baited two more without a strike and on the next saw another that refused to strike. These fish were all between 650 and 800 pounds, as near as we could estimate.

The next couple of days I saw nothing—so naturally I went back to that same church Sunday morning. This time I listened to my first sermon in Spanish. You can imagine how much I got out of it, but I did put five extra soles, a total of ten, in the plate, and came up to go fishing. I was fortunate in having Tom Bates as a companion on this occasion.

Around eleven o'clock we saw a fish, but before I could let out line and bait the proper distance (since I was still pulling the line and testing the drag on the reel) he struck. I threw off the drag and hooked him and after a fine active fight he jumped twenty-five or thirty times. I had him near the boat in forty minutes but again had the bad luck to break the footrest off the chair and had to substitute life preservers. Finally, after an hour's fight, I got him across the stern, where Bates gaffed him beautifully. This series of events, which indicates how vital a part luck plays, was the curtain raiser for what was to happen that afternoon.

We ran back to port with my fish and got a foot bracing off another boat which Louis Talavera adjusted to the chair in a jiffy. While he was at work I took pictures of the fish. He was next to the smallest caught at Cabo Blanco up to that time, weighing only 555 pounds.

We did not get out to the grounds again until two o'clock that afternoon and then ran north with the wind. Around three-thirty the crew on lookout thought they saw a tail. I didn't agree, but at three-fifty I sighted one from the cockpit a good half a mile away. It appeared so large that at first I thought the fish was a ray, of which there are a great many in these waters. In fact there are more manta rays or giant devil fish in these waters than anywhere else I've ever been—also more whales and various types of sea life.

I had put the Sierra mackerel bait out the regulation distance— some 200 feet—when this fine black marlin came up and grabbed it. I could not even hazard a guess as to his size at the moment. I hooked him with the same method I had hooked the others and he went off on a grand and glorious run and began jumping about a thousand feet ahead. After a thirty-five minute spell of greyhounding, tail walking and jumping (he made a total of twenty-three jumps), he settled down and swam rapidly north.

(You must realize of course that had I not broken the foot brace, gone in to obtain a substitute and returned to the fishing grounds precisely at this moment I probably never would have sighted this fish. And none of us on board realized how big he was.)

Some forty-five minutes later another fine fish appeared and swam along abreast of him for over half an hour. Judging from his tail he seemed to be almost as big. I was somewhat worried that he might cut the line though this seldom occurs with thirty-nine-thread. Finally I fought the fish for about an hour and a quarter. I didn't want to force him too hard, since I was very eager to take two black marlin in a single day. That is the maximum feat one can perform in fishing. By all odds my greatest thrill so far had been to take two swordfish on the same day. To a big-game fisherman this is the equivalent of a no-hit baseball game to a pitcher. It would mean that I had to my credit two of all the major species in a day—two black marlin to match my two swordfish, two blue marlin, two giant tuna, two striped marlin, two white marlin, etc.

About an hour and twenty minutes later my fish slowed down a bit and tried to sound. I was able to check him and arrest his downward run. He never got below 250 feet. After about an hour and thirty-five minutes of this I refreshed myself with a Coca-Cola. When fighting big fish we rod-and-reelers, unlike the ancient angler of Ernest Hemingway's *Old Man and the Sea,* have no desire to eat. Once in a while I've sucked on an orange, as hockey players do between periods, but found it enervating. Sometimes I may take a mouthful of water but I spit it out.

At the one-hour-and-thirty-five-minute mark I put added pressure on for the next twenty minutes. I placed my harness under my fanny, exerted a lot more drag on the reel and sat up in the chair. The weight of heavy drag on thirty-nine-thread can pull you out of the chair, so you sit right in the harness.

Women anglers are consistently being pulled up and therefore do a lot of their fishing in this fashion.

After about an hour and fifty-five minutes the leader came out of the water but I refused to let the crew touch it. The fish then sounded again. The sea was terribly rough by this time, and it was getting dark. The marlin had taken me about six miles north and some three miles inshore. I was off those wonderful boulders known as the Organos, for their high rocky ridges resemble the pipes of an organ. The condors were flying over them and playing around our boat with the usual boobies and man-of-war birds. Occasionally the penado petrel hovered around. The marlin that had been keeping company with my fish had disappeared by now and my leader wire again came out of the water—but again I cautioned the crew not to touch it. The gaffs on either side were in readiness, Bates prepared to do the gaffing on the port side and my boy McGill set to take the leader. Louis had

my chair and was ready to handle the gaff on the starboard side.
Captain Hajus, at the up-top controls, was doing a wonderful job of
piloting the boat. He had learned from all of us as well as from the
American guides. When the leader emerged for the third time, McGill
reached for and grabbed it, but could not maneuver the marlin within
gaffing range. He was yanked right around the stern. My heart was
in my throat at this juncture, for these are the crucial moments. It was
terribly rough and the tremendous weight of the fish was exerting an
appalling strain. Suddenly he broke loose again. Five minutes later
the leader again came out and this time I put both Louis and McGill
on it, with Tom Bates as the gaffer. The fish went under the stern
once and I thought it was goodbye. I feared the cable leader would
break across the stern but it went clear by some miracle. The boys
held the fish off and began to lift him. (The leader was twenty feet
four inches long—ten feet under that specified by the rules of the
International Game Fish Association.) Steadily they worked the fish
up inch by inch. The terrific weight and the turbulent sea made it a
very ticklish job. Marlin roll like crazy at that weight. Anxiously I
looked shoreward. Should I tell the boys to let go? I was in a position
to lead the fish in now and take it much more easily and safely in the
calmer water close in to the beach. I could run him in as we do at
Wedgeport on certain tides when the fish can go only in one direction
in the shallow water.

Why try to take him in seven or eight hundred fathoms of water,
I thought? The crew seemed to have control and to be anxious to do
so, but just then someone said to Bates, "Why don't you take the
leader?" I didn't want him lending a hand, because it might affect
the crew's morale for the future, but I was more than willing to let
him do the gaffing. Finally, inch by inch the leader was brought up and
McGill and Louis grimly held on. We were all soaked to the skin by
heavy water and the wind was still increasing. Up, up, the huge fish
came. I can see Tom Bates now—waiting, holding my favorite gaff—
one engraved "To Kip from Phil." Good old Phil Swaffield, ex-
president of the Catalina Tuna Club, one of my closest California
friends, who passed away some years ago, had given it to me back in
1940. It had been used to gaff my 853-pound swordfish in Chile and
my big Nova Scotia tuna and was now to be put to good use again.

The marlin came up leading better and Tom Bates cracked him
on the inside with an underwater jab. The motors were shut off, the
block and tackle on the big gin pole fourteen feet high on that side
were lowered and the tail rope rigged. The fish was losing blood that
dyed the water, so I could not determine as yet where he was hooked.
I stood up in the chair, of course, keeping the leader attached to the
rod and reel and holding it as I helped the others adjust the tail rope.

We began to pull in on the gin pole and it was tough work. One of the ropes almost fouled the top and Tom Bates went up to clear it. It took all five of us to get him up. The gin pole was fourteen feet high and the fish was longer. He was losing a great deal of blood as he hung there and we tied up his mouth so that none of the stomach contents would be lost. After heading the boat into the wind again we attempted to get him aboard and it took our combined strength to pull his head into the cockpit. The rest of him then slid on in and we got him straightened away. The tip of his wonderful tail, the largest I've ever seen, touched the engine box, and his bill—very short for a big black marlin—was smack up against the counter. He just fitted snugly in on one side, since these boats had been designed to handle two fish, a thousand pounds each.

Tom Bates and the crew shook hands with me and Tom said, "Boy, you've got yourself a fish. I think it's easily a new record." "I'm not after records," I rejoined. "All I can say is I'm thankful to have got two black marlin in one day and thank God you were with me!" (At no time while battling the fish had I thought he would go over 975 pounds.)

Our catch looked awfully well with the light from the gin pole shining down on him. It was now pitch-dark and we started to run back to port. I proceeded to rub myself down just as I had done on that fateful evening one year, five months, two weeks and a day earlier—but this time I sat and looked at my fish instead of at my hands. He was long and beautifully proportioned.

We made the mole around seven-thirty and there was good old Dick Norris once more awaiting my return. He bawled the hell out of me for staying out after dark twice in a year and a half. But this time he had something else besides a broken-down old man of the sea to help up the steps of the mole. He had a nice fish to lower the crane for. Its crew had stood by in expectation that my trip would be crowned with success. We jumped out of the boat onto the mole, where for once the children were not in evidence, as it was too late for them. We lowered the crane and lifted the black marlin out of the boat. As he came up he looked enormous, suspended in the air. They never appear more majestic than during that long lift up the mole.

The crew went out to moor the boat and stow the gear while Norris fetched the scales. "This is it." He grinned. While I still couldn't believe it possible it would have been a great privilege to catch a 1,000-pound fish after my many years of fishing.

After three weighings this splendid marlin was still 1,135 pounds and that was his final and official weight. He measured fourteen feet eight inches long, had a six-foot girth and the great tail a width of four feet ten inches. The crew paddled in aboard their balsa raft and looked up at me inquiringly. I called down, *"Uno uno tres cinco."* I'll never forget their expressions. Norris and Bates congratulated me, of course, and then took me up to the El Alto Club for a drink, and I must say that I drank three beers with great relish. Peruvian beer is really good.

I then drove back the thirty-two miles to Talara, dined with the Bateses and gradually became aware of the frenetic excitement my catch had kindled in Talara. Next morning I was back up again for the pictures but my luck had run out. At two-thirty that afternoon I hooked another fine fish with a blind strike, one of the fastest I have ever encountered. He jumped twenty-five feet in the air, twenty-five feet astern, doubled back and forth around the boat with his beautiful greyhounding leaps, rolling and turning and twisting the line all around him so that of course it could not stand up under such terrific strain and, after seven minutes, parted.

The following day, my last, I lost another fine fish after twenty-five minutes, when the hook pulled out. Thus ended two nine-day trips to Cabo Blanco with a total of sixteen black marlin sighted, ten strikes, nine hooked, and six caught. In that nine days I had accomplished the two things I wanted most to do: take a black marlin over 800 pounds and take two in one day. But on top of that I was winding up with the largest fish of any kind ever caught on rod and reel at that time in the entire history of fishing—the first 1,100-pounder ever to be boated.

I'm constantly asked how I felt and what were my reactions. I can say truthfully that my reactions on going to sleep that night and waking early next morning were somewhat the same as on the night I lost that other fish. Then I had awakened feeling chagrin and disappointment. Now I woke up with the jitters, thinking of all the things that could have gone wrong in the handling of great fish such as this had turned out to be. I thought also of other anglers far more deserving of taking such a prize. And I still wondered humbly why I had been singled out for this splendid fate.

It probably took twenty-four hours for me to rid myself of these mixed emotions, and I've taken quite a few big fish in my time—some of which I fought for hectic periods up to nigh on nine hours in length. At any rate that night I thanked the good Lord for answering my prayers. Many fishermen pray in times of stress and I know that I feel nearer to God and more religious when fighting fish than at any other time.

I did not bring my prize black marlin back to be mounted. I saved only the tail and bill, which I had mounted in Peru on a Peruvian-silver base and with a silver plate on the bill bearing name and date, and they adorn my mantel now. This was slightly at variance with the usual custom when mounting trophies but I wanted a very special memento of that wonderful country, its fine people and incomparable salt-water fishing which afforded me this great sport only nine and a half hours from home.

My black marlin was eaten by the villagers after being skinned by old man Tumi, dean of the commercials, whose son is one of our crack boat captains at Cabo Blanco. The fish was evidently very old, although it is difficult to estimate the age of any of these fish, where they spawn or where they are bound. Inside the fish was a harpoon dart, the wound it had made completely healed over. Evidently he had been struck by commercial fishermen many years before our fatal encounter. Again I thought of Hemingway's *Old Man and the Sea* and what he'd gone through.

As I write this, August 25, 1953, no fish has been hit by a shark at Cabo Blanco, so there has been no problem of mutilation of prizes taken in those waters. It was a little over ten months before my record was surpassed. I wore the same pair of gloves while taking all six fish, plus an extra one for the left hand, as the original wore out on the fourth black. However, I kept the tattered glove in the chair with me. I used the same reel I had used on the other fish. I wore the same blue shorts, the same sneakers and the same red silk handkerchief stuck in my shorts—and the next time I go out you can be assured that I will be attired in exactly the same manner.

I got back to the States as old Johnny Mize was signalizing his participation in the World Series by knocking out three home runs. I must say that old man Farrington with those three black marlin—all caught the same week—felt somewhat as he must have.

Trouting along the Catasauqua

FRANK FORESTER

Few of our prolific best-selling authors of today will write books that will rival, in longevity, the works of Frank Forester. In his day he was read avidly by young and old, and most of our serious anglers of today are well acquainted with his work. "Trouting along the Catasauqua," perhaps not his greatest tale, is about the most typical.

THUS FAR, since they had entered the wild and desolate ravine of the Catasauqua, they had passed no spot which could well have been adapted to the site of a human habitation, even of the smallest size and most inferior kind, and no vestige of a road was to be discerned by which access could be had to it from the settlements, except up the channel of the shallow and rapid stream. And

200

as the day gradually declined, and the sunbeams through the gaps in the hilltops fell higher and higher up the opposite mountain side, and dwelt no longer, even for a moment, in the bottom of the valley, Frank began to get somewhat curious as to the domicile to which he was wending his way under auspices so peculiar, and somewhat suspicious as to the nature of the feed which was likely to meet him in the middle of so absolute a wilderness.

Nevertheless, he held on, stoutly plying his paddle or his setting pole in silence, asking no questions of his dark ferryman, but greatly admiring the picturesque and devious path which he was traversing. Suddenly, after forcing the canoe, not without the dint of very considerable exertion, up a long shoot of clear, swift, glancing water, where the stream rushed, unbroken, over an inclined plane of smooth rock, the ravine turned an abrupt angle, formed by the projection of a bare, precipitous crag of yellow limestone, narrowing the channel to a third of its usual width, and excluding all upward view, due westward.

With a powerful sweep of his paddle, the steersman brought round the head of the light vessel, and she swung round the point in deep water, and lay in a large, circular tranquil pool, some three hundred yards across, embosomed in a sort of lap among the hills, of a milder character than anything which Frank had yet seen on the Catasauqua, and containing on the left bank a few acres of cleared land, pastured by a single cow, a rough Indian shooting pony, and half a dozen ragged-looking mountain sheep.

This pool, at the lower end, was perfectly still, as clear as glass, and very deep; but in two different places, at its upper extremity, where two narrow glens, or ghylls, as they would be called in the north country, entered the little amphitheater from the higher ridges to the south and the westward, the perturbation of its surface, the floating bubbles and foam flakes, and the whirling eddies, showed that two strong and rapid streams were discharged into it from above.

On the point formed by the union of these two tributaries, or constituents rather, of the Catasauqua, known as the Stony Brook and the Clattering Creek, which was a shelving bank of gravel at the water's edge, covered by a magnificent grove of the largest hemlocks Frank had ever observed, growing with their great trunks far apart, but their wide, feathery branches mingled above into a canopy of impenetrable verdure, stood in a small, sheltered nook, scooped, as it would seem, out of the sheltering wood, the cottage, which he recognized as the welcome bourne of his journey.

Cotton's Cabin, as the owner had christened it, after the friend and brother angler of dear old Izaak Walton, was the smallest and least pretending, as it was the quaintest and prettiest of primitive cottages. In front it presented a face of thirty feet in length, divided into three compartments, that in the center presenting an advanced gable of a story and a half in height, with a dormer window above the rudely arched doorway, with its quaintly carved inscription on the key block, and a gigantic pair of elk antlers affixed to the wall above it. In the spaces, on either side, which were but one story in height, was one large, latticed window, and no more. The whole edifice was framed of rude pine logs, with the bark still on them, those in the wings, if they may be so called, running horizontally, dovetailed into one another at the ends, those of the center standing perpendicularly, mortised into the plates and groundsills. The doorposts, lintels, and window frames were just as rugged of materials and as rustic of manufacture as the remainder of the building; and the roof, which widely overhung the eaves, was covered with scalloped slabs of pine bark, overlapping each other like shingles. A bright, fitful light glancing from one of the windows, out of the shadows of the hemlock grove, and a blue wreath of smoke winding up in strong contrast against the black foliage of the evergreens gave pleasant token of preparation and of hospital welcome in the wilderness. There was no sign of cultivation, no flower pot, no patch of vegetables near the house, only a narrow gravel walk winding up among the grape stems to the door from a small dock, at which lay moored another dugout, similar to that in which the voyagers were approaching, a couple of Indian birch canoes, and a light cedar skiff, double-headed like a whaleboat, built for a pair of sculls or paddles. But the ground under the trees was beautifully smooth, well kept, and cleared of fallen leaves, the hemlocks themselves were free from dead branches and dry, sapless limbs, and on the stems of one or two, in the foreground, the native vines and creepers had been trained with some care and grew luxuriantly, with their long trailers and bright hues offering a pleasant contrast to the dark formality of the evergreens. The only animals visible were a noble jet-black Newfoundland dog lying at length, with his head couched between his massive paws, on the doorsill, and a huge eagle owl, sitting on a rustic perch, to which one leg was attached by a long, light chain, devouring part of a fish which had been given to him, and occasionally wakening all the echoes of the hills by his solemn and melancholy shouts, *Waugh-oh! Waugh-oh!*, rendering the wild aspect of the place wilder and more outlandish.

"Dar de cabin, sah," exclaimed the mulatto, brightening up as they came into sight of the rustic lodge, "and dar old Cappun, de dog, and dar de owl and dar come Massa Langdale, too, I guess," as the door opened, and the owner, a tall, fine-looking young man of some eight and twenty or thirty years, made his appearance on the lawn, if it may be so called, attired sportsmanly in a tweed shooting jacket and trousers, a low-crowned felt hat and a pair of stout shooting shoes.

"How are you, Frank?" he hallooed in a clear, strong voice. "Devil-ish glad to see you at the cabin, now that you've got to it, which I suppose you gave up in despair of ever doing. I should have come down to pilot you up myself, but I've got a queer sort of cockney chap up here, only he's not a cockney, but a New York chap, that knows more about fishing than all of us together, to hear his own talk. He's a Wall-Streeter, I believe, but he came up to me upon the strength of a letter, and I can't get rid of him; but I fancy another day or two will finish him, for he frames, as you say in Yorkshire, very badly, and he's death on tackle. But come in, come in; ain't you thirsty?"

Whereupon, replying to his friend's greeting so soon as he found room to put in a word, and admitting that something long and cool wouldn't go far wrong, Frank followed his friend into the interior of the fishing hut, first pausing to note the invitation, carved in rude characters of old black letter, upon a slab, beneath the branching antlers, which ran thus, in the owner's antiquated doggerel:

COTTON'S CABIN
1850

Rest, angler, here y'r weary feet;
A brother angler bids you stay,
If hearty greeting, healthy meat,
Mild drink to moisten thirsty clay,
A-bed betimes and blythe uprising,
Be welcomes worth an angler's prizing.

The entrance, which was had through a hatch door, the upper half of which was glazed, admitted them into a small vestibule of some ten feet square, with a door in the center of each side. Its walls were plainly wainscoted with unpainted but neatly varnished pine wood, of which also were all the doors, window casings and woodwork of the house; the floor, composed of octagonal pine blocks, similar to those used in the old wooden pavement of Broadway, was covered by a neat red-and-white matting, in the center of which stood a solid octagon-shaped pine table, strewn with powder flasks, shot pouches, reels, fly books, and many of the implements and materials necessary for the angler's or shooter's art. The wainscoting was hung around with rifles, shotguns of several sizes and calibers, rods of all sorts and dimensions, from the huge eighteen-foot salmon rod and powerful trolling rod for the great mascalonge and pickerel of the lakes, to the neatest and lightest singlehanded trout rod, built especially for the use of the smallest mountain streams; with landing nets and gaffs of new construction, and Indian pipes and paddles, and fish spears, inter-spersed, swinging from the deer antlers affixed at intervals along the cornice, festooned with Indian-tanned hides of the deer, the wolf, the cougar and the loup-cervier, none of them, even at that day, rare or unfrequent visitants of those rude and thinly populated districts. Two glass-fronted corner cupboards in the upper angles of the room displayed, the one a beautiful assortment of lines, bottoms, foot links, hanks of salmon gut, reels, winches, hooks of every form and description, bait kettles, creels, and a complete assortment of costly feathers, furs, silks, gold and silver twist, and all the necessaries for flymaking; the other a show of all the sportsman can require for shooting, whether upland or lowland, mountain or forest, field or fen, sea or river, which would not have been overlooked in Cooper's most perfect showcases; four massive settles of the same fashion and material as the table, with deerskin cushions, completed the furniture of this primitive but pleasant and characteristic apartment.

The door to the left gave admission to a sitting room of the same size and corresponding furniture, with the exception that, instead of arms, antlers, and furry tapestries, its varnished but unpainted walls were adorned by some fine engravings from Landseer, and by two sets of well-filled bookshelves, one on each side of the great fireplace, in which blazed, not unpleasant, even at that season, in that wild spot, among those bleak and chilly mountains, a merry fire of pine knots and rock maple. Two double settles, one on each side of the fire, four cushioned armchairs, two tables, one in the center spread with a white cloth and laid with three covers, and one beneath the end window, for this room possessed two, covered with books, writing materials, a chessboard and a few knickknacks and ornamental articles; we will add a noble jet-black bearskin, playing the part of hearthrug, and the tale is told of the decorements, as Caleb Balderstone would have called them, of the salon of Cotton's Cabin.

It was not into this, however, that Lancelot led the way, but throwing open the right-hand door from the hall, "I am sure, Frank," he said, "after your burning race at the tail of the Erie teakettle and your long pull up the Catasauqua, you would rather have a cool bath than anything else, while the cool drink is getting ready. So *voilà* our common sleeping room, *voici* the bathing tub," pointing to a huge cedar tub, sparkling with almost ice-cold water, "and here comes Scipio Africanus, bearing your traps. So now to make yourself presentable with what speed you will, and then to supper, or dinner, if you like it better, with what appetite you may. And now as to the cool drink, will you London porter, will you cidercup, will you sherry, will you claret? The ardent we eschew, save in the fishing flasks, as an antidote to wet feet, chills and fever, and such blest appendages of the time, the place, and the profession. What say you?"

"Cider cup," replied Frank, briefly, who had already extricated a change of habiliments from the crammed valise, and divested himself

of his dusty jacket; and with the words, "I'll see to it myself," his hos-
pitable host left the chamber, followed by the conqueror of Hannibal,
showing his ivories from ear to ear, and chuckling to himself at he knew
not what. Meanwhile Frank, though he applied himself with all due
diligence to the renovation of his person, curiously observed this mountain bedchamber, and examined all its apparatus; for, wanderer as he
was, and acquainted, like Ulysses of old, "with the cities and the ways
of many mortals," yet of a verity, like of this, at home or abroad, far
or near, never had he seen.

Like the sitting room, of which he had caught a glimpse through
the open door, this chamber had two windows, one overlooking the
basin of the main river, in front, one looking from the east end through
the hemlock grove toward the Clattering Creek, one of the cataracts
of which could be seen among the evergreens, glancing like a pillar of
snow through the shadows. Like that also, opposite to the front window, this had a wide, open fireplace, with a few brands smoldering
on the hearth. But herewith all similarity to that or any other room
Frank had ever seen disappeared.

Beds, properly so called, there were none; but, in lieu thereof, two
oblong boxes of pine wood, about six feet, or a little over, in length,
by three in breadth, heaped to a foot above the brim, with an inviting
white pillow, and a Forty-second Tartan plaid by way of coverlet,
occupied the two spaces on each side of the fire; and one, in all respects similar, ran across the front of the room, with its foot toward
the door, occupying nearly two thirds of the area of the chamber. To
make up for this occupation of space, two massive slabs under the
windows projected over the foot of two beds, one supporting three
basins, ewers, and washing apparatus complete, and the other a toilet
glass, razors, brushes and combs, and all the needfuls for a gentleman's
uprising. Above the head of each bed an angular cupboard, supported
on brackets, at four feet from the ground, was ready to receive the
occupant's wardrobe; a tanned deerskin for a foot cloth and a four-
legged stool to each. Such was the bedchamber of Cotton's Cabin.

But such passing observation, for Frank's inquiring mind, was in-
sufficient; it struck his eye, at once, that the garniture of the bed
spoke little of feather bed, hair mattress, Whitney blankets, or down-
stuffed coverlets, wherefore see he must, before sleeping. To the brim,
or, by'r lady! a little above the brim of the bunks, perhaps two feet in
depth, were piled the soft and feathery tips of the fragrant hemlock,
with the stems downward, layer above layer, the softest and balmiest
bed on which ever reclined weary hunter. Above these was spread a
tanned deerskin, with the hair downward, sheets of the cleanest but
the coarsest linen, scented with the wild herbs on which they had been
bleached, and over all the warm and beautiful hill plaid, the quaint but

favorite wear of the eccentric but warmhearted owner of the cabin. Scarcely had Frank completed his survey, when Lancelot made his entree, followed by Africanus bearing an oaken salver, on which was a mighty pewter tankard, burnished until it shone like silver. It was filled, I commend it to you, noble reader, as the best and most cooling of summer beverages, with a quart of sound last year's cider from the cask, a half pint of brown sherry, a modicum of white sugar and one slice of lemon. The surface was brown as mahogany with grated nutmeg, and thereon floated a bunch of thyme, summer savory and sweet basil, bobbing about among great lumps of ice, glittering and lucent as the diamonds of Golconda.

"Was hael, Frank Forester," exclaimed the host, raising the tankard to his lips, not merely in ceremonial hospitality, as was seen by the length of the pull which followed, and then handing it to his guest.

"Drink hael, Sir Lancelot," elevating the tankard more and more, until its bottom corresponded to the plane of the horizon, and then lowering it with a grateful "A—h! that does a fellow good when he was as thirsty as I was just now. But how's this, Sir Lancelot? Is not this shabby treatment toward Wall Street, or don't the broker drink?"

"Only brandy," replied Langdale, glancing round to see that the door was shut. "Nothing stronger than that, nor anything much weaker, I fancy. He was afraid, it seems, he should find nothing fit to drink up here among the mountains, so he brought up a gallon of old Otard, which, seeing that I drink it not, he has well nigh consumed to his own check. I confess, I look to its going with some interest, surmising that, if gone, he will go soon afterward."

"A most considerate and delicate broker," laughed Frank.

"But for heaven's sake, Frank, not a word about Wall Street or brokers before him. In the first place, because I don't know, for certain, that he comes from the one or is the other. In the second, because, though a bit of an ass, he is not a bad fellow, and brought me a recommend from a capital good one. In the third, because if he plead guilty of both, it may be no fault of his that he hang out in a den of thieves and pursues a dirty calling, it may be he can dwell nowhere, and do nothing else. And in the fourth, especially, because he is under my roof, whatever he may be, and must neither be quizzed nor roasted, far less affronted."

"A second Daniel," Frank answered, with a mock obeisance. "I never roast or quizz anybody, much less muffs in my own friends' houses. Nor do I admire brokers so much that I love to talk either to them or about them. In this case I will eschew the word 'break' altogether; I will fracture my rod, should, which the gods forefend, such calamity fall out; rend my line; crack my gut; lux my hooks; and, should occasion be, batter or bang the head of any who shall deserve it; but devil a thing will I break, no! not even silence, if I cannot do so without saying 'broke.' "

"Well! well!" said Lancelot, "come along, you are rigged, I see; and dinner, such as it is, is ready. And you shall be made known in due form to Mr. P. St. Clair Robins, of New York. Is not that high?"

"Immense. What does P. stand for?"

"Peleg, I fancy. But he calls himself St. Clair only; for shortness, I suppose. In his signatures, however, out comes the detested P."

And, therewithal, passing across the little hall, and entering into the sole sitting room, which served the company for library, saloon, and dining room, they found the object of their conversation, a personable figure enough, elaborate of well-oiled beard and whiskers and some-what too accurately gotten up for a free-and-easy sportsman's feed like this, reading the last number of *The Spirit,* in the red light of the jolly wood fire.

"Forester, let me make you acquainted with my friend, Mr. St. Clair Robins; Mr. Robins, this is Frank Forester; you were looking over one of his books last night."

So they bowed, and shook hands and were mutually charmed, of course; neither of them caring a snap of his finger whether the other were crucified before breakfast; and, that duty done, Frank turned reproachfully to his friend—

"*Et tu, Brute!*" he said; "at least from you, I expected not this outrage. Among these unutterable hills and unpronounceable rivers, where few read and none write, I did hope to sink the abominable shop. Here, at least, I had hoped to escape the enemy."

Here Mr. St. Clair Robins looked at our friend wistfully and then at Lancelot doubtfully, as if hesitating whether he was crazy or in his cups.

But Lancelot laughed and inquired—"What enemies, Frank? Mr. Robins imagines you see snakes!"

"Pardon me, Mr. Robins, I never have been so unfortunate as to enjoy *del. tre.;* and even if I had, though being terribly afraid of all the serpent tribe, I am sure it is not they whom I should have seen. No! welcome snakes! save me from publishers alone. From the least wriggling dealer in cheap obscenity to the vast baronial constrictors, who, swallowing authors, vomit their torrents of folios; these are the terrors of the poor penman's waking hours, the tortures of his feverish dreams. Here I had hoped, fondly but fruitlessly, to hear of no books but fly books, no bookmakers unless on the Leger and the Derby, and lo! on my first visit into this most inhospitable cabin, there now! stop that, Lancelot; I foresee in the curl of your lip, an illusion to Uncle Tom! My appetite is taken away by base allusions to my miserable trade of grinding gammon to fill the—"

"Halt, there!" interrupted Lancelot. "We'll see about the appetite before we proceed, for I observe that Scipio has done his duty; how, it rests to be seen."

So they seated themselves cosily round the small round table, whereon appeared but a single dish, flanked by a plate of halved lemons, a decanter of sherry, and a long cork; in the blaze of the fire flashed a porter bottle, and at St. Clair Robins' right hand his favorite cognac stood sentry over his plate.

"No soup, Frank," said Lancelot, uncovering his dish, whereon reclined, on a neat white napkin, so exquisitely broiled that all the fair freshness of their silvery armor, sanguine spotted, all the inno-cent tricolor of their resplendent fins, was preserved intact, two lordly brook trout.

"Three-pounders, by the Lord Harry!" exclaimed Frank, almost bounding from his seat.

"Good boy, Frank," replied his host, approvingly. "Two, fifteen ounces and a half, this fellow," tapping the largest with the fish knife, "And the little one about one ounce lighter; but the little chap fought the harder fight. Did he not, Mr. Robins?"

"Nearly five minutes longer, I reckon," answered the Yorker. "Now that's a capital good trout, a'most as good as ours on the Island."

"You don't see many so heavy fish as those on the Island, nowa-days, Mr. Robins," interposed Frank; "two or three in a season at best. The general run is getting small, I hear, for I have not fished there many a year."

"Well I can't say," replied Robins; which was strictly true, for he had never wet a line in his life in any of those beautiful and now strictly preserved waters, though, like many others of his townsmen, he was very fond of talking about Lif. Snedecors and Sam Carmans. "Have you them as fine in England?"

"Our trout in England, in my day, were much larger, but much fewer in number and much shyer. A five-pounder was no wonder then; and who would not rather take two or three brace of such than ten or twelve dozen of half-pounders? Sometimes a monster is taken; one on record, caught in the Rennet or the Avon, above twenty pounds; and equally large fish have been caught in the Blackwater, in Ireland. Thames trout rarely run less than five, or over ten pounds; but they are rare and solitary fish. But a friend, who fished all Great Britain last year, tells me that, except in close waters, which he did not try, the trout are very numerous, but exceedingly small, owing, no doubt, to the waters being overfished. Another slice, Mr. Lancelot, and if you say sherry, I say sherry, too. What say you, Mr. Robins?"

"Allow me to take my brandy-and-water to your sherry."

"How about the appetite, Frank?"

"Pshaw! what have trout to do with appetite? Anybody can eat trout at any time; to catch them's the thing. Have you a fair sprinkling of such as these here?"

"There are always two or three brace in the pool, and a sprinkling in all the basins down the Catasauqua, and I have all the fishing to myself, no sportsmen having cottoned as yet, except for a flying visit, to these rude regions. There are some very large fish in the deeps of the Delaware, at the tails of the eddies, but no one will believe it, because they cannot be taken by bait at all, nor by a fly, except at moonlight, and I am not anxious to persuade them about it. I mean that we too should go down when the moon is full and have a dash at them. Stony Brook has some good pools, but the fish run smaller; a pound-and-a-halfer is a big one, and the average is not above three quarters. Mr. Robins had good sport this morning, up it."

"Twenty-one fish, eighteen pounds in all," said that worthy, complacently; "but it's the deuce and all on tackle."

"Full of fallen trees and logs?" asked Frank. "They are the deuce sometimes."

"No," replied Lancelot, "a beautiful gravel bottom, with swift eddies and nice whirling holes; here and there a fall of two or three feet, and here a glancing rapid over rock. It is the branches overhead that bother Mr. Robins. The brook is wholly overarched, and it is difficult to one who is not used to it."

"I believe you, it is," said Robins. "Why, I broke three of Conroy's best tips, and carried away I don't know how many leaders."

"Ah! that's bad. But you got a nice creelful, after all. Do you use fly?"

"No, sir; I stick to the good old-fashioned worm. But you won't try a glass of my Otard?"

"Thank you. I'll pledge you in a stoup of Sir Lancelot's Bordeaux; it used to be worth tasting."

"It is still, Frank; nearly the last that is left of the old Sneyd and Barton. Now, Master Scipio, what else have you got for dinner?"

"Pigeon pie, Massa Langdale, and broil' ducks. Mus' git on wi' dat, Massa," turning a deprecating glance to Frank. "Berry little game in de woods now; berry little Massa let me kill, anyhow."

"Pigeon pie and broiled ducks! I should as soon have expected turbot and lobster sauce, or larded sweetbreads."

"Scipio has only realized the poet's fancy; 'he has found out a gift for his fair, he has found where the wood pigeons breed,'" said Langdale; "and as for the ducks, they are only four of a brood of unfortunate flapper summer ducks, which I came across in a little tarn in the middle of a cranberry marsh, which is, in fact, the source of the Stony Brook. I knocked these over, and left a couple to console the anxious mother. But Scipio is quite right; this is the worst time of the year in which for me to entertain; for you must know we get mighty little butcher's meat here. Our rods and guns, backed by the pork barrel, feed us, in the main. A month or two later, I could have given you venison, ruffed grouse, and, by chance, a turkey or bear meat. Now, the devil an ounce will you get, unless it be a venison or bear ham. I believe I'll send Scip over the hills, one of these days, to Lanesboro, to see if he can't hunt us up a lamb or two."

"You have a road, then, to some civilized resort of man?"

"If you call it a road. It is the wildest, rocky wood path, impassable to anything less sure-footed than a Pyrenean mule, or old, ragged Mohawk yonder. It scales the ridge seven hundred feet above this, crosses the head of the Clattering Creek on two pine logs laid side by side, threads an intricate cranberry marsh, and comes down a regular rock staircase into the gorge of the Starucca, and so fifteen miles off into Lanesboro."

"And this Clattering Creek, what sort of water is it?" asked Frank; "that I may learn at once the whole lay of the land."

"A real mountain burn."

"I'm thinking of trying it myself tomorrow," said Robins. "Mr. Langdale tells me it can only be fished with bait, and that's what I'm best at. Besides, there are bigger fish in it."

"But fewer," answered Langdale. "No, Robins, I'd advise you to stick to the Stony, unless you'll try a cast of the fly with us over the pool and down the Catasauqua."

"No, no," replied St. Clair, half indignantly, "none of your flies for me, and no canoe work. But why do you advise me against it? You said there were no trees, bait fishing and big fish. What is there against it?"

"The toughest crag climbing and the most difficult fishing you ever tried."

"What like fishing is it, Lancelot?" asked Frank.

"Exactly what that capital sportsman, Colquhoon of Luss, describes in his excellent book *Moor and Loch,* under the title of the 'Moorburn.' "

"I remember," replied Frank. "Is it as bad as that?"

"Worse; but the fish much larger. I have caught them up to two pounds."

"I should like to hear about that. Can't you read it to me?" asked the Wall Street man, eager for information.

"I've no objection," said Langdale, "if Frank has not. He has read it fifty times already."

"I'm convenient," answered Frank, laying down his knife and fork, the last duck having disappeared.

"Well, then, here goes. Now, Scipio, look alive and clear away the table; bring us our pipes and coffee; and then we'll to bed, for we must be afoot by daybreak."

And with the word he rose, and, after turning over a few volumes on his crowded shelves, brought down the volume in question, with its pages underlined, and interlined, and filled with marginal notes and references. This done, he ensconced himself in the chimney corner, threw on a fresh log, and read as follows:

"In most of the small Highland burns, there is a succession of cataracts and pools, with a parapet of rock rising perpendicularly on each side, and often scarcely footing enough for a dog to pass. The greater proportion of picturesque-looking brethren of the angle would almost start at the idea of continuing their pastime under such disadvantages. They therefore make a circuit, and come down again upon the burn, where it is more easy to fish, and the ground less rugged. The trout in these places are thus left until many of them grow large, and each taking possession of a favorite nook, drives all the smaller fry away. The difficulty of reaching these places is, I admit, often great, the angler having sometimes to scramble up on his hands and knees, covered with wet moss or gravel, and then drag his fishing-rod after him. These lyns should always be fished up-stream, otherwise the moment you appear at the top of the waterfall or rock, the trout are very like to see you, and slink into their hiding-place. The burn, however, must always be low, as at no other time can you distinguish the snug retreat of these little tyrants, which, indeed, they often leave, during the slightest flood, in search of prey. By fishing up the stream, your head will be on a level with the different eddies and pools, as they successively present themselves, and the rest of your person out of sight. Hold the baited hook with the left hand, jerking out the rod, underhanded, with your right, so as to make the bait fall softly at the lower end of the pool. The trout always take their station either there or at the top where the water flows in, ready to pounce on worms, snails, slugs, etc., as they enter or leave the pool. Should a trout seize the bait, a little time may be given to allow it to gorge, which it will most likely do without much ceremony. If large, care must be taken to prevent it from getting to the top of the lyn, which may probably harbor another expectant. The best plan is, if possible, to persuade it to descend into the pool below. Having deposited the half-pounder in your creel, you will now crawl upon hands and knees, just so near the top of the lyn as will enable you to drop the bait immediately below the bubbling foam, nearly as favorite a station for an overgrown, monopolizing trout as the other. Except in such situations, the burn trout seldom exceeds a quarter of a pound, and may be pulled out with single gut, without much risk of breaking it. In these lyns, however, I have occasionally taken them upward of a pound, which is easily accounted for. As soon as the trout grows to a sufficient size to intimidate his pigmy neighbors, he falls back into the best pool for feeding, not occupied by a greater giant than himself, and as these lyns are almost always in precipices very difficult of access, he remains undisturbed and alone, or with a single companion, driving all others away, until he may at last attain to a pound weight.

"Now, I fear, brother angler, that you are in some respects what the indefatigable Gael would call a 'picturesque angler'; so I advise you in good faith, stick to the Stony Brook; fish it from the long fall carefully down. Scipio shall attend you with the landing net and plenty of worms and minnows; the last, hooked through the lip and back fin, will do you yeoman service in the lower pools; and Frank and I will join you in the afternoon."

"Agreed," said Mr. Robins; "I'll take your advice, I believe; and now I guess I'll turn in. Good night."

"Time, too," said Frank, laughing. "He was beginning to get a little white about the gills. Could that be his old Otard; he did not drink so much of it."

"Lord help you, no! he'd drink a gallon of it and no hurt. No! But he will persist in smoking Cavendish tobacco and kinnikinnick, because he had seen me do it, and, I believe, imagines that it confers some special powers of trout catching. But come, suppose we turn in, too; you'll be tired after your journey, and a good night's rest will give a steady hand and clear eye tomorrow."

"*Volontiers.*"

So they incontinently joined the Wall Street man, who declared, half asleep, that the bed was not so very bad, after all; while Frank, once ensconced in the fragrant sheets, swore, by the great god Pan, patron of hunters, that never had bed so sweet, so soft, so warm, in every way so excellent, received the limbs of weary hunter. And so, indeed, it proved; for, until Scipio made his entree, with his announcement, "Breakfast soon be ready, Massa; sun h'em 'mose up now," no one stirred or spoke during the livelong night.

Thereon they all turned, like the Iron Duke, not over, but out. Their sporting toilets were soon made; but Frank and Lancelot, in their old shepherd's-plaid jackets and trews and hobnailed fishing shoes, could not but exchange glances and smiles at the elaborate rig of their friend, which some Broadway artist had, it was evident, elaborated from a Parisian fashion plate, the high boots of exquisitely enameled leather, the fine doeskin trousers, the many-pocketed, pearl-buttoned shooting jacket of fawn-colored silk plush, the batiste neckerchief and waistcoat, point-device, with green-and-silver fishes embroidered on a blue ground, and, to complete the whole, a cavalier hat, in which, but that it lacked the king's black feather, Rupert might well have charged at Marston Moor or Naseby. He seemed, however,

so happy, that it would have been as useless as ill-natured to indoctri-
nate him; for evidently, as an angler, the man was hopelessly incurable,
though, as Frank observed, for Wall Street, he was wonderfully decent.

His weapon was a right good Conroy's general-fishing rod, but
without reel, and having its line, an unusually stout silk one, with a
superb salmon-gut bottom, which, in good hands, would have held a
twenty-pounder, made carefully fast to the top funnel; eschewing all
use of the ring and destroying all chance of the rod's regularly bending
to its work. But again, to counsel would have been to offend; so our
friends held their peace.

The smoked venison ham, broiled troutlings, dry toast and black tea,
which furnished their morning meal, were soon finished; and forth
they went into the delicious, breezy air of the quiet summer morning,
not a sound disturbing the solitude, except the plash and rippling of
the rapid waters, the low voices of the never silent pine tops, and the
twittering of the swallows, as they skimmed the limpid pool.

Up the gorge of the Stony Brook, followed by Scipio, with bait of
all kinds enough to have kept the kraten fat for one day at least, a
large creel at his back, and gaff and landing net in hand, away went
St. Clair Robins, gay and joyous and confident; and then, but not
till then quoth Forester—

"And whither we?"

"To the other side of the pool. You may see the big fish rising under
the alders, there, in the shadow of the big hill, from this distance.
That shadow will hang there until noon, while all this side of the
basin will be in blazing sunshine. Not a fish will bite here, I warrant
me, until three o'clock, while we'll fill our basket there with good
ones, certain. The best fish in the pool lies under that roundheaded
stone, just in the tail of the strong eddy, where the Clattering Creek
comes in, in the broken water. I rate him a six-pounder, and have
saved him for you all the spring. As soon as the sun turns westward,
and the hemlocks' shadows cross the white water, you shall kill him,
and then we'll away to the Wall Street man"; and therewith the
larger birch canoe was manned, paddled gently over to the shady side
of the pool and moored in about twenty-foot water, and then, the rods
being put together, the reels secured and the lines carried duly through
the rings, the following colloquy followed:

"What flies do you most affect here, Lancelot?" asked Frank.

"Any, at times, and almost all," answered Langdale. "In some
weather I have killed well with middle-sized gaudy lake flies; but my
favorites, on the whole, are all the red, brown, orange, and yellow
hackles, and the blue and yellow duns. And yours?"

"My favorite of all is a snipe feather and mouse body; next to that
the black and the furnace hackles."

"And will you use them today?"

"I will; the snipe wing for my stretcher. I mean to kill the big chap with him this evening."

"Be it so! To work."

And to work they went; but, though most glorious the sport to enjoy, or even to see performed gnostically, to read of it described is as little interesting as to describe it is difficult. Suffice it to say, that before the sun had begun to turn westward, sixteen brace and a half were fairly brought to basket by our anglers, one a three-pound-and-a-halfer, three two-pounders, there or thereabout; not a fish under a pound, all smaller were thrown back unscathed, and very few so small as that, all beautifully fed fish, big-bellied, small-headed, high in color, prime in condition. At one o'clock, they paddled leisurely back to the cabin, lunched frugally on a crust of bread and a glass of sherry, and awaited the hour when the hemlock's shadow should be on the white water.

At the moment they were there; and lo! the big trout was feeding fiercely on the natural fly.

"Be ready, Frank, and when next he rises drop your fly right in the middle of his bell."

"Be easy, I mean it." His line, as he spoke, was describing an easy circle around his head; the fish rose not. The second revolution succeeded; the great trout rose, missed his object, disappeared; and, on the instant, right in the center of the bell, ere the inmost circle had subsided, the snipe feather fell and fluttered. With an arrowy rush, the monster rose, and as his broad tail showed above the surface, the merry music of the resonant click reel told that Frank had him. Well struck, he was better played, killed unexceptionally; in thirteen minutes he lay fluttering on the greensward, lacking four ounces of a six-pounder. The snipe feather and mouse body won the day in a canter. So off they started up the Stony Brook, to admire the feats of P. St. Clair Robins. It was not long ere they found him; he had reached the lower waters of the brook, full of beautiful scours, eddies, whirlpools and basins, and was fishing quietly down it, wading about knee-deep with his bait, he was roving with a minnow, some ten yards down the stream, playing naturally enough in the clear, swirling waters. Some trees on the bank hung thickly over his head; a few yards behind him was a pretty rocky cascade, and above that an open upland glade, lighted up by a gleam of the westering sun; and, altogether, with his gay garb, he presented quite a picturesque, if not a very sportsmanly appearance.

"After all," said Frank, as, unseen themselves, they stood observing him, "he does not do it so very badly as one might have expected."

But before the words had passed his lips, a good fish, at least a pounder, threw itself clear out of the water and seized his minnow. In a second, in the twinkling of an eye, by a movement never before seen or contemplated by mortal angler, he ran his right hand up to the top of the third joint of his rod, which he held perpendicularly aloft, and with his left grasped his line, mid-length, and essayed to drag the trout by main force out of his element. The tackle was stout, the stream strong, the bottom slippery, the fish active, and, before anyone could see how it was done, hand and foot both slipped, the line parted, the rod crashed in the middle, the fish went over the next fall with a joyous flirt of his tail, and the fisherman, hapless fisherman, measured his own length in the deepest pool of the Stony Brook.

He was soon fished out, equipped in dry rigging, comforted with a hot glass of his favorite cognac; but he would not be consoled. He was off at daylight the following morning, and, for aught that I have heard, Cotton's Cabin beheld him nevermore.

As for Lancelot and Frank, how they fished the Clattering Creek at midday, and the rapids and whirlpools of the Catasauqua in the gray gloaming, and the broad reaches of the Delaware in the glimmering moonlight; and how they fed, and what they said, and how, in the end, they sped, is it not written in the Book of Lancelot, and will it not appear, when called for by a clamorous public?

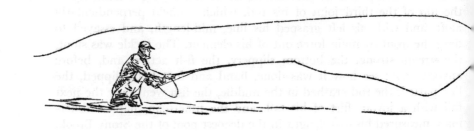

When Is
a Rainbow...

RODERICK HAIG-BROWN

Roderick Haig-Brown's Fisherman's Spring *is perhaps not as well known as some of his other volumes, but this selection from it, "When Is a Rainbow . . . ," offers an interesting discussion on a topic that has been the source of considerable argument among trout fishermen.*

SOME TEN or twelve years ago, in *The Western Angler*, I ranged myself firmly with those biologists and ichthyologists who feel that the world's trout can be assigned to three species—the brown trout of Europe, the cutthroats and rainbows of North America. Set slightly apart from these are the chars on one side, the Atlantic salmon and huchen on the other; the Pacific salmon have their own clear grouping, one shade further removed.

I still feel that this is a highly satisfactory arrangement, with as much of the truth of evolution and variation in it as can possibly be recognized by any useful system. And I believe the commonly recognized subspecies among the trouts, three each for the cutthroat and rainbow groups, also reflect, as accurately as is possible within a simple and useful frame of reference, the state of present knowledge of them. But while I should hate to destroy faith in this comprehensible state of affairs, I doubt if it is the final word, especially in regard to the rainbow group.

If it were simply a matter of structural differences, an academic affair of scale counts and ray counts and anatomical proportions, it might not be of great importance to anglers. It is much more than that; it is a matter of life histories and habits and performance in such wide variation that the anatomical differences seem almost insignificant. And therein lies the fisherman's worry.

The principle of scale count differences seems fairly satisfactory up to a point. The larger-scaled fish, with around 130 to 135 scales along the lateral line, are found at the coast—steelheads and coast rainbows. The intermediates, of which the Kamloops is typical and the Shasta perhaps equally so, with scale counts of around 145, are in interior waters. The mountain Kamloops and the Kern River trout with scale counts varying up to 160 or more are at still higher elevations. And the golden trout of Mount Whitney achieves the highest scale counts of all, often between 170 and 180.

So far, so good. It seems an obvious inference that the different scale counts reflect environmental changes in the same species of trout, varying mainly with altitude. When Mottley's experiments showed that scale counts could be varied up or down by varying hatching temperatures, the picture seemed admirably clear and settled. There was just enough to justify subspecific separation as a matter of convenience and on the assumption that persistence of the environmental factors would tend to emphasize the differences. But at the same time it had to be recognized that change of environment would probably modify the differences, and that in similar environment the fish would almost certainly adopt similar habits. The Kamloops trout, for instance, hatched in a coast steelhead stream, might be expected to assume the low scale of the steelhead and his seagoing habits.

The only remaining confusion in an otherwise pleasantly clear situation was the existence, side by side in the same streams, of the rainbow trout and the steelhead, which apparently had identical scale counts but very different habits. From the angler's point of view this was especially troublesome, since the seagoing steelheads attain much greater size and very different superficial appearance and obviously rate the distinction their common name gives them; yet science could offer no confirmation of this in a separate classification and no ready means of differentiation between a small migratory steelhead and a large resident rainbow. One could only say vaguely, "They're the same fish, of course. Some go to sea and some don't. It's probably hereditary, but . . ."

Obviously this is an uncomfortable state of affairs, a sharp challenge to any argumentative angler or any conscientious biologist. Fortunately, the biologists have begun to do something about it. Between 1938 and 1943, Ferris Neave, of the Fisheries Research Board of Canada, collected and segregated eggs from migratory steelheads and non-migratory rainbows of the Cowichan River system on Vancouver Island, then marked and released the fingerlings. He also checked the scale counts of a good number of wild fish of both types between three and six years old. The results showed small but consistent scale count differences between the types, with the steelheads always giving a slightly higher count than the resident rainbows (three or four scales along the lateral line, five to ten scales in the next line above). It was also quite clear from the movements and later recoveries of the marked fish that the offspring of the steelheads almost invariably went to sea at the expected times, while the offspring of the resident rainbows remained in the river.

There are also Kamloops trout in the Cowichen River system, introduced by the vaguely optimistic efforts of the British Columbia Game Department, an organization that maintains hatcheries and feels it has to put the results somewhere. Neave introduced others and marked them but was able to recover very few. Those that were recovered had the much higher scale count of the normal Kamloops, and there was not the slightest indication that any went to sea to become steelheads or later returned as steelheads.

The importance of these discoveries from a fish-management point of view is obvious. Resident coast rainbows are not a casual by-product of the steelhead runs, nor are the steelheads a simple variation of rainbow habit. The two fish are quite separate stocks and maintain hereditary differences in the same environment; protective measures for one will not necessarily help the other. And the rainbow of higher altitude maintains his hereditary difference when brought down to coastal waters, and apparently does not do nearly so well as the natives.

From the angler's point of view, things are just a shade more confused than they were already. He can no longer call his steelheads and rainbows "the same fish with different habits." They seem to be consistently, though slightly, different fish, with consistently different habits. But the structural differences are so slight that he can still distinguish between them only by their habits. And the difference in habit will not normally be clear to him until the fish are two or three years old.

The explanation, it seems, may well be "glands," as it seems to be in most matters of fish migration. One day the scientists will go to work and find out exactly which glands are the important ones and how they work and perhaps even that their functional peculiarity may be detected by external signs. In the meanwhile the angler must go on as best he can, making his identifications by the logic of where and how the fish is found and perhaps by some indefinable impression of its appearance which echoes experience and seems to tell him, "This is a young steelhead; this is a resident rainbow." Identification of this sort can be remarkably accurate, but not nearly so many men have the necessary measure of experience to be echoed as suppose they have.

I realize that this account does nothing to make things easier. Discovery has gone in the opposite direction to the one I expected, and it now seems that a smaller difference (three or four scales in the lateral line rather than ten or twelve) is both more stable and more significant than it had seemed the larger difference might be. I feel bound to record the discovery because I have previously recorded the other ones. And at the same time I feel bound to make an even more complex confusion by recording my own recent observations of rainbow trout variations in a single stream.

In the two or three miles of the Campbell River between Elk Falls (which fish have never been able to pass) and the salt water, I once supposed there were two important runs of steelheads, one in the winter months, one in May, and an insignificant residue of non-migratory fish, probably chance variants of the migrants. There were some other incidental strays, not too easily explained, but I set little store by these.

Now I can see some pattern and repetition in the strays. I expect something of the rainbows and steelheads in almost every month of the year, and I know that either my early observations were faulty or else the proportions of the various runs can change within a relatively short period of time. The major runs seem much as they always were, but the "strays" now seem to have a lot of brothers and sisters.

In December, January and February the true winter run is on. The fish vary in size from five or six pounds to twenty or more. They are probably of two races, one short and thick, one (the more numerous) long and slender. The degree of maturity varies a good deal; a dark fish, full of eggs or milt, may show up in December, and bright fish, apparently less developed, run during early March. These are variations one expects within a run, and while some of them may be more significant than they seem, one feels fairly comfortable in rating all the fish together as winter steelheads.

During February there may or may not be a sudden invasion of bright little rainbows, obviously from salt water, averaging about thirteen and a half inches in length and varying only by fractions of an inch from the average. They are immature fish, most of them nearly three years old, and they stay in the river only two or three weeks before disappearing as suddenly as they arrived. I have noticed this run three or four times in fifteen years. I may have missed it in some years because I was away at the time or because the river was too high to go fishing. But it does not occur every year. It occurs spasmodically in other nearby streams, and I think it is a sign of a steelhead stream in good healthy production. I feel reasonably sure that the fish themselves are the progeny of the winter run and that they will return later as normal winter fish.

The next run of possible significance comes in late February and early March, a sort of aftermath of the main winter run. The fish are very bright and clean and very small, usually weighing between four and seven pounds.

In May there is a run of fish that one thinks of as rainbows rather than steelheads, though they are obviously from salt water. The normal range is from one to four pounds, with an occasional six-pounder. The fish of two pounds or under are usually immature. Those larger than two or two and a half pounds are mature and seem to spawn within a month of their first appearance. It is rare to catch anything but a kelt of this run after the first week of June.

For many years I believed the Campbell had no true summer run of steelheads. Now I know a small number of big fish (I have caught them from eight to sixteen pounds) comes into the river during June, July and August. There are hardly enough of these fish to be called a run; in a lucky year one might catch five or six between the beginning of July and the end of September, then fish through the next season without firsthand evidence that they are in the river at all. But they are a run, quite possibly a typical summer run, apart from numbers, and I think it is possible their numbers may have increased slightly during the years I have fished the river.

During August and September yet another run of small fish comes into the river. They vary in size from three quarters of a pound to four pounds or more. Two and a half pounds is a big fish and usually mature; smaller fish are usually immature. My impression is that this run has increased considerably in numbers over the past ten years and is more widely spread through the river. The fish feed much more freely than those of the similar May run and come well to a dry fly. But the time of the year and the low level of the river may have something to do with this.

These add up to six distinct runs of Salmo gairdneri. In addition, I have caught a two-pound kelt in August which may or may not have been a remnant of the May run, and several kelts in late November which may or may not have belonged to the furtive summer run. And in June I have caught occasional very handsome rainbow trout in the tidal part of the river. I do not begin to know enough to make sense out of it all, but it is difficult not to suspect that each of these runs is controlled by heredity and that each may have other hereditary peculiarities that will one day be recognized by scientists. I do not think there is much we poor anglers can do about it except keep an open mind. It is important to remember that the rainbow group is highly complex and that the complexities are hereditary and stable rather than environmental and variable. For this reason it is important to pay close attention to both strain and environment in transplanting or stocking attempts; a migratory strain is likely to persist in its efforts to migrate, even when conditions are not favorable; a nonmigratory strain will not develop migratory habits simply by being put within easy reach of salt water; a high-altitude strain will probably do best at similar altitudes; a strain developed in water of high alkalinity quite possibly needs high alkalinity to thrive. There have been more disappointments in stocking rainbows than with any other fish, and it is quite evident now that most of them were caused by failure to select the strain best suited to the new conditions.

When to call a fish rainbow? I wouldn't know. When he isn't a steelhead, I guess. When he isn't a Kamloops or a mountain Kamloops or a golden trout. When he's caught landlocked in coastal waters. When he weighs less than five pounds in a stream open to salt water. Or maybe just the way we've always done it—when it seems like he's a rainbow.

Bonefish

VAN CAMPEN HEILNER

Few American salt-water anglers have the background possessed by Van Campen Heilner, who would rather hunt and fish than eat and would far rather enjoy all three than write about any one. He was one of the first Americans to establish a fishing lodge in the Bahamas, and his experiences there began long before big-game angling became a recognized activity. Few writers have provided as clear and interesting a dissertation on bonefish as the one offered in Heilner's Salt Water Fishing. *Since it was written, bonefishing has become a major activity in tropical waters, and tackle and methods have changed. It must be remembered that when he fished for these silver fighters, reels had no brake mechanism. The brake was the angler's thumb. Those were the days.*

O F ALL the fish which I have had the pleasure and sport of pursuing, and this includes a lifetime of angling for everything from brook trout to swordfish, my favorite is the bonefish. From my personal experience I can say he is the gamest fish for which I ever wet a line.

I started my angling in fresh water. Trout, salmon, black bass, muskies, pike and a host of others were old stories to me before I caught my first bonefish. For more than thirty years I have averaged a month a year surf fishing for channel bass and stripers. For seven years straight I trolled the waters off Catalina for swordfish, and caught them. With Zane Grey, William Scheer, Fred Alexander, Bob Davis and others we fought the great tuna off the Jersey coast out of Seabright dories over thirty years ago. Then they were known as horse mackerel and despised by the fishermen. When the Overseas Railroad had but recently crossed from the mainland of Florida to Key West, I wrestled with great leaping tarpon along the viaducts and the fresh-water rivers of the west coast. Yet to none of these will I yield the palm of fighting fury possessed by the bonefish. Each of the above deserves a niche in the piscatorial hall of fame. But in the center, on a pedestal all his own, belongs the one and incomparable, before whom all good anglers should uncover, the bonefish.

Without doubt my brother anglers will look upon these statements with amusement. "He must be a nut," I can hear you say. Well, I am. I admit it. But fortunately I am not alone, and all those, including many of my friends, who have concentrated on bonefish over a period of years are just as "nutty" as I. We belong to a select fraternity of maniacs who get a tremendous kick and thrill out of their insanity, and if the rest of the angling fraternity choose to regard us as demented, we are perfectly satisfied. We *know why* we are insane.

For over fifteen years I was the only angler who had a camp on the island of North Bimini in the Bahamas and there I have had an unusually excellent chance to fish for and study the elusive bonefish. With some of the world's finest marlin, tuna, and reef fishing at my door I have concentrated on the bonefish almost exclusively.

The bonefish, or banana fish, or to give him his Latin name, *albula vulpes,* which translated means "white fox," is one of the most widely distributed fish in the world. He occurs in warm seas all over the globe. In any part of the tropics from one side of the earth to the other you are almost sure to run across bonefish. As to his life history, not a great deal is known. In Florida and the Bahamas he has been angled for extensively, and it is from these records and experiences that most of our knowledge is derived.

In appearance he is a sort of cross between a carp and a grayling. His head is sharp and mean-looking. His color is silvery white shading to greenish blue on the back. His dorsal fin looks like a shark's as it cuts the water, and the upper lobe of his caudal sticks from the surface almost as high. In size he runs from a pound to sixteen pounds. A world's record fish of thirteen and three-quarter pounds, taken by

Burton F. Peek of Moline, Illinois, at Bimini in the Bahamas stood for years. The mounted fish may be seen in the American Museum of Natural History in New York. Another of sixteen pounds was taken in the Hawaiian Islands in 1948, and I fully expect to hear of one of twenty pounds almost any day.

Bonefish were unfamiliar to fishermen, in the larval stage, until Miss Gloria Hollister of the New York Zoological Society discovered one on a West Indian cruise.

Through the courtesy of Miss Gloria Hollister, Dr. William Beebe of the Department of Tropical Research and Mr. William Bridges, editor of the New York Zoological Society *Bulletin,* I am reprinting herewith from Miss Hollister's article on her observations made in Bermuda of the larval bonefish, which appeared in the 1936 issue of the *Bulletin.* Describing the catching of small fish life at night by means of an electric light hung over the wharf at New Nonesuch Island, Bermuda, she goes on to say:

No sooner had I returned to my night-light vigil than a small silver dot was reflected by the light. This I followed for some time, knowing that it was the eye of a fish but not knowing just what kind of fish it enlightened. Like the eel that had just been caught, it, too, was out of reach. But in a few minutes it was attracted nearer the center of the beam of light and then I saw a narrow, white, ribbon-like body trailing behind the glistening eye. It was the young of the world-known bone-fish, grubber, ladyfish, or *albula vulpes.* Many have been caught in this stage, when they resemble the young of certain eels and look not at all like their parents. At this particular time I happened to be working out the development of the skeleton of the *albula* from the very young to the adult. Hoping that this one would be an intermediate stage in our collection, I decided to catch it. After submerging the hand net slowly, and raising its rim around the fish, I held it there for a long time and watched this delicate spark of life. To lift the fish out of water would snuff out its life in a few seconds! As I watched it swimming around within the net I remembered the many that had come in our seine and surface nets and their short survival after being pulled in. Almost without thinking I slipped a small glass dish into the water within the net and gradually raised it around the fish. This was done without touching or shocking the fish by lifting it out of water even for a second. The dish with the fish was then submerged in a two-gallon tank. Before leaving that evening, the fish's length, shape, and general description were jotted down. The next morning on the way to the boathouse I prepared a vial of preservative in which to keep the little *albula* for study. Much to my surprise the fish was as lively as when captured the night before. I had even left it without an air supply.

Not dreaming that the *albula* would live over the second night, and wanting to study it in the laboratory, I again dipped it up in a small pint dish. Here it continued to live for two days without air supply, food, or change of water. I was amazed to see during this time how rapidly it was changing. It then dawned upon me that this larval *albula* should be given the best possible conditions. It was again placed in a two-gallon aquarium with a good supply of air and food, which consisted of plankton dipped up each evening from under the night-light. The young *albula* was two and one quarter inches long (55 mm) when it was caught on August 14. It was pure white and transparent and its small dorsal fin was way aft in position. According to daily measurements the fish grew more rapidly during the first four days; in fact, growth was less and less rapid on each successive day. Contrary to most fishes the growth in our living *albula* was by *decreasing* in length. During the first forty-eight *hours* it decreased more than one half inch and during the following forty-eight hours it shortened about one quarter of an inch. During the next four days the decrease in length was still less, being only a fraction of an inch, or 1 millimeter. During ten days this living *albula* larva changed completely before our eyes. It grew shorter and shorter, more round, more compact, more opaque and the dorsal fin developed from an insignificant one in a posterior position, to a prominent fin in the center of the body. The little fish began to acquire color which first showed as dusky blotches mixed with yellow which in turn changed to dusky silver. When our *albula* had decreased in length to about one inch or a little more than one third of its length when caught, it was a perfect miniature of its three-foot parent. It was identical in general form, position of the fins, proportion of the body, and hint of color.

Literature tells us about *albulas* that range from three or three and one half inches to two inches. This was recorded from preserved specimens. Our living *albula* decreased in ten days from two and one quarter inches to less than one inch, which gives us a hint of the amazing rapidity of transformation in this species of fish. From a one-inch miniature-adult the *albula* grew longer and larger; but we do not, as yet, know the length of time this takes. After having grown by shrinking for ten days our living *albula* was attacked by fin fungus, and in order to keep it for record and study it was preserved in spirits.

When the bonefish are small—from one to three pounds—they run in large schools, but as they grow older they seem to break up into pairs or even become solitary. The largest fish I have ever caught, or seen caught, were without exception alone or part of a pair. I have seen bonefish within an oar's length of my boat in clear, still water where I could observe them closely, which I am positive would run fifteen pounds or possibly larger.

Frequently large schools of small bonefish will gang up and form what is known as a "mud," a large patch of discolored water in the center of which the fish are feeding. If the angler can locate a mud and get ahead of it, as the fish move slowly with the tide, he can catch bonefish as fast as he throws out his bait. If no undue noise is made, the fish do not take alarm and the mud can be followed for long distances, similar to following a school of bluefish on the surface.

Bonefish are great lovers of shallow water. As soon as they feel the first thrust of the incoming tide they start to move in over the banks searching here and there for the tiny "ghost" crabs or other succulent bait hidden in the grassy bottom. They will force themselves into such shallow water that they can navigate only with the greatest difficulty, and I have frequently seen them struggling with half their backs out of water to pass over some particularly shallow piece of bank.

As the tide continues to flow they work further and further in until at high water they are scattered all about among the mangroves and sometimes 'way up in the heads of creeks which are dry at low water.

As the tide starts to fall off, they start to come off the banks, though at this stage they do not seem so hungry as before. Sometimes they will pass right over your bait without noticing it, or merely pick it up, to drop it immediately. However, there are no set rules for bonefish because they will never react the way you expect them to.

They continue to back off the banks as the tide drops lower and lower, until at dead low water you will find them settled off in deep holes or in the channels waiting for the never ending cycle of tides to repeat.

Bonefish average from two to five pounds. From six to eight pounds is a large fish; from nine to twelve pounds is a monster. The ten- to twelve-pounders are not common. At my camp we celebrate on anything over nine pounds. I am convinced that they reach a weight of twenty pounds.

Now that we know something of the appearance and habits of this wily "white fox," let us see how we go about catching him. While not an absolute necessity, as I shall explain later, our first requisite should be a good boat. This should not be over twelve or fourteen feet long and should be light and extremely flat on the bottom. Frequenlty it may be necessary to drag it by main force over practically dry ground.

It should be equipped with oars, two sharp-pointed stakes or two small anchors for fastening it bow and stern, and an outboard motor. I have two, one more powerful than the other, which I use when the bonefish grounds I wish to visit lie some distance from my camp.

Next are your rods. After several years of experimenting, we evolved a rod, which James Heddon's Sons make for us, which roughly compares with the standard for the 3/6 class of the Tuna Club. It is approximately six feet over-all and weighs about six ounces. An important factor is a rather long butt which, when you are fighting a fish, extends well down under your elbow and gives you considerable leverage. This should have about five guides in addition to the tip, as a seven-pound bonefish can put a considerable bend in your rod. All our rods are made of split bamboo and well varnished. This is a description of the rod which we have found most satisfactory for our use, but any light rod similar to that known as a "bay" rod will serve the purpose. I have frequently used a salt-water fly rod on bonefish and found it very sporty.

Next comes the reel. We have found a 1/0 reel filled to the brim with six-thread line to be just about right. A bonefish can run off an astonishing amount of line on his first rush and it is well to be prepared. If you are fishing in a locality, as frequently occurs, where there are lots of little mangrove shoots sticking out of the water, it is better to use a nine-thread line, as the bonefish will occasionally run around one of these and cause a severe sawing strain on the line. As a rule, however, a six-thread line will suffice. The matter of a star drag is optional. Not in order to keep a strain on the line, as this should be done with a thumbstall, but more to keep your knuckles from being skinned up when the fish makes one of its sudden rushes. If you are adept at letting go of the reel handle without injury, then do not use a star drag. Otherwise use one, but maintain the lightest of drags.

A small casting dipsey completes your rig but, in recent years when fishing in very shallow water, and "stalking" bonefish on foot, we have found it better to use no sinker at all, and to depend on the weight of the bait to cast out the line. When bonefish are in very shallow water, with part of their backs out, the "plunk" of a sinker scares them though they be a distance of several feet away. In deep water, however, or where there is any tide, a sinker should of course be used. A long-handled landing net, a meat grinder for grinding up chum, a hatchet for breaking up conchs, a woolen thumbstall, and you are all set.

The first thing is to procure bait. If you have a guide or "boy," he has attended to this by the time you have finished your breakfast. On the Florida coast the favorite bait seems to be hermit crab and live shrimp. In the Bahamas, although we have plenty of hermit crabs, we use conch. Sometimes we tip this off with a piece of ordinary blue-clawed crab, sometimes with a piece of crawfish. Conch is easiest to procure, stays on best, and makes good chum. If an occasional crab is drawn aboard while fishing, he is broken up and used along with the conch.

I shall not attempt to describe how to extract a conch from its shell. This is an art which requires considerable practice and can be done with dexterity by your native guide. A hatchet will help him considerably, but if none is available, he can do it by striking one conch against another and through the hole in the top just made insert his knife blade, with surprising results. I once saw a slightly inebriated gentleman give a conch a drink of whisky which brought him forth from his shell instantly.

After a great many of these large shells have been "deconched" the animal procured from them is then pounded furiously with a stick until it is pliable enough to go on your hook. Sufficient pieces are cut up for bait and the balance is run through the grinding machine into a box or pail to be used for chum. There is no special way of baiting the hook. The writer uses as large and as tempting a piece as he can get on it.

With plenty of bait aboard, rods and extra hooks and sinkers, you shove off from the dock just before low water.

It will take you one or two days to locate just where the fish are feeding, but once this has been done, you head for your favorite spot at once. When you get there, it may be absolutely dry. In this case you can do one of two things: get as near to it as you can and anchor; or drag your boat where you wish to have it and sit down and wait for the tide to come in. Generally you do not have so very long to wait. For as soon as you notice that the tide has started up you will commence to see bonefish.

Perhaps your first glimpse of them will be but a ruffled bit of surface. But if you are used to it you will spot it a long way off. Or it may be a fin cleaving the surface, or a whole procession of tails flicking out of water. "Here they come!" you whisper. Your guide commences to cast chum out in the general direction of the oncoming fish and you place your bait as nearly as you can in the middle of it. Pretty soon they are up with it and you can see the bonefish tails working around your bait. You wait, nerves tense, hardly daring to breathe. Suddenly comes a sly tug on the end of your line, just a quick little pull, no more. It comes so quickly and so easily that it has come and gone before you realize it. But it is in that split second that you must hook your bonefish. If you don't you will reel in your line to find your hook cleaned and the bonefish departed.

If you've been quick enough and have hooked him, you are in for some of the fastest moments of your angling career. The line actually flies through the water with a ripping sound that scares you. Your reel has become but a blur and the speed is so great that your thumbstall has become red-hot. Four hundred feet away the bonefish suddenly breaks water, turns and rushes at you as fast as he went from you. You reel until your wrist aches but you can't get in the slack. The bonefish shoots past one end of your boat, kicking up the spray as he goes, and a great belly sags in your line. You have never experienced anything like this before and you begin to wonder if you are playing a fish or a fish is playing you.

He's off again but this time the run isn't quite so long as the first one. Two hundred feet away he stops, and for the first time you can get your breath. You pump and you gain—pump and gain again. Now you can see him, cruising in a great semicircle—blackish green he looks in the water. But he sees you and the boat at the same time and the effect is as if he had been shot through with a high-voltage current. He's gone again and half your line with him. Wow! What a fish! He's run out more line in five minutes than any other fish could in an hour. And it looks as if he was never going to quit. But you keep working on him and this time it looks like the end. You get him almost to the boat and he starts a slow circling. Around the boat he goes and around again, nearer and nearer each time. Next time now.

"Get the net, Benjie. When I bring him around this time, gather him in. All right. Seven pounds? He felt like fifty."

You sit back, light your pipe and crack open a bottle of beer. A warm glow of pride and self-satisfaction suffuses your countenance. You've done a good day's work and so far as you are concerned you're willing to call it quits. Not so your guide.

"Great Lawd! Lookadare, boss! Nudder bonefish. Big fellah. See him dare!" You look, and sure enough. The excitement is contagious. You cast and wait again.

This bonefish bites in an entirely different manner. The first thing you know he's grabbed the bait and rushed off with it at breakneck speed. No tug. No pull. Just one awful snatch and zow! He's halfway to Nassau! This one is a horse of a different color. He just doesn't stop. Your thumbstall is burned clean through and your finger hurts. You thrust the reel and rod—the whole works—under water to cool it off. But it doesn't cool the ardor of your bonefish. Smaller and smaller dwindles the line on your spool.

"Pull the anchor. Pull up the stake! He's taking all my line."

Benjie struggles to obey. But he falls down in the boat and he can't get the stake up; it's jabbed down too far in the marl. You curse, you plead. Too late. The line comes to an end; there's one awful moment, then it snaps and flicks through the air like a wisp of smoke. Bonefish and six hundred feet of line have vanished into the blue.

You pick up and start sorrowfully back for camp. You say nothing. Benjie looks as if he were going to cry. You'd promised him five dollars for a ten-pound fish.

"Awful big bonefish, boss," he finally says. "Awful big."

And that's that.

The next day, or the following one, you return to your favorite spot but the fish are not there. You wait patiently, but as the tide creeps higher and higher and no bonefish appear you decide to go look for them. You stand in the bow, your rod held like a lance, and your guide poles you slowly across the banks. Hullo! What's that?

A hundred yards or so ahead you see some shadows against the white bottom. Are they bonefish or patches of grass? You shove a little closer. A tail flicks the surface. Bonefish! And working your way! You quickly stop the boat, gently lower the anchor and cast out your bait. Perhaps the cast scares them and they break in all directions like a covey of frightened quail. Perhaps they pass you by and pay no attention to either your bait or the chum. Or perhaps you are lucky and it is a day to be remembered. In any case, it's bonefishing.

Up early, out all day, poling across the flats for miles. One day you decide to "still-hunt" them. You strap a bait box on your belt, roll up your trousers, step overboard, and set out alone across the miles of flats to get a bonefish on your own. No boat, no net, no chum, nothing but an extra hook in your pocket, and your rod. To me this is one of the most fascinating and one of the sportiest ways to seek the king of game fishes.

For half an hour you trudge on through the ankle-deep water without a sign of game. You's not in the bay now, you're on the outside flats. If you see a bonefish he will be a big one and probably alone. Just then you do see one, but he's traveling quite fast. He's gone and an old soaker. You wade as fast as you can, but unless he stops you'll never catch up with him. But hold on! He's settled in a hole. What a stroke of luck! You tiptoe slowly forward.

The hole he is in is about a hundred feet long. And it must be two feet deep. When he's at the far end of it you can hardly see him. Up and down the length of it he swims, turning at each end like a tiger in its cage. But he can leave it anytime he wants to. He must have found something there that he likes. You wait until he has reached the far end again and softly cast your sinkerless bait almost to the middle. Back he comes. He's going past it. No, he isn't. He's stopped with a little swirl of sand that's plainly visible from where you are. He turns and noses head down for the bait. The lobe of his tail breaks water. There is a swift pull and you've hooked him!

Look at him go!

Was there ever such a fish? If the hook doesn't pull out he *can't* get away, this time. You'll run all the way to Haiti after him if necessary. But fortunately it isn't necessary. His first run was magnificent but you've turned him at last and the conclusion of each rush brings him closer and closer to your feet. Now he sees you and starts to circle. You pivot slowly like a ringmaster in a circus, your rod nodding and swaying a graceful beat in time to his swift plunges. But he's weakening. This time now. You hold the rod high in the air with your right hand, bend down and slip the fingers of your left hand through his gills. A ten-pounder. Your boat must be three quarters of a mile away. You hold up the fish and yell as loud as you can.

"A ten-pounder! A ten-pounder."

It's good to be alive, and bonefishing.

In all my years of bonefishing there are one or two incidents that stand out in my memory above all others. In my early days in the Bahamas, before we got it down to a science, we used the native sailboats for our fishing excursions, even to going outside on the reef and in the Stream. If you've never trolled out of a sailboat you've missed a lot of fun. You can go right through schools of fish without bothering them at all. Try it.

Well, on one bonefishing trip, things were pretty slow. It was about three in the afternoon and the sun was as hot as Tophet. My companion reclined in the stern, his hat pulled over his eyes, his rod resting across his knees. The omnipotent Benjie slumbered peacefully in the bilge. The sight of my two companions and the effect of two bottles of beer was too much for me, so I curled up in the furled sail, one leg over the boom, for a little concentrated sleeping. It was almost dead-low water and we were anchored "off in the deep" on the edge of the channel where bonefish generally go at that phase of tide.

A confused babble of sound gradually seeped through to my bemused brain.

"Come on, Van, get up! Wake up! Got a big one on. Big bonefish!"

I struggled mightily and dragged myself down from my perch in the sail. Harry was fighting a big fish, sure enough. The fish had out a lot of line and then, turning, headed straight for an old stake protruding from the water a hundred yards distant.

At this point Benjie distinguished himself with an act of quick thinking that has been a marvel to us ever since. We had a small canoe tied astern, and leaping into this he paddled toward the stake as if his very life depended on it, reached it two strokes ahead of the bonefish, and pulled it up. Harry netted his fish, a fine nine-pounder.

Another time I remember, my companion and I had pushed our skiff as far inshore as the tide would permit. We then got overboard and waded along the flats looking for bonefish on the incoming tide. For a long time we saw nothing. Then, as if by magic, bonefish tails were everywhere. Hundreds of them, thousands of them. I have never seen such a sight. No matter in which direction we looked, we could see schools of bonefish. Tails, fins, tails, working in across the flats. We cast and we cast, and before we were through we had brought to our feet and released fourteen bonefish. It was just one of those sights and one of those times that come but once in an angler's lifetime.

Then, perhaps, one of the most memorable times of all. A night of full moon. Supper over, someone suggested we go out for a try at bonefish. We crossed the bay to the far side, in quite close to the mangroves. The tide was almost full and the water must have been almost four feet deep. It was as bright as day. Every object on the ocean floor was plainly discernible. For a long time nothing happened. We fished and smoked and looked at the palm trees, tipped with silver in the moonlight. Then I caught a five-pounder. And then one of my companions had a strike.

This was one of those fish that just grabbed it and ran. And kept right on running. The wet line showered tiny drops of silver on the shining water. A heron croaked dismally over in the mangroves. No one said a word, and my friend fought a silent fight. On the Point, the beacon flashed in time to the bending rod. It was wild and beautiful.

At last we saw the bonefish, big and ghostlike in the crystal-clear water. He was a whopper. Around and around the boat and then down with the net and into it head first he went.

Ten and one half pounds! The record for that year. Those few hours on the moonlit flats, the palms rustling in the night wind, the big bonefish gasping away his life in the bottom of the skiff; there is a picture I can never forget.

Burning tropic sun, miles of flats glistening on the low water, fins and tails working in with the tide, a lone man-of-war bird circling high in the blue; moonlit nights with the dark shadows of mangroves stretching toward your boat, the singing reel and the bending rod; these are my memories of days and nights spent in pursuit of that true king of all game fish, the bonefish, the sportiest thing with fins!

Big Two-Hearted River

ERNEST HEMINGWAY

Hemingway was still grasping the first rung of the literary ladder when he wrote "Big Two-Hearted River," but no critic has even hinted that this story failed to boost him considerably higher. Simplicity and economy of style provide the unmatchable Hemingway atmosphere, even in an angling story.

T HE TRAIN went on up the track out of sight, around one of the hills of burnt timber. Nick sat down on the bundle of canvas and bedding the baggage man had pitched out of the door of the baggage car. There was no town, nothing but the rails and the burned-over country. The thirteen saloons that had lined the one street of Seney had not left a trace. The foundations of the Mansion House hotel stuck up above the ground. The stone was chipped and split by the fire. It was all that was left of the town of Seney. Even the surface had been burned off the ground.

Nick looked at the burned-over stretch of hillside, where he had expected to find the scattered houses of the town, and then walked down the railroad track to the bridge over the river. The river was there. It swirled against the log spiles of the bridge. Nick looked down into the clear, brown water, colored from the pebbly bottom, and watched the trout keeping themselves steady in the current with wavering fins. As he watched them they changed their positions by quick angles, only to hold steady in the fast water again. Nick watched them a long time.

He watched them holding themselves with their noses into the current, many trout in deep, fast-moving water, slightly distorted as he watched far down through the glassy convex surface of the pool, its surface pushing and swelling smooth against the resistance of the log-driven piles of the bridge. At the bottom of the pool were the big trout. Nick did not see them at first. Then he saw them at the bottom of the pool, big trout looking to hold themselves on the gravel bottom in a varying mist of gravel and sand, raised in spurts by the current.

Nick looked down into the pool from the bridge. It was a hot day. A kingfisher flew up the stream. It was a long time since Nick had looked into a stream and seen trout. They were very satisfactory. As the shadow of the kingfisher moved up the stream, a big trout shot upstream in a long angle, only his shadow marking the angle, then lost his shadow as he came through the surface of the water, caught the sun, and then, as he went back into the stream under the surface, his shadow seemed to float down the stream with the current, unresisting, to his post under the bridge, where he tightened, facing up into the current.

Nick's heart tightened as the trout moved. He felt all the old feeling.

He turned and looked down the stream. It stretched away, pebbly-bottomed, with shallows and big boulders and a deep pool as it curved away around the foot of a bluff.

Nick walked back up the ties to where his pack lay in the cinders beside the railroad track. He was happy. He adjusted the pack harness around the bundle, pulling straps tight, slung the pack on his back, got his arms through the shoulder straps, and took some of the pull off his shoulders by leaning his forehead against the wide band of the tumpline. Still, it was too heavy. It was much too heavy. He had his leather rod case in his hand, and leaning forward to keep the weight of the pack high on his shoulders he walked along the road that paralleled the railroad track, leaving the burned town behind in the heat, and then turned off around a hill with a high, fire-scarred hill on either side onto a road that went back into the country. He walked along the road feeling the ache from the pull of the heavy pack. The road climbed steadily. It was hard work walking uphill. His muscles ached and the day was hot, but Nick felt happy. He felt he had left everything behind, the need for thinking, the need to write, other needs. It was all back of him.

From the time he had got down off the train and the baggage man had thrown his pack out of the open car door, things had been different. Seney was burned, the country was burned over and changed, but it did not matter. It could not all be burned. He knew that. He hiked along the road, sweating in the sun, climbing to cross the range of hills that separated the railroad from the pine plains.

The road ran on, dipping occasionally, but always climbing. Nick went on up. Finally the road after going parallel to the burnt hillside reached the top. Nick leaned back against a stump and slipped out of the pack harness. Ahead of him, as far as he could see, was the pine plain. The burned country stopped off at the left with the range of hills. On ahead, islands of dark pine trees rose out of the plain. Far off to the left was the line of the river. Nick followed it with his eye and caught glints of the water in the sun.

There was nothing but the pine plain ahead of him, until the far blue hills that marked the Lake Superior height of land. He could hardly see them, faint and far away in the heat-light over the plain. If he looked too steadily they were gone. But if he only half looked they were there, the far-off hills of the height of land.

Nick sat down against the charred stump and smoked a cigarette. His pack balanced on the top of the stump, harness holding ready, a hollow molded in it from his back. Nick sat smoking, looking out over the country. He did not need to get his map out. He knew where he was from the position of the river.

As he smoked, his legs stretched out in front of him, he noticed a grasshopper walk along the ground and up onto his woolen sock. The grasshopper was black. As he had walked along the road, climbing, he had started many grasshoppers from the dust. They were all black. They were not the big grasshoppers with yellow-and-black or red-and-black wings whirring out from their black wing sheathing as they fly up. These were just ordinary hoppers, but all a sooty black in color. Nick had wondered about them as he walked, without really thinking about them. Now, as he watched the black hopper that was nibbling at the wool of his sock with its four-way lip, he realized that they had all turned black from living in the burned-over land. He realized that the fire must have come the year before, but the grasshoppers were all black now. He wondered how long they would stay that way.

Carefully he reached his hand down and took hold of the hopper by the wings. He turned him up, all his legs walking in the air, and looked at his jointed belly. Yes, it was black too, iridescent where the back and head were dusty.

"Go on, hopper," Nick said, speaking out loud for the first time, "fly away somewhere."

He tossed the grasshopper up into the air and watched him sail away to a charcoal stump across the road.

Nick stood up. He leaned his back against the weight of his pack where it rested upright on the stump and got his arms through the shoulder straps. He stood with the pack on his back on the brow of the hill looking out across the country, toward the distant river, and then struck down the hillside away from the road. Underfoot the ground was good walking. Two hundred yards down the hillside the fire line stopped. Then it was sweet fern, growing ankle-high, to walk through, and clumps of jack pines; a long undulating country with frequent rises and descents, sandy underfoot and the country alive again.

Nick kept his direction by the sun. He knew where he wanted to strike the river and he kept on through the pine plain, mounting small rises to see other rises ahead of him and sometimes from the top of a rise a great solid island of pines off to his right or his left. He broke off some sprigs of the heather sweet fern and put them under his pack straps. The chafing crushed it and he smelled it as he walked.

He was tired and very hot, walking across the uneven, shadeless pine plain. At any time he knew he could strike the river by turning off to his left. It could not be more than a mile away. But he kept on toward the north to hit the river as far upstream as he could go in one day's walking.

For some time as he walked Nick had been in sight of one of the big islands of pine standing out above the rolling high ground he was crossing. He dipped down and then as he came slowly up to the crest of the ridge he turned and made toward the pine trees.

There was no underbrush in the island of pine trees. The trunks of the trees went straight up or slanted toward each other. The trunks were straight and brown, without branches. The branches were high above. Some interlocked to make a solid shadow on the brown forest floor. Around the grove of trees was a bare space. It was brown and soft underfoot as Nick walked on it. This was the overlapping of the pine-needle floor, extending out beyond the width of the high branches.

The trees had grown tall and the branches moved high, leaving in the sun this bare space they had once covered with shadow. Sharp at the edge of this extension of forest floor commenced the sweet fern.

Nick slipped off his pack and lay down in the shade. He lay on his back and looked up into the pine trees. His neck and back and the small of his back rested as he stretched. The earth felt good against his back. He looked up at the sky, through the branches, and then shut his eyes. He opened them and looked up again. There was a wind high up in the branches. He shut his eyes again and went to sleep.

Nick woke stiff and cramped. The sun was nearly down. His pack was heavy and the straps painful as he lifted it on. He leaned over with the pack on and picked up the leather rod case and started out from the pine trees across the sweet-fern swale, toward the river. He knew it could not be more than a mile.

He came down a hillside covered with stumps into a meadow. At the edge of the meadow flowed the river. Nick was glad to get to the river. He walked upstream through the meadow. His trousers were soaked with the dew as he walked. After the hot day, the dew had come quickly and heavily. The river made no sound. It was too fast and smooth. At the edge of the meadow, before he mounted to a piece of high ground to make camp, Nick looked down the river at the trout rising. They were rising to insects come from the swamp on the other side of the stream when the sun went down. The trout jumped out of water to take them. While Nick walked through the little stretch of meadow alongside the stream, trout had jumped high out of water. Now as he looked down the river, the insects must be settling on the surface, for the trout were feeding steadily all down the stream. As far down the long stretch as he could see, the trout were rising, making circles all down the surface of the water, as though it were starting to rain.

The ground rose, wooded and sandy, to overlook the meadow, the stretch of river, and the swamp. Nick dropped his pack and rod case and looked for a level piece of ground. He was very hungry and he wanted to make his camp before he cooked. Between two jack pines, the ground was quite level. He took the ax out of the pack and chopped out two projecting roots. That leveled a piece of ground large enough to sleep on. He smoothed out the sandy soil with his hand and pulled all the sweet-fern brushes by their roots. His hands smelled good from the sweet fern. He smoothed the uprooted earth. He did not want anything making lumps under the blankets. When he had the ground smooth, he spread his three blankets. One he folded double, next to the ground. The other two he spread on top.

With the ax he slit off a bright slab of pine from one of the stumps and split it into pegs for the tent. He wanted them long and solid to hold in the ground. With the tent unpacked and spread on the ground, the pack, leaning against a jack pine, looked much smaller. Nick tied the rope that served the tent for a ridge pole to the trunk of one of the pine trees and pulled the tent up off the ground with the other end

of the rope and tied it to the other pine. The tent hung on the rope
like a canvas blanket on a clothesline. Nick poked a pole he had cut
up under the back peak of the canvas and then made it a tent by
pegging out the sides. He pegged the sides out taut and drove the
pegs deep, hitting them down into the ground with the flat of the ax
until the rope loops were buried and the canvas was drum-tight.

Across the open mouth of the tent Nick fixed cheesecloth to keep
out mosquitoes. He crawled inside under the mosquito bar with various things from the pack to put at the head of the bed under the
slant of the canvas. Inside the tent the light came through the brown
canvas. It smelled pleasantly of canvas. Already there was something
mysterious and homelike. Nick was happy as he crawled inside the
tent. He had not been unhappy all day. This was different, though.
Now things were done. There had been this to do. Now it was done.
It had been a hard trip. He was very tired. That was done. He had
made his camp. He was settled. Nothing could touch him. It was a
good place to camp. He was there, in the good place. He was in his
home where he had made it. Now he was hungry.

He came out, crawling under the cheesecloth. It was quite dark
outside. It was lighter in the tent.

Nick went over to the pack and found, with his fingers, a long nail
in a paper sack of nails, in the bottom of the pack. He drove it into
the pine tree, holding it close and hitting it gently with the flat of
the ax. He hung the pack up on the nail. All his supplies were in the
pack. They were off the ground and sheltered now.

Nick was hungry. He did not believe he had ever been hungrier.
He opened and emptied a can of pork and beans and a can of spaghetti into the frying pan.

"I've got a right to eat this kind of stuff, if I'm willing to carry it,"
Nick said. His voice sounded strange in the darkening woods. He did
not speak again.

He started a fire with some chunks of pine he got with the ax from
a stump. Over the fire he stuck a wire grill, pushing the four legs
down into the ground with his boot. Nick put the frying pan on the
grill over the flames. He was hungrier. The beans and spaghetti
warmed. Nick stirred them and mixed them together. They began to
bubble, making little bubbles that rose with difficulty to the surface.
There was a good smell. Nick got out a bottle of tomato catchup and
cut four slices of bread. The little bubbles were coming faster now.
Nick sat down beside the fire and lifted the frying pan off. He poured
about half the contents out into the tin plate. It spread slowly on the
plate. Nick knew it was too hot. He poured on some tomato catchup.
He knew the beans and spaghetti were still too hot. He looked at the
fire, then at the tent, he was not going to spoil it all by burning his

tongue. For years he had never enjoyed fried bananas because he had never been able to wait for them to cool. His tongue was very sensitive. He was very hungry. Across the river in the swamp, in the almost dark, he saw a mist rising. He looked at the tent once more. All right. He took a full spoonful from the plate.

"Chrise," Nick said. "Geezus Chrise," he said happily.

He ate the whole plateful before he remembered the bread. Nick finished the second plateful with the bread, mopping the plate shiny. He had not eaten since a cup of coffee and a ham sandwich in the station restaurant at St. Ignace. It had been a very fine experience. He had been that hungry before, but had not been able to satisfy it. He could have made camp hours before if he had wanted to. There were plenty of good places to camp on the river. But this was good.

Nick tucked two big chips of pine under the grill. The fire flared up. He had forgotten to get water for the coffee. Out of the pack he got a folding canvas bucket and walked down the hill, across the edge of the meadow, to the stream. The other bank was in the white mist. The grass was wet and cold as he knelt on the bank and dipped the canvas bucket into the stream. It bellied and pulled hard in the current. The water was ice-cold. Nick rinsed the bucket and carried it full up to the camp. Up away from the stream it was not so cold.

Nick drove another big nail and hung up the bucket full of water. He dipped the coffeepot half full, put some more chips under the grill onto the fire, and put the pot on. He could not remember which way he made coffee. He could remember an argument about it with Hopkins but not which side he had taken. He decided to bring it to a boil. He remembered now that was Hopkins' way. He had once argued about everything with Hopkins. While he waited for the coffee to boil, he opened a small can of apricots. He liked to open cans. He emptied the can of apricots out into a tin cup. While he watched the coffee on the fire, he drank the juice syrup of the apricots, carefully at first to keep from spilling, then meditatively sucking the apricots down. They were better than fresh apricots.

The coffee boiled as he watched. The lid came up and coffee and grounds ran down the side of the pot. Nick took it off the grill. It was a triumph for Hopkins. He put sugar in the empty apricot cup and poured some of the coffee out to cool. It was too hot to pour and he used his hat to hold the handle of the coffeepot. He would not let it steep in the pot at all. Not the first cup. It should be straight Hopkins all the way. Hop deserved that. He was a very serious coffee maker. He was the most serious man Nick had ever known. Not heavy, serious. That was a long time ago. Hopkins spoke without moving his lips. He had played polo. He made millions of dollars in Texas. He had borrowed carfare to go to Chicago, when the wire came that his first big well had come in. He could have wired for money. That would have been too slow. They called Hop's girl the Blond Venus. Hop did not mind, because she was not his real girl. Hopkins said very confidentially that none of them would make fun of his real girl. He was right. Hopkins went away when the telegram came. That was on the Black River. It took eight days for the telegram to reach him. Hopkins gave away his .22 Colt automatic pistol to Nick. He gave his camera to Bill. It was to remember him always by. They were all going fishing again next summer. The Hop Head was right. He would get a yacht and they would all cruise along the north shore of Lake Superior. He was excited but serious. They said goodbye and all felt bad. It broke up the trip. They never saw Hopkins again. That was a long time ago on the Black River.

Nick drank the coffee, the coffee according to Hopkins. The coffee was bitter. Nick laughed. It made a good ending to the story. His mind was starting to work. He knew he could choke it because he was tired enough. He spilled the coffee out of the pot and shook the grounds loose into the fire. He lit a cigarette and went inside the tent. He took off his shoes and trousers, sitting on the blankets, rolled the shoes up inside the trousers for a pillow and got in between the blankets.

Out through the front of the tent he watched the glow of the fire, when the night wind blew on it. It was a quiet night. The swamp was perfectly quiet. Nick stretched under the blanket comfortably. A mosquito hummed close to his ear. Nick sat up and lit a match. The mosquito was on the canvas, over his head. Nick moved the match quickly up to it. The mosquito made a satisfactory hiss in the flame. The match went out. Nick lay down again under the blankets. He turned on his side and shut his eyes. He was sleepy. He felt sleep coming. He curled up under the blankets and went to sleep.

In the morning the sun was up and the tent was starting to get hot. Nick crawled out under the mosquito netting stretched across the mouth of the tent to look at the morning. The grass was wet on his hands as he came out. He held his trousers and his shoes in his hands. The sun was just up over the hill. There was the meadow, the river, and the swamp. There were birch trees in the green of the swamp on the other side of the river.

The river was clear and smoothly fast in the early morning. Down about two hundred yards were three logs all the way across the stream. They made the water smooth and deep above them. As Nick watched, a mink crossed the river on the logs and went into the swamp. Nick was excited. He was excited by the early morning and the river. He was really too hurried to eat breakfast, but he knew he must. He built a little fire and put on the coffeepot. While the water was heating in the pot he took an empty bottle and went down over the edge of the high ground to the meadow. The meadow was wet with dew and Nick wanted to catch grasshoppers for bait before the sun dried the grass. He found plenty of good grasshoppers. They were at the base of the grass stems. Sometimes they clung to a grass stem. They were cold and wet with the dew and could not jump until the sun warmed them. Nick picked them up, taking only the medium-sized brown ones, and put them into the bottle. While he was picking up the hoppers the others warmed in the sun and commenced to hop away. They flew when they hopped. At first they made one flight and stayed stiff when they landed, as though they were dead.

Nick knew that by the time he was through with breakfast they would be as lively as ever. Without dew in the grass it would take him all day to catch a bottleful of good grasshoppers and he would have to crush many of them, slamming at them with his hat. He washed his hands at the stream. He was excited to be near it. Then he walked up to the tent. The hoppers were already jumping stiffly in the grass. In the bottle, warmed by the sun, they were jumping in a mass. Nick put in a pine stick as a cork. It plugged the mouth of the bottle enough so the hoppers could not get out and left plenty of air passage.

He had rolled the log back and knew he could get grasshoppers there every morning.

Nick laid the bottle full of jumping grasshoppers against a pine trunk. Rapidly he mixed some buckwheat flour with water and stirred it smooth, one cup of flour, one cup of water. He put a handful of coffee in the pot and dipped a lump of grease out of a can and slid it sputtering across the hot skillet. On the smoking skillet he poured smoothly the buckwheat batter. It spread like lava, the grease spitting sharply. Around the edges the buckwheat cake began to firm, then brown, then crisp. The surface was bubbling slowly to porousness. Nick pushed under the browned undersurface with a fresh pine chip. He shook the skillet sideways and the cake was loose on the surface. I won't try and flop it, he thought. He slid the chip of clean wood all the way under the cake, and flopped it over onto its face. It sputtered in the pan.

When it was cooked Nick regreased the skillet. He used all the batter. It made another big flapjack and a smaller one.

Nick ate a big flapjack and a smaller one, covered with apple butter. He put apple butter on the third cake, folded it over twice, wrapped it in oiled paper and put it in his shirt pocket. He put the apple butter jar back in the pack and cut bread for two sandwiches.

In the pack he found a big onion. He sliced it in two and peeled the silky outer skin. Then he cut one half into slices and made onion sandwiches. He wrapped them in oiled paper and buttoned them in the other pocket of his khaki shirt. He turned the skillet upside down on the grill, drank the coffee, sweetened and yellow-brown with the condensed milk in it, and tidied up the camp. It was a nice little camp.

Nick took his fly rod out of the leather rod case, jointed it, and shoved the rod case back into the tent. He put on the reel and threaded the line through the guides. He had to hold it from hand to hand, as he threaded it, or it would slip back through its own weight. It was a heavy, double tapered fly line. Nick had paid eight dollars for it a long time ago. It was made heavy to lift back in the air and come forward flat and heavy and straight to make it possible to cast a fly which has no weight. Nick opened the aluminum leader box. The leaders were coiled between the damp flannel pads. Nick had wet the pads at the water cooler on the train up to St. Ignace. In the damp pads the gut leaders had softened and Nick unrolled one and tied it by a loop at the end to the heavy fly line. He fastened a hook on the end of the leader. It was a small hook, very thin and springy.

Nick took it from his hook book, sitting with the rod across his lap. He tested the knot and the spring of the rod by pulling the line taut. It was a good feeling. He was careful not to let the hook bite into his finger.

He started down to the stream, holding his rod, the bottle of grasshoppers hung from his neck by a thong tied in half hitches around the neck of the bottle. His landing net hung by a hook from his belt. Over his shoulder was a long flour sack tied at each corner into an ear, The cord went over his shoulder. The sack flapped against his legs.

Nick felt awkward and professionally happy with all his equipment hanging from him. The grasshopper bottle swung against his chest. In his shirt the breast pockets bulged against him with the lunch and his fly book.

He stepped into the stream. It was a shock. His trousers clung tight to his legs. His shoes felt the gravel. The water was a rising, cold shock.

Rushing, the current sucked against his legs. Where he stepped in, the water was over his knees. He waded with the current. The gravel slid under his shoes. He looked down at the swirl of water below each leg and tipped up the bottle to get a grasshopper.

The first grasshopper gave a jump in the neck of the bottle and went out into the water. He was sucked under in the whirl by Nick's right leg and came to the surface a little way down stream. He floated rapidly, kicking. In a quick circle, breaking the smooth surface of the water, he disappeared. A trout had taken him.

Another hopper poked his head out of the bottle. His antennae wavered. He was getting his front legs out of the bottle to jump. Nick took him by the head and held him while he threaded the slim hook under his chin, down through his thorax and into the last segments of his abdomen. The grasshopper took hold of the hook with his front feet, spitting tobacco juice on it. Nick dropped him into the water.

Holding the rod in his right hand he let out line against the pull of the grasshopper in the current. He stripped off line from the reel with his left hand and let it run free. He could see the hopper in the little waves of the current. It went out of sight.

There was a tug on the line. Nick pulled against the taut line. It was his first strike. Holding the now living rod across the current, he brought in the line with his left hand. The rod bent in jerks, the trout pumping against the current. Nick knew it was a small one. He lifted the rod straight up in the air. It bowed with the pull.

He saw the trout in the water jerking with his head and body against the shifting tangent of the line in the stream.

Nick took the line in his left hand and pulled the trout, thumping tiredly against the current, to the surface. His back was mottled the clear, water-over-gravel color, his side flashing in the sun. The rod under his right arm, Nick stooped, dipping his right hand into the current. He held the trout, never still, with his moist right hand, while he unhooked the barb from the mouth, then dropped him back into the stream.

He hung unsteadily in the current, then settled to the bottom beside a stone. Nick reached down his hand to touch him, his arm to the elbow under water. The trout was steady in the moving stream, resting on the gravel, beside a stone. As Nick's fingers touched him, touched his smooth, cool, underwater feeling, he was gone, gone in a shadow across the bottom of the stream.

He's all right, Nick thought. He was only tired.

He had wet his hand before he touched the trout, so he would not disturb the delicate mucus that covered him. If a trout was touched with a dry hand, a white fungus attacked the unprotected spot. Years before when he had fished crowded streams, with fly fishermen ahead of him and behind him, Nick had again and again come on dead trout, furry with white fungus, drifted against a rock, or floating belly up in some pool. Nick did not like to fish with other men on the river. Unless they were of your party, they spoiled it.

He wallowed down the stream, above the knees in the current, through the fifty yards of shallow water above the pile of logs that crossed the stream. He did not rebait his hook and held it in his hand as he waded. He was certain he could catch small trout in the shallows, but he did not want them. There would be no big trout in the shallows this time of day.

Now the water deepened up his thighs sharply and coldly. Ahead was the smooth dammed-back flood of water above the logs. The water was smooth and dark; on the left, the lower edge of the meadow; on the right the swamp.

Nick leaned back against the current and took a hopper from the bottle. He threaded the hopper on the hook and spat on him for good luck. Then he pulled several yards of line from the reel and tossed the hopper out ahead onto the fast, dark water. It floated down toward the logs, then the weight of the line pulled the bait under the surface. Nick held the rod in his right hand, letting the line run out through his fingers.

There was a long tug. Nick struck and the rod came alive and dangerous, bent double, the line tightening, coming out of water, tightening, all in a heavy, dangerous, steady pull. Nick felt the moment when the leader would break if the strain increased and let the line go.

The reel ratcheted into a mechanical shriek as the line went out in a rush. Too fast. Nick could not check it, the line rushing out, the reel note rising as the line ran out.

With the core of the reel showing, his heart feeling stopped with the excitement, leaning back against the current that mounted icily his thighs, Nick thumbed the reel hard with his left hand. It was awkward getting his thumb inside the reel frame.

As he put on pressure, the line tightened into sudden hardness and beyond the logs a huge trout went high out of water. As he jumped, Nick lowered the tip of the rod. But he felt, as he dropped the tip to ease the strain, the moment when the strain was too great, the hardness too tight. Of course, the leader had broken. There was no mistaking the feeling when all spring left the line and it became dry and hard. Then it went slack.

His mouth dry, his heart down, Nick reeled in. He had never seen so big a trout. There was a heaviness, a power not to be held, and then the bulk of him, as he jumped. He looked as broad as a salmon.

Nick's hand was shaky. He reeled in slowly. The thrill had been too much. He felt, vaguely, a little sick, as though it would be better to sit down.

The leader had broken where the hook was tied to it. Nick took it in his hand. He thought of the trout somewhere on the bottom, holding himself steady over the gravel, far down below the light, under the logs with the hook in his jaw. Nick knew the trout's teeth would cut through the snell of the hook. The hook would embed itself in his jaw. He'd bet the trout was angry. Anything that size would be angry. That was a trout. He had been solidly hooked. Solid as a rock. He felt like a rock, too, before he started off. By God, he was a big one. By God, he was the biggest one I ever heard of.

Nick climbed out onto the meadow and stood, water running down his trousers and out of his shoes, his shoes squelchy. He went over and sat on the logs. He did not want to rush his sensations any.

He wriggled his toes in the water, in his shoes, and got out a cigarette from his breast pocket. He lit it and tossed the match into the fast water below the logs. A tiny trout rose at the match as it swung around in the fast current. Nick laughed. He would finish the cigarette.

He sat on the logs, smoking, drying in the sun, the sun warm on his back, the river shallow ahead entering the woods, curving into the woods, shallows, light glittering, big water-smooth rocks, cedars along the bank and white birches, the logs warm in the sun, smooth to sit on, without bark, gray to the touch; slowly the feeling of disappointment left him. It went away slowly, the feeling of disappointment that came sharply after the thrill that made his shoulders ache. It was all right now. His rod lying out on the logs, Nick tied a new hook on the leader, pulling the gut tight until it grimped into itself in a hard knot.

He baited up, then picked up the rod and walked to the far end of the logs to get into the water, where it was not too deep. Under and beyond the logs was a deep pool. Nick walked around the shallow shelf near the swamp shore until he came out on the shallow bed of the stream.

On the left, where the meadow ended and the woods began, a great elm tree was uprooted. Gone over in a storm, it lay back into the woods, its roots clotted with dirt, grass growing in them, rising a solid bank beside the stream. The river cut to the edge of the uprooted tree. From where Nick stood he could see deep channels, like ruts, cut in the shallow bed of the stream by the flow of the current. Pebbly where he stood and pebbly and full of boulders beyond; where it curved near the tree roots, the bed of the stream was marly, and between the ruts of deep water green weed fronds swung in the current.

Nick swung the rod back over his shoulder and forward, and the line, curving forward, laid the grasshopper down on one of the deep channels in the weeds. A trout struck and Nick hooked him.

Holding the rod far out toward the uprooted tree and sloshing backward in the current, Nick worked the trout, plunging, the rod bending alive, out of the danger of the weeds into the open river. Holding the rod, pumping alive against the current, Nick brought the trout in. He rushed, but always came, the spring of the rod yielding to the rushes, sometimes jerking under water, but always bringing him in. Nick eased downstream with the rushes. The rod above his head, he led the trout over the net, then lifted.

The trout hung heavy in the net, mottled trout back and silver sides in the meshes. Nick unhooked him—heavy sides, good to hold, big undershot jaw—and slipped him, heaving and big sliding, into the long sack that hung from his shoulders in the water.

Nick spread the mouth of the sack against the current and it filled, heavy with water. He held it up, the bottom in the stream, and the water poured out through the sides. Inside at the bottom was the big trout, alive in the water.

Nick moved downstream. The sack out ahead of him sank, heavy in the water, pulling from his shoulders.

It was getting hot, the sun hot on the back of his neck.

Nick had one good trout. He did not care about getting many trout. Now the stream was shallow and wide. There were trees along both banks. The trees of the left bank made short shadows on the current in the forenoon sun. Nick knew there were trout in each shadow. In the afternoon, after the sun had crossed toward the hills, the trout would be in the cool shadows on the other side of the stream.

The very biggest ones would lie up close to the bank. You could always pick them up there on the Black. When the sun was down they all moved out into the current. Just when the sun made the water blinding in the glare before it went down, you were likely to strike a big trout anywhere in the current. It was almost impossible to fish then, the surface of the water was blinding as a mirror in the sun. Of course you could fish upstream, but in a stream like the Black, or this, you had to wallow against the current and, in a deep place, the water piled up on you. It was no fun to fish upstream with this much current.

Nick moved along through the shallow stretch watching the banks for deep holes. A beech tree grew close beside the river, so that the branches hung down into the water. The stream went back in under the leaves. There were always trout in a place like that.

Nick did not care about fishing that hole. He was sure he would get hooked in the branches.

It looked deep, though. He dropped the grasshopper so the current took it under water, back in under the overhanging branch. The line pulled hard and Nick struck. The trout thrashed heavily, half out of water in the leaves and branches. The line was caught. Nick pulled hard and the trout was off. He reeled in and, holding the hook in his hand, walked down the stream.

Ahead, close to the left bank, was a big log. Nick saw it was hollow, pointing upriver; the current entered it smoothly, only a little ripple spread each side of the log. The water was deepening. The top of the hollow log was gray and dry. It was partly in the shadow.

Nick took the cork out of the grasshopper bottle and a hopper clung to it. He picked him off, hooked him, and tossed him out. He held the rod far out so that the hopper on the water moved into the current flowing into the hollow log. Nick lowered the rod and the hopper floated in. There was a heavy strike. Nick swung the rod against the pull. It felt as though he were hooked into the log itself, except for the live feeling.

He tried to force the fish out into the current. It came, heavily.

The line went slack and Nick thought the trout was gone. Then he saw him, very near, in the current, shaking his head, trying to get the hook out. His mouth was clamped shut. He was fighting the hook in the clear flowing current.

Looping in the line with his left hand, Nick swung the rod to make the line taut and tried to lead the trout toward the net, but he was gone, out of sight, the line pumping. Nick fought him against the current, letting him thump in the water against the spring of the rod. He shifted the rod to his left hand, worked the trout upstream, holding his weight, fighting on the rod, and then let him down into the net. He lifted him clear of the water, a heavy half circle in the net, the net dripping, unhooked him, and slid him into the sack.

He spread the mouth of the sack and looked down in at the two big trout alive in the water.

Through the deepening water, Nick waded over to the hollow log. He took the sack off, over his head, the trout flopping as it came out of water, and hung it so the trout were deep in the water. Then he pulled himself up on the log and sat, the water from his trousers and boots running down into the stream. He laid his rod down, moved along to the shady end of the log, and took the sandwiches out of his pocket. He dipped the sandwiches in the cold water. The current carried away the crumbs. He ate the sandwiches and dipped his hat full of water to drink, the water running out through his hat just ahead of his drinking.

It was cool in the shade, sitting on the log. He took a cigarette out and struck a match to light it. The match sank into the gray wood, making a tiny furrow. Nick leaned over the side of the log, found a hard place, and lit the match. He sat smoking and watching the river.

Ahead the river narrowed and went into a swamp. The river became smooth and deep and the swamp looked solid with cedar trees, their trunks close together, their branches solid. It would not be possible to walk through a swamp like that. The branches grew so low. You would have to keep almost level with the ground to move at all.

You could not crash through the branches. That must be why the animals that lived in swamps were built the way they were, Nick thought.

He wished he had brought something to read. He felt like reading. He did not feel like going on into the swamp. He looked down the river. A big cedar slanted all the way across the stream. Beyond that the river went into the swamp.

Nick did not want to go in there now. He felt a reaction against deep wading with the water deepening up under his armpits, to hook big trout in places impossible to land them. In the swamp the banks were bare, the big cedars came together overhead, the sun did not come through, except in patches; in the fast deep water, in the half-light, the fishing would be tragic. In the swamp fishing was a tragic adventure. Nick did not want it. He did not want to go down the stream any further today.

He took out his knife, opened it, and stuck it in the log. Then he pulled up the sack, reached into it, and brought out one of the trout. Holding him near the tail, hard to hold, alive, in his hand, he whacked him against the log. The trout quivered, rigid. Nick laid him on the log in the shade and broke the neck of the other fish the same way. He laid them side by side on the log. They were fine trout.

Nick cleaned them, slitting them from the vent to the tip of the jaw. All the insides and the gills came out in one piece. They were both males; long gray-white strips of milt, smooth and clean. All the insides clean and compact, coming out all together. Nick tossed the offal ashore for the minks to find.

He washed the trout in the stream. When he held them back up in the water they looked like live fish. Their color was not gone yet. He washed his hands and dried them on the log. Then he laid the trout on the sack spread out on the log, rolled them up in it, tied the bundle and put it in the landing net. His knife was still standing, blade stuck in the log. He cleaned it on the wood and put it in his pocket.

Nick stood up on the log, holding his rod, the landing net hanging heavy, then stepped into the water and splashed ashore. He climbed the bank and cut up into the woods, toward the high ground. He was going back to camp. He looked back. The river just showed through the trees. There were plenty of days coming when he could fish the swamp.

Storytelling on
the Thames

JEROME K. JEROME

Jerome K. Jerome wrote Three Men in a Boat, *and many insist he should have stopped right there, since he never could have done better. This angling chapter from his delightful book is ample justification for many of his less absorbing writings.*

THE NEIGHBORHOOD of Streatley and Goring is a great fishing center. There is some excellent fishing to be had here. The river abounds in pike, roach, dace, gudgeon, and eels, just here; and you can sit and fish for them all day.

249

Some people do. They never catch them. I never knew anybody catch anything, up the Thames, except minnows and dead cats, but that has nothing to do, of course, with fishing! The local fisherman's guide doesn't say a word about catching anything. All it says is the place is "a good station for fishing"; and, from what I have seen of the district, I am quite prepared to bear out this statement.

There is no spot in the world where you can get more fishing, or where you can fish for a longer period. Some fishermen come here and fish for a day, and others stop and fish for a month. You can hang on and fish for a year, if you want to: it will be all the same.

The *Angler's Guide to the Thames* says that "jack and perch are also to be had about here," but there the *Angler's Guide* is wrong. Jack and perch may be about there. Indeed, I know for a fact that they are. You can *see* them there in shoals, when you are out for a walk along the banks: they come and stand half out of the water with their mouths open for biscuits. And, if you go for a bathe, they crowd round, and get in your way, and irritate you. But they are not to be "had" by a bit of worm on the end of a hook, nor anything like it—not they!

I am not a good fisherman myself. I devoted a considerable amount of attention to the subject at one time, and was getting on, as I thought, fairly well; but the old hands told me that I should never be any real good at it, and advised me to give it up. They said that I was an extremely neat thrower, and that I seemed to have plenty of gumption for the thing, and quite enough constitutional laziness. But they were sure I should never make anything of a fisherman. I had not got sufficient imagination.

They said that as a poet, or a shilling shocker, or a reporter, or anything of that kind, I might be satisfactory, but that, to gain any position as a Thames angler, would require more play of fancy, more power of invention than I appeared to possess.

Some people are under the impression that all that is required to make a good fisherman is the ability to tell lies easily and without blushing; but this is a mistake. Mere bald fabrication is useless; the veriest tyro can manage that. It is in the circumstantial detail, the embellishing touches of probability, the general air of scrupulous—almost of pedantic—veracity, that the experienced angler is seen.

Anybody can come in and say, "Oh, I caught fifteen dozen perch yesterday evening," or "Last Monday I landed a gudgeon, weighing eighteen pounds, and measuring three feet from the tip to the tail."

There is no art, no skill, required for that sort of thing. It shows pluck, but that is all.

No; your accomplished angler would scorn to tell a lie, that way. His method is a study in itself.

He comes in quietly with his hat on, appropriates the most comfortable chair, lights his pipe, and commences to puff in silence. He lets the youngsters brag away for a while, and then, during a momentary lull, he removes the pipe from his mouth, and remarks, as he knocks the ashes out against the bars:

"Well, I had a haul on Tuesday evening that it's not much good my telling anybody about."

"Oh! why's that?" they ask.

"Because I don't expect anybody would believe me if I did," replies the old fellow calmly, and without even a tinge of bitterness in his tone, as he refills his pipe, and requests the landlord to bring him three of Scotch—cold.

There is a pause after this, nobody feeling sufficiently sure of himself to contradict the old gentleman. So he has to go on by himself without any encouragement.

"No," he continues thoughtfully; "I shouldn't believe it myself if anybody told it to me, but it's a fact, for all that. I had been sitting there all the afternoon and had caught literally nothing—except a few dozen dace and a score of jack; and I was just about giving it up as a bad job when I suddenly felt a rather smart pull at the line. I thought it was another little one, and I went to jerk it up. Hang me, if I could move the rod! It took me half an hour—half an hour, sir!—to land that fish; and every moment I thought the line was going to snap! I reached him at last, and what do you think it was? A sturgeon! A forty-pound sturgeon! Taken on a line, sir! Yes, you may well look surprised—I'll have another three of Scotch, landlord, please."

And then he goes on to tell of the astonishment of everybody who saw it; and what his wife said, when he got home, and of what Joe Buggles thought about it.

I asked the landlord of an inn up the river once, if it did not injure him, sometimes, listening to the tales that the fishermen about there told him; and he said:

"Oh, no; not now, sir. It did used to knock me over a bit at first, but, lor love you! me and the missus we listens to 'em all day now. It's what you're used to, you know. It's what you're used to."

I knew a young man once, he was a most conscientious fellow, and, when he took to fly fishing, he determined never to exaggerate his hauls by more than twenty-five per cent.

"When I have caught forty fish," said he, "then I will tell people that I have caught fifty, and so on. But I will not lie any more than that, because it is sinful to lie."

But the twenty-five per cent plan did not work well at all. He never was able to use it. The greatest number of fish he ever caught in one day was three, and you can't add twenty-five per cent to three—at least, not in fish.

So he increased his percentage to thirty-three and a third; but that, again, was awkward, when he had caught only one or two; so, to simplify matters, he made up his mind to just double the quantity.

He stuck to this arrangement for a couple of months, and then he grew dissatisfied with it. Nobody believed him when he told them that he only doubled, and he, therefore, gained no credit that way whatever, while his moderation put him at a disadvantage among the other anglers. When he had really caught three small fish, and said he had six, it used to make him quite jealous to hear a man, who he knew for a fact had caught only one, going about telling people he had landed two dozen.

So, eventually, he made one final arrangement with himself, which he has religiously held to ever since, and that was to count each fish that he caught as ten, and to assume ten to begin with. For example, if he did not catch any fish at all, then he said he had caught ten fish— you could never catch less than ten fish by his system; that was the foundation of it. Then, if by any chance he really did catch one fish, he called it twenty, while two fish would count thirty, three forty, and so on.

It is a simple and easily worked plan, and there has been some talk lately of its being made use of by the angling fraternity in general. Indeed, the Committee of the Thames Anglers' Association did recommend its adoption about two years ago, but some of the older members opposed it. They said they would consider the idea if the number were doubled, and each fish counted as twenty.

If ever you have an evening to spare, up the river, I should advise you to drop into one of the little village inns, and take a seat in the taproom. You will be nearly sure to meet one or two old rodmen, sipping their toddy there, and they will tell you enough fishy stories, in half an hour, to give you indigestion for a month.

George and I—I don't know what had become of Harris; he had gone out and had a shave, early in the afternoon, and had then come back and spent full forty minutes in pipe-claying his shoes, we had not seen him since—George and I, therefore, and the dog, left to ourselves, went for a walk to Wallingford on the second evening, and, coming home, we called in at a little riverside inn, for a rest and other things.

We went into the parlor and sat down. There was an old fellow there, smoking a long clay pipe, and we naturally began chatting.

He told us that it had been a fine day today, and we told him that it had been a fine day yesterday, and then we all told each other that we thought it would be a fine day tomorrow; and George said the crops seemed to be coming up nicely.

After that it came out, somehow or other, that we were strangers in the neighborhood, and that we were going away the next morning.

Then a pause ensued in the conversation, during which our eyes wandered round the room. They finally rested upon a dusty old glass case, fixed very high up above the chimney piece, and containing a trout. It rather fascinated me, that trout; it was such a monstrous fish. In fact, at first glance, I thought it was a cod.

"Ah!" said the old gentleman, following the direction of my gaze, "fine fellow that, ain't he?"

"Quite uncommon," I murmured; and George asked the old man how much he thought it weighed.

"Eighteen pounds six ounces," said our friend, rising and taking down his coat. "Yes," he continued, "it wur sixteen year ago, come the third o' next month, that I landed him. I caught him just below the bridge with a minnow. They told me he wur in the river, and I said I'd have him, and so I did. You don't see many fish that size about here now, I'm thinking. Good night, gentlemen, good night."

And out he went, and left us alone.

We could not take our eyes off the fish after that. It really was a remarkably fine fish. We were still looking at it, when the local carrier, who had just stopped at the inn, came to the door of the room with a pot of beer in his hand, and he also looked at the fish.

"Good-sized trout, that," said George, turning round to him.

"Ah! you may well say that, sir," replied the man; and then, after a pull at his beer, he added, "Maybe you wasn't here, sir, when that fish was caught?"

"No," we told him. We were strangers in the neighborhood.

"Ah!" said the carrier, "then, of course, how should you? It was nearly five years ago that I caught that trout."

"Oh! was it you who caught it, then?" said I.

"Yes, sir," replied the genial old fellow. "I caught him just below the lock—leastways, what was the lock then—one Friday afternoon; and the remarkable thing about it is that I caught him with a fly. I'd gone out pike fishing, bless you, never thinking of a trout, and when I saw that whopper on the end of my line, blest if it didn't quite take me aback. Well, you see, he weighed twenty-six pound. Good night, gentlemen, good night."

Five minutes afterward, a third man came in, and described how *he* had caught it early one morning, with bleak; and then he left, and a stolid, solemn-looking, middle-aged individual came in, and sat down over by the window.

None of us spoke for a while; but at length, George turned to the newcomer and said:

"I big your pardon, I hope you will forgive the liberty that we—perfect strangers in the neighborhood—are taking, but my friend here and myself would be much obliged if you would tell us how you caught that trout."

"Why, who told you I caught that trout!" was the surprised query.

We said that nobody had told us so, but somehow or other we felt instinctively that it was he who had done it.

"Well, it's a most remarkable thing—most remarkable," answered the stolid stranger, laughing: "because, as a matter of fact, you are quite right. I did catch it. But fancy your guessing it like that. Dear me, it's really a most remarkable thing."

And then he went on, and told us how it had taken him half an hour to land it, and how it had broken his rod. He said he had weighed it carefully when he reached home, and it had turned the scale at thirty-four pounds.

He went in his turn, and when he was gone, the landlord came in to us. We told him the various histories we had heard about his trout, and he was immensely amused, and we all laughed very heartily.

"Fancy Jim Bates and Joe Muggles and Mr. Jones and old Billy Maunders all telling you that they had caught it. Ha! ha! ha! Well, that is good," said the honest old fellow, laughing heartily. "Yes, they are the sort to give it *me*, to put up in *my* parlor, if *they* had caught it, they are! Ha! ha! ha!"

And then he told us the real history of the fish. It seemed that he had caught it himself, years ago, when he was quite a lad; not by any art or skill, but by that unaccountable luck that appears to always wait upon a boy when he plays the wag from school, and goes 'way out fishing on a sunny afternoon, with a bit of string tied onto the end of a tree.

He said that bringing home that trout had saved him from a whacking, and that even his schoolmaster had said it was worth the rule of three and practice put together.

He was called out of the room at this point, and George and I again turned our gaze upon the fish.

It really was a most astonishing trout. The more we looked at it, the more we marveled at it.

It excited George so much that he climbed up on the back of a chair to get a better view of it.

And then the chair slipped, and George clutched wildly at the trout case to save himself, and down it came with a crash, George and the chair on top of it.

"You haven't injured the fish, have you?" I cried in alarm, rushing up.

"I hope not," said George, rising cautiously and looking about.

But he had. That trout lay shattered into a thousand fragments—I say a thousand, but they may have been only nine hundred. I did not count them.

We thought it strange and unaccountable that a stuffed trout should break up into little pieces like that.

And so it would have been strange and unaccountable, if it had been a stuffed trout, but it was not.

That trout was plaster of Paris.

Bass Are Bass

ARTHUR R. MacDOUGAL, JR.

Few angling readers of today are unacquainted with Dud Dean and with Arthur R. MacDougal, Jr., his creator. "Bass Are Bass" is written in his normal vein, but it's a different type of story.

H OW ABOUT some bass fishing?" I asked Dud, one suggestive morning in June.

Dud Dean simply shook his head.

"Why not?"

"Jist ain't interested. Never see a bass, as I rec'lect."

"But it is said, that pound for pound—"

"Aya, I've heard that one, an' it don't sound reasonable to me. Thar ain't no pound of nothin' that can put up a bigger an' better show'n a white-water salmon."

"Get your rod," I challenged, "and I'll show you that the black bass need not dip his colors to anything that swims."

But Dud simply leaned back against one of the shade trees along our main street, and began to fill his antique pipe.

"Look here," he said, squinting at the sky. "I can see that ye're itchin' to go fishin', Mak, an' I know where thar's some prime salmon jist waitin' to grab a Jock Scott. I mean *salmon*, mind yer!"

256

I countered with, "A fellow just told me about a pond where we can catch black bass—bass that will outstage any of your salmon." You see, I wanted to inveigle Dud. A day's bass fishing with the old veteran promised so much.

Dud stared at me. For a moment his sense of humor was paralyzed. I had blasphemed against his prince of fresh-water fishes.

"By crotch, Mak, yer can't mean that! What's chewin' in your head?" Then, recovering from his shock, he added with a grin, "Mak, I'm 'shamed of yer."

"But," I persisted, "you wouldn't deny a fact, would you? I am offering to prove that pound for pound—"

"Crotch, Mak, a fish ain't a fact. It's a fish. A whole lot of foolishness c'ud be avoided in this world, if folks w'ud keep their facts an' fish separated."

Well, it looked as though I were trying to drive my logs against a head wind, as Dud would have put it. "Hang it all, Dud," I said, "I want to take you bass fishing. Try it once!"

"How many miles is it to this bass pond of yours?"

"It's over in the back part of Solon—say, ten miles."

"As near as that? Fust thing we know, somebudy'll be plantin' them warm-water fish up here. An' I've been given to understand that they're sunthin' desperate on trout. Which puts me in mind of what Hen Barnaby told the jedge when he fined Hen for contempt of court. Says Hen, 'Mister, thar ought to be a law ag'inst sich a blarsted outrage.'

" 'That'll cost yer five dollars more,' says the jedge, 'an' every time yer open your head ag'in, it'll cost yer five more'n that.'

" 'Kin I ask jist one question?' says Hen.

" 'It is irregular,' says the jedge, 'but I'll permit it.'

" 'What I want to know is,' says Hen, 'are you God Almighty, er jist a plain two-legged critter like me, only a darn-sight meaner?' What I was thinkin' of was that thar ought to be a law ag'inst puttin' them bass—"

"But what do you say?" I broke in. "Will you give the bass a tryout?"

"Wel-el, ter tell the truth, I d'know but that I'd try most anythin' right now, becuz Nancy's gittin' worked up fer another house cleanin'. It's in the air. She's sniffin' out the corners, an' squintin' erbout fer imaginary cobwebs. D'know but I'd go cusk fishin' to escape that, although cusk fishin' is so low-down that it's ag'in the law in Hell Huddle, an' sh'ud be everywheres."

And so it came about. When Dud showed up, he was carrying his best rod. That was significant. But he persisted in maintaining his skepticism of bass.

"Yer know, Mak, I feel ornery," he said, "I feel as low-down as I did the day I skipped school, years ago, an' found out in the afternoon that it was a holiday anyway. Here we be, you an' me, goin' bass fishin'. The mighty has fallen flat, as Doc Brownin' useter say."

I passed that off with a grin. I could afford it. I had accomplished my objective that day. Once on the road, an expression of deep contentment settled over Dud's fine face. And as we rolled along the road, I fell to thinking about the many trips I had enjoyed in the company of this mellow, home-town philosopher. I have spent many days afield in such good company.

A chuckle interrupted my reveries. "I was jist thinkin'," Dud explained, "erbout the fust automobile Nancy an' me bought. Prob'ly yer ain't noticed it, but Nancy has got opinions of her own. One of 'em is that a woman can do anythin' a man ever done, an' do it better. So when automobiles came erlong in this country, it galled her awful to hear folks talk as if no woman c'ud ever learn to drive one. An' she got it inter her head that we'd got to have one. At fust, when she brought up the subject, I argued that I c'ud never learn to drive one of them things. But that jist made Nancy look scornful.

"Wel-el, bad news blows wherever it listeth. An' one day a feller come to our house, all dressed up like it was Sunday. He was sellin' automobiles, of course. The one he had was all trimmed up 'ith brass an' doodads. The bulb on the horn was 'most as big as a football. Nancy was taken 'ith the looks of the whole rig. She took lessons on it, till finally that slicker told her that she c'ud drive it as good as any man that ever come down the pike. That clinched the deal. I fergit what the whole thing cost, but we bought it.

"A few days after that, Nancy an' me started out. We got erlong slick as a beaver, at first, but everythin' we met had a devil of a time. For instance, we met old Ben Hall comin' erlong, leadin' a black-an'-white cow. I was scared, becuz it looked like Ben an' the cow warn't never goin' to turn out.

" 'Blow that horn,' I says. 'That's what a horn is fer.'

"Nancy musta been a little scared herself, becuz she did jist what I told her to do. I never saw a cow as quick as that one. She jerked Ben right off his feet, an' the goldarn idgit hung to the rope. The last I see of them, Ben was wrapped 'round an apple tree, but the cow was jist goin' over a fence in the next field.

"Nancy never said a word, an' we kept right on, like nothin' had happened. Bineby, I see that we was comin' to a bad turn in the road ahead. An' we was goin' so fast the tears was runnin' out of my eyes. Crotch, we must have been goin' twenty miles an hour!

" 'Here comes a turn,' I sings out. 'Look out fer that bad turn in the road! Slow down. D'yer hear?'

"If she slowed down a mite, I c'udn't see it. But I guess that she w'ud have made that corner, if she had changed the wheel after we got 'round it. But she didn't.

"Thar was a nice little white house on that turn. An' it had a white picket fence eround the front yard. We went through that fence like it was built of matchsticks. Thinks I, 'A fence like that is no protection at all.' An' the next second we hit the house sunthin' wicked. But it never budged a bit.

"It was a Sunday afternoon, an' the old couple that lived thar came runnin' out, 'ith their arms up in the air, like they was willin' ter surrender 'ithout an argument. But when the old feller see that it was us that had hit his house, instead of sunthin' supernatural, he begin to swear. He was a pitchur, 'ith his long hair awavin' in the breeze. An' his flow of language beat anythin' I ever heard, except Doc Brownin's. Thar was a while when I thought that the old codger had an edge on Doc, but he got to repeatin' hisself, 'long at the last. I guess he had the talent, but lacked Doc's eddication.

"Nancy's hat was down over her eyes, but she give it a poke, and when she see where we was, she acted like somebudy had played a dirty trick on her. 'Dudley,' she says, 'git down an' crank this machine.'

"So I climbed down, an' cranked. An' that automobile started like it had never stopped. I got in ag'in an' Nancy got all set ter back out. She tramped 'round on them pedals, like an organist gittin' ready ter play 'The Lost Chord.' An' we backed out of that yard as neat as a crab c'ud. Then we got stalled ag'in, afore Nancy had got straightened away. So I got down, an' cranked some more.

"By that time, a crowd had gathered from nowhere. Thar was a lot of loud talkin'—most of it from the old feller, who hadn't run down none. I s'pose it all made Nancy nervous. Anyhow, she stepped on a pedal, intendin' ter back up a little more. An' by crotch if we didn't shoot back inter the yard ag'in. An' if we was goin' twenty miles an hour, when we hit that house the fust trip, we was doin' thirty when we struck it the second time.

"The old lady of the house had been down on her knees, sort of moanin' over a bed of red geraniums we had run over on our first trip in. She never had no time to straighten up, but jist crawled out of our way by the skin of her teeth.

" 'Thar, by gad!' yells the old man at her. 'Yer git inter the house, er they'll kill yer!'

"But I can't say that even the house seemed like a real safe place ter me, by that time. I warn't jist calm after we'd fetched up, an' I says ter Nancy, 'If ye're goin' to do that ag'in, I'm goin' to git out an' walk home.' Soon's I said it, I was sorry, becuz I see that Nancy was 'bout ready to bawl.

"Jist then, a young feller stepped up an' says, 'Havin' some trouble, er jist tryin' her out?'

"By crotch, that was jist erbout the last straw, as Dan Nye said, tellin' how bad his hay fever had been, an' I was jist agoin' to git out ter show that young squirt sunthin', when he added that he was an automobile mechanic, which was what we needed, as sure as a ship ever needed a sailor. Wel-el, he offered to back us out an' git us squared off fer home. Which he did. Then he offered to drive us home, but Nancy 'lowed that she was perfectly capable from thar on, thank yer. After we'd gone a few rods, I begin to git back a little confidence. An' by crotch if we didn't sail erlong nice, until we got to our house. Seemed like stoppin' was one of Nancy's troubles. So we rode inside the barn, 'ithout openin' the doors. An' the blarsted thing never stopped, until we fetched up ag'in a post."

We were going down Gilman Hill when Dud finished his story. One gets a partial view of Iron Bound Pond from that elevation.

Dud, who apparently had not noticed the road while he had been recalling his first automobile trip, sat up straight. "Why didn't yer say we was comin' over to this pond?" he demanded. "I've been told that thar's some good salmon in this water."

"Bass, too," I added.

We left our car at the foot of the hill, and then walked down to a black, weather-beaten house, where, I had been informed, we might hire a boat. The negotiation was simple. And at the landing we picked the most attractive craft. Dud took the stern seat, asking, with an oar poised paddlewise, "Where?"

I explained that I had been instructed to fish the lower end of the lake; that the bass were supposed to favor that section.

"They w'ud," grunted Dud.

But in spite of his show of indifference, I noticed that Dud toyed with his nice rod, as he put it together.

"A split bamboo," said my old friend, "is a great contraption. The other day I was readin' a list of great inventions. The feller that made it up claimed that each invention he listed had turned some tide of hist'ry, but the goldurn chump never mentioned the split bamboo."

I passed my fly book to Dud. "Here are some bass flies," I said, "which are also great inventions."

Dud looked at the bass flies dubiously. "They look like I expected," he said. "An' they ain't fit to put on the end of a light leader, let alone usin' on a good rod. Guess, if you don't mind, that I'll stick to my own. I'll jist fool 'round 'ith a Jock Scott. Maybe thar's some *real* fish somewheres erbout this pond."

I selected a bass fly with a silk body, bound with silver, and wearing regulation wings and hackles. Dud watched me, out of the corner of his eye, but continued his own beautiful casting without further comment.

The next two hours seemed to confirm my opinion that our coldwater bass would not take a fly, although I had been assured that they would. We moved about, but hung to the lower end of the lake. Finally Dud remarked, with evident disappointment, that the salmon must be few and far between in Iron Bound Pond.

"Maybe I had better try one of them frog-ketchin' rigs of yourn, Mak. I jist see a fish feedin' over by that bunch of grass, but most likely it's nothin' but a pickerel."

Again I offered my fly book.

"These ain't flies," Dud muttered, "but here goes, as Clum McGlouster said, time he fell off the barn roof. Is this here thing s'posed to float, er sink?"

I turned to inspect the fly he had picked out. It was one that a friend had tied, and he had used the tip of a red squirrel's tail, with a bit of hackle from a white Leghorn rooster. All in all, I felt compelled to admit it the most unlikely fly in the book.

Without waiting for a reply to his question, Dud cast. "It's floatin' purty good," he commented.

"Let her float," I said.

Dud twitched the fly lightly. Something swirled up from the deep water. Spray broke, as though a miniature depth bomb had gone off, and a nice little bass smashed Dud's fly on the rise. For a moment the fish stood out against the afternoon light, vibrating from gills to tail. Then it hit the water, tossing the hook from its mouth.

An odd look of surprise appeared on Dud's lean face. "The lowdown tud," he muttered in an undertone.

Then he addressed me. "Turned that trick purty slick, didn't he? Guess I'll have another try at him, like Doc Brownin' said, time a three-year-old colt kicked him flat."

Dud dropped his next cast upon a small stool of grass. At a hint from his rod, the fly dropped into the water. Nothing happened, although the thing had been perfectly done, and Dud said with a ludicrous trace of anxiety in his voice, "Yer don't s'pose I gummed up the works, do yer?"

And at that moment I connected with a two-pound bass—not a big bass, but a bass. As Dud said, later, "A hooked salmon kinda scoots up inter the air, like it knew jist how it oughter be done, but a bass jist rears up an' lets her go, like it didn't care a dang how it's done."

When Dud had netted my fish, he examined it with interest. "By crotch," he muttered, but volunteered no more. I looked off to the east, grinned, and winked at nothing in particular. And then we continued our casting. Presently I hooked another bass, but fumbled it. And soon Dud took a bass that would weigh a pound and a half. As I netted it, I looked to Dud, supposing of course that he would direct me to turn it loose.

"Dang it, Mak, I know what ye're thinkin', it ain't big but I aim to keep that bass. Some of the fellers might want to look at him. Yer know, it's been a month of Sundays since a fish slipped me as neat as that fust big 'un did."

The fish that Dud referred to could not have weighed over two pounds, but I refrained from saying so. Dud was warming up to bass fishing! But the day was far spent.

It is superfluous to mention that spell which haunts the woods and inland lakes at twilight. Night and day are one for a moment. Day lingers. Night procrastinates. Lights become duns. Colors of sunset become diluted tints. Sounds assume a new resonance, with the harsh notes whittled down. The day balances its books, and turns over the accounts to the night and the stars. Twilight is the prelude before the deep rest from growing toils. It is the return of the eternal lull.

"Geehosaphat!" exclaimed Dud. "Did you see that?"

It was the swirl of a mighty fish in the dark water.

"Ain't that a sight! Right under our noses! It was a salmon, er maybe a trout. Acted ter me like one of them old bottom sinners that cruises up once in a blue moon ter see if the sky is still on top of the world."

As he talked, Dud pulled out his own immense fly book and searched through its pages.

"Ten to one," I said, "it was a black bass."

Dud did not look up, but said, "Guess yer didn't notice that fish, Mak. It was a fish that 'ud weigh five pounds er more. . . . Now here's a female Black Gnat—black wings, white edges. That's a nice fly, Mak. Bright colors fer salmon, sure, but don't fergit to try a Gnat, now an' then."

"For trout, maybe, for salmon, sure, but for—"

Dud interrupted me. "Aya, for salmon, sure!"

"It's a total loss," I said.

"Fer how much?"

"Any amount, if you want to gamble."

"Sish. Make it ten thousand, Mak."

Of course I couldn't stand a figure like that, even in fun, but before I could alter it a startling commotion occurred in the vicinity of Dud's fly. In fact a he-fish had smashed Dud's Gnat, as though it were a tiny ship riding at anchor with all her lights hung out. Fish like that do not come often, in these days, for the simple reason that it takes several years to raise one. When Dud set the little hook, the fish plunged away like a heavily loaded ferryboat. But please don't let that figure convey the impression of ungainliness!

"Whoa, thar!" said Dud. "You ain't goin' inter them bushes if I can help it. Doggone it, Mak, why don't I have more faith, er less confidence. I've gone an' put on a leader that's too light fer a fish like this."

The bass came out of the water, tossing itself into the air like a punted football. For a brief moment it stood out in the twilight.

"If that ain't a fat salmon, I'll eat him," drawled Dud. "Them black salmon is always bottom feeders. He's loaded heavy, an' he fights deep. Seems like he's got a whole bagful of new tricks. Right now, I can feel him standin' still, an' shakin' his head, like a dog 'ith canker in both his ears. Acts like he was mad as a forked bull."

The fighting fish was beginning to rush circles about the boat. Dud was busy gathering in line that he must soon allow the fish to take again. But Dud was having a big time. Grin after grin chased across his face.

I waited for the remark I had heard so many times, under similar circumstances. At last it came:

"Crotch, Mak, this fish thinks it can git away from me! Hope that hook don't wear a hole in his mouth, an' fall out. Got to keep a tight line, if he ties me up in a hundred knots. Seems like I never see a salmon pull so. Yer can see it ain't no bass, becuz no bass 'ud last this long, even if I can't put all the strain on him that I w'ud if I had a fittin' leader. Nothin' in fins can match these salmon. Cousins, they are, to the kind that useter run up from the sea. Great fish they was, Mak. Grand fish, they be!"

I kept my peace. In the half-light, I could see the grin etched all over Dud's face. Now and then he blew great gulps of air through his lips, tilting his gray mustache askew.

"Mak, I ain't had so much fun, seems like, since the fat lady, over to Embden Fair, tipped back in her chair an' fell off the platform. Look at that cuss toss his head, when he comes up to swear at me."

I uttered an enthusiastic tribute. "It's a fine bass!"

Dud was as near to anger as I ever saw him.

"Holy Moses, Mak! That ain't no bass! Stop sayin' it, er I'll be mad at yer, fust thing yer know."

I watched the fish break and leap a half-dozen times thereafter, but each smashing plunge upward occurred in the shadows, and I could not be sure it was a bass. Still the tactics were reminiscent of bass. And I held, in silence, that it *was* a bass.

The battle began to lag. "I'm afraid that it's sunset an' evenin' star fer this fish," said Dud. "I hate to lick 'em, an' I hate to git licked. That's fishin'!"

There were a few more dogged plunges, and an abortive leap, and the old warrior rolled on his side at the surface.

Dud swung him into the boat, where I could easily reach him with the landing net.

"See," I said triumphantly, "it *is* a bass!"

Dud stepped to the middle of the boat, and we both looked down at the beaten fish. "Must be a salmon," he insisted.

"Look at it!" I exclaimed.

Dud got down on his knees, to see his fish the plainer, in the dim light. "Shucks," he grunted, "I thought it licked too easy fer a salmon."

I carelessly slid the net toward the fish.

"He's all done," said Dud, "but save him. I want to show him to the boys. Some of 'em never saw a bass."

Then a coiled spring seemed to let go in that bass. An astonishing explosion of energy occurred. Dud and I threw back our heads, but Dud's face got a liberal splashing of pond water. Getting to his feet hastily, he exclaimed, "By crotch! What swallowed that fish?"

But of course the spurt of life was short, and that game old bronzy had to come in at last. Again I slid the net under him—that time cautiously—and lifted him into the boat.

Dud sat down, wiping his face.

"Have you got that bass? Can't get away to save hisself, can he? Licked, ain't he?"

"Absolutely," I answered.

"Well, then, by crotch, is he dead?"

"No, but I'm going to hit him over the head with this paddle."

"No, sir! Don't yer do it! Goldurn him! Let him go! The old son of a gun."

Feebly moving his tail, his gills working gaspingly, the old bass sank out of our sight. The inky waters welcomed him home again.

"Thar!" said Dud. "That's over. But jist the same, I'd have liked to show him to Nancy. I don't s'pose she ever see a bass."

"Can a bass fight?" I asked.

"Well," began Dud, as he took down his rod, "that reminds me of Robby and Mike Fitzpatrick. They bet on a dogfight. The dog that Robby picked had some advantages.

" 'By the lovely, lovely,' says Robby, 'my dog licked yourn.'

" 'By the roarin' Jorus,' says Mike, 'not from where I was standin', he never!' "

"But," concluded Dud, "it's up to me to say that a bass is a bass. An' what d'yer say if we try 'em ag'in, someday?"

Spinning for Fresh and Salt Water Fish

A. J. McCLANE

THE LOOPER, MID
18TH CENTURY
*European "winch"
operators impro-
vised by spinning
(strip casting) this
way.*

*Although the purist may frown, and mumble under
his breath, spinning has attained a firm foothold
on the margin of almost every American lake and
stream, as well as the coastal beach. This exploration of the origins of the complex contraption
knows as the spinning reel should be of interest,
even to the opponents of the machine. In this
chapter entitled "History" from* Spinning for
Fresh and Salt Water Fish *A. J. McClane has
once more established his place as one of the most
able of our modern angling writers.*

AN UNIDENTIFIED CHARACTER, who wanted to toss the seventeenth-
century version of a dipsey sinker farther than the other characters who fished with him, started the whole business. Not
that throwing sinkers was much fun, but it was very disconcerting
when you realized that reels had been invented fully two centuries
before and they still did nothing but rotate in one direction—backward. This frustrated jetty jockey needed a spool that would go forward, but the mechanics of gearing were unknown; so in lieu of engi-
neering, our hero applied common sense and ignored reels completely.
His only interest was in getting the bait off the beach.

The principle of the fixed-spool reel originated among the anglers
of southern Europe in the seventeenth century. In or about the same
period, the Indian tribes of the Pacific Northwest discovered and employed the same device—a frame of wood. True enough, it was not
a spool but it was fixed, and for the first time in two hundred years
it permitted the "casting" of a bait. The Siwash was a net fisherman
by nature, and necessity; so frame fishing blossomed and died long
before American tackle designers could realize the value of casting

line off a stationary object. So far as the Indians were concerned, they would swap the idea for a bag of clams, as theirs was a rodless method and not efficient for mopping up a salmon run.

The Basques of Spain, the French, Italians, and Swiss were anglers by preference, as rods had been in use in the Old World for nearly five thousand years, and the development there was of a sporting nature. This original frame was fourteen by eight inches in size, these figures being based on ease of operation in the average hand. So threadline fishing had its roots in Europe.

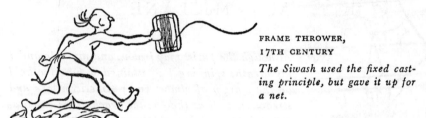

FRAME THROWER,
17TH CENTURY

The Siwash used the fixed casting principle, but gave it up for a net.

Frame fishing is reminiscent of the method used by drop line artists along the coastal United States today. The modern pier pigeon wraps about fifty yards of line around a frame of wood and, after arriving at his local hot spot, rolls the line off the wood, carefully piling the coils of line at his feet. A six-ounce sinker and a short length of line are then twirled overhead cowboy-style and released when enough momentum is created to pull out all the loose coils. Of course, nobody can be certain where the flying sinker will find its mark. Even the Siwash was a more cautious hand line fisherman three centuries ago. These ancients wrapped their line around a frame of wood and wisely turned the frame, so that the uncoiling line faced the direction of the cast. This eliminated the need to take the coils off before the cast was made, as the kelp line merely peeled over the end.

European anglers went a step further and added to the technique a sticklike rod, on the end of which was attached a ring similar to the modern tiptop. The frame was held in the left hand and the lure thrown with the stick in the right. Oddly enough, the rod idea was derived from the fly fishermen, who had been hard at work for three thousand years, but the fly fishermen ignored the tiptop and continued to tie the line to the end of the rod. At any rate, our Mediterranean riffle bird conceived the first casting stick; and even though he caught more herring than ever before, he was soon looking for greater distance.

In the early eighteenth century, the Basques were using the "bird cage," a device that looked exactly like a canary parlor turned sideways. A handle was built on one end, and the angler pointed this weapon in the same fashion in which we now mount a fixed-spool reel. The multiplying reel was still in its dormant state. In fact, the "winch" hadn't progressed much beyond the design popularized in the late fifteenth century, which was a single-action skeleton-type reel, crudely hammered from brass. It did nothing but retrieve, and it didn't do a good job of that.

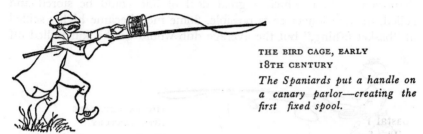

THE BIRD CAGE, EARLY
18TH CENTURY
The Spaniards put a handle on a canary parlor—creating the first fixed spool.

The bird cage, however, required that the angler hold the instrument in his left hand while his right hand was occupied with co-ordinating the rod with the left. Here at least the spool was cylindrical, if no less confusing. After the cast was made, the angler had to grab the line near the rod butt with his right hand and, still holding the rod and playing the fish, make rotating motions with the bird cage while guiding the line with the same busy right hand. This was truly a study in perpetual motion: everything moved in opposition to everything else.

Up to this point in fishing history, about 1750, you can see that there were two schools of anglers: those who cast with ease and retrieved with great difficulty (the fixed-spool clan); and those who retrieved but couldn't cast more than two rod lengths away (the winch boys). The principles were there—but how to combine the two?

Now, the fly fishermen knew that the fixed-spool adherents were getting their distance because they had whipped the problem of friction. I use the term "fly fishermen" in the same sense in which we now refer to a fellow who starts the day off with a fly rod but is apt to end up using spinners, bait, or whatever conditions call for. It is the rod that qualifies him for the title. The fly fisherman of the eighteenth century used a long, flexible rod, ranging from eighteen to twenty feet in length and weighing from two to two and a half pounds, with which he dapped crickets, flicked flies and dunked worms come a flood. His reel was made of brass or wood and went forward with the greatest difficulty.

He found that he could simulate the casting of his fixed-spool brother by running the line in long spires between his fingers, in much the same fashion in which many people strip-cast today. His "fly rod" then could propel a worm as slick as a pike's nose (for a short distance) and retrieve with comparative ease. This was the practical technique, but nobody was particularly happy with it; the maximum distance attainable was limited to the amount of line you could hold between your fingers. No, you had to do more than combine principles, but they did start people thinking.

The Scotchmen entered the scene wearing trays on their pioneering diaphragms, upon which a great deal of line could be stored and coiled, making longer casts possible. Some men became highly skilled at "basket fishing," but the average dub would get his kilt pulled off

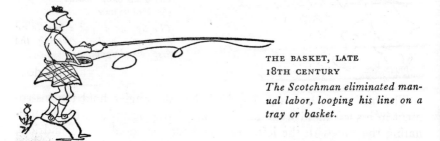

THE BASKET, LATE
18TH CENTURY
The Scotchman eliminated manual labor, looping his line on a tray or basket.

as the uncoiling line faced vertical instead of horizontal, and snagging one's basket was common. This innovation didn't make a great mark on the page of progress, but it was a leg up. Variations of this technique are still used by goofers, or salmon egg fishermen, on western coastal rivers.

The Swiss liked the idea; so they borrowed the Spaniard's bird cage and the Scotchman's basket, combined the two, and came up with the first belt reel. This was late in the eighteenth century. Fly fishermen now had guides on their rods, but reels were still winches and rotated in one direction—backward. The belt reel had minor successes in various parts of Europe, but here again it was a mechanical failure.

With the bird cage now on the belt, the angler looked like a cooch dancer getting wound up. More hips were thrown out of joint by playing trout than climbing the Matterhorn. There was no pickup on the reel, and it was necessary to wind the line back by hand. The reel was fully fifteeen inches in diameter, requiring as much stomach muscle as it did arm motion to keep the lure moving. So the fixed-spool reel alternately jumped from hand to stomach throughout the eighteenth century. It wasn't until 1949 that the belt reel became refined in the hands of Bob Worden of the Yakima Bait Company in Washington. The modern "belly winder" is a metal drum with a crank handle, roller pickup and drag—a monstrous mechanical triumph that found its place in big Western rivers for spinning, fly and bait fishing.

From 1780 to 1810, primitive brass, single-action reels were widely used both here and abroad, but the cogwheel gearing broke down all too frequently. This crude design was the progenitor of the modern bait-casting reel, but as yet there was no dependable multiplying action, and a bait could not be thrown more than twenty-five or thirty feet. The first casting reel appeared in this country in 1810, designed by an American watchmaker, George Snyder. The history of the multiplier goes on through men like Meek, Miliam and Talbot, Wheeler and McGregor, leading to the popular acceptance of bait-casting in 1860. Anglers could now cast and retrieve, but our fixed-spool friends were still unhappy. To them, the biggest bug in casting dynamics was friction and its mate—backlash.

THE BELT REEL, LATE
18TH CENTURY
The Swiss combined bird cage and belt and came up with the first belt reel.

In 1884 a gentleman by the name of Peter Malloch from Perth, Scotland, incorporated the principle of a fixed spool with that of the revolving spool. The Malloch reel looked like an ordinary bait-casting reel of that era, but it had a large ring guide mounted several inches in front of the spool. When making the cast the angler first grasped the spool and flipped it so that the end of the spool faced the direction of the ring. When retrieving, he pivoted the spool back to the orthodox reeling position. The Malloch was in effect built on a turntable and used as both a multiplying and a fixed-spool reel. The large ring served to keep the spiraling line under control when casting, as rods were still equipped with the small-diameter ring guides around which the line might easily twist.

The theory was good, but the reel created more problems than it solved. The Malloch reel appeared at a time when light lines were coming into vogue; they twisted naturally but on the Malloch were assisted by the reel itself. Each time the angler pivoted his spool from the casting position (which was parallel to the axis of the rod) to the retrieving position (which was at right angles to the axis of the rod), he reeled in all the twists made by casting, as well as those created by the rotation of the lure in the water.

To give you an idea of what the angler of 1920 was up against, here are some letters to the editor taken from the *Fishing Gazette,* a British angling paper:

The line gets kinked of course only in that part of the line which is cast off the reel—find out what your average length of cast is, and if it is, say, 35 yards, have two loops on the line 35 yards from the end, and when the line gets kinked, instead of taking all the line off and reversing the spool, simply unloop the 35 yard bit of line and reverse it. The action of casting then unwinds the kinks. When that part of the line used in casting gets worn, it will be easy to replace it with a new piece."

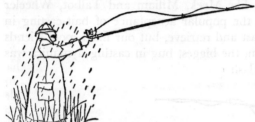

THE MALLOCH REEL,
19TH CENTURY

Peter Malloch combined a rotating spool with a fixed spool to get it on the rod.

Of course, this was a great deal of work, and soon anglers were whipping their genius into a frenzy:

There is no need for your suggestion of the loop at 35 yards down the line, with the attendant delay—simply reverse the drum. It is just a matter of education to wind the reel the opposite way. I forgot to say a swivel at the head of the bait and one at the end of the trace next to the reel line are required, and if any lead is used it should be the cylindrical tapered kind—not any lead of the underhung variety, thus allowing the spin of the bait to take out the twist put in by casting.

Detach the trace and spinning bait, go to the head of the pool or the fastest running water close to hand, and let out 35 yards of line or thereabouts in the stream. The current will straighten out the line in a few minutes. In a lake or very slow water this would be no good unless one was in a boat and trailed the line.

Nobody commented on what to do if you were on a lake and didn't have a boat. Needless to say, the fixed-spool reel was a dinger in 1920. You have to remember that there was no such thing as braided nylon or nylon monofilament in the early days—just soggy silk, linen, or imitation gut, any one of which remained straight for two casts, then suddenly spiraled into a jungle of backlash all over the reel. The Malloch had no pickup finger; the angler pressed the line against the rim of the spool with his own forefinger and released it when making the cast. Mr. Malloch was looking for his golden egg in a field of birds' nests.

The principle had been crystallized, however, and creative anglers jumped into the swim. Viscount Henry de France plunged ahead in 1903 with the "rustic reel," which had a spool that remained stationary throughout the cast and retrieve. It was obvious that the Malloch theory of pivoting the spool directions killed more fishermen than fish; so Henry whipped up a stationary cylindrical spool to hang under the rod and conceived what looked like an extra-large crocheting needle to keep his left hand busy. The line was passed through the ring at the end of the needle, the needle pressed against the cylinder until the cast was to be made, and released when the lure went on its wobbly course. Here, in effect, was the first fixed-spool reel in principle and practice. To retrieve, the disciples of this honorable gentleman wound the line back on the spool with the needle. Henry won many casting honors in his day, but crocheting trout in the stream was a nuisance.

THE RUSTIC REEL, EARLY
20TH CENTURY

France ignored the revolving spool and retrieved line with a crocheting needle.

The Viscount's idea got kicked around, then landed in England, where Alfred Holden Illingworth, who had been quietly tinkering with a new idea for several years, came out with a more mechanical model in 1905. His reel was a complete departure from traditional designs. Heretofore people had begun with a conventional looking reel and worked on that basis. But the strange contraption Illingworth devised looked more like the spindles used in his family's woolen mills. The spool was conical in shape, made of wood, and in one respect it has never been surpassed—there was no spool flange such as we find on modern reels, and the line would peel off with no friction. Illingworth is credited with the first roller or manual pickup. This pickup was incorporated on the rim of the housing upon which the angler dropped his line. When reeling, the housing rotated around the spool, thereby winding the line in place. There was no shuttling motion of the spool in his first reels, however, as it was a narrow drum, and the line was merely dumped in and squeezed between the plates. This caused much binding of the line, but at least the crocheting needle had been eliminated.

The Illingworth No. 1 had a lot on the ball, and its inventor captured first place in the International Casting Tournament in 1908 with an aggregate of three casts, scoring 309 feet against the second man with a score of 258 feet. This was in the light-bait event (three drams). Illingworth's greatest achievement lay in the fact that he didn't attempt to incorporate the two spool principles (revolving and fixed), but worked his design on the fixed-spool alone.

Letters to the editor then took a new turn:

I am very much troubled with the fine line sinking down into the coils on the drum, and occasionally have a sudden pull-up with a loss of gear owing to this. To overcome this, I made an "Illingworth" in which the drum was set at a slight angle with the revolving arm. This drum, instead of being fixed, made one revolution for every 100 (about) of the revolving arm. The effect of this was to lay the line from side to side of the groove in the drum, overlapping each other in much the same way a ball of twine is wound. As a casting reel it is about perfect, and an hour's trial satisfied me that it was more suitable for my cabinet than for the water's edge.

But soon anglers found that they could cast remarkably well with the Illingworth because the "shuttling spool" (cross-winding) had been added, thereby eliminating the lines jamming one coil under another.

The race was on.

The Illingworth, product of three centuries of experimentation, was a huge success—so much so that it was banned from most English rivers. Now that the impossible was possible, nobody wanted it. Or at least nobody who was anybody wanted to be seen with it. People caught more fish than they ever did before, because more people went fishing. So technical progress was relaxed while technician and angler discussed each other's morals. This dubious argument is still going on today.

Introduction,
The Complete
Fly Fisherman

JOHN McDONALD

John McDonald started out to collect material for an article on fly fishing and wound up with a weighty volume on an individual whose work was encountered in the course of research. Most dedicated American fly fishermen knew something of Theodore Gordon. McDonald thought they should know more. The Complete Fly Fisherman was written to this end. His introduction to this book presents the article he originally had in mind and embodies the real essence of fly fishing in this country.

THE BEST THING about Gordon is that he wrote well and with remarkable knowledge about contemporary fly fishing. As the principal creator of the structure and style of the American imitation trout fly, and the one who introduced and adapted the dry fly to the U.S., he also occupies a unique position in the sport. This historical connection gives his work—despite the fact that he died in 1915—an authentic intimacy with our present practices. For it was he who developed much of what we now do. Time moves slowly in fly fishing. The last time it moved appreciably in the U.S. was with Theodore Gordon.

Gordon was a flytier as well as fly fisherman and a journalist of the stream. His rare dedication to the sport came about by virtue of an illness that barred him from the conventional life of a stockbroker and kept him in the mountains. That at any rate was his excuse for giving his good mind exclusively for many years to the subject of fly fishing. Gordon first appeared on the scene in the late nineteenth century in an English journal, *The Fishing Gazette,* and until his death was widely regarded here and in England as the leading American angling authority (in fishing, "authority" is a manner of speaking). Since then Gordon has become legendary. Few fly fishermen today are directly familiar with his work. I trust that some of them will find it both useful and pleasing to rediscover him in these notes and letters.

Gordon's work speaks for itself, and since I have put it together for reading pleasure rather than for the more complicated interests of criticism or scholarship, there is little that I want to say about the text. I should like, however, to try to describe the fly-fishing situation in which Gordon appears—particularly with reference to the trout fly.

On the stream, the fly fisher makes his own history. Off the stream, his talk about flies opens a treasure box of antiquity, full of fish stories, views of embattled theorists, memories of immortal fly fishers and all the numberless books that have made fly fishing the most literary of sports. The trout fly of today grew out of the trout fly of yesterday. From a dim background in medieval France and Renaissance England, it has had a line of development and a breakdown into schools of thought from which the flies of today take their character.

Fly fishing has three elements: equipment, knowledge of stream life, and presentation. The equipment centers on the artificial fly; knowledge of stream life encompasses insects and trout; presentation is skill, acquired and magical, in presenting the fly to the trout. Fly-fishing argument, which is fabulous, revolves around the comparative value of these elements. At the heart of the argument is the trout fly, its patterns and forms giving tangible expression to fly-fishing theory. Most trout flies are "imitation," resembling natural insects, or "fancy," resembling in their abstract patterns merely the generality of insect life.

In its classic form, the trout fly is modeled on an insect. Like an insect, it has, in full regalia, wings, body, legs (called "hackle"), and tail. Trout-fly fishing began, according to the lore, in antiquity, when some angler, seeing a fish rise up to take an insect off the water, dropped his worm and tried to use an insect as bait. It did not work, of course, the insect being too fragile to remain on the hook under the required conditions of casting and manipulation—and so began the historic, irreconcilable split between fly and bait fishing. (The exceptions to these are "dapping," a little-known, delicate art of fishing with natural flies, and occasional plain bait fishing with the heavy stone fly.) Certain bird feathers were found to be similar to insects in color, marking, texture, and weight. Tying a feather on a hook to represent insect wings, spreading the fibers of another as legs, attaching strands of the fiber for the tail, and winding fur around the hook for the body, the ancient anglers produced a sufficiently delicate yet sturdy likeness of an insect.

The trout fly is either wet or dry. The wet fly is relatively flat, two-dimensional, with soft flowing hackle. It is fished literally wet, that is, below the surface. The dry fly is three dimensional and can be stood up on its stiff hackle and tail. It is fished literally dry, often with the aid of waterproofing, and cocks up like an insect on the water. The dry fly is almost always fished upstream (ordinarily it would quickly drag, downstream); the wet fly is fished up, down, or across. Once the subject of controversy, both the wet and the dry fly are now generally found in the equipment of the sophisticated angler.

The angler's problem today, as always, is in his choice of flies. Most fly fishers use only a small number, perhaps not more than fifteen or twenty. But which ones and why? Some five hundred standard patterns in the U.S. are listed by *The Sporting Goods Dealer*. Mary Orvis Marbury (*Favorite Flies and Their Histories*), member of a celebrated flytying family of Vermont, fifty years ago expressed "perplexity" and "dismay" at the "accumulation of the ages"—and that was before the dry fly was really known in the U.S. Today it accounts for probably half of our trout flies. Standard and nonstandard patterns together run into thousands.

This number and diversity represent various approaches to fly fishing. Every new thought or method has inspired new flies, even where conditions have remained constant, as in the chalk streams of southern England. Consider then the provocative inconstancy of the North American continent and its inhabitants: its waters wild and domestic, fast and slow, high and low, varying in altitude, temperature, food supply, and species of trout; its regional habits grooved in fishing traditions expressed by the fancy yellow-white-scarlet Parmachenee Belle fly of Maine, the precise, subtle, bronze-blue-gray Quill Gordon of the Middle Atlantic states, the roughly delicate, mottled brown-and-gray Adams of Michigan, or the coarse, durable, hair-woven Mite family, a relatively conservative symbol of the West. Grafted to these natural vagaries of flytying is a widespread commercial exploitation of patent-medicine fishing with sure-kill fabrications. The important thing for the angler is to understand enough about fly theory to know what he is doing. A million flies will not confuse the sound angler. He begins where fly fishing began, with nature.

IMITATION OF THE NATURAL

The relationship of trout flies to natural insects is the rule, the first principle of fly fishing—exceptions afterward. The primary food of the trout is the insect life of the stream. Underwater food has been called the trout's beef, the winged fly its caviar. And it may be so, for many fishermen have seen that a trout taken on a fly may already be full to bursting—an experience that suggests that the trout may have either a sporting or an epicurean instinct, in addition to ordinary hunger. This observation may serve also as a tip that fly-fishing information is highly speculative.

Early fly fishers pioneered loosely in entomology, vaguely studying insect forms and colors. Science later identified insects by form in black and white. The fly fisher, with his special interest in color, could have paid more attention to scientific method, for he got himself into such an unholy mess with his beautiful language of watery duns, pale evening duns, hare's ears, and March browns that he was not able to speak clearly across the centuries, as the scientists do with their Latin and Greek, or even across the Atlantic or between the states.

The big five of trout-stream insects—the May fly, caddis fly, stone fly, true fly, and alder fly—and their several stages of life are not of equal value to the fisher. In their preadult stages (nymphs or larvae), these insects live under water, where their herbivorous appetite performs the service of converting plant into animal life. The stream bed is generally littered with larvae and nymphs, and trout spend most of the year rooting among them for the better part of their food. In recent years fly fishers have shown an increased interest in the nymph, and the wet fly is thought often to be taken by the trout for a nymph or a minnow rather than a winged insect. The chief interest of fly fishers, however, is in the adult, winged flies that appear in the spring and summer, especially between the lilac and the laurel, the heart of the fly fisher's season. Most trout flies represent winged insects.

Two groups of winged flies are favored most by the trout, the May fly and caddis fly. The latter, unfortunately, does most of its hatching near or after nightfall, and is therefore usually on the stream after the fly fisher has gone home. And so, beyond but by no means to the exclusion of all others, the trout fisher has traditionally prized and copied the gorgeously hued aristocrat of the stream, the May fly. The May fly lives most of its life of a few weeks to more than a year under water, as a nymph, and gets its scientific name, Ephemeroptera, from its fleeting adult life. As an adult it has two further stages of life: the fly fishers' dun (science: subimago) and spinner (imago). Sometime in the fly fishers' season the May-fly nymph makes a dash for the surface, often with a trout in swift pursuit, splits the nymphal shuck, airs its wings, and takes off for the woods, a dun. In this form, the fly fisher knows many species. Some fly fishers prefer the dun to all others, as it is found so frequently on the stream. The dun is a great and historic fly, progenitor of countless trout-fly patterns. Hills (*A History of Fly Fishing for Trout*) has traced the artificial duns of Berners' ancient treatise down the centuries to the present time. The dun is out again in profusion each month of May.

After spending a few hours or days in nearby trees, the May-fly dun molts and is transformed into a spinner, more brilliant than the dun and slightly altered in size and shape. The spinner returns to hover over the stream in a rhythmic mating dance of birth and death. Before the end the female deposits her eggs in the water, caviar in truth for the trout.

Duns and spinners vary by country, region, stream, and season. Fly fishers often get to know them on their favorite stream, though the date of hatch is unpredictable. It is not always possible to match the natural insect even from a full fly box. The strict use of imitation flies is the ideal of many anglers. But because of the many difficulties and the problem of obtaining good floating materials in certain colors, anglers are generally satisfied to use a fly that at once resembles several species. This traditional practice of matching a single or similar species accounts at one stroke for the largest number of trout flies.

No matter how flies are chosen or fished, some kind of speculative underwater view is implied. Man lives in air, trout in water, and the surface of the stream is like the borderline of metaphysics. The theory of strict imitation, asserted or hidden in simple practice, is that the trout has a fine sense of color, form, and size. The imitators uphold one or another of these capacities. Their rather formidable assumption is challenged notably by P. B. M. Alan (*Trout Heresy*), who submits that "the trout has no more brain than a lizard," and that as, say, between the shades of an olive dun, it has "no powers of discernment whatsoever." To Alan the legend of the wise trout is man's conceit, "for if trout can outwit us, the lords of creation, he must be superior to us in cunning."

FANCY FLIES

Detractors of the trout's sensibility often fish with fancy flies such as the Scarlet Ibis and Parmachenee Belle, suggestive not of species or group but merely of fly life. One can get entangled here, however. The Parmachenee Belle, for example, was created in the 1870s to imitate the fin of a brook trout; no one will ever know what the trout has been taking it for all this time. Fancy flies are fished without regard for the insects on the water. Both fancy and imitation flies take trout, yet the reconciliation of the theories behind them would be the most revolutionary event in the history of fly fishing. It would be easier to reconcile Plato and Aristotle. Today the popular fishing writer Ray Bergman (*Trout*), takes the genial view that any standard pattern will do. Another, Lee Wulff (*Leaping Silver*), believes that the trout sees no color so much as a silhouette, and fishes his flies accordingly. Charles M. Wetzel (*Practical Fly Fishing*), is a color imitationist. Ray Camp of the New York *Times* likes to try out new flies. The good Western flytier, Dan Bailey, prefers flies for streams. Jim Deren fishes all the angles. The six are masterful fishermen and by all accounts net many fish. One ought to get a skeptical conclusion out of this. But be careful: belief inspires confidence, and confidence inspires the angler.

Basically there are but two schools of fly fishing, imitation and presentation, both closed systems of thought. They work this way: The imitationist, with due allowances for skill, believes that his trout rise to the naturalness of his flies. He explains the basket of the presentationist as the result of trout mistaking the fancy or unnatural fly for some known insect. In extremity, he will deny that there is any such thing as a fancy fly; all are imitations in one way or another, and the basket would be fuller if the presentationist paid more attention to the insects. The presentationist, on the other hand, graciously attributes the basket of his adversary not to his flies but to his fishing skill. The tallest tales of fishing experience will not crack the logic of these views.

Regional fly practices defy all theory. Dry flies are predominant in the East after the snow water and April freshets have run off, but toward the West flies grow wetter and wetter. Imitation flies have prevailed for fifty years from the Beaverkill in New York to the Brodhead in Pennsylvania. They turn fancy north along the seaboard to Maine and Canada. In the whole sweep of the Rockies, flytiers are wonderfully enterprising and unorthodox. They often leave the delicacy of fur and feathers for the durability of hair, squirrel tail, and bucktail. Large, rough, and radically spectacular, their flies express the directness and enthusiasm of wild-country fishing.

THE OLD MASTER

The main tendencies of modern American flytying largely stem from Theodore Gordon, the old master of American fly fishing, familiar now only by his signature, the Quill Gordon fly. Gordon's influence is very much alive in the peerless school of Sullivan County (New York) flytiers, standard-bearers of the imitation fly: Reub Cross, who learned flytying from him; Roy Steenrod, author of the Hendrickson fly, and Herman Christian, both Gordon's fishing companions; the Walt Dettes, man and wife; and the Harry Darbees. (By indirection it extends to most contemporary American flytiers.) In delicacy, precision, and style, the craft of these modern masters is out of the old master, Gordon. But the knowledge of him and his meaning to contemporary fly fishing are lost behind these opaque curtains of culture that obscure everything that happened before 1917. Gordon died in 1915 and was swept from sight like a spent spinner. He never wrote a book, and his numerous "Little Talks on Fly-Fishing" faded away in the files of *Forest and Stream* and *The Fishing Gazette,* of which he was the American correspondent from 1890. He was born in Pittsburgh in 1854 with a silver spoon in his mouth and fly-fished in the limestone creeks of Pennsylvania from the age of fourteen.

Gordon lived a remarkable life, unheard of in our day. A man of taste and intelligence, a good, restrained, yet warm and exciting fishing writer, a reader who knew Chaucer as well as Walton and Thoreau, Thad Norris (*The American Angler's Book*) as well as Frederic Halford (*Dry-Fly Fishing in Theory and Practice*), and a devoted follower of the great Francis Francis (*A Book on Angling*), Gordon fled civilization for a retreat on that famous trout stream, the Neversink, in New York State. He put one thing only into his mind—the stream—and sustained it there unflaggingly for a great many years. An inexplicable performance, probably never duplicated by anyone anywhere. He made an elegant backwoodsman. His one fishing photograph, taken around 1895, suggests a more than ordinary discrimination in clothing and equipment. He spat blood during his last three years and died of t.b. What we really know of him is that he lived a sweet, good life, perhaps the only man ever to express with his whole life the ideal of the anglers' brotherhood. His contemporaries called him the American Walton and the Sage of the Neversink. Like everything else, fishing has been used for unworthy purposes, and the only luxury of discordance Gordon allowed himself was to snub the angling snobs.

Whatever his spiritual purpose, Gordon did not entirely succeed.

His early writing is more cheerful than his last. He did not wholly escape the civilization from which he fled. The destruction of forests —bringing ice jams and floods—and pollution of streams, all killing to the trout, bothered him more and more. The increasing purchase of riparian rights and consequent closure of long stretches of streams for private use he felt was a violation of the anglers' code. And although his fame brought him many invitations, he usually turned away from posted and specially stocked waters with the remark that they were too easy to fish and no test of skill. He respected the clubs for their role as trout preserves. But he loved difficult fishing, and enjoyed most the days when the trout, especially the big ones whose lairs he knew, were elusive.

A Fish Story

Gordon is the subject of many anecdotes. His small slender figure was beloved by the people of Sullivan County, where he and his rod were most often seen bobbing along paths and streams. His haunts were the Neversink, Beaverkill, Willowemoc—the big three of eastern trout streams—and the Esopus and Big Indian. But he had fished too in the dear Brodhead of Pennsylvania, south to Florida, north to Maine, west to Ohio and Michigan. Gordon himself tells a fishing story, incidentally revealing of his stream manners. In the early spring of 1907, when the water was too high and roily for flies in the main stream, he turned off into a tributary—a useful hint for early-season fly fishers—and soon came upon a little Negro girl fishing a pool with stick and string. He was stalking and she did not notice him. He thought to signal her. "I did not wish to poach upon her pool, but, as a matter of form, dropped my fly at the edge of the stone and not three feet from the small maiden's toes. It was seized at once by a half-pound native trout, which had been lurking under her pedestal, and I am not sure who was more surprised, the child or myself."

But Gordon's stature in American fly fishing and trout flies is measured by more than spiritual matters. He was operating at the heart of things from 1890 onward as an inveterate fisher, writer, and professional flytier. A craftsman and an innovator, he came upon the scene at an opportune time for a great man, and he lived up to the occasion. Two disparate traditions that today make up the central course of our flytying and fly fishing were then operating independently of each other. The first of these was the long line of English fly fishing from the time of Berners, which was then making its greatest turn with the development of the dry fly. The other was American fly fishing, which was then still locked in the wet fly, used mainly either in indigenous fancy patterns or in imitation patterns tied on British models. Gordon brought about the juncture of these traditions.

On the English side, trout flies go back to the fifteenth century. We know from Hills' ingenious and masterful history that eleven of Berners' twelve flies, the first on record, can be traced through the ages to the present time. The flies were wet and strictly imitative. Other equipment consisted of long rods and twisted hairlines. From Berners in 1496 to Cotton in 1676 (Walton was not a fly fisher), there was practically no change except the addition of a number of flies. The seventeenth was a literary century, lit up by Walton, Cotton, Wotton, and other great fishing writers. The eighteenth century stopped writing, except such valued items as Gay's verses, and got to work supplying the tackle essentially as we have it today: short rods, reels, silk lines, and drawn-gut leaders. It was a technical century; the artistry of flytying stood still.

ACTION UPSTREAM

The nineteenth century was the fly fisher's epoch. Literature and fishing came together in the romantic appreciation of nature. The study of science brought fly fishers' entomologies in color, notably Ronalds' monumental work, *The Fly Fisher's Entomology*. Flytiers set to work with their models drawn in front of them and expanded their range with numerous species of insects. Pulman (*Vade Mecum of Fly-Fishing for Trout*) pulled the dry fly out of his hat, complete in 1841, though for all anyone knew it might as well have been a rabbit. It was an extraordinary achievement, but a little ahead of its time.

Then came Stewart (*The Practical Angler*) and the first leap forward in fly-fishing history since its origin. Until Stewart, fly fishers relied on the color and shape of flies to catch their fish. Stewart introduced action. How did he do this? By turning upstream, something that many Western American fly fishers have yet to do. Some fly fishers had been upstream men since Cotton's time. But Stewart went upstream and made an argument for it. Upstream fishing is superior fishing, wet or dry, for many reasons, but essentially for one: facing upstream the fisher controls the position of the fly; therefore the fishing is more precise, the element of luck is greatly diminished.

THE DRY FLY

The effect on fly fishing was profound, for upstream fishing was a prelude to the dry fly. The dry fly must float naturally, an action almost impossible to obtain downstream. From Pulman, who first held it up, to Halford, who quit his business, took off his coat, and fought thirty-five years for its exclusive use, the dry fly had a rapid and spectacular development. During the last half of the nineteenth century it came to maturity. Color and form were debated all over again. Halford wrote the second great entomology, with color plates to identify shades of color. Thereafter the color in fly dressings could be specified by plate number. The effect was standardization, which Americans, fond of it in so many other regards, are still without. When Halford got through, a wet-fly fisher on a chalk stream in southern England "skulked like a poacher." Hills is moderate, yet here is his summation of the dry fly: "It altered both the practice and the temperament of the angler. It called different qualities into request. It has charm and an allurement which the older sport did not possess. In what does its charm lie? Partly in the fact that all the moves in the game are visible."

The dry-fly rage was on when Halford received, in 1890, a letter from Theodore Gordon, making inquiries about this new phenomenon. Halford replied, enclosing a paper into which he clipped a full set of his dry flies, each carefully identified in pen and ink, and the dry fly winged its way to the New World.

In the U.S. sport fishing had been practically unknown before 1830. Fish was food. The fly was not widely used, or at least not talked about, until the 1860s, when it suddenly boomed. The Americans had learned most things from the English, who lazily "fished the rise," that is, waited until the trout showed itself and then cast over the rise. But the Americans strode their fast-water streams and went after the trout wherever they lay, rise or no rise. The fishing was good, too good, and the fancy wet fly was often sufficient to the occasion, until the 1870s, when the native brook trout of the East were suddenly fished out.

The great American fisher of the century was "Uncle" Thad Norris, experienced in books and native practice. He knew about everything there was to know in his time, put it all down in 1864, and thereby established the school of early American fly fishing with a rounded theory and practice. Like Stewart, from whom he must have learned it, he was fishing upstream, sometimes even drying his wet fly in an effort to make it float. That was the nearest that an American came to getting in on dry-fly development—a gesture.

By 1879 the brook trout were all but gone and the hardier brown trout not yet transplanted from Europe. The editor of *Forest and Stream* threw in the sponge with a long editorial dirge, ending, "This is probably the last generation of trout fishers." Norris' crowd had got all the trout, and the next generation and succeeding ones had to learn conservation. Eastern fishing, the larger part of early American fishing, grew in difficulty for more reasons than one. The immigrant brown trout was wiser than the native brook. Neither fancy flies nor wet flies were enough. Fly fishers of the nineties faced upstream and waited for something to happen.

THE MODERN FLY

It was a historic moment, then, in 1890, when Gordon opened Halford's letter and fingered his flies. Gordon was as American as a brook trout. His first practical book had been Norris'. From it he had learned to tie his first flies. Like Norris and his predecessor, Stewart, he was an upstream man. He had fished through the decline of the brook trout and the rise of the brown, and so cherished the native species that he flatly refused to accede to its scientific designation, charr. It was a trout. He had seen sights unseen by the modern angler, "water covered with dimples made by the rising trout as far as my view extended."

The significant thing is that Gordon had fished the wet fly dry, the natural outcome of an acute upstream man fishing over rising trout. Instinctively he dried the fly, as Norris had done. But the construction of the fly was wrong. At best the wet fly when dry keels over like a victim of DDT and floats inert on the surface. Gordon was a reader of English as well as American books. It was natural, logical, and inevitable that a man of his temper, consecrated to angling, should have heard the echoes of Halford's crusading din across the water.

Gordon saved Halford's fly donation as models of construction for the tying of his own flies. His job had just begun. First, Halford's flies imitated English insects, different from ours. Gordon set out to correct this in his own way. Lacking any kind of formal fly fisher's entomology, he studied what entomological knowledge there was, and began to observe duns on the water. It is thus owing in part to the lack of American color-printed entomologies that he observed flies under natural conditions and, tying their imitations impressionistically on the spot, gave rise to our contemporary style of American flies—the cockiest, and among the prettiest, most natural flies in the world.

He became for a time a strict imitationist—that is, he tried for an impression of individual species. Although he grew so well acquainted with insects in his long sojourn by the stream that he could carry the impression of hundreds of them in his memory, he gradually turned moderate, the effect in part of becoming a professional flytier. He came to grant that under all but the most difficult circumstances an imitation covering a group of species was sufficient for good fishing. Many of his species flies are now used as group types. He never went against the fancy fly in theory, recommending it for wild waters. Flies according to the conditions, he said. His own preference, however, was for tough conditions. After all, when you have fished intensively for a half century you may be excused for preferring it tough.

A further Gordon contribution grew out of the fast stream: The English, fishing the rise in quiet water, can afford to use a softer hackle than Americans, whose flies are always being ducked by whitecaps, froth, converging currents, and all the movements of the stream. Gordon sought a stiffer hackle, a matter of greater selectivity in cock necks, and tied it as sparsely as the conditions would allow. From this the fly developed greater delicacy and buoyancy. The key to the American dry fly today is still buoyancy, and, assuming you start with a light wire hook, that means hackle. American flytiers now introduce stiff hackle into their flies, even at the cost of departing in color from strict imitation of natural insects.

Other men made contributions to American fly fishing after 1890. Since Gordon never put his work between covers, the laurel for the first book on the dry fly went to Emlyn M. Gill (*Practical Dry-Fly Fishing*) who hatched out the dry-fly cult in 1912. Here, as in England, the cult put on a great, if belated, campaign to sink the wet fly forever. Its titular leader was Gill's friend, George La Branche, whose book, *The Dry Fly in Fast Water,* is regarded by many as the American classic on the subject. One of the all-time greats of American fly fishing, La Branche made a unique contribution to the technique of fast-water fishing: the decoy method of floating a fly many times over the supposed lair of a trout for no less a purpose than to create an entire artificial hatch. His celebrated fly is the Pink Lady. Yet Gordon, who fished the dry fly from 1890, tied it, talked it, and wrote about it, never joined the cult or turned away from the art of the wet fly fished upstream. When the dry-fly rage came on, he resisted it. In England the "wet" man Skues (*Minor Tactics of the Chalk Stream*) had fought the "dry" man Halford, and the two made a balance. Gordon's range was wider. He performed the joint services of a Halford and a Skues.

In brief, then, the classic American trout fly of today comes down to us in the English line from Berners through Cotton (Walton's disciple) to Stewart, to Halford, to Gordon; and in the American line from Berners through Cotton to Stewart, to Norris, to Gordon. It continues down to us from Gordon through the creations of contemporary flytiers, some of whom have been mentioned here.

Whatever your preference in trout flies, take Gordon's advice and "cast your fly with confidence."

Fishing the Dry Fly
on Quiet Waters:
A Character Study

VINCENT MARINARO

*Few participants in any form of sporting activity
are as stubborn and dedicated as the so-called dry-
fly purist, and few angling writers have offered as
convincing a justification of purism as Vincent
Marinaro in* A Modern Dry Fly Code. *If trout
and salmon angling is—as some insist—an experience in applied philosophy, Marinaro's "Fishing the Dry Fly on Quiet Waters" is its critique,
and with no apology to Kant.*

M INERVA SPRANG full-grown and armed from the brain of
Jupiter. The mythical goddess did not enjoy a more complete
birth than many of the limestone streams of central Pennsylvania. Issuing with great force and volume from the Stygian caverns
in the soft lime rock, they present an aspect of maturity no less entire
at the immediate source than at any other point in their course.

Constancy of flow is their great virtue, implemented and made secure by union, over- and underground, with other streams of a similar speculative origin. Blessed by nature with a boundless store of the elements which are conducive to the flourishing of underwater life, they are unsurpassed in their capacity to nurture and maintain a stock of trout and other fishes in extraordinary quantity and growth. Weeds are profuse and varied, insuring the continuance of those lesser underwater creatures which thrive in their midst and constitute the finest larder ever designed by man or nature for the trout family.

There was a time, according to the ancient annals, when the average weight of brook trout caught in these waters was near two pounds and the yearly total of such trout for a single fisherman was numbered in the thousands, an impossible thing now, in these sterile times of premature harvest and inordinate demand by an ever increasing horde of fishermen. Yet the inherent richness of these waters remains unchanged, sometimes evidenced by the astonishing size and condition of brown trout, recently introduced, which have escaped for a time the searching and ever present barbs of the relentless multitude.

There was a time, too, when the encroachments of civilization and the urgent needs of man did not interfere with the normal purity and clarity of these streams, as they have of late, with the regrettable result that miles of these valuable streams remain unproductive and barren of fish life. Wherever they can be found in their original state of excellence they continue to be the favorite haunts of fly fishermen as they were a hundred years ago and more, particularly the dry-fly fishermen, who have discovered them to be pre-eminently suited to the use of the dry fly by virtue of the habitual presence of surface insects and the willingness of the trout to rise freely to them.

Fortunate indeed are those who, by force of circumstances or choice, are able to pursue and enjoy a form of angling which is exactly suited to their inclinations. When a happy condition of this sort exists, it seems almost inevitable that the angling practices of that locality will occasion a constant and intelligent study by its devotees in order to create the refinements which so greatly increase the pleasures of angling. In some instances there may be a sufficient number of those individuals, keenly observant and studious by nature, who bend their combined efforts in study and experiment to evolve and formulate a new and interesting method of angling.

By all accounts, these are the factors which gave rise to the birth and bloom of the art of dry-fly fishing. Cradled and nourished in the chalky downs of the Hampshire district of England by men whose names have become a byword to fly fishermen everywhere, it has risen to a plane so lofty as to border on the aesthetic!

It seems quite clear, in retrospect, that the dry fly would never have occurred in its present exacting form without the existence of the chalk and limestone streams of England or streams of a similar nature elsewhere. Unquestionably this was the stage, the proper setting arranged and prepared for the advent of men like Halford, Lord Grey, and Marryat. Without this background—the slow-flowing, smooth-surfaced, limpid waters of Test and Itchen—without the luxuriant waterweed and the consequent abundance of water-bred insect life, notably the Ephemeridae, there would have been no plastic, no clay so to speak, for these men to shape and mold. There would have been no dry fly. It does not matter that these men might have come in an earlier or later century. The important thing was, and is, the existence of these unique rivers.

So, too, in the present instance it is appropriate to establish a proper basis or background to authenticate, as it were, the origin and development of new dry-fly patterns and their application to these and similar waters. In more recent times these efforts have been centered largely on the beautiful Letort, at Carlisle, Pennsylvania, and the sister streams nearby.

What shall I say of the Letort? Certainly it is beautiful, not with the wild beauty of our mountain freestone streams, decked out in their garish display of laurel and rhododendron, but rather with the calm and serene beauty of pastoral scenery. Nestled in a little valley, with gently rolling hills on both sides, it meanders slowly and evenly, its placid surface hardly ever ruffled even by the westerly winds which prevail thereabouts. Even a heavy downpour creates no severe change other than a barely perceptible fullness and a slight milkiness which disappear in a short time, a matter of hours.

I never cease to marvel at this phenomenon, particularly when I recall a certain fishing hut, which has its foundations resting on a level bank about ten feet from the stream and hardly six inches above the level of the water! Yet, within my memory and that of many who often fish there, no water has ever been seen underneath the hut.

The reader must not suppose, however, that these features indicate a lack of character in the Letort. It could not be so, in consideration of its great depth and vast weed beds and channels exerting their subtle influence underneath the calm exterior, creating currents and cross-currents, intermingling them in a sinuous manner which, barely noticeable to the casual visitor, causes no end of astonishment and despair in his efforts to overcome drag. The Letort is a hard taskmaster and does not treat lightly any violation of dry-fly technique. Any suggestion of drag, heaviness in the cast, or thick gut is magnified many times on such a calm surface, and the penalty is absolute and total failure.

On the other hand, a successful angler is rewarded handsomely in the event of a proper approach, position, and cast. It could not be otherwise in a stream where trout grow to such noble proportions in a short time and rise freely to the smallest of dry flies, and where the rises themselves are of such a character as to startle the most phlegmatic of natures. I must confess that I have never become used to them, even the quiet and dainty rises. One moment the artificial is floating quietly and gently, and the next instant there may be a sudden heaving and bulging of the water, accompanied by a sound of basso-profundo depth that cuts into the consciousness with a sharpness which is a little unnerving, but also exhilarating. Even where the rise form is a tiny sip or dimple, awareness comes suddenly to the angler from the violent lunge of the fish and the ratchety sound of the reel. I suppose it is the severe contrast of the quiet of the stream and its surroundings with the commotion and noise of the rise which affects me in this manner, for I do not experience the same thing when fishing rough water. Then, too, there are those occasions, which are very frequent on the Letort, when I can observe every movement of a feeding trout —see him aquiver the instant my artificial lands a foot or two in front of him, watch him detach himself from his observation post, undulating backward and lifting slowly to take the fly at the precise instant they both meet at the surface, as though the trout had calculated the interception by triangulation! These are the worst times for me. Being somewhat nervous by temperament, I cannot subdue the building up of nervous pressure engendered by the visible and deliberate rise. The usual result in these cases is a violent reaction on my part intended to be a strike, something I fervently wish I had never learned, and the matter is concluded by a sudden parting of the ways between the trout and me. Again there are those moments of indecision on the part of the trout when the backward undulating movement is continued for perhaps three or four feet from the usual point of interception, the nose of the trout barely touching my artificial while he scrutinizes it carefully, and all the while my anxiety is mounting with the realization that the point where free float ends and drag begins is fast approaching. In other respects the Letort presents an aspect of constancy in hatches and rising fish which is extremely gratifying to the angler-entomologist-researcher.

On some waters the prospects of finding trout regularly and habitually taking surface food are slim indeed. As for daily routine, it simply does not exist, being the exception and not the rule. Anglers who fish those waters and who like to employ the dry fly are constrained to fish to a position rather than to an individual fish, as I understand it, searching, with a fly of impressionistic design, each pocket and eddy, or any likely place where a trout might be lying in wait to seize a chance morsel as it goes by.

On the other hand, trout of the limestone waters constantly exhibit a preference for surface food that is rituallike in point of time and place. In recent years it has been an object of special interest to me to determine the extent of this habit. I have taken every opportunity during the course of my fishing excursions to note the time of day and the number of successive days on which rising fish could be observed, and I lost no opportunities to make similar observations on those vacation periods when I lived on the stream itself for as long as a week at one time. On these latter periods it was my custom on leaving the hut in the morning to take readings of water and air temperature, note barometric pressure, and then patrol a beat of one half mile of water, taking note of the time and place of any rises during my tour; I repeated this whole routine once in every hour during the day.

Water temperature seemed to be the most decisive factor in determining the regularity of rises. The temperature at seven or eight o'clock in the morning always gave a reading of 50 or 52 degrees Fahrenheit. Each successive hourly reading thereafter revealed a rise in temperature of 2 degrees, until about two o'clock in the afternoon, when the peak was reached at 60 degrees or 64 degrees. At approximately eleven o'clock, when the readings were 56 to 58 degrees, the first rises could be seen, few in number and taking place at longish intervals. As the temperature increased the number of rises increased, the intervals between rises of the individual fish shortening considerably; the peak of activity was reached when the highest reading of 64 degrees was taken. It was interesting to note that brown trout were not the first to begin the search for food. At the lower end of the beat there is a part of the stream which seems to be especially suited to brook trout, for a fair number of them can always be found there. The inception of the feeding period at ten-thirty or eleven o'clock, concurring with the temperature reading of 56 to 58 degrees, always took place at this location and was evidenced by the movements of brook trout only. At one or two o'clock, when the temperature of the water gave a reading of 62 to 64 degrees, the brown trout made their appearance and from that time until approximately five o'clock both species fed with sustained regularity.

This performance continued day after day; as nearly as I could determine, the only factors that caused any interruption in these conditions were changes in barometric pressure, and thunderstorms. These fish are positively allergic to thunder and other heavy vibrations of any sort. An occasional blasting operation in a nearby limestone quarry will put them down for such a long time that the angler is forced to occupy himself elsewhere until their confidence is restored and their feeding resumed.

Armed with this sort of knowledge, those who fish these waters are in an excellent position to adjust the time and place of a fishing jaunt to conform to the well-established habits of these trout, but I hasten to advise that there is no guarantee that they can be caught!

Familiarity with all of those facts has provided me with an unending source of amusement at the expense of a stranger or infrequent fishing guest. It is no great trick to inform him in a sober and offhand manner that he will find trout rising in a certain place at a certain time and confound him further by sending him off to try for a fish that rises at a certain hour just three feet below a box elder and two feet from the right-hand bank. I fear that these doings have earned for me, in a few cases, a reputation for clairvoyance and wizardry in trouting matters that fits me badly, particularly since every once in a while I am invited to try for the fish and fail miserably to take it!

All of this makes this sort of fishing a reasonably constant and predictable affair not only with respect to the activity of the trout and the state of the water but also with respect to the presence of insect hatches, water-bred, and insect flights, land-bred.

Let others less fortunate envy the British and their olive dun and its spinner, that wonderful fly which by common acknowledgment seems to thrive and appear in great numbers on all the English dry-fly rivers. The olive is very scarce in America and its imitation is of questionable value, but in these parts dry-fly anglers may rejoice in the existence of a pale, watery class of May fly, both the pale-winged and the blue-winged variety, which forms the backbone of dry-fly fishing on limestone waters. In a very good year, when hatches are especially heavy during the peak of emergence, they can be seen streaming upward from the surface of the water, their bodies catching and reflecting the full rays of the sun, winking and glowing like a thousand hot golden sparks. There is cause to rejoice further in the fact that they emerge almost daily from early May until the end of the season. Oftentimes, their behavior on the surface of the water is characterized by considerable effort and exertion in order to dispel the nymphal shuck, until finally they glide along in full repose with wings erect, like little ships with sails unfurled. That all of this is a form of conduct highly absorbing to fish as well as anglers is confirmed by the presence of rising trout everywhere, which take the insect with a peculiar noise, much like the sound of a cork popping out of a wine bottle.

Equally interesting to both angler and trout is the appearance of the Hendrickson, locally called Slate Drake, which usually obliges the grateful angler by emerging on or about that auspicious day, April 15, the beginning of the trout season. The pale wateries might be depicted as dainty, the Green Drake as a clumsy, lumbering beast, but gallant is the word which describes the Hendrickson.

No sight is prettier than to see a string of these creatures come sailing along, wings erect and proud and slanted at a rakish angle, bodies rocking mildly with each little wavelet, causing the tall wings to tip and bow, now this way, now that, as they turn with the current.

On the Yellow Breeches Creek, before the first Hendrickson is seen the caddis flies have already put in their appearance. The variety and number of caddis at this time of year is astounding. Light-colored ones and dark ones, small and large, they fill the air above the water in countless hordes, dipping, fluttering, and flying aimlessly as caddis flies will. They are often so thick that the form of an angler a hundred feet away is reduced to an indistinct blur. It is not unusual for an angler to leave the stream after a day's fishing at this time and discover that his waders, from top to toe, are covered with a solid mass of green egg sacs, acquired from the deposit of the industrious caddis. The memory of such an experience is indelibly inscribed on the mind of the unlucky angler when he discovers the tenacious character of these egg sacs in his futile attempt to remove them.

These various caddis represent a very powerful attraction to the trout, causing them to gorge and regorge as they see fit. But let the first Hendricksons make their appearance and the order of the day is changed completely. The caddis are entirely abandoned and the trout immediately direct their attentions to the Hendrickson, displaying a ravenous appetite, which is astonishing in view of their previous gluttony.

Here indeed is an extraordinary situation. The great profusion of caddis, the advent of the Hendrickson, the change of taste by the trout —all of these are conditions calculated to produce doubt and uncertainty in the mind of the angler. An artificial which easily deceived the trout taking caddis earlier in the day is no longer successful; and if, as the angler suspects, the trout are taking Hendrickson, how is he to know when and where? Fortunately, some order out of this confusion is possible. If the angler carefully observes the rise-form of individual trout, he may learn that there is a remarkable difference between the rise to caddis and the rise to Hendrickson. Trout taking caddis do so with a slashing strike, throwing a bit of spray accompanied by a thin, watery sound; in the case of the Hendrickson there is a deliberate sucking rise, causing a single boil or ring on the surface and creating a sound which has a deep, resonant quality. But a word of caution is necessary here, for oftentimes a trout which has just diverted his attention from caddis to Hendrickson will continue to exhibit a rise-form of the slashing kind for a short time. Once the feeding on Hendrickson is fairly under way, the trout will gradually reform his pace until it resembles the correct rise-form to the Hendrickson.

It is a regrettable day, a regrettable hour when the last of these fine insects is seen at the end of the emergence period, which lasts for perhaps three or four weeks. Given a good head of trout in the stream and provided that weather and water conditions are suitable for the entire period, there is no fishing to any insect which is more likely to stir the interest and imagination of the angler.

Do not suppose, however, that the passing of the Hendrickson and the coming and going of the pale wateries put an end to the anticipation and fulfillment of the dry-fly angler's chosen pursuit. Even in late season, when the larger May flies are less and less in evidence, the surface of these waters is literally carpeted with terrestrials of one form or another, providing a source and inducement for surface feeding that rivals the earlier duns and spinners; and in some ways it must be admitted they are even more important to the dry-fly fisherman than the Ephemeridae because of the attraction of their larger, meatier bodies, analogous to the same attraction which exists for the trout during the season of the giant May fly, Ephemera guttulata, or more familiarly the Green Drake, which occurs in tremendous quantities on our limestone waters. In particular, I would commend to anglers of the limestone waters everywhere the marvelous fishing to be had during the grasshopper season, a phase of dry-fly fishing little known but highly developed in these parts, which makes the short bacchanalia of the Green Drake very pale by comparison, if only because of the lengthy period during which grasshoppers are available. In like manner, I can speak of the newer and equally fascinating form of dry-fly fishing provided by that otherwise unwelcome newcomer the Japanese beetle, which at present is largely confined to the Eastern seaboard but, by all accounts of the entomologists, is gradually but inevitably moving westward and in time should appear on all the waters of this continent. True, it spells agricultural calamity wherever it appears, a consequence deplored by this author, who would gladly agree to its complete extinction; but if it blows an ill wind in the agricultural quarters, it blows with equal force for good in the angler's favor. During the annual period of its presence, lasting for perhaps three weeks, it appears in such tremendous quantities as to belie description, clinging to and devouring avidly every form of leafy growth. In some cases, where its attentions are concentrated on an especially palatable object such as a buttonwood tree, the ultimate result, in a comparatively short time, is similar to the midwinter starkness of hardwoods, but covered with lacework. The activity of these beetles is not confined to inland shrubbery but progresses to the very edge of all waters, where they can be found on the tips of any overhanging of trees or shrubs which inhabit the streamside; and in consequence, they are constantly dropping and being shaken onto the water by various influences, creating in this fashion a situation much like a hatch of duns, with the same succulent appeal to the attentions of the trout. Do not suppose that the presence of beetles and the activity of trout are restricted to the edges of the stream or near the banks. Let there be a current angling away from the bank or an obstruction causing such a current, and a stream of beetles is forthwith diverted even to the center and farther on some of our widest rivers, stirring and exciting a chain reaction of feeding activity. Then let there be other currents at these farther points, splitting and splitting again, diverging fanwise, carrying beetles in every direction to every feeding position in the river. These are not my observations alone but also those of many anglers of my acquaintance who wade and fish the broad Susquehanna for bass—reliable fellows, who can confirm these statements and who have done so by making numerous autopsies on bass caught in mid-river, disclosing stomachs gorged and distended by Japanese beetles and nothing else.

Many of those who live outside the orbit of the Japanese beetle may experience little or no interest in this account, and naturally so when there is no opportunity to observe it and fish to it, but I daresay that, if and when it finally arrives in consequence of its steady migration in those localities presently uninfested, there will be ample occasion to recall these words with a new significance.

Equally important, and no less abundant on limestone waters— perhaps more so than grasshoppers and Japanese beetles—is another class of insects so tiny in form as to be almost invisible on ordinary inspection, giving rise to the existence of a curious phenomenon that involves some of the most fundamental concepts of fish habits and angling technique.

Most of us, as a rule, regard 18 and 20 sizes in dry flies as being extremely small, but this is a situation that demands even smaller artificials. In fact, size 22 is still too large. But besides the matter of size, there is a strange twist in the manner with which they are taken, something which is seldom observed or accurately appraised. But once a friend and a very keen angler offered this remarkable opinion: that a great many times when we think a fish is nymphing, it is really taking very tiny insects, living or spent, from the surface. A statement of this sort, casually given, is likely to be accepted as a rare happenstance or an unusual incident which an angler might encounter at one time or another, but which is not really worthy of the angler's attention. Whatever may be its application on other waters, however, for the quiet meadow streams it is a monumental pronouncement representing and embracing a tremendous segment of regular angling procedure.

To explain the matter fully, I must revert to my early days on the limestone waters, when my visits were rather infrequent and I had no more serious purpose than to catch fish. I can recall now with some amusement the perplexity of myself and my friends on those days when we were confronted with feeding trout everywhere in sight, but trout feeding in such a manner as to render indeterminable the kind and source of food and the level from which it was being taken. At that time I did not have a particularly good knowledge of the various rise-forms, but believed from what I had read and heard that the trout were engaged in nymphing. The rise-form in evidence seemed to fit the standard description exactly—a slight humping or bulging of the water, no apparent break in surface, and no surface food visible. I flattered myself at the time for having solved the problem so neatly and immediately proceeded to offer to the fish every conceivable form of artificial nymph that I could find in my box, including some that had no counterpart in nature. All to no avail. This same comedy was repeated many times and my disappointment increased with every occurrence, except for a short-lived interval of renewed hope when a new pattern of nymph came on the market and I tried it, only to fail again.

At one time I believed that trout were feeding on snails in this manner, for they can sometimes be seen floating along just beneath the surface of the water; * and because I was aware of the great quantity of these creatures in those waters and the trout's fondness for them, I had a right to assume that they were the source of food and the reason for the peculiar rise-form. But subsequent observations indicated that the bulk of this food is plucked forcibly by the trout from stones and abutments to which these animals cling, while only a small proportion of them are taken when floating free. At Big Springs and in the Yellow Breeches, certain gravelly and rocky stretches are so densely populated with snails that the wading angler often experiences a distinct crunching sensation underfoot, but they are dislodged from their anchorage so seldom and in such small numbers that they could not be the cause of the mysterious surface activity of the trout.

Matters rested this way for some time until one memorable day a few years ago, when I was again confronted with this problem. I was on the Letort at the time in the company of Charles K. Fox, whose unusual skill and resourcefulness were severely challenged by this peculiar problem that I had failed to solve. It was shortly after he had acquired the beautiful stretch of the Letort which he now owns, and since he was anxious to familiarize himself as much as possible with the sporting possibilities, we spent a considerable number of days together, making many observations, fishing continuously and enjoying ourselves tremendously. Uppermost in our minds was the age-old problem of the bulging, humping trout. On this day they

---

* It is my impression that snails do not float freely in the water. Upon examination, these floating objects were discovered to be empty shells which were probably cast off or abandoned by the snails, leaving them light and buoyant enough to rise to the surface and float away.

were performing in the same mysterious fashion and we were making the usual offerings—nymphs of all kinds and sizes, wet flies whole, and wet flies trimmed—all of them fished with change of pace, dead drift, jerked in short strokes and long strokes, fished high and fished deep, but none of it produced a single fish. There were at least a dozen good trout within my immediate vicinity and I went from one to another in the same futile routine. Charlie was engaged in like manner, passing me at intervals and returning to try for another fish and giving me a questioning glance each time to which I am sure my own hopeless, unspoken query was sufficient answer.

The day might have ended in the usual manner except for the fact that my disillusionment reached a critical point and I quit fishing entirely, content to lay aside my tackle. Stretching myself prone on the bank with my eyes not more than one foot from the water, I beguiled the time by watching a small trout nearby feeding in the manner of his brothers. I had no particular object in watching the water, but I do it often, enjoying the mesmeric effect of smoothly gliding water and the pleasant lassitude it induces. I do not know how long I stayed this way on the bank, but it was long enough for me to acquire a sense of unreality about my surroundings and the water before me so that eventually I began to see things on the water which should have been only a figment of imagination—tiny little duns, dozens of them, some struggling to dispel the nymphal shuck, others sailing along in perfect repose with wings unfurled; other creatures too, minute beetle forms, moundlike in shape and shiny in appearance. I allowed this picture to dwell in the half-consciousness for some time until a sudden sharp awareness invaded my mind, causing me to forcus my attention on the water more closely. Gradually a suspicion of the truth dawned upon me. The sight before me was not figment, it was real.

A mild excitement stirred me and I hurried back to the fishing hut, where I found the thing I needed so badly—a square mesh bag, with one-eighth-inch mesh, which seemed a little too large but, doubled, made a mesh of approximately one sixteenth of an inch. I found two sticks of suitable length and thickness which I inserted in the bag, and by holding the two sticks apart I was able to maintain sufficient tension on the cloth to provide me with a satisfactory screening device. With this equipment, crudely fashioned but seemingly practical, I returned to the stream and chose a likely place for my experiment, a place where the flow of water was concentrated in a narrow channel, in order to intercept the greatest possible amount of surface drift. I inserted the net about half its length below the surface and was considerably annoyed to discover that so fine a mesh could offer so much resistance to even the gentle current of the Letort; the resistance caused the water to roll back upstream for a short distance, where the downstream current caught it and forced it to curl around either side of the net, carrying with it all of the flotsam I had hoped to entrap. Eventually I discovered that allowing the top of the net to lean downstream at a considerable angle lessened the resistance a great deal, thereby permitting a goodly amount of surface water to seep through the mesh and deposit the mysterious burden which interested me so much. I maintained this position for perhaps fifteen or twenty minutes, enduring the discomfort of icy water on my hands and wrists, then withdrew my catch and, carrying it to a place where the light was good, proceeded to examine the deposit as carefully as possible.

It did not take me long to find that my suspicions were confirmed, and I was properly elated. Clinging to the fine mesh of the cloth in great numbers and arranged in a straight line across the netting where it had coincided with the surface current were many tiny insect forms, unbelievably small—perfectly developed little duns no more than an eighth of an inch in any dimension; beetle forms, no more than three thirty-seconds of an inch long; reddish-gold ants in the winged state, so small that their slender waists were almost invisible; but most amazing of all, a respectable number of large black ants, fully a half or five eighths of an inch long. I could not understand immediately why I had never detected the presence of the large ants in my previous examinations and I returned to the stream again to discover the reason for this defection. After a careful inspection, I found to my surprise that the large ants did not float on the surface of the water but drifted awash, partly submerged and flush with the surface, wings sodden and blending with the background in such a way as to make them completely invisible to the angler.

The significance of these revelations was plain to me, and I envisaged a whole new line of thought and approach; but the task at hand was not completely finished, for it was imperative that I should establish the connection between the mysterious rises and the newly found food forms. I called to Charlie, who was engaged elsewhere at the time, acquainted him hurriedly with all that had occurred, and explained the necessity of obtaining a few trout for the purpose of making autopsies. He readily agreed, and we renewed our attempts to lure and capture these trout with livelier hopes, but with a different approach, although in a somewhat apprehensive state of mind because of the rapidly failing light. I searched in my fly box for a very small fly, dressed on the lightest of hooks, and finally selected one in size 20 with a reddish-tan fur body and a rusty dun hackle. I trimmed away all of the wing and almost all of the hackle except for two or three barbules on each side of the body, attaining in this manner the desired emphasis on the body and insuring the likelihood that it would float low and flush with the surface in the manner of the naturals. I lost no time in presenting this unusual lure to a feeding fish, noting quickly that it floated properly, for I could barely see it on the surface of the water, and promptly raised, hooked, and landed a trout of medium size.

In like manner, I succeeded in taking three more fish and lost a fifth in the weeds before I could turn its head and skulldrag it across the weed beds as I had done with the others. It was not pretty fishing, and ordinarily I would not have been guilty of such forceful and ungraceful manners on a trout stream (and I confess, too, that my trout were of a size which should have been returned to the water for the good of the fishing); but I was desperately in need of these specimens. The autopsies were performed without delay, before the digestive processes had time to render the stomach contents unrecognizable, and I found to my satisfaction that the entire bulk of the food taken consisted of the minute forms which I had netted earlier. I might add that the very smallest of the ants were present in great numbers, with a good representation of the wee duns and only a few of the very large ants. I cannot say for certain that any one of these insects was preferred over another by the trout, who seemingly took whatever came to them in the line of drift. The predominance of the little red ant in the autopsies may only mean that they were greater in number than the others on the water, in the same proportion as they were ingested by the trout.

If there is any doubt about choice of the correct pattern to be presented, it should be resolved in favor of the one which imitates most closely the insect which is most in evidence at any given time, and this seems to be a sound and logical rule to follow. However, I would like to caution my readers that this rule is not infallible and sometimes does not apply when there is a variety of large insects on the water. There are some seasons, notably the Green Drake season, when the trout often prefer a smaller, darker dun emerging at the same time; and I can recall a similiar instance, which takes place regularly on the Yellow Breeches stream in Cumberland County, when the concurring prevalence of the Hendrickson and several species of caddis flies, all in great profusion, makes it extremely difficult to determine the preference of the trout. As noted before, it is absolutely necessary for the angler to recognize the rise-form which identifies the taking of any particular species if he is to select the proper artificial.

I cannot emphasize too strongly the findings which I have reported in the preceding account of the peculiar feeding habits of trout when minute insects are being taken. It accounts for a great deal of the fishing to be had in the latter half of the season on rich meadow waters, to an extent and of a nature not heretofore appreciated by the anglers of these parts. It was an especially lucky stroke that I happened to be present when there was such a great number and such a variety of these minute insects. I have not seen an assortment of this kind since that day. In all likelihood there was a fortuitous overlapping of hatching or flight periods of these tiny creatures on that particular day. But rest assured that they are nearly always present on the surface of the stream, even though they are almost invisible. In the normal course of things they occur, a single species or perhaps two at one time, during their appointed season. Some are of short duration, although one amazing little red ant, in the winged state, appears almost daily and continues until November. The imitation of this insect in the floating pattern looms with increasing importance in fly-fishing practice on these waters; it should be tied as small as possible—size 20 short shank or 22 regular shank, or even size 24.

The little red ant still remains somewhat of a mystery; I have never actually seen it in flight, nor has anyone else as far as I know, although I have heard rumors to the effect that anglers have seen clouds of little red "bugs" on the Letort at the ungodly hour of five o'clock in the morning.

This abundance of minute forms is not confined to the Letort or the Newville water. Once when I was fishing the Yellow Breeches in May, I remarked about the appearance of the water, which seemed to be covered with a layer of fine particles, as though a giant hand had shaken salt and pepper on the surface, and I carelessly ascribed it to a shower of sooty grit and dust from the passing engines of a rail line immediately adjacent to the stream. Later in the day, I took the opportunity of examining a particularly fine specimen of the Light Cahill floating on the water, ladling it out with the palm of my hand, and was startled to discover that, along with Ithaca, my hand was entirely covered with the tiniest of the Ephemeridae. I repeated the operation several times, each time with the same result.

I can recall other occasions, on other streams—Honey Creek in Mifflin County and, for another, that wonderful dry-fly stream, Spruce Creek in Huntingdon County—where I was badly beaten by trout that performed in the strange fashion which I have already described.

Lest there should be some misconception about this phenomenon, particularly if someone should liken it to the kind of fishing which accrues from the heavy fall of spinners or imagos of the larger Ephemeridae, be advised that it bears no resemblance whatsoever to that kind of fishing. The rise-form of trout feeding on spent imagos may be similar, but there is the tremendous difference that a heavy hatch of duns preceding the fall of spinners, and easily observed, forewarns the angler of the kind of fishing to be expected in a day or so. He need not be present to see and capitalize on the return of spinners, for oftentimes trout will feed actively on the following day when there are no

insects in sight and when the spent forms are lying adrift in the backwaters and eddies, flush with the surface and almost invisible. If trout
are observed feeding quietly in the bulging, humping manner, the
angler, being forewarned, may safely conclude that the spent artificial
is the proper choice for presentation. I insist, too, that no comparison
should be made with the case of trout feeding delicately on smuts, for,
small as they are, they can usually be seen in clouds, milling about
above the water and rising and dropping in unison. If a trout waiting
below and just beneath the surface can be seen making a quiet and
dainty rise, it is fair to assume that he has taken one of these tiny
insects and will probably take more. The circumstances are too easily
related in this case to leave the source of food in doubt.

The imitation of all of these minute insects, as well as the larger
May-fly duns and spinners, has been an object of great concern to
me. I feel that there is a great need for specialization in the field of
terrestrial insects and the minute forms—a specific treatment, heretofore neglected, with the object of creating satisfactory artificials intended to be used when their employment is indicated, and further-
more a formulation of the proper tactics to insure their success when
presented to the fish.

Some progress has been made in this direction, warranting the
belief that a solid foundation has been laid, lacking only those small
refinements to achieve perfection. On this score I have not hesitated to
capitalize on the noble assistance of many interested and sympathetic
friends. Once, when I was wandering about the Letort during the
grasshopper season, I had a chance meeting with Gene Craighead and
his brother Charlie, both fine anglers and both of them highly absorbed, as I was, in the spectacle of several large trout feeding with
wild abandon on grasshoppers, which not only could be seen all
around the meadow in great quantity but also were finding their way
into the stream in surprising numbers. Our conversation was largely
limited to the problem of devising a proper imitation of the grasshopper, and I confessed that up to that point I had not attained anything of a satisfactory nature. Thereupon Charlie informed me that
he had considered the problem somewhat and the night before had
completed the tying of several patterns which might be successful. I
was inclined to be skeptical but nevertheless accepted two of them,
which he graciously offered to me from his fly box. One was of
a greenish-yellow coloration, about an inch and a quarter long, with
brownish wings tied flat. There is a wide range of coloration in grasshoppers of the same species, but Charlie insisted that the yellow one
was best. Gene has succeeded in identifying the natural as Melanoplus
differentialis, a common type, after Thomas.

I did not use Charlie's imitation that evening, but I now have every reason for remembering that particular gift for a long, long time to come. It is no longer in my possession, being now the property of one of the legendary trout of the Letort unless it has rusted away and fallen from that capacious mouth. I got into him several days later, when he was gorging on the natural, pulping and slashing at every one that came down his line of drift. The grim contest that ensued lasted for two hours and a half, necessarily so, for I was using 4x gut and had to let him have his way in order to conserve my tackle. He was a tremendous fish, awesome in point of length, girth, and dignity. Crisis after crisis took place during this epic struggle—times when he dashed through one weed bed into another, my leader dragging heavily from the burden of weed caught by this maneuver, other times when he darted in one direction or another, looping the line around an obstruc-tion by making a wide turn and returning to his original position. Then there were times when he revolved interminably in a tight little circle, slapping viciously at the leader at each turn, forcing me to gauge to a nicety the exact psychological moment when the leader should be slackened in order to soften the blow. All of these emer-gencies I was able to meet with proper countermeasures, but he finally broke me after the leader had been worn thin at the jaw line and when he was wallowing hoglike in a little bay where I expected to beach him. I had to stand helplessly, watching him feebly inch his way into the current and safety, his head lolling and his massive tail arching slowly from side to side. I dare not guess at his weight for fear of inviting the questioning glances of my polite friends. In any event I have a reliable witness to that memorable engagement, one who will swear to at least one half of what I say!

I found little comfort in the proffered condolences of my sympathetic companion and I could only increase my discomfort by recalling a similar incident which befell me one clear evening, years ago. The memory of the awful thing that rose and engulfed my fly at the tail of a long pool and the subsequent break was considerably sharpened by my present loss of the Letort giant. My musings drifted into specula-tions about this and other trout which have become a substantial part of the legend and folklore surrounding this amazing little stream.

Could my fish have been that monster that rose, wraithlike and sinister, from the murky deeps and hung suspended and motionless on the surface, his huge dorsal fin protruding from the water, before the pop-eyed and incredulous gaze of farmer Jones, who was walking his pasture at the time? And did he know, by his wisdom acquired from contentions with mankind, that farmer Jones was seriously debating the choice of pitchfork or rifle to end his existence, when he sank out of sight at the critical moment?

Could he have been that other monstrosity before whom a lady fisher, that Diana of the Letort, dared to cast her feathered offering, which was accepted, thereby making her an unwilling and tremulous appendage while he towed her slowly but relentlessly downstream for two solid hours, finally leaving her in tearful despondency?

Or was he that appalling creature that I saw from a high bank, one clear summer day, my footsteps suddenly halted and all motion stilled by the apparation of a giant trout slowly easing his way through the clear waters of the Letort? I remember thinking at the time that a yardstick would not measure him. Here memory cannot go much further, for there was only that one terrifying instant when he rose slowly and majestically, looked at my fly and refused it, then gently sank out of sight forever. Few of us have enjoyed the great good fortune that attended Don Martin's glorious achievement when finally he landed his stream-bred fifteen-and-a-half-pounder at Newville.

With good fortune or bad, a single incident of this nature, necessarily rare, does not establish conclusively the excellence of the aforementioned grasshopper pattern, but it goes a long way toward convincing me that it has merit and should serve as a model whose virtues must be copied.

But many pitfalls await the man who is bent on discovering and imitating all of the insects upon which trout feed. I venture to say that of all the insects which inhabit our streams none are more plentiful or more freely taken than cress bugs, Mancasellus brachyurus. They exist and multiply in unbelievable quantities in these waters, harbored in comparative security by the dense weed beds of elodea, and are available to these trout any day, any season of the year. They are truly the bread-and-butter of trout diet in these limestone waters.

Consider the following seemingly implacable logic. If this insect is the most plentiful of all and if this is the one the trout take in greatest volume, *ergo* it should be the one to imitate above all others and, what's more, should occupy the most important position in a new series of artificial patterns.

Who would censure me for following this line of reasoning? Who would dispute the propriety of trying to imitate this interesting creature? What angler flytier would not rejoice at the opportunity of expending time and labor on such an imitation, with the prospect of enjoying marvelous sport with it even though it must be fished wet style? These were the considerations which prompted me to try to imitate the cress bug, but believe me, abstract logic of this kind, without practical considerations, sometimes commits us to the worst kind of folly. Rest assured that more time and effort were spent on this one insect alone than on all of the others combined, and always with the same negative results. Repeated failures with the various concoctions only served to dampen and finally destroy the earlier confidence with which I began this task, and everywhere I went, limestone anglers increased their demands for a successful pattern of the cress bugs. They, too, were afflicted with the same kind of logic that guided my investigations.

For a long time, longer than I care to remember, I was not aware of the hopelessness of trying to imitate Mancasellus. I clung to the belief that it was only a matter of gaining the right size, color, shape, and translucency. But all variations in these respects were worthless.

The reason for failure did not lie in the mechanical execution of the imitation. The reason went much deeper—in fact, into the darkest recesses of the weed beds. For I finally discovered that Mancasellus is not a free swimmer. It is rarely found in mid-water, never on top, occasionally on the bottom. Hence the trout never get it except by burrowing into the dense weed beds and picking it off the stalks and branches of elodea, chara, and other weed growth.

It must now be clear to everyone that to cast an imitation of Mancasellus, no matter how perfect, into the weed bed itself in order to attract a feeding trout is worse than trying to find the proverbial needle in a haystack; for in the latter case there would be but one needle but in the former, countless numbers of the living likeness of the imitation that no trout could possibly find.

At this point an interesting question must have occurred to the reader, as it did to me. If a good imitation of Mancasellus were to be cast, not into the weed beds, but to a trout feeding in mid-water where his vision is not obstructed, would he not recognize and accept it confidently as the kind of food that he knows best? Unfortunately, the answer is no! Because of the physical characteristics of these waters and the feeding habits of the fish, the trout are rarely found in mid-water. The dense weed beds of elodea fill the streams from bank to bank and the growth almost reaches the surface of the water in mid-summer, but there is always a very deep but narrow channel where the main current runs, and sometimes multiple diverging channels running parallel to the main one. The trout habitually lie in the bottom of these channels, whether feeding or at rest, and rarely take a feeding position over a weed bed itself. To do so would be an assumption of risk that these wild creatures cannot afford, since the water over the weeds appears to be very shallow and provides no cover. If these fish are inclined to feed, they must do one of two things—take their food off the weed bed itself, or come to the top for surface food. Confinement to the deep, narrow channels does not allow for much wandering about for mid-water foods, and besides, this kind of effort is not necessary. But I must say, to the unending delight and satisfaction of all those who fish these waters, the trout often prefer to come to the top when surface food is present. This conclusion is inevitable since we know that Mancasellus is always present and easier and safer to secure. The reason for this preference is not difficult to determine when one considers that the cress bug, in spite of its large size, is for the most part composed of a hard, shell-like covering and very little meat. On the score of food value, he is really second choice to anything else on the surface and certainly not to be compared with the fat duns, grasshoppers, Japanese beetles, and the like.*

I earnestly hope that this account of the cress bug will serve to dissuade all of my brother anglers from any further attempts to employ or manufacture imitations of this insect, for such imitations are bound to be worthless in actual use. This I must emphasize in spite of the occasional success that some anglers enjoy with imitations that they are pleased to call cress bugs. In any event these successes occur when the imitation is used on certain gravelly stretches, free of weeds, where the artificial of Mancasellus ranks no better than any one of the modern nymph artificials.

There are other peculiarities in the character of the water and the feeding habits of these trout which must be considered in devising new patterns. The placid surface, the gentle current, and the clarity of the water form a combination that bodes ill for the angler whose fly pattern is not correct, for the trout attune themselves to these conditions and reflect all of them in the deliberateness of their movements, the careful inspection of each passing object, and their surreptitious manner of actually taking food from the surface. Sometimes the take is so nearly imperceptible as to seem doubtful to the keenest of eyes, and the education of the limestone fisherman is never complete until he has come to see, recognize, and catalogue in his mind every little disturbance of the surface that spells trout taking top-water food. He must learn to know that tiny flick, that little curl of the water that appears and is gone in a flash. Sometimes it is a little roll, or humping of the surface, but he must never, never mistake this for a nymphing trout, as we noted earlier in this chapter. This is a true surface rise and the water is, in fact, broken, although the angler will probably never see the actual rupture of the surface.

It is a peculiar sensation to anyone who has a sound knowledge of these things to sit and watch a phenomenon of this nature while a parade of anglers go by, never seeing, never knowing that over against

*These conclusions are offered as perfect examples of the qualitative preference which trout seem to exercise when there is a choice of foods. I am fairly certain that the quality of various insect foods is the most important factor in explaining the selectivity of feeding trout. Such selectivity can exist between foods above and below the surface as well as on the surface. It does not really make any difference to a trout whether his food is wet, dry, or slightly damp; it is likely that he never knows. These distinctions exist only as a procedural index to which the fisherman must constantly refer in order to reach the level of the feeding fish with the proper lure.

the far bank a lusty three-pounder is feeding industriously at regular intervals for perhaps four or five hours.

Even though armed with this knowledge, the expert is oftentimes unaware of the presence of surface-feeding trout. The following incident is appropriate for the purpose of illustration: Three veteran limestone anglers sat on the bank of the Letort on a day in mid-July during the 1946 season, not more than twenty feet from the nearest edge of the stream. They had been there for several hours, chatting, smoking, and watching the water carefully. One of them finally noticed a small disturbance of the surface against the far bank. A short interval elapsed and again the disturbance appeared. The angler retrieved his tackle, made the proper approach and sent his fly to the desired spot. A fine fish of some two and a half pounds was raised, hooked, and landed and an immediate autopsy was performed. All of the stomach contents were perfectly recognizable. Digestion had not taken place to any degree and the following food forms were revealed: fifteen or sixteen ants, five or six houseflies, three or four lightning bugs, two cress bugs. The alternative figures represent allowances for broken parts. It is significant that this trout had been feeding continuously in the presence of these very keen dry-fly anglers, and it is more significant that all but two of the food forms were of the surface variety; and yet this activity went on unnoticed for a considerable length of time.

Is it any wonder that such trout are not to be taken so easily! More than this, however, is required of the angler who seeks the maximum in sport with trout of the limestone waters.

The matter of proper presentation of the fly is a thing which really belongs to a book on the art of fly casting. That subject is not within the province of this volume, but surely some reference to this subject must be made herein in order to insure good results from the new patterns; for no matter how perfect an imitation may be, if it is not delivered in the proper manner it is bound to fail, along with the reputation of its designer.

The matter of presentation calls to mind another peculiarity of Letort trout, in particular, with reference to the manner of taking the dry fly, and must be divided into two distinct phases: (1) the observation post, and (2) the taking position. In the vast majority of cases, these trout do not lie close to the surface at feeding time but occupy a position very deep in the channels, as noted before. When the fly is pitched—note carefully—in front of the observation post—not the taking position—the first movement is a gentle swaying motion rearward, utterly graceful and continuing low in the channel for a distance of some two to four feet; then there is a sharp lift of the body upward and the fly is intercepted at the taking position.

Time after time I have commiserated in silence with a brother angler who persisted in casting to a taking position, not realizing and not appreciating the fact that he was casting his fly, very accurately, let it be said, but uselessly to a spot some three or four feet behind the trout; and they simply will not come back that far to take a fly. This is an excusable error, for it is given only to the most rigidly trained and keenest of eyes to know that the shadowy detachment occurring in the depths of the channel is a trout moving backward under the fly.

On the other hand, it sometimes happens that the trout will often halt the sharp upward movement just short of the fly, reverse himself and follow the fly for three or four more feet downstream, no doubt for a closer inspection. Nothing is more trying to the angler than this exasperating habit; for, although the threat of drag in a normal drift

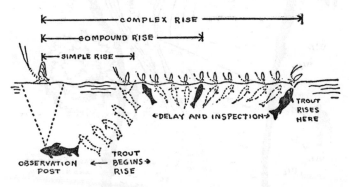

of three or four feet is worry enough, when it is stretched to seven or eight feet the problem is considerable. There is always impending the crisis when free float ends and drag begins, and the trout may have chosen that moment to decide that the fly is authentic. The result in most cases is a disdainful flick of the tail as the trout drops low and slithers back to his original position, the observation post. If the unfortunate angler encounters this misfortune often enough, it begins to assume a nightmarish quality, to such an extent that it will disturb the composure of the sturdiest of natures, not infrequently manifesting itself in actual physical tremors.

There is yet another variation of this feeding habit which the angler must recognize in order to present the fly properly. Sometimes the line of drift flows straight downstream, then angles sharply away toward the center of the stream; this is often caused by an obstruction near the bank, a weed bed, or a bend in the stream. Sometimes the change of drift originates in the center and is directed toward the banks. In either event a trout may occupy an observation post at the exact point where the flow begins to break away. In these cases, the first movement of a trout is not directly backward, but consists of a gentle, undulating

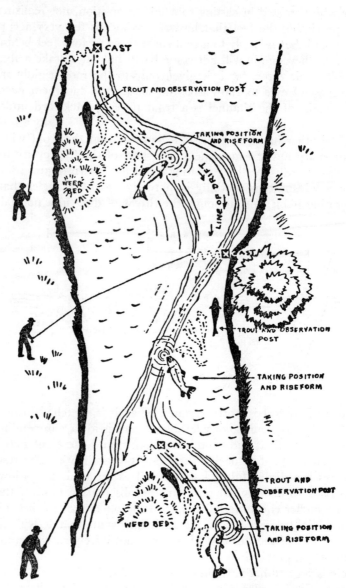

movement sideways, progressing across the stream and low in the
channel for three or four feet; then comes the sudden, sharp, upward
lift and the fly is taken.

The unsuspecting angler may easily be deceived into casting his
fly directly upstream, thinking that the observation post is ahead of the
taking position, when in truth the cast should have been made four
feet to the side of the taking position and two feet ahead.

The case of the box-elder trout is a graphic illustration of this point. I first saw this fish one sunny afternoon in mid-June. His taking position was four feet below the trunk of a box elder and four feet out from the bank. I watched him feed for a while, then decided to try for him. When a number of casts proved of no avail, I ceased all further attempts until I could make a study of this particular fish. On my next visit to this spot, I was elated to discover that he was feeding in his usual quiet, unobtrusive manner. A study of the currrent at this point revealed that the line of drift was concentrated at the trunk of the box elder, then broke sharply away toward the center. I felt sure that this trout's observation post was some four or five feet upstream and very near the trunk of the box elder, thereby requiring a cast a foot or two above the trunk and a float of six or seven feet in order to take him. I could not have picked a more unfavorable day for this trial. A westerly wind was steadily blowing half a gale directly cross-stream toward me so that in order to reach the desired spot with my fly it was necessary to shoot the cast through an opening in the branches of the box elder some three feet in diameter. Time after time my casts were buffeted about, blown back and misdirected. My fly landed on every spot near this trout but the right one. I stopped casting entirely, gently waving the rod back and forth, hoping for a cat's-paw in the wind in order to make at least one accurate cast. A momentary lull finally came along, and seizing the opportunity I shot the line through the opening with all the speed I could muster. I was rewarded with a perfect cast and almost immediately I could barely perceive the shadowy outline of the fish as he moved sideways and slightly backward to intercept the fly. The surprise engendered by the unexpected success of the cast and the actual rise of the fish induced a momentary loss of poise, causing my hands to freeze to the rod and line while the trout made a sudden lunge and broke me. This same fish, a fat three-pounder, was subsequently captured by Charlie Fox in his usual skillful manner and exhibited evidence of a fresh scar on the lower left jaw.

For the above reasons, I will continue to advocate the use of slack-line casts rather than the curve casts, wherever the former are possible. The great fault with the slack-line casts lies in the fact that there is the likelihood of lining the trout with the leader, directly overhead; but this can easily be avoided by making the casts at right angles to the stream or nearly so. The long drift afforded by a slack leader will oftentimes overcome the difficulties of the delayed rise.

The application of the slack-line delivery to a variety of circumstances makes it especially valuable. Let me mention another of these situations which is common on limestone streams.

Let us suppose, for example, that the angler is standing on the left bank, looking upstream. Directly across-stream, against the far bank, there is a small bit of backwater or bay in which a trout is feeding very delicately on tiny duns, but feeding so close to the weeds which border the stream that part of the rise-form itself is dissipated against the weed stalks. The feeding trout seems to be actually touching the weeds in these instances as he takes in one insect after another, and usually he will not move a single inch from this line of drift. Let us suppose further that there is a narrow piece of fast current between the angler's position and the little bay or backwater. Obviously, the caster's problem is to place the fly tight against the bank of weeds without actually touching them but not more than a half inch or one inch away from them, at the same time insuring a long free float to circumvent the possibility of drag by the intervening current. Curve casts are absolutely useless in these cases since the curve itself lies in the slow back water, affording no pressure against the upstream side of the curve to equalize the pace of leader and fly. What really happens is that the line is immediately seized by the current, causing leader and fly to describe an arc, actually traveling upstream, then they are whipped around and taken by the fast water out of sight.

To my knowledge, there is no situation more exasperating than this one, especially if the angler allows his determination to exceed his patience. Time after time, ignoble defeat is the lot of expert and novice alike under these conditions and the temptation to abandon these fish entirely and forever is common to both. However, the angler need not despair of ever taking these fish, for there is at least one maneuver that is successful part of the time. It is questionable that anyone will ever score heavily on fish of these habits, but if the angler wishes to try he can employ a special slack-line cast which is executed according to these directions.

Let the angler take his position directly across from the trout in such a way as to face the opposite bank squarely. Aim the cast high above the weeds and deliver it far beyond the trout, *over the land* on the opposite bank for perhaps ten feet, bringing it to a halt with a decided abruptness that will cause it to recoil sharply toward the angler, thereby achieving a series of close-packed loops on the surface of the backwater and allowing the fly just barely to clear the weeds on the return and fall within an inch or so of the weedline. Theoretically it is a successful cast, since the series of loose coils pay out slowly into the fast current, allowing the fly to pursue a natural and leisurely drift in the backwater. In actual practice, the placement of the fly within an inch or so of the weedline by this indirect method is a rare bit of luck even the most expert would appreciate. Of course, this procedure is unnecessary if it is possible to cross to the other bank where a short line can be cast with ease to such a fish, but some of these streams, particularly the Letort, are too deep to permit such a crossing.

One more observation in connection with this cast is worthy of note; that is, in order to obtain maximum benefit from the slack line, the forward cast must be delivered with considerable force, stopping its forward motion sharply, thereby causing it to jerk backward and fall in loose curves on the water. I have never been able to do it properly with soft rods and light lines. In recent times, I have resorted to heavier lines and stiffer rods in order to accomplish my purpose.

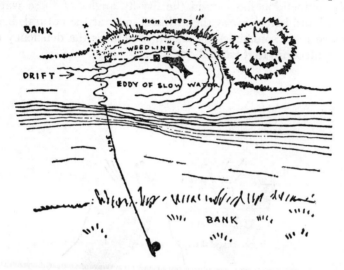

During the season of 1947, I acquired and used exclusively a fly line with a belly dimension of .070 inch, or triple A. This was variously described by my friends as clothesline, bull rope, lariat, and so forth; but I can truthfully say that I never enjoyed a more successful season with these difficult fish, and that I ascribe a great measure of this success to the use of this combination, simply because I can throw a better slack line.

Such is the character of the fish and the fishing on the Letort and other limestone waters—exacting to a high degree, where tackle and technique must be finely adjusted and, above all, the artificial pattern must be correct. This last requirement is always uppermost in the minds of those who practice the dry fly on these waters; and any effort to improve patterns has always met with the approbation and encouragement of these fine anglers.

It is the natural consequence of adherence to the principle of *following the hatches*, systematically pursued from date to date in accordance with the tabulated emergence periods of the important insects. It means more than fishing to all of the hatches of a single stream, good and poor, for the entire season. It means, rather, a constant pilgrimage from stream to stream at the appointed time when the heaviest hatch of fly for each of them is in progress or about to begin. I do not know how much this principle is followed elsewhere, if at all, but for these anglers of the limestone streams it is more than a habit; it is a religion.

Little wonder, then, that for them the artificial has become an object of special concern, suffering as it does the eternal competition of the naturals for the attention of the discerning trout.

This competition has caused the dry-fly angler of these waters to look hard and long, now at the artificial, now at the natural, bringing into sharp focus sometimes the merit, sometimes the deficiency of the dainty confections that we call dry flies.

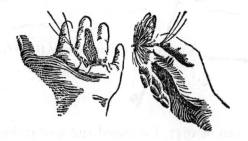

Three Bottles
of Claret

W. C. PRIME

*W. C. Prime was one of your grandfather's favo-
rite angling authors. Prime might be said to have
fished and written in the classic—or traditional—
manner. He did not write for the man in the street.
Rather, like many English fishing writers, his
books were intended for the "gentleman" angler.
"Three Bottles of Claret" might be described as
one of the lighter chapters from* I Go A-Fishing,
which is not a frivolous book.

IT HAD BEEN a delicious afternoon on Profile Lake; one of those
days when the very glory of the other country seems to come
down among our mountains. The little lake had presented, as
usual on such evenings, a gay and brilliant scene. It was a lake of
Paradise. A dozen boats were out with parties of ladies or with an-

glers, some of the latter fishing with floats and worms, some casting
flies, and now and then getting up fair trout. I had passed the time
after a fashion that is somewhat lazy and luxurious, lying at full length
in the bottom of my boat, drifting idly around while I read an old
book, occasionally sinking into a doze and dreaming. As evening came
down the various parties left the lake, and at last in the twilight Dupont came up in his boat alongside of mine, and we found ourselves,
as often before, alone on the lake.

Among all my memories of trout fishing there are none more pleasant than the memories of those evenings on Profile Lake, when my
friend and I, with our boats at anchor a few rods apart, have cast our
flies long after the darkness prevented our seeing their fall, and whether
we got rises or not were content to see the stars come over the mountains, or the moonlight descend into the ravine and silver the surface
of the lake.

This evening was profoundly still; not a breath of air disturbed the
leaf of a tree. One could hardly hope to find a Profile Lake trout so
foolish as to take a fly on such a glassy surface. I was lazy and indolent,
but Dupont was making long and steady casts, always graceful, and as
sure as graceful. I paused and watched him. I could just see in the
twilight the fall of his tail fly, some fifty feet away from his hand, as
it touched the water close inshore under a great rock, and I felt in my
own arm the thrill which was in his as I saw the slightest commotion
on the surface, and knew that a good fish had risen and "sucked in"
the fly without striking it. It was a very pretty contest then, with his
light Norris rod and a fish that would weigh over a pound. The silence
was profound. No sound on water or land or in the air. Few night
birds are heard in our forests thereabouts, and in the cool evenings the
insects are still. So I looked on while he patiently wearied and landed
his fish—a good size for this overfished lake, where the trout have
little chance to grow large. It is in some respects the most wonderful
trout pond I have ever known. In the rush of travel hundreds of men
and boys, and many ladies, take trout here every summer. Few days
in July and August see less than ten or fifteen rods on the lake. We
have estimated an annual catch of at least three thousand trout in this
small pond, and the supply seems equally great each year. This is
largely due to the protection of the smaller pond above the lake, which
is the breeding place, and where no fishing is permitted.

I had taken nothing. In fact, I had not made a dozen casts. But
now I began to work, laying the flies away in the shoal water near the
inlet. It is the advantage of fly fishing that one can cover so large a
space of water without moving position. It is an easy matter in still
weather to whip every inch of a circle of a hundred and fifty feet
diameter.

The fisherman who tries the water of a new lake, uncertain whether there be any trout in it, should, if possible, cast at evening near an inlet. He will often find the largest trout in water not over six inches deep. It is probable that at this hour of the day the large trout are on the feed, and seek near the inlet the smaller fish as well as insects. I remember an evening in Northern New Hampshire, when Dupont and myself took twenty-seven trout between sunset and an hour after dark, every one of which weighed over two pounds, and every one took the fly in water about ten inches deep. There was a brilliant full moon that night, and they rose later than usual. An old Adirondack guide has frequently told me that in those waters large trout rise freely to the fly between one and three o'clock in the morning. I have never been able to verify his saying, for I have never loved fishing well enough to toil all night at it as did the apostles, nor to get out of bed very long before day. I have, however, not infrequently cast for a half hour before the dawn on water where trout were abundant, and I never got a rise until day was fairly shining. But I am not willing to place my limited experience against the assertion of the guide, backed as it was by the statement of sportsmen that they had known him to go out of camp at midnight and return before daylight with a load of trout. In some of the streams of the Pacific coast I have been told trout are taken with bait at all hours of the night in streams where one is seldom taken in daylight. All this goes to the question whether fish sleep, a question not yet satisfactorily answered.

I could not provoke a rise, and it grew dark apace. I threw my line back for a long cast. It was very near being a case of broken rod, for there was a sharp jerk as the flies went through the air, the line came in all in a heap, and something fell into the water close to the boat. I picked up the slack and hauled in—a bat. The wretch had taken a small black gnat, and the hook was in his throat. So much for casting a fly in the dark. It was the last cast I made that evening. We went ashore and strolled up the dark road to the hotel.

The windows blazed their light into the gloom of the Notch, making a strange contrast to the darkness of the forest road from which we emerged. The sound of the music in the drawing room drove all forest ideas out of one's head. It was nine o'clock, and the dancing had begun. The Profile House is a small world in the midst of the mountain solitudes. Including guests and persons employed about the house, there were nearly eight hundred men, women, and children there that night, and every station in life was represented.

Have I anywhere in these sketches mentioned my old friend, Major Wilson? He was sometimes one of our group at the Rookery in years past, but since he had grown to full age he seldom ventured far from his own dinner table. Why should he, since he esteemed it the main luxury of life? Do not imagine him a useless man, a mere *bon vivant*. He was a hearty old man, a patron of art, and very generous withal. A man is none the worse for loving a good dinner. Gastronomy is as much one of the fine arts as trout-fishing or sculpture. It is very depraved taste which despises good cookery. Table decoration, furniture, and provision form almost the only safe standard by which to estimate national or individual civilization; for civilization is not, as some people imagine, a question of morals or religion. Christianity is not synonymous with civilization; neither does its introduction civilize a nation. It deals with the individual man, not with communities. Men call New York a Christian city, England a Christian country, the people of the United States a Christian people. This is pure nonsense. There are not more than one in ten, perhaps not more than one in a hundred, of the people who are in any proper sense Christians; whose morals, manners, or characters have been directly touched by the refining influences of personal Christianity. Obviously the influence and example of the Christian has its effect on his companions, but that is no reason for calling a people Christian who have only a small sprinkling of Christians among them. Nor can we stand a comparison with some heathen nations. Christianity cannot afford to be saddled with the absurd and barbarous customs of our social life, or with the manners and customs of so-called Christian peoples, especially when it appears that the civilization of Japan is in many respects in advance of that of England or America. We have innumerable habits and manners which are barbarous. The dress of a gentleman or of a lady in New York in this year 1873 is barbarous, whether regarded by standards of taste, comfort, or usefulness. A dress coat was no more absurd a costume on the West Coast African, who wore nothing else, than it is on the diner-out of New York. A stovepipe hat is so thoroughly ridiculous that no barbarous nation has ever invented anything remotely resembling it.

Seek a standard where you will, and, after all, it will be found that the manner and matter of feeding is a tolerably safe one by which to measure comparative civilization.

The Major had been a week or two at the Profile House, living at his ease, and rather content with the table, which was not by any means a poor one, and solaced for any minor failures by his own wine. He did not wander much among the mountains, but contented himself, book in hand, with the sunshine on the broad piazza, and evenings in his own rooms, where his man John, who had been his personal servant more than thirty years, took care to make him comfortable. His rooms were near mine, and that evening after Dupont and myself had dined—for I make it dinner however late the coming home occurs —I went to see the Major.

One can be very comfortable in a summer hotel if he will take a little trouble and go to a little expense. One cannot be comfortable at any summer hotel in America or the world without these. The rooms of my friend were two ordinary bedrooms, one of which he used as a *salon*; and by a very little exertion it had been made into a cozy and rather brilliant room. The table was literally covered with books and periodicals, for the Major had a hunger for reading which could never be satisfied, and every mail brought him packages. He was tearing off the envelope from an Innsbruck book catalogue as I entered the room, and I recognized the label of an old acquaintance.

"So you get catalogues from Carl Pfaundler, do you? I have picked up some good things in his shop."

"Yes. I have a pretty extensive list of booksellers sending me their catalogues, but it's getting to be rather a nuisance. I've about done with buying old books. Come in; find a chair—John, a chair—help yourself to the claret. You dined late, I fancy. Did you get me a good trout for breakfast?"

"Not a trout. I took a bat on the wing. Did you ever eat bat?"

"Never. I suppose it would be about the same thing as mice. Mice are not good; the flavor is musky. Rats are much better, and very decent eating, if they are properly fed. I don't know why bats might not be made eatable. They are carnivorous; but dogs are good food, if well cooked. However, we don't need to try experiments in this land, where the markets are better than in any other country on earth."

"I'm glad to hear you say that, Major. I have said it often, and it's pleasant to be backed by a man of your gastronomic taste."

"Who disputes it? Surely no one who knows anything about eating. There are articles, of course, which are to be found in other countries superior to the same article here; but America is the only land for general good eating. One gets fearfully tired of a European kitchen, even with all the resources of Paris in the palmiest days of the Brothers. But here the varieties of fish and flesh are inexhaustible; and fruit— nowhere in the world is there a fruit market comparable with that of New York. An English sole is not equal in flavor to a flounder taken in clear water at Stonington, and a turbot is no better than a tautog. Shad, sheepshead, Spanish mackerel, red snappers, bass, bluefish—a fresh bluefish is glorious—where will you stop in the list of fish that abound on our coast, every one of which is better than any salt-water fish known on the other side of the Atlantic?"

"Excepting sardines."

"Well, I may perhaps except sardines."

"May? None of your prejudices, old fellow. There's no dish of fish to be invented equal to sardines, fried and served as they used to do it in the old San Marco at Leghorn. I lament the closing of that house with profound regret. I have gone down from Florence more than once to pass a night there just for the sake of the delicious breakfast I used to get on those sardines. No one else cooked or served them so in any town on the French or Italian coast."

"I remember fifty years ago seeing them catch sardines along the shore at Naples."

"Yes, I have sat many a morning in the window at the old Vittoria, looking out on the sea and watching the sardine nets come in, glittering with diamonds; and I have taken them with a rod at Leghorn."

"I never found trout south of the Alps. Why is that?"

"Simply because you never looked for them yourself. The hotels rarely furnish them; but you can get them in Lombardy if you want them. I have taken trout in the Izak above Trent, and at Botzen."

"My dear boy, what a muddle your brain must be in about historic places. The idea of talking about trout fishing at Trent, a place with which one never associated any idea but of profound ecclesiastical and theological significance."

"There's a charm in trout fishing, Major, which you would have appreciated if your education had not been neglected. It has never failed me; and I have studied no small amount of history as I strolled along the bank of a trout stream. Were you ever at Salzburg?"

"There several times, and always fared well at the Hôtel de l'Europe."

"Ah yes, you think first of the hotel. So do many old travelers. So I confess do I sometimes. A poor inn is a fearful obstacle to the enjoyment of art or antiquity. But there are trout streams around Salzburg, and some fine trout in them; and I have passed some of the pleasantest days along those streams, looking up at the grand pile of the Untersberg, in whose caverns the two emperors sit face to face, sleeping, but now nearly ready to wake. I was fishing there in June, 1871, and wondering what could happen to rouse the mighty Charles, and a month later the thunders of Weissembourg must have shaken the imperial slumbers. But Ischl, Major, Ischl—were you ever at Ischl? It is the most lovely spot in Europe. Go there before you die, and don't go to the Hôtel Bauer on the hill, but to Sarsteiner's, the Kreutz, a capital inn, with old books in the halls, and pictures of all sorts of places, and large bedrooms and saloons, and a kitchen that is not to be surpassed in or out of the Tyrol. It will suit you. The valley of the Traun is a glorious place, and the river is the only river my eyes ever saw which is indisputably superior in beauty of water to our White Mountain streams. The delicate apple-green tint does not harm its transparency. You can see bottom in twenty feet of water. It flows like a liquid chrysoprase, and the trout and grayling in it are superb. Mr. Sarsteiner controls all the fishing in the valley, and is himself an angler, a man of reading and extensive travel, and is interested in fish breeding. The fishing is close at hand too. I went out of the house one evening about seven o'clock, and walked in five minutes to the other side of the Traun, just above the bridge and opposite the promenade, where the river glides swiftly down over a pebble bottom. It was nearly dark, but in fifteen minutes I had a half-dozen good trout which the boy stowed safely in a barrel; for in Switzerland and the Tyrol, when you go afishing, you have always with you a boy who carries a small barrel in which it is his duty to keep the fish alive until they are transferred to the tank which every inn keeps stocked with plenty of trout. It had gotten to be quite dark, and I was casting a large white moth across the swift current, when I got the heaviest strike, with one exception, that I ever felt from a trout in Europe. He made a splendid struggle; but the little Norris rod did its duty, and I brought him to barrel in a few minutes—that is to say, I landed and unhooked him, and handed him to the boy while I hurried to cast again. I had made only one cast when the boy shouted, 'He's too big for the barrel'; and I turned to laugh at his vain endeavors to crowd his tail into the hole. He was, in fact, two inches longer than the barrel, which had not been made in expectation of such fish. So I slipped him into his short quarters, and gave up the sport, and in five minutes he was the admiration of a crowd in the kitchen of the Golden Cross, swimming around in a small tank into which cold spring water poured a steady stream. He weighed only two and three quarter pounds English; but Mr. Sarsteiner told me that, though he had seen larger trout there, he was one of the largest, if not the largest, that he had ever known taken with a fly in the Tyrol. All the way up the river to Lake Haldstadt there are plenty of fine trout, and I have enjoyed many a day's sport along the beautiful stream."

"Now for the exception."

"What exception?"

"You said it was the heaviest strike, with one exception, that you ever felt in Europe."

"I'm a little ashamed of that other. You remember the Rhine above the falls, from Schaffhausen to the Château Laufen? I was fishing it one evening, years ago, in a boat, with a strong German boy to row. I had to keep a sharp lookout, for the current is wild, and it is not quite sure that, if you are careless, you may not go over the falls. By the by, Major, with all our boasting, we haven't many cataracts in America as fine as the Rhine Falls. It's a grand piece of scenery. It looks better from below than above, however, if you happen to be in a heavy boat with a stupid boy as oarsman. We were just on the edge of the swift water, and I told him to hold on by the bushes and keep the craft steady while I cast. He obeyed, until a tremendous swirl and swash startled him as a trout struck the fly. The rush was so sudden that the boy was absolutely scared, so that he let go the bushes, and the boat swept right across the line at the same instant that the trout went down. My second joint broke close to the butt ferrule, and we went like lightning toward the falls. I dropped my rod to seize an oar, and threw my whole weight on it. The boat yielded, took the cant I intended, and plunged bow on into the bank, where I seized the bushes and held on till the young Teuton came to his senses. Meantime the second joint and tip had gone overboard, and the reel was paying out. I brought in line very gently, and grasping the lower end of the second joint, dropped the butt, and proceeded to try an old and difficult plan of using the hand instead of a reel. As soon as I got in slack enough I felt the fish. He was at the bottom, and made a rush when he felt the first steady pressure of the tip. It took me twenty minutes, with second joint and tip, to kill that trout, well on to four pounds' weight, and the largest I ever killed east of the Atlantic. That same evening I took twenty more trout, and no one of them went over four ounces."

"I am one of the few," said the Major, sipping his claret appreciatively, and then tossing the full glass down his capacious throat, as if to wash a way out for talk—"I am one of the few who once loved angling, but have lost their taste for it. I've been latterly thinking the matter over, and—can you justify yourself in it? Isn't it cruelty to animals? You know these are days in which men are getting to have notions on that subject."

"I've no objection to their notions, and I have the highest opinion of the Society for the Prevention of Cruelty to Animals; but we must guard our sympathies that they do not go too far. No man of decency will be guilty of wanton cruelty to a beast. I have a warm love for some beasts. My dogs, my horses, have I not loved them? But there is much nonsense afloat on the subject. I rate the life of a beast somewhat lower than that of a man, and his comfort in the same ratio. I must often work even when I am sick. Rheumatism bothers me, and I have frequently to walk and even run when I am lame. Yes, perhaps it is gout. We won't discuss that; but lame or not I must work. Business requires it. I would drive a lame horse for the same reason. A poor carman can not afford to let his horse rest, any more than he can afford to rest himself, on account of a slight ailment. It's an error therefore to suppose it always wrong to get work out of a suffering animal. So, too, I would kill a horse to accomplish a result which I valued at a higher rate than the life of the horse, if I could not accomplish it in any other way. Some philanthropists, good men, but thoughtless, who would never dream of blaming a man for earning his bread and that of his children when he was sick and suffering, but would rather commend him, would fine and imprison him for working his sick horse with the same necessity impelling him.

"They should try to make a reasonable distinction in these matters between wanton cruelty and the necessary work that we must get out of a sick animal. I never saw a nobler beast, or one to which I was more thoroughly attached than my bay horse Mohammed; but great as he was and much as I loved him, do you not believe I would have ridden him through fire and tempest till he fell down dead, if it were necessary to save his mistress, who loved him as well as I, a pain or a sorrow? Should I let her suffer to save a horse from suffering? Does your notion of charity extend so far as that? Mine does not. I might give myself pain to save him pain; but her?—Never. Mohammed would have said so too if he could have spoken. I know he would.

"In war this whole subject is understood well, and no one thinks of finding fault with the destruction of the lives of beasts to accomplish the purposes of men; for in war human life is freely expended to purchase results. Who would blame an officer for using his lame, sick, dying mules and horses to the last moment to accomplish an object in the face of the enemy? It is then a mere question with beasts and with men, how much must be sacrificed to do the work. Would you require them to let sick mules rest in hospital, if they had no others?"

"Then you don't approve of stopping cars and omnibuses in New York, and compelling the passengers to dismount and find other conveyances, because the horses are lame?"

"Not at all. It is well meant, but it is bad in principle, and injures the society which does it. It would be right and proper to take a note of the horses and their owners and drivers, and make the necessary complaint in the police court, and if the animals were treated with wanton cruelty punish the guilty. But the time of a passenger is often worth thousands of dollars per minute, and the probability of such value outweighs all considerations of comfort to horses. In the days of the horse disease, when all the cities were suffering, it was both necessary and proper to use sick horses for transportation. It was a pure question of money value then. Shall a merchant allow ten thousand dollars' worth of perishable goods to decay for the sake of saving the health or the comfort of a cart horse? Yet the absurd proposition was forced on the public that it was their duty to sacrifice their own comfort, property, and health to the comfort of the horses. Nonsense. If you had a sick child, would you hesitate to kill a horse if necessary to get a surgeon or a physician in time to save the child's life? If you had a loaded wagon full of perishable articles of great value, would you hesitate to use your lame horses, or kill them if necessary to save your property? Let use teach kindness to animals, men and beasts, and make it infamous to treat them with unnecessary or wanton cruelty; but don't let us get our ideas mixed up on the subject, so that we place the comfort of the beasts above that of the men. For all our purposes the comfort and the life of a beast have a measurable value. The owner is the judge of that value to him."

"But how about killing fish for sport?"

"In the name of sense, man, if God made fish to be eaten, what difference does it make if I enjoy the killing of them before I eat them? You would have none but a fisherman by trade do it, and then you would have him utter a sigh, a prayer, and a pious ejaculation at each cod or haddock that he killed; and if by chance the old fellow, sitting in the boat at his work, should for a moment think there was, after all, a little fun and a little pleasure in his business, you would have him take a round turn with his line, and drop on his knees to ask forgiveness for the sin of thinking there was sport in fishing.

"I can imagine the sad-faced, melancholy-eyed man, who makes it his business to supply game for the market as you would have him, sober as the sexton in *Hamlet,* and forever moralizing over the gloomy necessity that has doomed him to a life of murder! Why, sir, he would frighten respectable fish, and the market would soon be destitute.

"The keenest day's *sport* in my journal of a great many years of sport was when, in company with some other gentlemen, I took three hundred bluefish in three hours' fishing off Block Island, and those fish were eaten the same night or the next morning in Stonington, and supplied from fifty to a hundred different tables, as we threw them up on the dock for anyone to help himself. I am unable to perceive that I committed any sin in taking them, or any sin in the excitement and pleasure of taking them.

"It is time moralists had done with this mistaken morality. If you eschew animal food entirely, then you may argue against killing animals, and I will not argue with you. But the logic of this business is simply this: The Creator made fish and flesh for the food of man, and as we can't eat them alive, or if we do we can't digest them alive, the result is we must kill them first, and (see the old rule for cooking a dolphin) it is sometimes a further necessity, since they won't come to be killed when we call them, that we must first catch them. Show first, then, that it is a painful necessity—a necessity to be avoided if possible—which a good man must shrink from and abhor, unless starved into it, to take fish or birds, and which he must do when he does it with regret, and with sobriety and seriousness, as he would whip his child, or shave himself when his beard is three days old, and you have your case. But till you show this, I will continue to think it great sport to supply my market with fish.

"Between ourselves, Major, I am of opinion that Peter himself chuckled a little when he took an extra-large specimen of the Galilee carp, and I have no doubt that he and James, and even the gentle and beloved John, pulled with a will on the miraculous draught of fishes."

"Probably you are right; but I have lost my love for the sport. I can hardly say how it came about with me. I think it was the result of a long illness which I had in my middle life, and from which I recovered slowly, and in such strict confinement that the love of reading grew on me, and other employments lost the zest which I once found in them. I sometimes wonder now how you can read all winter and go afishing all summer as you do. I can't separate myself from my books."

"You are growing quite too bookish of late years, if you will pardon me for saying so, my old friend."

"As how?"

"I mean that you are getting to be dreamy in your manner, and you don't seem to realize the common events of life. You live so much among thoughts and imaginations that you're getting to be quite useless as a companion, except when one wants to talk or listen."

"I haven't lost my appreciation of claret."

"So I perceive."

"Your glass is empty. Help yourself."

"Thanks; I'm doing very well."

"Talking of books and fishing, Effendi, did you ever come across the *Dyalogus Creaturarum?*"

"Yes, I have the Gouda edition of Leeu, 1482 I believe is the date."

"There's a comical little picture of a fisherman in it, illustrating a fabled talk between two fish. I don't know whether there is any older picture of the gentle art in existence, but that is worth noting as a historical illustration, for the angler there uses a float."

"The literature of angling is abundant, and art has always found ample range in its illustration. I have seen a score of pictures of fishing on ancient Egyptian monuments. Many modern artists are enthusiastic anglers. And in what kind of life could they find more of the beautiful? Look at a trout. Is there any object more exquisitely beautiful?"

"Yes, a small rattlesnake."

"Gaudy, Major, and brilliant, but the brilliance of the diamond and ruby compared with the soft glow of the pearl. Do you know these little Pemigewasset trout are so exquisite in their pearl and rose colors that I didn't wonder the other day at the exclamation of a very pretty girl in the chariot on the way to the Flume, when they pulled up by me down the river and asked to see my basket. 'Oh, I want to kiss them,' she said."

"You didn't know her?"

"Never saw her before, or since."

"It was a fresh remark. I like it. I wonder who she was. It's a pleasant thing now and then to hear a bit of nature out of red lips."

"Your experience in the utterances of red lips is rather limited, Major. I was telling you just now that you live too much on books and too little on realities."

"On red lips, for instance?"

"Exactly. An old bachelor like you has great opportunities in life. You might take to fishing even, and perhaps some day, when you have a full basket, a pretty girl may ask you to let her look at the speckled beauties, and then—what might not happen as a consequence?"

"Bah! I've been through it all."

"You?"

"I."

"Fishing and—"

"Red lips—yes. Redder than this blood of the grape, and a thousand times as maddening. What do you boys of these late years fancy you can teach me, either in sports of the forest or loves of the town? I had drunk all the wine of that life up, and the cup was empty before you were born."

The Major was excited, and his dates were evidently confused. But it was refreshing to be called a boy, and I urged him on. He told stories of old sporting days, which proved that he was no idle boaster when he said he had gone through all that. He grew fairly brilliant as he talked.

"I remember," said he, "the very last night I ever passed in the forest. It had been some years then since I had given up my rifle and rod, but an old companion persuaded me to join him in November in Sullivan County, in New York, and I went up the Erie Railroad to Narrowsburg, and struck out into the woods for a ten-mile tramp to our appointed place of meeting. I knew the country as well as you know these mountains, but at evening I had loitered so that instead of being near the cabin of our old guide I was three miles away; darkness was setting down fast, and a heavy snowstorm was evidently coming on. I, who had often said I would never camp out again so long as roofs remained among the inhabitants of earth, found myself wishing for the darkest hole in a rock or a hollow tree. Is it that the ground is not so soft a bed as it used to be, or have we grown harder?

"Night and gloom thickened around me. My eyes, from watching the clouds, retained vision of them longer than one who opened his suddenly at the place and time would have believed possible. The trees had passed through the various shapes and shadows which they assume in the twilight and first darkness. They were grim, tall giants, some standing, some leaning, some fallen prone and lying as they fell, dead and still; and some had gone to dust that lay in long mounds, like the graves of old kings. I kept on, pushing my way steadily, for there was no spot that I could find fit for a resting place, and I had hope of reaching a good point for the night halt by proceeding. I hit on it at length. There was a hill down which I went, tripping at every fourth step, and plunging into indescribable heaps of brush and leaves and stones, until I came out suddenly on the edge of a piece of burnt land, which a fire had gone over last summer. A pile of fallen trees lay on the very border of the unburned forest, and I sought shelter among them from a driving blast, which now brought snow with it in quantities. I faced the tempest a moment, and thought of that passage in which Festus described the angels thronging to Eden and 'alighting like to snowflakes.' I wished that there were more similarity, and that the flakes were fewer and farther between. But there was a terrible reality in the night and storm, which drove poetry from my brain. At this moment I discovered a pile of hemlock bark, gathered by someone to be carried to the tanneries. It was the first indication of this being an inhabited part of the world; but it was no proof that inhabitants were near, for these piles of bark are often gathered in remote parts of the forest. But it was a great discovery. There was enough of it to roof the City Hall; and in fifteen minutes there was as neat a cabin built among the fallen timber as any man could desire under the circumstances. It was artistically built too, for I had built such before; and, by the by, I recollect one which Joe Willis once constructed, in which the chimney arrangements proved unsafe, and we awoke at about daylight among the flames of our entire establishment. True, he laid it to my restlessness in the night, and actually charged me with getting my feet into the fire and scattering the coals, while I dreamed of the immortal—who was it that won immortality by setting fire to the Temple of Diana? But it was false, atrociously false. I was dreaming of——, but let that pass.

"The wind grew furious, and the snow came thicker, finer, and faster, but none reached me as I sat in my shelter, open indeed on one side, but fully protected there by a fire built at a safe distance, which blazed as a pile should blaze that was the funeral pyre of more than one of the forest giants.

"And now the sound of the wind in the forest grew terrible in the grandeur of its harmonies. A lonesome man, far from my fellows, the sole human companion of the storm, the sole human witness of the fury of the tempest, I sat, or lay, half reclined on the heap of brush that I had gathered for a bed, and with my hand screening my face from the intense heat of the fire, looked out into the abyss of darkness, and watched the snowflakes driving from far up down toward the flames, as if they sought instantaneous and glad relief from cold and wretched wanderings; and I wondered whether, of intelligent creatures, I was alone in that wild, grand, and magnificent scene.

"Sometimes I thought I could hear human voices in the lull of the storm; but oftener I imagined that the inhabitants of other worlds were near, and that they were unearthly sounds which were so strange and abrupt and startling; and when I closed my eyes I was certain that, among all the confusion, I could hear the rushing wings of more than ten legions of angels; and in a moment of still calm, one of those awful pauses that occur in furious storms, in the deep, solemn silence I heard a cry, a faint but wild and mournful cry, and it seemed far off, farther than the forest, farther than the opposite mountain, beyond the confines of the world, and the cry grew into a wail—a wail of unutterable anguish, agony, and woe—such a wail as might have been Eve's when the flaming sword flashed between her and Abel; and it came nearer, nearer, nearer, and it filled the air, the sky, the universe it seemed, and thrilled through my soul till I sprang to my feet, and dashed out into the blinding, mad tempest. It was so long since I had heard it, that I had forgotten that voice of the mountain wind; but now I remembered it as the blasts swept by me, wailing, shouting, laughing, shrieking, and I retired to my warm nook, and laughed back at the storm, and slept and dreamed. I never slept better.

"I awoke at daybreak, and the storm was over. A blue break in the clouds let through the light of a November moon, clear, soft, and exceedingly beautiful. Dawn drove the moonlight out of the forest, and I pushed on then and got my breakfast with old Steven in his cabin. I have never slept in the forest since that night. Help yourself to the claret, Effendi. It seems to me it's growing cold. Yes; I have led that life, and liked it well enough once."

"You've told me of your forest experiences, Major, but you rather fight shy of the subject of the red lips."

"I tell you I have tasted the wine of red lips to intoxication; but there were lips that I never touched whose utterances were more intoxicating."

The Major sat looking into the fire; for though it was August we had bright wood fires in the evenings, as we often do at the Profile House. He looked very steadily at the coals on the hearth, shivered once as if he were cold, bolted two glasses of claret in quick succession, and I waited, confident that I should hear his story at last. Soon he began to talk.

"Draw your chair close up. Light another pipe, and fill your glass. It is a cold night. My old bones shudder when I hear the wind wail over the house and through the trees. Capital claret, that! John, come in here. Open another bottle of claret, John. What, not another! Certainly, man, I must have it. This is only the second, and Mr. —— has drank half, of course. Not drank any! You don't mean to say that he has been drinking nothing all the blessed evening? Effendi, I thought you knew my rules better than that. But you always would have your own way.

"One more bottle, John—but one. It shall be the last; and, John, get some Maraschino—one of the thick, black bottles with the small necks, and open it. But you know how, old fellow, and just do your best to make us comfortable.

"How the wind howls! My boy, I am seventy-three years old, and seven days over. My birthday was a week ago today.

"An old bachelor! Yea, verily. One of the oldest kind. But what is age? What is the paltry sum of seventy years? Do you think I am any older in my soul than I was half a century ago? Do you think, because my blood flows slower, that my mind thinks more slowly, my feelings spring up less freely, my hopes are less buoyant, less cheerful, if they look forward only weeks instead of years? I tell you, boy, that seventy years are a day in the sweep of memory; and 'Once young forever young' is the motto of an immortal soul. I know I am what men call old; I know my cheeks are wrinkled like parchment, and my lips are thin, and my head gray even to silver. But in my soul I feel that I am young, and I shall be young till the earthly ceases and the the unearthly and eternal begins.

"I have not grown one day older than I was at thirty-two. I have never advanced a day since then. All my life long since that has been one day—one short day; no night, no rest, no succession of hours, events, or thoughts has marked any advance.

"I have been living forty years by the light of one memory—by the side of one grave.

"John, set the bottle down on the hearth. You may go. You need not sit up for me. We will see each other to bed tonight. Go, old fellow, and sleep soundly.

"She was the purest angel that flesh ever imprisoned, the most beautiful child of Eve. I can see her now. Her eyes raying the light of heaven—her brow white, calm, and holy—her lips wreathed with the blessing of her smile. She was as graceful as a form seen in dreams, and she moved through the scenes around her as you have seen the angelic visitors of your slumber move through crowded assemblies, without effort, apparently with some superhuman aid.

"She was fitted to adorn the splendid house in which she was born and grew to womanhood. It was a grand old place, built in the midst of a growth of oaks that might have been there when Columbus discovered America, and seemed likely to stand a century longer. They are standing yet, and the wind tonight makes a wild lament through their branches.

"I recall the scenery of the familiar spot. There was a stream of water that dashed down the rocks a hundred yards from the house, and which kept always full and fresh an acre of pond, over which hung willows and maples and other trees, while on the surface the white blossom of the lotus nodded lazily on the ripples with Egyptian sleepiness and languor.

"The old house was built of dark stone, and had a massive appearance, not relieved by the somber shade in which it stood. The sunshine seldom penetrated to the ground in the summer months, except in one spot, just in front of the library windows, where it used to lie and sleep in the grass, as if it loved the old place. And if sunshine loved it, why should not I?"

The Major's voice faded, his head slowly fell forward.

I left him sitting there, his head bowed on his breast, his eyes closed, his breathing heavy. My own eyes were misty. The mood might never come again. I would never know this story.

In the hall I found John, sitting bolt upright in a large chair.

"Why, John, I thought the Major sent you to bed long ago."

"Yes, sir; the Major always sends me to bed at the third bottle, sir, and I always doesn't go. He's been telling the old story, now hasn't he, sir?"

"Yes."

John laid his long black finger knowingly up by the side of his nose and looked at me.

"That story never gets telled."

"Why, John—you don't mean to say—eh?"

"All the claret, sir?"

"John, my man, go in and take care of him. He is either asleep or drunk. Curious, that! Why didn't I think that a man was hardly to be believed after the second bottle, and perfectly incredible on the third."

It would be difficult to describe all that I dreamed about that night.

The Silver Trout

A Legend of the River's Side

SIR R. H. ROBERTS

Sir R. H. Roberts' "The Silver Trout" has been described as one of the few instances in which angling mingles with the metaphysical. The writing itself is definitely dated, but despite this fact, and somewhat because of it, it's immensely appealing.

IT WAS the height of the London season. The sun glared down into the streets from a clear blue sky, with never a cloud to shelter one from its burning rays. I sat in my studio lazily repainting the foreground of a bit of Dartmoor scenery, cursing the fate that kept me, a poor artist, in town whilst I ought to have been making studies from Nature in the country, when my door was unceremoniously thrown open, and an old Oxford chum burst in.

"Hullo, old man! what's the matter? Why didn't you answer my letter?"

"For the very best of reasons," I replied. "I never got it."

"Confound that servant of mine. I daresay he has it in his pocket now. However, there's lots of time. Come, pack up your things, get your fishing tackle and painting things and come with me for a week. I've arranged everything. Got anything to drink? This is awfully thirsty weather."

"My dear friend, it is impossible. In the first place, I can't afford it, and—"

"Oh, bosh! who asked *you* to afford it; and since when is it that such formality has sprung up between Charles Haughton and Jack Leslie? Where the dickens do you keep that drink?"

"My dear Jack, you'll find it in that cupboard; but, as to your offer, I must really decline."

"Decline be hanged," he cried, opening a bottle of soda water. "Come, old man, you can pay me back when that picture's sold. By the way, how much do you want for it? Never mind answering now, but hurry up, and whilst you're packing I'll tell you where we are going."

It was no use, for when Jack Leslie made up his mind there was no resisting him, and, as the sequel proved, this little holiday had very nearly a very serious effect upon my future life.

"Have you ever been down to ——shire?" asked Jack, whilst standing with his back to an imaginary fire in an empty grate, with his coattails under his arms.

"Never," I replied.

"Well, then, you'll enjoy yourself. I'm going down to stop at a farmhouse with the jolliest old couple you ever knew. They've only one bedroom, but there are two beds in it. I've sent down some liquor and some other little comforts; for the rest, we must depend upon the fowl yard and the dairy; and last, but not least, I've got three and a half miles of the loveliest trout stream within a hundred miles of London. Now, old man, which prospect suits you best—this stifling studio or my farmhouse in ——shire, eh?"

"My dear Jack, your description settles me at once, if I really ever had any hesitation."

"By the way, there's a lovely old mill down there that ought to pay you for the whole trip."

All I had to do was to overhaul my tackle, and whilst doing this I was debating in my mind what the odds were in favor of fishing against painting; and I am free to confess that the chances of the former predominated. All this time Jack Leslie was looking over a portfolio of sketches and sipping his brandy and soda.

"I'll tell you what it is, Charley, if you won't mind my saying so, there's a want of life in your studies. Why don't you stick in a girl wearing a red petticoat and a blue bodice, every now and then, or something like that? This is a jolly sketch (holding it up); 'A Cast Upstream.' The man's capital."

"Well, old man, you're right, and I'm going to make some studies of rustics, &c., on this occasion." Little did I know what this would lead to at the time.

A smart-going hansom soon landed us at the station, where a first-class carriage was quickly piled with our impedimenta, and in a couple of hours' time, after having been whirled through that most lovely scenery which the home counties alone can afford, we arrived at our destination.

Standing on the platform, rigged out in his Sunday clothes, stood our host, as fine a specimen of the British yeoman as one would wish to see.

"How be you, Muster Leslie," he commenced, giving Jack a hearty shake of the hand; "and you, sir, you be the painter, I suppose. You're welcome, sir"; and, without waiting for a reply, and anticipating Jack's question, he continued: "The trout be a rising that mad, Muster Leslie, you can scarce see the water for 'em. You knows I b'aint much of a fisherman; but says I to my old woman, says I, 'Muster Leslie will have rare sport.' But coom on, sir, cart's a waitin', and maybe you'll like a seat."

"No, thank you, Joshua, my friend and I will walk. It's only a couple of miles," he added, turning to me, "and part of the road runs by the riverside, going by the old mill. There's no such thing as a fly down here, old man, so you must walk unless you like to be jolted to pieces in that cart." We soon struck the river. What a sight to gladden the heart of any angler, much more an unfortunate, worn-out artist. Fringed here and there with rows of willows, whilst an occasional old pollard stretched its gnarled trunk across the water, creating darksome shadows, a swift-running stream, from fifty to one hundred feet in width, flowed smoothly between and over long banks of swaying weeds; sometimes over a gravelly bed, creating a gentle stickle; anon gliding over an alluvial bottom; now losing itself in a sharp bend, making a deep but clear eddy on the one side and a still pool on the other, and finally, after a tortuous course, each nook and bend of which promised a harbor for big fish, the rapidity of the stream was lost in the waters of an old milldam. Here and there, too, on either bank grew a sturdy oak or a thornbush, whilst a paling ran out into the stream, each post making a refuge for a fish behind it.

And then the mill, how shall I describe it? There are mills and mills; but the only mill the fisherman loves to think of is that one the very sight of which tells him intuitively that, round and about it, in the mill head and in the mill tail, the heavy fish do congregate. Yes! the dear old wooden mill, with its red-tiled roof, toned down with moss and lichen, the small quaint windows, the open door just above the sluice, looking up the river; the whole building painted white, except where the projecting angles are covered with the equally white flour dust; the hum of the grindstone, as it is impelled by the old wheel; and the miller's boy, lazily smoking his pipe and leaning across the footbridge watching the swallows as they skim across the millpool, whilst an occasional circle here and there tells one that the trout are feeding. Dear reader, can you see the picture? I shall never forget it, for it is here that I encountered much which had a most profound influence upon my future life. Do you believe in the supernatural? Do you believe in Fate?—in Kismet? If so, listen, for I am about to tell you a story, which you can believe or not, as you like—a story of love and a ghost fish.

I shall not pause to describe the farmhouse where we stayed, or its surroundings. There are hundreds of them to be seen, with all their wealth of comfort and solidity, in the home counties. Four walls and a roof on top, four windows, a green door and a brass knocker, with a gravel path up to that said green door, pretty well covers the architectural and other descriptions. Suffice it to say that comfort and plenty reigned supreme, and that for cleanliness and civility, Mr. and Mrs. Joshua Whitcomb ought to take the palm in any community.

We soon settled down, Jack and I, in our comfortable bedroom, unpacked our traps, taking, of course, our fishing paraphernalia down with us to the common sitting room, where a cozy table spread out for the evening meal awaited us. After supper Jack and I naturally fell to the task of sorting our tackle, which soon covered the table, whilst old Joshua, seated in an armchair, lit his pipe and joined us in a glass of grog.

"Well, Joshua," said Jack, extricating a mass of flies and casting lines from a tin box, "and how is Mr. Tomlin, the miller?"

"Well, sir," replied Joshua, sipping his grog, "he be main the same as ever, only a bit more cantankerous about that there mill head. You know the old story, and it do seem as he grows older as if he believed more in it."

"Oh! to be sure; the queer story, or absurd nonsense, I ought to say, about the silver trout. You don't mean to say he still keeps to that?"

"Indeed, but he do, sir, and more serious nor ever."

"The silver trout," said I. "What on earth does that mean?"

"Oh!" replied Jack, "that is a mystery which forms part and parcel of the attraction which I intended you to enjoy during your stay down here. Well, old man, it's almost a ghost story—at least, a fishy one."

"That it be, Muster Leslie; my old woman and I don't lay much store by such fal-lals, yet it do seem kinder strange and onnatural."

"What's the mystery?" said I, beginning to feel interested.

"Well," replied Jack, "I'm not quite well up in it, but Joshua here knows all about it, as, indeed, does the whole countryside, for the matter of that; so Joshua, while I get this blessed tangle out, freshen your glass, and tell Mr. Haughton the tale."

Thus requested, Joshua refilled his glass, settled himself in his arm-chair, and told us the following strange story.

"Well, gentlemen, you must know that old Bill Tomlin—I say old, for he must be nigh on to threescore and ten—and his father before him, have owned the mill, and the meadow above the millhead, for many years. When old Bill was nigh on to forty-five he married, and the folks they stared, because Bill had always been a wild kind of a chap, and not sich an one as would make a good husband. Well, gentlemen, one day, just after haymaking, Bill went up to London, and when he come back he brought a wife back wi' 'im. The neighbors and country folk round about warn't much pleased. They said there was lots of nice girls about, and what did he want to go and bring a stranger down to the old mill. Still they was all main anxious to see her, out of curiosity like, and Bill he was only too glad to let 'em do so; and well he might, for a prettier, modester, kind-hearteder, Christianer young woman I never set my eyes on than Mrs. William Tomlin. Lord bless yer! Muster Leslie, if this gentleman had seen her he ud 'ave made his fortun a paintin' her. When I see'd her first, says my old woman to me, 'She's kind o' delicate, Jos'; but I laughed, and said that ——shire air would soon bring the roses to her cheeks; and so it did, and Bill he drove a roaring trade, and all the country round come to see his beautiful wife, and things went well wi' 'em. Well, gentlemen, in time, the Lord, in His goodness, give him three children; but, alack! sirs, they was all girls, and never a boy came, to hand the old mill over to; and when the third little one was born—that's Dora that is now, Muster Leslie—as you know, poor old Bill lost his wife. Well, gentlemen, from that day it seems as if nothing but misfortune come to Bill Tomlin—not as his business got bad, but somehow he seemed to change. First, he wouldn't grind everybody's corn; then he wouldn't let anybody fish in the millhead or the meadow; and one day, when he caught the curate afishing there, he threw him right into the river, and never went to church arter. Why, I don't know, for the curate was main sorry. Well, the daughters they grew up, and, as time went on, they bloomed and blossomed into beautiful flowers, like their poor mother, and full of that sweetness and gentleness that had made her loved by everyone. You'll excuse me, gentlemen," said old Joshua, wiping his eyes with his coat sleeve, and taking a strong swallow from his glass, "but I get kinder foolish when I think of her and her little ones, as is all gone 'cept Miss Dora as is, bless her heart!"

"All gone?" said I, interrupting him, for I was now fairly interested.

"Yes, sir, I'll tell you all about it. It's a queer tale; and while I think of it, Muster Leslie, don't fish the mill head tomorrow. I know old Bill wouldn't like to deny you; but he's been very cranky the last few weeks, and maybe you would excuse him."

"All right, Joshua, go ahead with the yarn. You tell it better every time I hear you."

"Thank you kindly, sir. Well, the girls grew up, and about three years ago the old Squire he died up at the Manor House, and the place, with the shooting and sporting, was let to an officer, who come down and took possession. Well, somehow he made acquaintance with old Bill, who was always a bit of a sportsman, you know, and he commenced to talk to Bill about improving the river, and said as how he wanted to put some new trout in. Bill didn't like this, as he was always very conservative; but somehow the Captain he got round him, and some beautiful fresh trout was turned in just above the bend of the old mill head. I wish them trouts had been all boiled before they was put in. I wish—well, excuse me, gentlemen, I'm d——d if I do know what I *do* wish," said the old man, striking the table heavily with his hand; "but, mind you, I don't believe it. I goes to church regular, and I tell you I don't believe it. About this time Bill was took ill of a fever, and while he had that fever there came upon him a feeling that those trout as was turned in was agoing to work mischief. One night he got out of his bed when no one was watching, and got an old net down as he kept for keeping the jack out of the water, and he tried to drag the mill head above, and was found nigh dead on the bank. I must tell you, gents, that some of these trout had been caught, and they were quite white and silvery, not like our own trout down here, but quite different. The Captain he said it was because they were not used to the change. Howsomdever, while Bill lay ill, Clara, his eldest daughter, she went off, and has never been heer'd on since. The Captain went away at the same time, and he give up the Manor House too. Then a painter gentleman come down—excuse me, sir," said the old man, looking at me—"no disrespect; he took the Manor House, and he come down, and he painted the old mill, and old Bill, and the old mastiff, and my missus, and the parson, and the church, and most everything round; and Bill Tomlin, who had just got over his illness, and was sore tried about Clara, he seemed to take to the painter gentleman. Well, the painter was main fond of fishing, and somehow he found that the mill head and tail, and the meadow above was the best ground, especially when Miss Mary—that was the second daughter—was about. Since Bill Tomlin's illness, the neighbors said he was queer in his head. I never saw it. Only he made hard bargains about grinding the corn, and put up ever so many posts warning people from fishing. But one day he come down to me, and I got a bit scared. Says he to me, 'Josh, do you know there's a silver trout in the mill head, and if I don't catch him, I shall lose Mary. She and the silver trout is agoing somehow. They're going through the wheel into the race, and then the corn will be ground blood-red.' I tried to soften him down; but no, I must come, he said, that night, and help him with the net. Of course, I promised him, never intending, and I saw him back to the mill, and I told Miss Mary I thought her father was kinder strange; but the painter gentleman was there, and she seemed only to heed him. Next morning Miss Mary was gone and the painter too, and old Bill lay on his bed near to his death, talking nothing but about a silver trout in the mill head. That is two year ago, gentlemen, and Bill is better, although he ain't heard of Clara or Mary. Dora, as you know, is at home, Muster Leslie; but what is queer is that there *is* a silver trout left in the mill head, and that old Bill won't let anyone fish there for fear of catching it."

"Why not?" I asked, deeply interested.

"Because, sir, Bill says when that trout is caught he'll lose his life and his only daughter."

"What bosh!" exclaimed Jack. "Here, let's have another drain and to bed; I'll bet we'll catch this same silver trout." Upon which old Joshua rose, and, in a most sepulchral voice, and with deep meaning, said:

"For the love of heaven, gentlemen, don't, don't try. The silver trout is not a fish; it is the spirit of poor Mrs. Tomlin as has gone into a trout, so as to be near all she loved, and I'm sure of it."

Old Joshua's story haunted me all night. I could not sleep, and was up with the sun in the morning. As I threw open the window and leaned out, the scene reminded me of a similar one, which an Irishman—a natural poet—whom I met in the west of Ireland, thus quaintly described:

> One morning bright and glorious,
> When the wild birds sang a chorious,
> And all nature was uproarious,
> In the charming month of May,
> When the lambs and trouts and horses,
> That know not what remorse is,
> And the salmon, whale and porpoise
> They gamboled in the sea.

Jack Leslie was snoring hard, and I had not the heart to wake him; but back to bed I could not go. That prophetic warning of old Joshua's seemed to jangle in my ears—"Don't fish for the silver trout"; and yet the very fact of being told not to do so made me more anxious to find out something about this strange old miller and his daughter.

The mill wasn't far off. How would it be to walk down there and be back in time for breakfast? I might make a sketch, and I might—well, I didn't exactly know what might happen.

I was soon dressed and on my way to the mill. It was, I should say, about five o'clock, and a lovely morning. There was not a breath of wind, and the day augured badly for fishing. However, "Many a bright, sunshiny morning turns out a dark and cloudy day," says the old fishing song, and so I hoped it would. A short half hour's walk brought me to the mill. I walked up onto the bank at the mill head, which was like a sheet of glass, except where, here and there, the gentle suck of a trout made a tiny ring upon the still surface. Well, here was the spot of last night's curious story, and here must be the "silver trout," without the shadow of a doubt. I looked with curiosity at the water, reflecting the while as to the exact spot whereabouts that fish might lie. Just then a short cough caused me to look up, and I saw an old man, very much bent, and leaning on a stick, standing on the opposite bank, carrying a basket in his hands. He evidently had not observed me, so, taking it for granted that this must be the miller, I hid behind an alder bush and watched him. First of all the old man knelt down upon the bank, and commenced muttering, all the while keeping his gaze fixed upon the water. Then he took something out of the basket, which he threw into the water. A commotion and a splashing ensued, and I could plainly see the tail of a large trout as it broke the surface.

"The Silver Trout!" I mentally exclaimed, and a rare big fish, too. My angler's spirit was in arms. I vowed not only to catch that fish, but also to solve the whole mystery. Whilst thinking over how this was to be done, I heard one of the sweetest of voices calling from the mill, "Father! father! why didn't you wait for me?" and immediately afterward there came tripping on the scene a girl that you see only once in a lifetime; at least, I think so.

"Well, how's the dear old trout today?" she asked; "and are you—" Just then she caught sight of me behind the alder bush. "Father, there's someone on the other side of the stream." The old man looked up, and, shading his eyes with his hand, said:

"So there be, girl. Coom away; don't ee stand glaring there. Coom away, Dora, I say. I dreamed about it, girl, I did, and I saw them both and the silver trout. Coom away; the Captain will excuse us."

"That's not the Captain, father."

"Oh, yes it be; he told me last night he was coming to fish, and bring— Well, no matter."

"Come, father, breakfast will be ready; let us go in."

"Aye, aye, the Captain; he'll not be long, he'll not be long"; and, muttering to himself, he disappeared through the door into the mill with the young girl, who, I naturally concluded from what I had heard, was Dora, his youngest daugter.

It was now getting on to eight o'clock, and the appearance of the weather had entirely altered. A southwesterly wind had sprung up, and dark clouds were coming up from that direction. There was a sough in the withy heads on the banks, and the rushes and flags crackled as they swayed with the breeze. I at once started for home, and as I went I thought of the strange coincidence that had introduced me at once to the principal actors in the drama which I had listened to the night before—the miller, his daughter, and last, but not least, "the silver trout."

When I got back, I found Jack Leslie on the lawn busily putting his rod together. I did the same, for he had brought my tackle down as well. He asked me where I had been, and I answered, somewhat reticently, that I had strolled down to look at the river, and to see if the fish were feeding.

What a fishing morning it was, as we stepped out on the gravel path after breakfast. The weather had now assumed that aspect which the fly fisherman always prays for, and but seldom gets—a warm, southwesterly wind, with driving showers, alternate darkness and sunshine.

"Now, old man," said Jack, "there is little to choose as to water, only that the lower half has the advantage of the mill head; but as I think we'd better not touch that—at any rate, on the first day—after what Joshua told us last night, you'd better go to the head of the water, and I'll take the lower bit."

"Oh, no," I replied; "we'll do as we always do, and toss." For I had determined to fish that mill head, and to learn a little more, if possible, of the miller and his daughter.

"Call!" cried Jack, as the coin went spinning in the air. For once I felt nervous.

"Woman, it is."

"You're right; well, of course, you'll go to the top."

"Not a bit of it. I fancy that about the middle of the day I shall want to make a sketch of the old mill, as I shall be tired by that time; so go ahead, old chap, and we'll meet at lunch time."

"All right, we can change tomorrow; meanwhile, here we are about the middle of the water, only I rather think I've got the better of you, for the mill head and the meadow above take a good slice of water away, so I ought to show more fish than you at lunchtime; but mind, don't fish the meadow or the mill head; we'll do that when I've had a chat with old Tomlin. *Au revoir.*"

I watched Jack Leslie, as he left me, swishing his rod and whistling "The Flowers in the Spring," from *The Mikado,* and then I made my way to the river.

The fish were rising everywhere, and the Olive Duns were coming down in myriads, whilst here and there an Alder fly flopped heavily on the water. It is a curious fact that on large rivers the Alder is comparatively small, whilst on small rivers or streams it is generally large, at least so it has always seemed to me.

The very sight of those rising fish—and some of them looked heavy ones—filled me with excitement and increased my desire to catch them. The miller and his daughter, the Silver Trout, and old Joshua's story, all gave way to the one prominent feature—fishing. Besides, Jack Leslie had gone, as he said, to the best water, and, good or bad water, had I not forgotten as much as Jack Leslie ever knew about trout fishing, and so I stood upon the bank with a doublehanded trout rod in my hand, taking stock of the river and its surroundings.

I may be wrong, and am always open to practical conviction; but, on such a river as I was fishing, and, indeed, on any of the streams in the home counties, I am confident that a doublehanded rod is the proper implement. My reason is I can stand farther back from the bank, and so command the water; and that when the line is thrown the length of the rod enables me to keep clear of teazels, or what not, that encumber the bank nearest to me.

How often have I stolen up, crawling and creeping, to a rising fish with a singlehanded rod, and, when almost within reach, have been caught up in a teazel, and had to extricate the line at the cost of scaring the fish, while with a doublehanded rod, say of fourteen feet, this ought never to occur.

I scanned the water carefully before putting up my cast, and it seemed to me as if I could do no better than mount the Oliver Dun at the end of a fine gut collar, which was stained with green baize. I selected what I considered as perfect an imitation of that ephemera as fur and feathers could represent. A fish was rising under the bank immediately opposite to me, and I put the fly over it in a delicate and gingerly manner—not a stir; twice it went sailing over its very nose—never a move. The fourth time the fish rose almost immediately after the fly had passed, clearly proving that I had not scared it by any previous operations. However, it was evident this was not the fly. Just then a shower came on, and suddenly the fish stopped rising; the surface of the river, which a moment before had been covered with circles, was now completely tranquil.

I sat down, and as I did so an Alder fly lumbered onto my cheek. Perhaps *this* is it, thought I; and on went an Alder.

Now, I have seen Alders and Alders, but, except amongst my personal friends, never have I seen them tied after my own fancy. For the benefit of my readers, I give them the pattern:—Body, orange floss silk, over which a bronze Peacock herl is twisted, so as to leave the orange floss silk visible between each two turns, a small portion of the silk being left at the tail, but not as a tag. Wings taken from the Bustard, matched to the color of the natural fly and dressed flat. Horns, two strands of a soft black hackle.

Much as I love the fly, on this particular occasion it was no good. I tried hard over every rising fish; no go. What, then, were they rising at? The problem was soon solved, though by accident. Whilst in the act of creeping up to a rising fish I kicked against a bunch of rushes and flags, out of which fluttered a heavy, light-colored fly, which, taken by the wind, dropped into the middle of the river, and was immediately seized. I soon caught another, and found it to be the Sedge fly. On went the Sedge, and two minutes after I had the satisfaction of drinking the health of a lovely two-pound trout as it lay in the bottom of my landing net.

Then commenced the fun. After each shower the fish rose freely, and stopped the moment the raindrops pattered on the water. Unconsciously, I approached the prohibited ground, the meadow next to the mill head. As I clambered over the fence I marked a heavy fish down close to the opposite bank immediately under an old pollard. "That's a whopper," I mentally exclaimed, "and if there is any virtue in 'fine and far' I'll add you to my basket."

A slight detour into the meadow brought me a little below and opposite to the fish; down I went on my knees, and as I did so the trout rose again. The moment the fly went over it up it came and I struck, but the line came back without the welcome strain; that I had not touched it I felt certain; would it come again? I let it rest for a couple of minutes, during which time I saw no signs of the fish, and then, trembling with excitement, I once more cast over the spot.

This time the hook went home, and with a shake of the head and a heavy roll away went the trout downstream. Across the water at the end of the meadow a chain had been stretched, and it was evident, if I could not stop the fish before it got there, I must lose it; but to arrest the career of a five-pound trout—as I felt certain this one must, at least, be—was no easy matter. Whizz went the winch, my good old greenheart rod was bending almost double, and still the fish made for the chain, which, to add to my difficulties, was covered with weeds.

I dared not show the butt any more, and began to despair of the capture, when the fish suddenly stopped, and came racing back upstream like a mad fellow; so fast, indeed, that I had to run back into the meadow in order to keep a tight line.

The cause of this mad rush was soon explained. Coming through the gate on the opposite side was the same young girl I had seen in the morning with the old miller, and in her white muslin dress and large Leghorn hat, with a background of pale-green willows, she made as fair a picture as one would wish to look upon. Her entry upon the scene had, for the moment, diverted my attention, although, with true fisherman's instinct, I still kept a tight line upon the fish.

"He'll be into the weeds in a minute, if you don't mind," cried a tuneful voice, "you've got hold of one of the big ones"; and then she went on excitedly, "I'm sure you won't be able to land him yourself; I'll be round in a minute," and off she went back again through the gate.

Well, thought I, this is an adventure with a vengeance; and then the tug-tug, jigger-jigger of the fish reminded me I had something else to think of; besides, what a mortification it would be to lose the fish under such conditions. Just then Dora Tomlin joined me, having possessed herself of my landing net, which was sticking up in the next meadow.

"I used to be a good hand, sir, with a landing net," she commenced, in a sort of apologetic manner, "and I felt sure you would not be able to land that fish without someone, and so I—and so—but perhaps you'd rather—" and she blushed and stammered.

I proceeded at once to explain to Miss Tomlin how glad I was of her assistance, that nothing on earth should induce me to take that fish without her aid. I think, in my confusion, I told her that I was always in the habit of having a lady to land my fish, and much preferred them to a keeper or male attendant, and was going on in a like strain, when she stopped me with—"There! he's making for the old pollard stump. Take care, or you'll lose him."

The extra pressure I put on brought the fish up, and it sprang into the air, showing its noble proportions.

"What a beauty!" exclaimed my companion. "I hope you won't lose him."

The fish was now getting tired, and, marking a clean spot just below where I was standing, I coaxed it downstream. What was my surprise to see Miss Tomlin, without a word of instruction, get below the fish, drop the net into the water, and wait until, exhausted and gasping, I brought it within reach. Then, without the slightest hurry, she slipped the net under, and landed the trout on the bank.

That I was not only delighted and surprised goes without saying, and whilst admiring my capture, I expressed a hope that I was not trespassing, as I now, for the first time, observed the locality I was in. This led to a conversation and to a mutual introduction. When my fair companion heard that I was an artist her delight knew no bounds. Would I paint a picture of the mill? and would I let her watch me while doing so? and would I mind her asking me not to fish the mill head? It was a whim of her father's who was not very well. If she'd asked me to stand on my head in the middle of the river I should have done so at once, I think. Somehow or another we had seated ourselves upon the bank, and the finest trout in the world would have had no attractions for me, nor do I think I should have thought anything more about fishing had not a "halloo" in the distance warned me that I was on earth with mortals and not in heaven with an angel, and that that mortal was Jack Leslie. She heard it too, and, getting up, wished me good day with a sweet smile, adding:

"I lost my brooch the other day, leaning out of the boat on the other side, just opposite here, when the water was muddy, and so I came to look for it today."

As she was going I ventured to ask permission to call upon her and show her some of my sketches, which she granted, and so we parted.

A few minutes after Jack appeared with five and a half brace of trout. I had only one and a half brace. Did I tell him the reason? No, dear reader. Would you?

It was very lucky for me that Jack's eye was fixed upon my last capture. If he had not been intent upon admiring the proportions of that fish he could not have failed to perceive the flutter of a white muslin skirt in the next meadow, as it disappeared in the direction of the mill. As for me, I became suddenly intent upon unpacking the contents of the luncheon basket.

"I say, old man," said Jack, suddenly turning upon me, "I thought we had agreed that you were not to fish this meadow."

"Well, yes," I replied, mendaciously fishing out a lettuce from the bottom of the basket; "but, you see, I don't know the water as well as you do; and I saw this beggar rising, and I really did not stop to look at the locality—come on, let's have lunch."

"All right, old man," and, coming toward me, he remarked: "That's about as perfect a specimen of the *Salmo fario* as has ever been taken out of these waters. How the dickens did you land it? What the devil is this?" he queried, stooping to pick up a lady's glove, with eight buttons.

Of course, if that glove had had only one button, or even two, I might have found an excuse; but, no, this one seemed to me to have about forty. The situation was rather awkward. "By Jove! it *is* a lady's glove," I ventured, looking at it as if I'd never seen such a thing before. "What a lot of buttons it's got, and—and what a little one!"

"Yes," said Jack dryly, and looking me straight in the face, "my impression is the same. It *is* a lady's glove."

"Well, never mind what it is. I'm awfully hungry; come on." I at once proceeded to demolish the wing of a chicken.

That brute Jack stuck that delicate and adorable glove on the top of a thistle, and gave a prolonged whistle that irritated me: it was not so much the whistle as the way in which he looked at the glove and then at me when he did so.

"I suppose it will be the correct thing," I ventured, "to give that fish to the miller, won't it?"

"Yes, I'll send the boy down with it, with my compliments," he replied, opening a bottle of Bass.

"You'll send it? Confound it! I caught it, and I ought to take it."

"But you don't know the miller and there'll be a row; besides, I shall be able to take this glove down at the same time. I fancy it must belong to Miss Tomlin; so while you go and fish the upper water after lunch, I'll stroll on down to the mill and apologize for your trespassing."

I was very fond of Jack Leslie, and would have done anything in the world for him, but this was too much.

That Miss Tomlin should have her glove returned by anyone else than myself I could not for a moment endure, and so I said, with as much equanimity as possible, "Well, all right, you take the fish and I'll take the glove."

"Why?" he retorted, and there was a world of meaning in the query.

"Division of labor, you know. Besides, I want to make Mr. Tomlin's acquaintance; I want to ask permission to make a study of the mill, and then, you know, you said you'd arrange for me to have a throw on the mill head, and with this wind there must be a fine curl on it. Besides, there's no particular hurry, is there? I fancy the lower end here, and, as you seem to have done so well up above, it's a pity you shouldn't stick to it for the rest of today."

Jack Leslie got up without answering a word; he filled his pipe, very carefully, lit it, and then took up his rod, basket and net, and, raising his flask, he said—"Haughton, you go to the top of the class. Here's your good health," and sauntered off to the upper water.

I employed myself leisurely packing up the *débris* of the lunch, and then dispatched the boy with it to the farmhouse. Fortunately there was no one in sight. The glove being still on the thistle, I edged gradually nearer and nearer, and finally, after a furtive glance around, I pounced upon it.

Why I should have taken such an interest in this glove I did not then know. After all, it was only a lady's glove, and all I had to do was to put it in my pocket, go on fishing, and return it when the proper time came. Why I looked at it, smoothed it, and then smelled it, I can't make out; but I did, and then, to tell the truth, I kissed it.

Just at that moment a shower came on, and I hid the precious gantlet in my bosom, taking refuge under the hedge. The shower passed, the fish began to rise again, but the river had no longer any charms for me. I took up my rod almost mechanically and sauntered to the edge of the stream. Heavy waves rolled over the shallows, as the fish started on catching sight of me, but I heeded nothing. I lazily flicked the fly on to the water without aim or reason. I was thinking of Dora Tomlin, of the circumstance that had brought us together, and as I thought I remembered the incident of the brooch which she had come to seek. Why should I not look for it?

Here was an inspiration which was seized with avidity. I flung my old good Blacker rod down. I divested myself of my coat, fishing basket, &c., and began cautiously to examine the water. She had indicated the spot, but, after careful searching, from my side I could see nothing of it. I must cross, but where? The stream was uneven as to depth, and apparently treacherous as to bottom. I looked up and down; the chain was my only chance; besides, by going below the spot I should not muddy the water. On reaching the spot I found there were two chains, one placed considerably below the water, which seemed to me to offer the facility I required. I commenced my journey by placing my feet on the lower chain and grasping the upper one. All went well till I neared the center, when, to my horror, I found the lower chain gradually giving way. Yes, the water was already trickling in over the tops of my waders. I struggled, I floundered, but it was no use, in I went up to my armpits: but, still grasping the upper chain, I got to the opposite bank, and crawled up covered with weeds, looking like a drowned rat.

All the romance of half an hour ago had been washed out of me, and I thought of nothing except my situation if Jack Leslie should return, or even Dora Tomlin. I pulled off my wading stockings and emptied them, wrung my clothes, and then literally hung myself out to dry. Fortunately, the sun was very warm as I walked briskly up and down the bank to assist the drying process. In my peregrinations I passed the spot where the brooch was supposed to have been dropped. Did my eyes deceive me? No, there was certainly something shining at the tail of that weed, and in less than no time I was in the water and back on the bank, holding triumphantly in my hands a silver brooch, beautifully modeled in the shape of a trout. Had I indeed caught the Silver Trout? And then the prophetic words of old Joshua occurred to me, that "on the day a silver trout was taken out of the river the miller would lose his life and his only daughter."

It was true I had got the brooch and that my clothes and waders were dry enough to put on, but how was I to get back to the other side of the river? I could, of course, go round by the mill, but there

I ran the risk of meeting Dora, and, of course, I should have to account for being without my coat, and of necessity return the brooch. Just then I remembered that there was a small footbridge, some two meadows up, that I had not thought of, and I at once made my way toward it, all the while ruminating as to what I should do with the brooch and whether I should tell Jack Leslie anything about it. Then there was the glove business; what was I to do about that? I was prepared to be most unmercifully chaffed by Jack; that I knew was inevitable, but how to get out of the business without compromising myself, I knew not.

Pondering on these matters, I arrived at the footbridge and was about to cross, when a roar of laughter caused me to look up, and there, as ill luck would have it, was Jack Leslie, fishing in the adjoining meadow.

"What on earth is up now? And what are you doing without your coat?"

As a rule I am not in want of an answer under any ordinary situation, but this was a poser. Jack Leslie came toward me, and I braced myself to meet the situation.

"What are you doing on that side of the river, old man; and where the deuce are your coat and traps? What's the matter with you, man? Why don't you answer?" he shouted, as I was hesitating.

"I suppose I am not responsible to you for all my actions," I answered sulkily. "I crossed over the river to look at something I saw on the opposite side."

"Oh, indeed, and to do that you took off your coat and went round by the mill, I suppose?"

"No, I didn't go round by the mill. But there, don't bother, Jack, that's a good fellow. Fact is, I fell into the river trying to cross by the chain, and I'm going home to change. By Jove! Look at that lovely fish feeding under the willow. You are a duffer if you can't catch him!"

In a moment Jack had forgotten everything, and I left him creeping up the bank intent on the capture of that trout, whilst I made my way to where I had left my traps. Arriving at the spot I at once determined to return to the farmhouse and change my clothes, and as I went I questioned myself as to what was the meaning of the interest I felt in this miller's daughter. What was she to me? Hadn't I seen lots of pretty girls—much prettier than Dora—and yet I had never bestowed as much thought upon them as I had upon Dora— Dora! The very name sounded so soft as I whispered it to the summer wind. Yes, Dora was an awfully pretty name!

I walked slowly back to the farm. Under usual circumstances, had I been going to change my clothes, I should have used much more dispatch, but now, somehow, I felt as if I didn't care to get back to my fishing. What! not go back to the river? Why, what had come over me? Trout fishing was the one dream of my life, as I painted away in my dreary studio; a day's trouting was looked forward to and prepared for weeks before; but today, somehow, I thought I was tired—that I had fished enough for the first day; that my waders were not dry, and, in fact, that I would fish no more that day.

But I was not too tired to take a canvas, my color box, sketching easel and umbrella, and walk back to the old mill at the rate of five miles an hour. Now I did not particularly want that umbrella, as there were plenty of trees, but it occurred to me that a white umbrella stuck in a conspicuous place on the bank of the mill head must attract attention from the mill. Yes, probably the miller's boy will come out and see what it was, or the cook, or the gardener, and then, perhaps —well, we would see.

I planted myself in the most open spot, and in full view of the window of the miller's house. I placed my canvas on the easel, and I commenced sketching the outline of the mill. Somehow or another my eyes were more often kept upon those windows than upon my canvas, and the perspective of the lines I had already traced were most woefully out of drawing. Just then the old miller appeared in the porch, followed by his daughter. Were they coming this way? My heart was absolutely thumping against my ribs. Yes, they were coming. What should I do? What should I say? As they approached, I felt I was blushing like a boy.

"You see, Miss Tomlin, that I have taken advantage as soon as possible of the permission given me, and have left Mr. Leslie to fish by himself."

"You are quite welcome, sir. Indeed, any friend of Mr. Leslie's is always welcomed here."

A sudden thought flashed across my brain. Could I have made a mistake? Was the girl who had crept into my heart in so short a time also beloved by my friend? And why not? Had not Jack known them for years? Could anyone see Dora Tomlin and know her without loving her? I must be mad—I was a fool, a dolt, an idiot. Miss Tomlin interrupted my thoughts by introducing me to her father, at the same time adding, "He is not quite right in his mind, and takes you for someone else; pray humor him."

I bowed, scarcely knowing what to do or what to say. The old man seemed to take no notice of me; but, keeping his eyes fixed on the water, muttered: "The time is near; I am coming, wife. The Captain is here. He has come at last, but he is alone. It is better, wife, to hide our shame." Then, turning to me, he said, abruptly:

"Why did you stop away so long, and where is she?"

Dora answered, "Dear father, this is Mr. Haughton, a friend of Mr. Leslie's."

The old man passed his hand across his forehead, and then, coming to me, held out his hand, and, in a rational voice, he said, "You are welcome, sir. Indeed, any friend of Mr. Leslie's is always welcomed. I hope you have had good sport? There are plenty of fish, and good ones, if you can catch them."

"Oh! Mr. Haughton," cried Dora, "are you going to begin to paint; because, if so, I should like to stop and watch you—that is, if I may?"

Half an hour ago, had Dora asked me that, I should have replied in quite a different way; but that speech of hers about Jack Leslie rankled in my mind. "Certainly, Miss Tomlin," I said, "if you wish it; but, to tell you the truth, I don't feel up to work, and I was on the point of stopping as, somehow or another, I cannot draw today."

"Then perhaps you will join us in a cup of tea; it is about time. Your things will be all safe here." And, in a lower tone, added, "You must not mind father. He has suffered a great deal, as I daresay Mr. Leslie told you. Will you come?"

There was nothing for it; I had better go. Besides, I could return the glove and the brooch, and see what effect that might have, and so I followed Dora Tomlin and her father into the coziest of parlors, full of woman's surroundings and occupations, with the sweet scent of flowers coming through the windows and the urn steaming upon the table. I must confess I felt a sort of tightness at the heart as I watched Dora Tomlin's graceful figure presiding over the teatable. Could there be anything between her and Jack? That was the all-absorbing question.

"I expect Mr. Leslie in to tea," she remarked quietly.

"Do you really?" I answered, hardly knowing what I did say.

"Yes, he generally comes in before the evening fishing, as he calls it."

Well! what was there in that? Why shouldn't he come in to tea in the same way that I had? Just then Jack passed the window.

"Ah! here he is; I thought he wouldn't forget teatime."

As Jack Leslie entered the room the old miller was seated upon a couch close to the window, looking out onto the mill head. Dora was at the teatable and I was leaning against the mantelpiece. I see the picture now. Jack paused at the door.

"Well, I'm sure," he cried, "you have not taken long to make acquaintance. I looked for you as I came down the river, for the purpose of bringing you in and introducing you, but I see that's unnecessary. May I venture to inquire how this came about?"

"Presently, *Jack*," answered Dora. "Sit down and have your tea."

Jack! She called him *Jack!* It was all over. My romance was gone. That one word had shattered my hope, my dream, and Dora was no more to me at that moment than any other girl. I made up my mind at once.

"Well, you see, Jack," I said, "I came down to sketch, was invited by Miss Tomlin to tea, and I thought I would take the opportunity of returning her a glove she had lost whilst landing my trout for me, and a brooch I found which must be hers."

Jack indulged in a prolonged whistle.

"A brooch, did you say?" cried Dora.

"Yes, a Silver Trout."

"A Silver Trout!" cried the old miller, springing to his feet. "Who knows anything about the Silver Trout? Did you say you had caught the Silver Trout? Do you know what you have done? You have committed murder, cold-blooded murder; you are an assassin; you—you—"and the old man fell back upon the couch gasping for breath.

We were at once by his side. The bell was rung and a man sent immediately for the doctor. The old miller lay insensible, a small stream of blood trickling slowly from his lips. Gradually his eyes opened, and were fixed upon Dora and Jack.

"Lift me up," he murmured. "It has come true. I knew it." Then taking Dora's hand, he placed it in Jack's. "Take care of her, Jack—the Silver Trout. I am coming, darling wife; I am coming, to you," and sank back a corpse.

I have little more to add. I was terribly shocked at having been the innocent cause of such a catastrophe, and to my dying day shall never forget it. It is needless to say that Jack explained to me afterward the situation. How he had wooed and won Dora long ago, and how he had intended to tell me all about it at supper in the evening. And so the legend came true. The day that a Silver Trout was taken out of the river the miller would lose his life and his only daughter.

Mr. Theodore Castwell

G. E. M. SKUES

The late G. E. M. Skues was one of the early exponents of the dry fly in England, and he did much to encourage American anglers in this method of taking trout. His many writings on fishing are, for the most part, serious discussions on the many phases of trout and salmon angling, a number of them having initially appeared in the Journal of the Fly-Fishers' Club, a serious organization which has its counterpart here in the New York Anglers' Club. Those followers of his serious work will find it almost impossible to credit him with the authorship of "Mr. Theodore Castwell," in which he displays some of the craft of O. Henry.

M R. THEODORE CASTWELL, having devoted a long, strenuous and not unenjoyable life to hunting to their doom innumerable salmon, trout and grayling in many quarters of the globe, and having gained much credit among his fellows for his many ingenious improvements in rods, flies and tackle employed for that end, in the fullness of time died and was taken to his own place.

St. Peter looked up from a draft balance sheet at the entry of the attendant angel.

"A gentleman giving the name of Castwell. Says he is a fisherman, your Holiness, and has 'Fly-Fishers' Club, London' on his card."

"Hm-hm," says St. Peter. "Fetch me the ledger with his account."

St. Peter perused it.

"Hm-hm," said St. Peter. "Show him in."

Mr. Castwell entered cheerfully and offered a cordial right hand to St. Peter.

"As a brother of the angle—" he began.

"Hm-hm," said St. Peter. "I have been looking at your account from below."

"I am sure I shall not appeal to you in vain for special consideration in connection with the quarters to be assigned to me here."

"Hm-hm," said St. Peter.

"Well, I've seen worse accounts," said St. Peter. "What sort of quarters would you like?"

"Do you think you could manage something in the way of a country cottage of the Test Valley type, with modern conveniences and, say, three quarters of a mile of one of those pleasant chalk streams, clear as crystal, which proceed from out the throne, attached?"

"Why, yes," said St. Peter. "I think we can manage that for you. Then what about your gear? You must have left your fly rods and tackle down below. I see you prefer a light split cane of nine foot or so, with appropriate fittings. I will indent upon the Works Department for what you require, including a supply of flies. I think you will approve of our dresser's productions. Then you will want a keeper to attend you."

"Thanks awfully, your Holiness," said Mr. Castwell. "That will be first-rate. To tell you the truth, from the Revelations I read, I was inclined to fear that I might be just a teeny-weeny bit bored in heaven."

"In h-hm-hm," said St. Peter, checking himself.

It was not long before Mr. Castwell found himself alongside an enchantingly beautiful clear chalk stream, some fifteen yards wide, swarming with fine trout feeding greedily: and presently the attendant angel assigned to him had handed him the daintiest, most exquisite, light split-cane rod conceivable—perfectly balanced with the reel and line—with a beautifully damped tapered cast of incredible fineness and strength, and a box of flies of such marvelous tying as to be almost mistakable for the natural insects they were to simulate.

Mr. Castwell scooped up a natural fly from the water, matched it perfectly from the fly box, and knelt down to cast to a riser putting up just under a tussock ten yards or so above him. The fly lit like gossamer, six inches above the last ring; and next moment the rod was making the curve of beauty. Presently, after an exciting battle, the keeper netted out a beauty of about two and a half pounds.

"Heavens," cried Mr. Castwell. "This is something like."

"I am sure his Holiness will be pleased to hear it," said the keeper.

Mr. Castwell prepared to move upstream to the next riser when he noticed that another trout had taken up the position of that which he had just landed, and was rising. "Just look at that," he said, dropping instantaneously to his knee and drawing off some line. A moment later an accurate fly fell just above the neb of the fish, and instantly Mr. Castwell engaged in battle with another lusty fish. All went well, and presently the landing net received its two and a half pounds.

"A very pretty brace," said Mr. Castwell, preparing to move on to the next string of busy nebs which he had observed putting up around the bend. As he approached the tussock, however, he became aware that the place from which he had just extracted so satisfactory a brace was already occupied by another busy feeder.

"Well, I'm damned," said Mr. Castwell. "Do you see that?"

"Yes, sir," said the keeper.

The chance of extracting three successive trout from the same spot was too attractive to be forgone, and once more Mr. Castwell knelt down and delivered a perfect cast to the spot. Instantly it was accepted and battle was joined. All held, and presently a third gleaming trout joined his brethren in the creel.

Mr. Castwell turned joyfully to approach the next riser round the bend. Judge, however, his surprise to find that once more the pit beneath the tussock was occupied by a rising trout, apparently of much the same size as the others.

"Heavens," exclaimed Mr. Castwell. "Was there ever anything like it?"

"No, sir," said the keeper.

"Look here," said he to the keeper, "I think I really must give this chap a miss and pass on to the next."

"Sorry, it can't be done, sir. His Holiness would not like it."

"Well, if that's really so," said Mr. Castwell, and knelt rather reluctantly to his task.

Several hours later he was still casting to the same tussock.

"How long is this confounded rise going to last?" inquired Mr. Castwell. "I suppose it will stop soon."

"No, sir," said the keeper.

"What, isn't there a slack hour in the afternoon?"

"No afternoon, sir."

"What? Then what about the evening rise?"

"No evening rise, sir," said the keeper.

"Well, I shall knock off now. I must have had about thirty brace from that corner."

"Beg pardon, sir, but his Holiness would not like that."

"What?" said Mr. Castwell. "Mayn't I even stop at night?"

"No night here, sir," said the keeper.

"Then do you mean that I have got to go on catching these damned two-and-a-half pounders at this corner forever and ever?"

The keeper nodded.

"Hell!" said Mr. Castwell.

"Yes," said his keeper.

Angler, Beware!

EDMUND WARE SMITH

*The creator of the One-eyed Poacher of Privilege
and the Tomato Can Chronicle is familiar to every
dedicated reader of angling literature. Edmund
Ware Smith, like many others, has found Maine
a fertile source of both characters and fish.
"Angler, Beware!" is a definite variation from the
normal "line," but perhaps this has given it a
broader appeal.*

NOWADAYS, even in the wood-burning towns of the north country where trout still come heavy and often, you'd have to
hunt hard to find a doctor that believes there's anything in
prenatal influence. A few tenacious old midwives living on the river
above Frederickton may insist that a boy born during the first salmon
run will be a great fisherman; but most of the bright young medicos

use sulfanilamide, drive streamlined convertibles, and have read *Devils, Drugs and Doctors.*

Sue Crane's obstetrician was even more modern. Aside from an annual two weeks in Bar Harbor, he had never been north of the Boston Lying-In. Having worked with the great De Normandie, then of Marlborough Street, he didn't give prenatal influence a thought. Prenatal care was the thing. With the able co-operation of Sue herself, he brought young Judson Crane into the world, slapped the breath of life into him, and went out to the reception room to see if he could do anything for the stricken father.

You remember William Edward Crane, of course. Inventor of the Crane-Wing fly, and author of *Stream Technique and Fly Rod.* Bill Crane and his lifelong fishing comrade, George Pattengill, were pacing up and down, clinging to each other for comfort, when the doctor arrived. They were dressed in waders, flannel shirts, and hats. During their hours of travail, the waders had dried out in the steam heat, and you could smell mud and rubber. It would have been difficult to tell at first glance which man was the father. Both seemed on the verge of collapse.

"How is she?" said Bill Crane, paling as the doctor entered.

"She's great, Bill! Did a splendid job, all the way through. I congratulate you on your wife—and your baby."

"What kind is it?" asked George Pattengill, his forehead clammy with dread.

"Boy. A corker, too! Just under eight pounds. Got a back like a wrestler."

It was George who fainted—relief and ecstasy in equal parts. Had the newborn been a girl, George probably would not have regained consciousness. He had tried to teach a girl—she was a graduate of that finishing school in Farmington, Connecticut—how to cast a fly, which is why he had remained a bachelor. George now came to, muttering something sentimental about the newborn's first trout. The doctor, administering brandy, again noticed that his two nervous cases were dressed for fishing. He frowned.

"Sue mentioned that things began happening on some riverbank," he said.

"I shall never forget it," murmured George Pattengill from the day bed. "Sue was sitting under the big pine, just above the cement bridge on the Manhan. I had just raised a fair-sized brown. I should say he'd go about—"

"What's the idea?" interrupted the doctor, turning to Bill. "Taking your wife fishing at such a time! Haven't you got any sense at all?"

"No. Yes. I mean—oh, gosh! I don't know," said Bill. "It's opening day on trout, don't you see? Sue wouldn't let me stay home with her.

Said it would spoil our fishing—George's and mine. 'Course I couldn't go and leave her alone. So, she . . ."

The day bed creaked as George Pattengill rolled over and sat up. He looked better, but was still a sick man. "It's beautiful," he breathed. "The whole thing is beautiful. It's poetic, that's all. Think, Bill. Your son, born on opening day, and all of us out there together—fishing —when it started. That is, I mean, of course, you and I were fishing. Not Sue."

"No," said Bill bleakly. "Not Sue. She was reading."

"Used to fish, didn't she?" asked the doctor.

"Before we were married. She reads now."

A wan light showed in George Pattengill's eyes. The poetry in him was not yet exhausted. "If only she had been reading La Branche, or Hewitt on the dry fly, the aura would have been perfect. I mean to say, the prenatal influence of such a powerful combination of—"

"Rot!" said the doctor. "You know better, George! Or you should. What was she reading?"

"I don't know. I just know it wasn't La Branche, or Hewitt, or Skues, or anything to do with fishing. It was probably—"

"My God!" cried Bill Crane, dementedly plucking George's sleeve. "I remember now! I—George! It was *Moby Dick!*"

"*Moby Dick,*" echoed George, reaching for the brandy. "Oh, Bill!"

Whether or not there was anything to the Crane-Pattengill theory of prenatal influence, young Judson Crane, at age three, could actually cast a fly out of his lap and some distance beyond. His father, of course, had given him a fly rod before he could walk, and George Pattengill—Uncle George now—had provided him with a complete set of celluloid trout for bathtub use. In the ordinary sense, little Jud Crane never wore rubber pants. He was taught to call them waders.

"See, Mummy! See! See!" he cried one summer day, following an especially good downwind cast on the back lawn.

"That's lovely, dear," said Sue, not quite looking up from her book. "Daddy will be so proud. And Uncle George will burble."

Later in the day Jud's mentors returned from business and went immediately to the back lawn to see how the boy was coming along. He performed splendidly, and with spirit.

" 'Nother year or two," said Bill, "and we'll have him with us on the stream."

George Pattengill watched his protégé in a kind of steamy trance. "Look at him! Bill. And Sue. I want you both to just notice how he's getting his wrist into it."

"How wonderful," said Sue, setting aside her book. The year was 1929, and the book was Thomas Wolfe's *Look Homeward, Angel.*

A connotation in the title vaguely disturbed Sue. She was to have a more definite qualm about the same author's *Of Time and the River,* which appeared six years later. Now, a little stoically, she said, "You three boys are going to have wonderful times together, aren't you?"

"You didn't include yourself, dear," said Bill Crane, turning anxiously to his beloved. "We're together, always, you know. You must think of us as four, not three."

"But I do, Bill. You know I do."

At seven, Jud Crane had mastered the roll cast and some of the simpler curve casts in still air. He was catching trout regularly, and his picture had appeared many times in rotogravure. Usually you saw him standing between his father and George Pattengill, a lanky, graceful, serious-looking boy. You looked at the three of them, and you knew they were the sort of fellows who took trout. Then, in the background, slightly out of focus, yet somehow dominant, you noticed Sue Crane. She was lovely-looking, her eyes invariably on her son. She held a book in one hand and a bottle of fly dope in the other. She was never mentioned in the captions.

During the winter of his ninth year, Jud Crane learned to tie his own flies. Each evening he mounted his vise on the edge of the living-room table and went to work. From a nearby chair, Bill constantly watched the advancement of his son's art. On a March night, when sleet tinkled on the windowpanes, Jud completed a good specimen and turned to his father for approbation. But this time Bill's chair was empty.

"Where's Dad, Mum? I thought he was right here."

"He went into the study five minutes ago."

"Is anything the matter?"

"I think he's tired. He's been quiet this evening."

"Well," said Jud, holding the finished fly toward his mother, "how do you like this one?"

"How lovely, dear! It's a . . . a—don't tell me—Royal Coachman!"

"No, Mum. It isn't. It's a Crane-Wing—the one Dad invented."

"Of course. How stupid of me," said Sue, and went to get the vacuum cleaner to rid the blue rug of feathers, lint and tinsel.

Jud stared after her for a long, puzzled moment, then darted for the study. He found his father lying on the sofa gazing at the ceiling.

"Hi, Dad. Are you awful tired?"

"Huh?" said Bill, sitting up. "Tired? Me? Why?"

"Well, you scratch your head when you're tired, and your hair's rumpled."

Bill Crane wasn't exactly tired. He was troubled. The fact was that he had recently noted the first of several disquieting symptoms having to do with his relationship to fishing. Bill had lunched that noon with George Pattengill and a visiting fly man from the Anglers' Club of New York. They had discussed a trout's cone of visibility in clear water. During the conversation, it had suddenly occurred to Bill that Hargrave's glass tank photographs and diagrams had settled the subject—exhausted it, you might say—ten years ago. After Hargrave, there was really nothing more to be said. Yet George Pattengill and that other fellow had said it for two solid hours. George's voice, hoarse with the lust of angling theory, had haunted Bill all afternoon. In trying to rid his ears of the echo, Bill felt a twinge of disloyalty both to George and to a trout's cone of visibility.

But Jud's appearance in the study had a refreshing effect. Now, the shadows vanished from his mind, Bill waxed enthusiastic over his son's expertly tied Crane-Wing. He did not notice that the boy listened in a preoccupied way.

"That's a beautiful fly," said Bill. "Can't fault it. Why, you've even got your hackles slanted just right. Uncle George ought to see this. It'd please him. You're going places, son."

With startling irrelevance, Jud said: "Dad, doesn't Mother like fishing?"

"What? What's that? 'Course she does! Loves to come with us, and watch us, and everything. What do you mean?"

"Well, heck—sometimes she seems awful still."

"Don't let that worry you at all. We're a right little, tight tight little unit—you and Mother and Uncle George and I. Always will be."

"She just seems to read, though, Dad."

During the next few seasons Sue Crane read a great deal on the banks of many rivers. She became not only a student of contemporary literature, but an authority on fly dope. She tried all the new brands and in time came to regard fly dope as perfume, which she secretly labeled *eau d'ennui*.

In May of one of these seasons Bill Crane had his second symptom, or qualm, concerning his attitude toward fishing. It was vague and unexplainable, like the first. He had waded out of the Westfield River one afternoon and ploshed up to where Sue was sitting on a cold stone.

"What are you reading, dear?" he said.

"*Anthony Adverse*. Been saving it. Go away, darling. You're dripping on me."

A squeal of delight reached them from across the river. "Darned if Jud hasn't tied into another one," said Bill, and went down the bank again into the stream. A trout rose to a natural within thirty feet of him. He didn't notice the trout. There was a gorgeous white cloud lifting above the ridge. Bill noticed the cloud. He couldn't remember noticing a cloud before, while fishing. Nor could he recall coming out of a stream during a rise to inquire what Sue was reading. With a faint shudder, he at once resumed casting.

In the winter of that very year, George Pattengill prevailed on Bill to write *Stream Technique and the Fly Rod.* Sue Crane was thus driven into reading her first book on fishing. Loyalty to her husband and son, and a taste for the proper use of the English language, compelled her to read the typescript, galleys, and page proofs.

Stream Technique and the Fly Rod was a smash hit. It came out in March and sold eight thousand copies in three weeks. The book was dedicated simply and devotedly: "To My Wife and Son."

George Pattengill, now quite bald, and more solemn than ever, had expected that *Stream Technique* would be dedicated roughly as follows:

TO GEORGE PATTENGILL,

my dearest friend and most inspiring comrade on the trout rivers of eastern North America. Without his encouragement and expert criticism this book could not have been written. His advice has been an unfailing bulwark of comfort. To those who have been fortunate enough to fish with George, it will be apparent that his genius is largely responsible for the brilliant chapters on stream entomology, leader calibrations, water temperatures, and the sense perceptions of trout. And I would like to take this opportunity to express an even more personal gratitude to George, for it is none other than he who has so loyally assisted in the angling education of my son.

When George read the real dedication, he was hurt. But he didn't mope very long. He bravely admitted and resigned himself to the fact that in the family bond there was something a lonely bachelor couldn't fully grasp. Besides, the opening of trout season was near.

On the backswing from his disappointment, George went the least bit loopy. He arranged a dinner party in one of those rooms upstairs in Locke-Ober's café in Boston. The walls were oak-paneled and hung with sporting prints. George bought champagne for Sue Crane, Bill and himself, and an orangeade for Jud. He stood up and raised his glass. "I want to say just a word," he said.

"Sure, George," said Bill uneasily. "It's quite an occasion."

"Shoot, Georgie," said Sue, very gently. "Quick. I'm hungry!"

Jud, slender and shining in a new suit, sipped his orangeade and eyed his pseudo uncle worshipfully.

Nervously plucking at his collar, George began, "The eve of Jud's birthday, coinciding with the eve of the open season on trout, and practically coinciding with the publication of *Stream Technique and the Fly Rod*—" George paused, plucked, drew breath and resumed— "finds the four of us together again. And I count it a special privilege to make Jud a birthday present, a present that will last him faithfully through the years to come. I am sure it will give him as much pleasure as rods of similar craftsmanship have given his father and me."

With a gesture a little too yearning to be effective, George reached under the table and produced an aluminum-cased rod. He conferred the gift on Jud, and stepped back perspiring.

"Georgie! You shouldn't have done that!" said Sue.

"I have wanted to for a long time," said George hauntingly.

"Good Lord, George! It's a Spencer—a genuine!"

"Three and one half ounces of sheer beauty and power," said George.

"Oh, gosh, Uncle George!" cried Jud, uncasing the rod and caressing the joints. "It's wonderful! I just can't wait till tomorrow. Oh, gosh, thanks, Uncle George."

"Just now," said George, his head at a reverent angle, "I am thinking of a day eleven years ago. Your father and mother and I, Jud, were fishing the Manhan above the cement bridge. We—"

"I wasn't fishing, Georgie."

"No, Sue. You weren't. For it was on that day that a sacred— I mean to say, you were concerned with the divine process of—"

"Georgie, dear. On that day Jud was born. Is that what you're trying to say?"

"Yes," said George, wringing his napkin. "And now that Jud has a Spencer, I thought it would be upholding a sort of tradition—just ours, you know—if we all went out to the Manhan tomorrow and wet a line together."

"Oh boy!" said Jud, sighting along the perfectly aligned guides of his rod. "Swell!"

Sue gave a rippling laugh. "All right, Georgie. I'll bring a blanket and a book."

During this conversation, Bill Crane had been strangely silent. He wore a set smile. He was in the grip of another symptom. It was almost a premonition. How long, he wondered, had Sue been calling George Georgie? Something in the way she said it gave you a kind of perspective. Or maybe it was the fact that a genuine Spencer cost a hundred and fifteen dollars. Or maybe it was the way the light shone on George's head and spilled down over the round, kind, earnest, yet somehow arid face.

"About the book," George was saying to Sue, his voice muted. "Could you make it *Moby Dick*, Sue? Just to sort of round out things?"

"No," said Sue.

Bill Crane had a miserable time getting to sleep that night. At first he attributed his restlessness to lobster, then to the fact that tomorrow was opening day—then to the curious feeling he had had about George. There was no denying it: A subtle inflection in Sue's voice had made him see George, himself, *Stream Technique,* and—yes, yes!—fishing through detached eyes. Bill grappled his pillow and pondered. What the deuce was wrong? Nothing, really. Not a darn thing. Good old George! Swell of him to give Jud that beautiful rod. Just like him. Heart of gold. And couldn't he take trout on a dry fly! Wow!

Bill finally dropped off; but at a shuddery, predawn hour he awoke with a start. He sat bolt upright, thus dragging the covers from Sue.

"Bill, darling. Do lie still. I'm freezing."

In the frigid, graying light, Bill stared around the bedroom.

"Did George ring the doorbell?" he asked.

"No. And if he did, he can just wait outside till five o'clock."

Bill imagined old George waiting on the front steps in the cold. The picture made him wince. "Did Jud call?" he said.

"Of course not. I'd have heard him."

"Did his alarm clock go off?"

"No! Pity's sake, Bill. Don't be an egg. Go to sleep. What's the matter with you?"

"I . . . Darned if I know. Nightmare, maybe."

"It's opening day on trout, if you ask me," said Sue, wryly.

Bill swung out of bed, tucked the covers around Sue's shoulders, kissed her, and went downstairs. He switched on an excessive number of lights, but was in no way cheered by them. Jud's fishing gear— wader, creel, wading boots and hallowed Spencer lay neatly on the sofa. By habit and custom Bill's tackle should have been laid out beside Jud's. It wasn't. Funny, Bill thought; must have left it in the hall closet. Darn funny, on opening day.

On the way to the hall closet, Bill stopped at the living-room table and riffled the pages of a copy of *Stream Technique and Fly Rod.* Usually this pastime comforted him. This time it didn't. It didn't do anything at all. Bill knew now that he was on the verge of a revelation which might be too appalling to face. But an instant later, when the revelation came, he not only faced it but welcomed it. He said the words inwardly and was mildly astonished that they didn't rock the house. He went to the front hall, looked at himself boldly in the mirror, and spoke the words aloud in a low, steady voice: "I don't give a damn if I never go fishing again!"

For a time Bill ecstatically savored his new freedom. The thing had come about quite painlessly. He realized that it had been eating away at him for a long time. There wasn't a regret. The writing of *Stream Technique* had simply been the final blow, but long before that he had been quietly corroding. Now, thank God, it was all over. No more ice water leaking through his waders. No more getting up in the middle of the night. No more interminable conversations about leader lengths, nymphs, bugs, flies, and a trout's cone of visibility.

"Think," mused Bill, "what poor Sue has been through all these years! Simulating interest, just for Jud and me and poor old George. What a girl!"

Bill stepped gaily across the living room, hs bathrobe flaring. He picked up another copy of *Stream Technique*—the house was full of them—and hurled it into a distant chair. It lay there, pages fluttering, like a bird with a broken wing.

"Here I am," Bill told himself, "at the height of my fishing career, and I hate fishing. Boy-oh-boy-oh-BOY!"

But Bill Crane was not at the height of his fishing career, or anywhere near it. Presently he understood why. He reached his understanding through an imaginary conversation with George Pattengill.

"George," he said in fancy, "I'm through. You can have my Spencers, and my Caverdi reels, and all my other—"

"What?"

"Just as I say, George. Fishing bores me."

In Bill's piteous though somehow delectable dream, he saw the pallor spread slowly over George's face.

"But the Crane-Wing fly, Bill," George seemed to say, "and *Stream Technique*, and—"

"Hell with 'em all."

George swayed. In the phantasy Bill rushed to him and eased him into a chair. George's voice was very weak. "Your—your whole reputation, Bill, throughout New England and eastern Canada. What about that?"

"That bores me, too, George. Have a brandy?"

George's next question, though still imaginary, gave Bill Crane such an actual jolt that he nearly needed brandy himself.

"What about Jud?" asked George, his eyes suddenly narrowing. "Going to let your son down, Bill? Going to break the boy's heart? Are you?"

Bill's pulse thumped. This was reality. So was the buzzing in his ears. And so the tinkle of Jud's alarm clock. It was opening day! Bill gave himself a poignant smile in the front-hall mirror as he passed on the way to Jud's bedroom. The boy was stepping out of his pajama bottom when Bill entered.

"Hi, Dad! Hi! Hi! Gee, I can't wait to get going."

"Neither can I!" said Bill. "Happy birthday! Yippee! Let's go!"

Bill Crane's casting that morning on the Manhan was effortless, disinterested, and nothing short of magnificent. At at least sixty feet, he was laying 'em two inches from an alder frond that trembled near the surface of the stream. Cross-wind, too!

"Gad, Bill," said George Pattengill, "you're hot. You're really sweet, man. Never saw you in such wrist. Practically fluid."

"Huh?" said Bill, gazing off at Jud, who was working a riffle just above. "What's that, George? Oh, yuh, sure. Thanks."

Bill was especially attentive to Sue. He hadn't told her of his revelation for two reasons. The first was that he couldn't be sure his release was permanent. The second was that he feared Sue might take steps to lure Jud away from his beloved sport. She might argue, and with good point, that one small boy's fishing shouldn't poison the free hours of both his parents. If Sue really got herself braced, Bill could see the three of them vacationing on a hotel porch in the mountains. No, he had better not tell her. At least, not yet.

Sue sat under the big pine wrapped in her blanket, her nose looking cold, and the pages of *One More Spring* whipping in the breeze. Every other time Bill turned to look at her, a trout socked his trailing fly. Now that there was no thrill in it, Bill couldn't keep them away. He hooked a brown that morning, while gazing at Sue, that was as large as any within the memory of local pipe smokers. He had his limit by nine o'clock.

"Gee, Dad!" cried the adoring Jud. "How in heck do you do it?"

"That," intoned Uncle George, "is what you call stream generalship."

The novelty of fishing purely for sacrifice didn't nourish Bill Crane very long. His compensation was in Jud's happiness, and in the strengthening of the bond between them. But he had come to loathe fishing as much as if not more than he had once loved it. One day on the Deerfield, when fellows with flies in their hats had gathered around to admire a four-pound rainbow he had accidentally hooked while lighting his pipe, Bill felt mean enough to have poured acid in George Pattengill's leader case. Seeking respite, he climbed the riverbank and sat down beside Sue.

"Bill, dearest. Don't bother about me. Go right back to the river and have fun." He went.

The next season, in prizes for big, bigger and biggest trout, Bill won four hundred dollars' worth of fishing tackle. He was by now conducting a number of fishing columns in magazines and newspapers. He had a public, as well as a son. But this drudgery wasn't the worst that Bill endured. George Pattengill blithely arranged dates for Bill to address fish-and-game clubs in winter. George and Jud always sat beside Bill on the platform, while Sue attended the nearest movie. After his lectures, looking a little gaunt and haggard, Bill would often have to give a casting exhibition in some bleak gymnasium smelling of old basketball shoes.

There was no peace in winter, or even sleep. In nightmares Bill would hear Jud's clear, urgent young voice saying, "Dad, let's go fishing!" In the nightmares, and also in the daytime in season, Bill would answer, "You bet! Great idea! We'll get Mother and Uncle George and start."

His one satisfaction was in knowing that he was doing the right thing for Jud. Pretty soon now the boy would be grown up. He would go fishing with friends his own age, and Bill could rest, certain that he had left his son a solid treasure of companionship. Bill told himself that when that time came, he would write a slim, stark volume entitled *Hell with Fishing*. Then he would put a blow torch to his tackle and take up gardening.

The year of Jud's enrollment in boarding school was the most dramatic of Bill Crane's career as husband, father, and fisherman. Jud was to be away from home for the first time in his life, and Bill determined to give him something really big to honor the occasion. He took a martyr's delight in laying plans, and in breaking the jolly news.

"Son," said Bill severely, "stop studying your algebra, and tell Mother and me what you'd like best in all the world."

It was an early-June evening. Jud looked up from his algebra book to see his father and mother smiling at him. He glanced from one to the other, his face brightening. "Don't you know?"

"Haven't the faintest idea," said Bill.

"You're trying to kid me. You know darn well what I want. I want a good, long fishing trip with you and Uncle George."

"How strange!" said Sue.

"Sure is," said Bill, "because it just so happens I've engaged four of the best guides on the Nepisiguit River. There's trout in that river—squaretails—that'll go six pounds. We start the twenty-sixth of this month. We'll be gone three weeks."

"The Nepisiguit!" cried the boy. "Three weeks! Oh, Dad!"

The joy in his son's voice was balm almost adequate to the wounds Bill had suffered throughout three deadly seasons. He hoped Jud's enthusiasm would have a similar sustaining effect on Sue. It was going to be a tough trip.

Jud was regarding his mother thoughtfully. He started to speak, hesitated, and finally said, "Are you going to be with us all the whole time, Mother?"

"Of course, dear. Why not?"

"I was just wondering," said Jud, fidgeting, "if you'd like it."

Always when Jud had voiced this doubt, Sue had gaily laughed it away. Now Bill noticed that she was steeling herself. There was a barely perceptible tightening of her lips. Bill could understand. Three weeks on a wilderness river in fly season was a lethal stretch.

"Of course I'd like it!" said Sue.

"I mean really like it," the boy persisted, nervous in his effort to make himself clear. "I mean the way Dad and I and Uncle George like it. You know, Mother—the fishing part. You don't ever seem to fish. You 'most always seem to just read."

Bill had a bad moment while Sue delayed her answer. Just when he was sure she would revolt, the tightening of her lips grew more pronounced, her chin firm. "I love being with you and Dad, dear," she said.

"And Uncle George, Mother?"

"And Uncle George," said Sue, her lips now practically a straight line.

Bill remembered this conversation many times in the weeks prior to departure. It had done something to Sue—undermined her. She grew increasingly silent, and at times even grim. Bill sensed the tension in her and dreaded that she had reached the breaking point—the moment of open rebellion. He could feel her cringing from three weeks in the close company of George Pattengill. Bill understood only too well. Not that George wasn't a good fellow. It was just that—well, as a matter of fact, George was still talking about a trout's cone of visibility.

A few days before departure, George rather startlingly announced that he would be unable to get away for the full three weeks. Bill felt that the news would come as a relief to Sue. He was relieved himself, and a little ashamed of it. But Sue's reaction to the glad tidings was not as he had hoped.

"Dearest," he said, after Jud had turned in, "old George is acting strangely. He may be in love. He—"

"Maybe!" said Sue. "He is! I'll tell you who with, too: he's in love with George Pattengill and fish! Fish! Fish!"

"Wait a minute, Sue. You'll wake Jud. Relax, dear. It isn't going to be so bad, after all. George isn't—"

"Damn George!"

"I'm trying to tell you that George isn't coming up till the second week. He told me this afternoon."

Sue curled up in her wing chair and bowed her head in her arms. Bill was disappointed. His good news seemed to have brought her little, if any, relief. He decided to adopt a gay manner.

"I asked George what was the matter," Bill went on laughingly, "and he blinked at me, and the sweat came out on his head. He said, 'Bill, I simply can't get away, that's all.' I asked him if his trouble was financial, and he said, 'No.' Then his face got round, and he stared up at that salmon that's mounted over his desk. I couldn't help thinking how he kind of looks like the salmon—the eyes, I guess. Then he swallowed, and mopped his head with his handkerchief, and said, 'Time is of the essence.' That's all."

Bill felt that his description of George was a concession to Sue's opinions. He felt he deserved at least a chuckle. He didn't get it. As if she hadn't heard a word of what he had said, Sue asked in a dull, toneless voice, "Where is this Nepsiquiti River?"

Bill was thunderstruck. "Why, Sue! You know where it is. You've heard George and me—"

"I wasn't listening. Where is the Nepsiquiti River?"

"Nepisiguit, Sue. Not Nepsiquiti."

"Where is it?"

Bill thought it best to humor her. "Northern New Brunswick," he said patiently. "It empties in Chaleur Bay at Bathurst. From Bathurst we go sixteen miles upriver on the abandoned mine railroad. You'll love that, Sue. There's just a flatcar. At the abandoned mine the canoes meet us, and—"

"That's enough. Are there any flies?"

"Flies? Oh, you mean black flies? Why . . . uh . . . maybe—a few."

"Bill," said Sue, facing him, and speaking with a kind of ghastly gentleness, "I'm not going."

"What?"

She repeated very slowly: "I—am—not—going."

Bill saw that she was bracing herself for his storm of indignation. Smiling at her with infinite understanding, he simply said, "All right, old dear. I know how you feel, and I'm sure Jud knows. That boy's really keen. I'll break it to him gently."

"You know how I feel?" said Sue, almost shrilly. "You? You don't even begin to know! Did you ever sit on pine needles and damp stones from April to September? Did you? Bill Crane! I've got fly bites on my legs dating back to 1920!"

"Yes, dear," said Bill, strolling along the fringe of the blue rug. "You've been a good soldier! Jud and I'll go it alone. We'll get along."

Sue came down to the dock to see them off for St. John. As the boat slipped away from the pier, they looked over the rail at her. She was staring up at them, her eyes streaming.

"Aw, gee, Dad," said Jud. "She's crying."

Far down the pier they spied a familiar figure lumbering toward them and waving a panama. They waved back frantically.

"Uncle George!" yelled Jud, his voice drowned in the steamer's throaty blast. "See you in a week!"

George's pudgy arm had suddenly stopped waving. His panama hung, so to speak, at half mast. He had noticed Sue Crane. He stopped beside her. Bill saw him reach out his hand as if to pat her shoulder. Sue whirled. Bill thought he saw Sue's lips frame the words "Don't touch me!"

Poor old George, thought Bill. Then, turning to Jud, he said, "Well, boy—we're off!"

A few days later, Bill Crane and his son were taking trout on the fabulously beautiful Nepisiguit River. They were camped in those neat, peeled spruce cabins on the high bluff at the Narrows, four miles above the abandoned mine, where the river sings down through the ledges.

For the first time in his life, Bill Crane had taken a book on a fishing trip. The book was Walter Edmonds' *Chad Hanna,* and aside from the parts where Chad went trout fishing, Bill enjoyed the book mightily. When he and Jud were within sight of each other, Bill fished. But when he could sneak around a bend, he would climb out on the bank, apply fly dope, and settle down with Chad Hanna.

The evening of the day before George Pattengill was scheduled to arrive, Jud reported seeing a very large trout in the pool near the head of the Narrows. The next morning he said, "Dad, I'm going up there and really work on that mossback. Bet you his tail was five inches wide."

"Wow! Go get him! Want me to come along?"

"Well, I . . . I kind of want to solve him singlehanded, Dad. Then I'll have something to tell Uncle George tonight."

"That's the stuff, Jud. Know just how it is. Guess I'll stay around camp for a while, and then maybe work the lower pools."

"Okey, Dad. So long. Tight lines!"

For an hour after Jud had gone up the trail to the upper pool Bill lazed around talking to the guides. Then he decided to take *Chad Hanna,* slip downriver a couple of bends, and finish the book. He had been hoarding the last three chapters.

"Seen that book I was reading, Zeb?" he asked his guide.

"No, I ain't. But seems like 'twas layin' on your bunk this morning, Mr. Crane."

"It was," said Jud's guide. "But Jud took it with him. I seen him tuck it in his creel."

"You . . . you what?"

"The boy took it in his creel, sir."

"Oh. He took it in his creel?"

"Yuh."

"Oh. I see."

"Like for me to go up there an' get it for you, Mr. Crane?"

"No, Zeb. Thanks. You fellows stay right here and whittle. I'll walk up there and get it myself."

Ten minutes later, peering through the branches of a little fir that grew on the shore of the upper pool, Bill Crane saw his son lying full length on the sun-warmed ledge, *Chad Hanna* spread open before him. The boy was completely absorbed. His Spencer rod, forgotten, leaned against a bush, the line trailing in the water. A small trout had taken the fly. Its antics, unnoticed by Jud, twitched the rod tip violently. Bill drew a long breath, stepped out onto the ledge, and said, "Hello, son."

Jud scrambled to his feet. His face turned crimson, and his lips worked nervously. "Gee, Dad—thought you were down below."

"When did you get sick of fishing, boy?" asked Bill.

"Sick of fishing? Me? Why, gosh, Dad. What the heck do you mean?"

Bill came close. He put his arm around Jud's shoulders, and hugged the boy against him. "Well, it's this way: I've hated fishing for three years that I know about. How about you? Come on! Confess!"

"And . . . and all this time you've been fishing because of me, Dad?"

"Something like that. But I loved that part of it. How long have you been fishing because of me?"

Jud smiled. He nudged himself close against his father's side. "Heck, ever since I can remember. But it was kind of nice, though, Dad. I like doing things with you and Mother, even when I hate the things."

Father and son stood off and looked at each other.

"You know," Bill said, "I think this is about the happiest moment of my life—except, maybe, when you were born."

"Me, too, Dad. Gee, you're a swell guy."

Bill swallowed and said no more. He had never realized how close a father and son might feel through detesting a common hobby.

"Oh, gosh all hemlocks, Dad! Wait till we tell Mother! She'll have ten million cat fits."

"I can hear her laughing right now," said Bill.

"Poor Uncle George, Dad. What will he say? He'll suffer awful. Bet you he will. He'll be so lonely."

"Good Lord! I'd forgotten about that. We better not say anything to him at first. We'll have to handle him with kid gloves."

George Pattengill was on the cabin porch when Jud and Bill got back. This was strange, on the face of it, because George wasn't due till evening. Moreover, George seemed distracted—and at the same time complacent, and even a little fatuous. Bill guiltily told himself that it was a combination only George could achieve.

"Left East Boston Airport at daylight," said George, "landed in Chaleur Bay. Got here ten minutes ago."

"Great to see you, George. Expensive trip, wasn't it?"

"Worth it. Come here. Want you to look down there at the lower pool."

They stepped to the edge of the bluff. A solitary fisherman stood waist-deep in the pool below. George pointed a shaking finger. "Look!"

"One of the Rollins boys?" said Bill, puzzled and annoyed. It wasn't like old George to ring in a stranger.

"Looks like Tiny Rollins," said Jud. "Looks like— Dad! It's—"

"George!" gasped Bill. "My God, George! Is that one of the Rollins boys? Or . . . or . . . is it my wife?"

"It's Sue Crane," said George, as if he were unveiling a statue.

"Mother!" said Jud. "Dad! Look at her cast that fly!"

Bill and his son exchanged a glance. Sue hadn't seen them yet. She was casting over a pocket fifty feet away, and she was casting beautifully. Bill and Jud watched her in stunned silence. No wonder they had mistaken her for one of the Rollins boys. Her hair was tucked up under her felt hat, and they could see a smooch of dirt on one cheek. A cloud of black flies, unnoticed, busied themselves around her. But more than that, far, far more, there was the tense, slightly demented expression on her face—the gleaming, telltale eagerness. Bill glanced again at his son, and his heart warmed to the boy's slow wink. Jud, too, had recognized the signs of the true, passionate, and permanent angler.

"Sue!" Bill yelled. "Oh, Sue! Sue!"

She didn't hear him. A twelve-inch trout had looped into her fly, and she had him on. Her rod curved in exactly the right arc. She played the trout expertly, slipped the net under him, and looked up to see her loved ones. She didn't wave her hand at them. She waved her hat!

"Yoo-hoo! O, da-a-a-rlings!" she called, wading ashore.

Jud went racing down the steep trail to meet her. Bill started to follow, but George prevented him.

Bill Crane was now aware that George had been talking for some time. George's monologue was both an explanation and a paean of self-praise. The main facts reached Bill in a badly blurred condition, but he was gradually separating them while Sue and Jud were exchanging hugs on the riverbank below.

It seemed, according to George, that Sue had come to him in secret the day after Jud had been told of the Nepisiguit trip. She had said to him, "George, Jud is distressed because I don't fish. He's unhappy because I don't participate. It's going to mar his trip, maybe even ruin it. I am going to learn to fish, if it kills me. It may kill you, too, George. You're going to teach me."

George said that he had never seen such savage determination in the eyes of woman. He had given her secret lessons every afternoon.

At this point in George's narrative, Bill again started down the bluff toward his wife and son. George pinioned him. "Wait, Bill. I want you to know everything."

"Hurry, George!"

"Bill, if I may say so, she was awful! No other word. Three weeks without a spark. I almost—"

"Why didn't she ask me to teach her?"

"Dread of failure. And it is my belief that it might have led to serious domestic strife, or worse. Because after only ten lessons we stopped speaking to each other. That was the day Sue broke the tip of a Spencer by hitting the ground on the backcast. The backcast, mind you, Bill."

Bill made a third lunge toward the trail leading down the bluff. George again restrained him by force. "Bill, you must hear me, first. Let her tell Jud. You can see how happy she's making the boy. Look at the way they're smiling at each other."

"Yuh. Sure, George. Hurry."

"Three days before we were to leave on the trip," George continued, "I saw a glimmer of hope. A faint one, Bill. That was the day she tried to strike me. But I had tied her elbow to her side, so that she couldn't use that frightful, full arm sweep. I had just told her, gently of course, that I had never dreamed anyone could be as awkward as she. Right after that, she struck at me with the rod. In that instant, she got her first sense of timing. Instead of hitting me, what she did, with her elbow tied, was to get a respectable cast—her first. She didn't realize it, but I did. It was poetry, Bill—poetry."

"George! That was the day you told me you couldn't get up till the second week."

"Yes. It was a turning point. She needed a bit more time. Time was—"

"Of the essence."

"Exactly. These last nine or ten days have proved it. I prevailed on her to stay. She said she wasn't going anyway."

"I remember, George."

"I was constantly by her side, Bill. Of course I wouldn't have done it for anyone else. I gave her everything I knew. It was beautiful to see it taking shape in her, and growing. One day she smiled. The radiance simply spread over her. She had got out thirty-five feet, and the fly stayed on. The basic fire, the love, must have been there all the time. Must have been lying dormant in her for twenty years. What you have just witnessed is the mere flowering of . . ."

This time Bill Crane made good his escape. An instant later he held his wife in his arms. "Sue, dearest! You're a marvel. That was pretty casting—pretty!"

"Oh, Bill! I'm so glad! Jud said I was good, too. When I think of what I've missed!"

"Plenty good years ahead for all of us."

"That's just what I told her, Dad," said Jud. "I told her about my big trout in the upper pool, too. But she won't go near him."

"Cast for another fellow's trout?" cried Sue. "Nothing doing!"

Apparently, in Sue, one of angling's highest principles was already fixed. Bill's arms tightened. He stared over her shoulder into his son's tanned, wistfully smiling face. In each other's eyes, father and son saw their futures reflected. Year after year they would arise in the cold dawn. They would don flannels, waders, and a spirit of Spartan gaiety. It would be an ordeal by ice water, alarm clocks, tapered silk, and split bamboo. Their reward would be another's happiness, and the knowledge that, together, they held the key. The trout in the upper pool was but the beginning. Bill smiled and straightened up.

"Guess it's your trout, Jud. But if you want any help . . ."

"I'll take this one solo, Dad." The boy came around to face his mother. How strangely real rang his eagerness. "Come on, Mother. Dad. Let's go!"

The Lotus Eaters

SPARSE GREY HACKLE

The author of "The Lotus Eaters" and the follow-
ing selection, "Murder," is not a prolific writer, yet
it was most difficult to make a selection from the
regrettably thin works of Sparse Grey Hackle. A
friend described this writer's angling and writing
by classing him as "a purist with emotional lapses."
The editor, knowing the man behind the pseu-
donym, cannot agree. Sparse both fishes and writes
as he pleases. Had he lived two hundred years ago
Thomas Paine would have had a fast run for his
money.

No RECORD remains of the early history of the club which
a group of wealthy Brooklyn brewers and trout fishermen
incorporated in 1895 as the Fly Fishers Club of Brooklyn. But the late Chancellor Levison, who was a member, told Dick
Hunt that the group fished Brodhead's Creek from the Henryville
House in the seventies and when the brook-trout fishing played out
there in the nineties, moved to the Beaverkill and made their headquarters at Ben Hardenburgh's farm.

Legend says that Ben built a log cabin on his farm for a wealthy
man who wanted a love nest; that after Ben had discovered what
was going on and had run him off, the Brooklyn fishermen took it
over for a dormitory; and that when they had a mass disagreement
with Ben some years later, they formed their own club and bought the

368

cabin for their clubhouse. At the same time, the club took its pick of the trout water for a price little more than the traditional red apple.

As now constituted, the club has several acres of rolling ground, on the eminence of which is the same log cabin, with a separate mess hall behind it; two and a half miles, both banks, of the sweetest dry-fly water on the entire length of the Little River, more than half of it in fee and the rest on long-term lease; privileges of entry and water supply in connection with the late Ben Hardenburgh's farm; and a sound, well-built dam at the foot of the Home Pool which goes out with the flood water each year.

The charter provides for twenty-five members but unwritten law limits it to twenty, the present total; after a lapse of many years, there actually is now one member from Brooklyn. The shares of stock, one to a member, are valued at $100 each and the dues are $25 a year, besides an assessment whenever the dam goes out. But to stem any rush for the bargain represented by this combination of superb fishing and low cost, it should be noted that a flaming sword bars the entrance to this angler's Eden. It is the membership, the most unique thing about this unique institution.

For these are lotus eaters. They live in a little world apart, a world which they found perfect upon entering and which, consequently, they strive to keep unchanged. Does there come one with wealth and social position? They do not comprehend the terms. Angling genius, and the prestige of authorship? They glance up incuriously, and return to their concerns. Sportsmanship, pleasing personality, fellowship of spirit? They regard him with unfocused eyes and murmur that they already have these qualities in the club. Here is one institution by which it is no reproach to be blackballed, for the present members are all agreed that if they themselves were now outsiders coming up for membership, they would be blackballed without exception. This is not a manifestation of caprice, misanthropy or sadism. It is merely the outward expression of the spirit of the club, that everything is perfect the way it is— let us keep it that way.

This passion for the past carries the members to inordinate lengths, some of which may be described. For instance, the great one-room cabin bears no wall decorations except a thousand nails at which one may pitch his kit and hang it up, a series of penciled outlines of big fish, and a grocery-store calendar for the year 1910. Even to stretch a hand toward this ancient fly-specked relic elicits outraged cries and warnings from all present. The rough board floor is covered with a mud-caked rug of nondescript color; when Malcolm Runyon and the present writer essayed to remove and beat the tattered fabric, Scotty Conover, doyen of the club, leaped upon it in a heroic attitude and exclaimed, "That rug was put down in 1912, the year I joined the club. It has never been off the floor since, and it is not going to be taken up now!" The fireplace below the foot-thick flagstone mantel shelf is about the size of a one-car garage and contains a layer of ashes at least three feet thick. We removed about a foot of this deposit before we were discovered and restrained, and although we finally escaped expulsion, we never wholly lived down the opprobrium that descended upon us.

A new member who naïvely offered to have the cabin wired for electricity at his own expense shocked the members into literal speechlessness, and his sacrilege was blamed for a crack which appeared in the fireplace. The club's shame is the handsome new (twenty years old) mess hall, which had to be built simply because the old one burned down. But fortunately it is offset somewhat by the condition of the backhouse, which was torn from its mooring to the cabin and knocked askew years ago when the pilot of the county snowplow was induced to open the lane. Becoming a bit overinduced, he turned too short and the plow engaged the corner of the backhouse. It has been allowed to remain just as it dropped when Wally Fassett reached over and disengaged the clutch, and the members boast of its generous ventilation and erratic geometry.

Aside from the hearth fire, the sole artificial illumination in the cabin is an old-fashioned kerosene hanging lamp which was salvaged from a country church. Directly beneath it is a small table upon which each member, as he enters, deposits his bottle.

Additionally there is a pitcher of the icy spring water which flows perpetually from a pipe in the front yard—water that is agony to the teeth and a frigid benediction to the palate. No one can recall clearly how long the lamp and the table have been there, but all agree that the lamp has leaked kerosene upon the table—and into the water pitcher—ever since it was filched. You may think that the leak might be repaired, or that the table might be moved, or at least that the pitcher might be shifted, but that is because you do not know the Brooklyn Fly Fishers. Every highball that has been consumed in the club during all those years has featured a slight but terribly definite flavor of kerosene.

The same willingness to sanctify a traditional disability prevails in the dormitory, the single room constituting the upper floor of the cabin. Here unyielding cots bear mattresses of geologic age, each with its hills and valleys disposed in an individual terrain. Each member has learned how to wind himself between the lumps of his own bed and sleep comfortably in that contorted attitude, and if a newcomer takes another member's bed he will hear bitter protestation.

To be at the club for Opening Day is to realize how their devotion to the past inures the members to present hardship. The hardy anglers spend the evening in front of the blast-furnace fireplace, fortifying themselves internally to prevent their entire rear aspects from freezing solid. When the inner stiffness approximates the outer, each picks up a huge load of gray camp blankets and a kerosene lamp and climbs to the loft. How they have failed to burn down the cabin long ago by this procedure is a mystery.

Some take off a few clothes and there was once an exhibitionist who got into pajamas, but the standard procedure is to take off nothing but the shoes and the hat. Daybreak finds not even an ear or a nose visible, but one cowering figure, more valiant or less enduring than the rest, finally will force himself out of bed to dash downstairs, chunk up the fire, and clench his chattering teeth on the neck of a bottle. When the fire begins to make an impression on the room temperature, the other sleepers come dashing down to seize their bottles and back up to the blaze. The lavatory is the spring-water pipe in the yard. In warm weather they strip down and wash there, shaving with mirrors propped against the porch railing, but on Opening Day they just rinse their hands.

Two things may be noted about that porch in passing. One is that every bottle ever emptied at the club reposes beneath it—it is a broad porch, nearly surrounding the cabin, with very little room left under it. The other is that its railing is a favorite spot for the members to cool off on in their pelts after a sweaty afternoon in waders—a spectacle which once sent flying two schoolmarms who had come to inspect the "quaint cabin," thinking it unoccupied.

Two henchmen occupy the club's little world, along with the members. One is Joe Hardenburgh, whose farmhouse lies hidden beyond the apple trees; he "keeps an eye on things" in addition to working a hardscrabble farm on which crops are dragged up painfully, rather than raised. This laconic descendant of the patroon who received the far-flung Hardenburgh Patent is best depicted by his reply to an invitation to attend an auction. "I got everything I want now," he said. The other is Bert Cable, the best short-order cook in the world, who looks after the mess hall during the season. He ran the famous White House Restaurant in Roscoe for years and, in fact, starts a restaurant whenever he feels like it, selling it out when he gets tired of it. Like Joe, Bert doesn't really work for the club; he just comes up to help out his friends. They are a true part of the atmosphere of this ethereal cosmos.

For so it is. This is the land of the lotus, to enter which is to come under the spell of a dreaming languor, an enchantment of restfulness which makes the world outside hazy and unreal. The energetic visitor ascends the lane in a shower of gravel, hustles in with his equipment, sits down on the porch to catch his breath—and is lost. In this natural bower, where nothing can be seen but trees and sky, he idles to watch the line of the hills, to hear the birds at their housekeeping and the river whispering on its stones. He murmurs vague conversation, wanders about the cabin, and dawdles before the fireplace. He smokes the pipe of contemplation over his empty plate. When he goes to his locker for his waders, he forgets his purpose; and if he starts for the stream at all, he does it late and reluctantly. No one ever strides down to the river at the Brooklyn Fly Fishers. At best, he saunters.

The river itself fits into the spell. This is the Little River, the Beaverkill above its junction with the Willowemoc, the stream to which its alumni return again and again, forsaking the certainty of lordly preserves. The Big River, from the junction at Roscoe to the junction at East Branch, is a challenge, whereas the Little River is an invitation. It takes stronger legs and longer chances to wade the Big River, a bigger rod and a better arm to cover its waters. It is here that the ten- and twelve-pound monsters are taken and the five-pound bass that makes the startled angler think he has hooked into a trout twice as big. Here the stalker can watch an hour, a day or a week until he sees a great trout feeding and then wade armpit-deep and try to keep sixty feet of line off the water as he works out the single cast which will either raise the fish or put him down.

Fishing the Big River is a sport, but fishing the Little River is a recreation. This dozen miles of the loveliest trout water in America, with the Balsam Lake Club at the top and the Brooklyn Fly Fishers at the bottom, is what the old-timers referred to when they wrote about the Beaverkill, the classic water of the Golden Age.

It is still just as it was, at least from the infall of Berry Brook down to the Brooklyn water, and the Rockland bridge half a mile below it. A road follows it from Roscoe to the source, but above the Rockland bridge it is a washboarded red-dirt track with an ugly habit of tipping cars into the river, so that visitors to the state campsite above Berry Brook prefer to go in on the paved road from Livingston Manor. All that disturbs the melody of the living countryside along the river road is the bouncing of an occasional farm truck.

And as the river has not changed, neither have the Brooklyn Fly Fishers, for whom the Golden Age still exists. Not for them the state water farther upstream, nor the open water below the Rockland bridge. For years the club leased the beautiful Tempel water in the latter stretch, but finally gave it up because "nobody ever went down there." No, no one wants to go to any other water. The club leprechaun, Johnny Woodruff, may sneak off to night-fish the Picnic Grounds, and the club juvenile, Ed Myers, may spend his energy on expeditions to the Summer House Pool, but these are the exceptions. Sometimes the members speak knowingly of Foul Rift and the Lone Pine, the

Deserted Village and Painter's Bend, but when you pin them down you discover that they have not fished those pools in the Big River since their boyhood.

Another way remains in which the club still stays faithful to the Golden Age. It is the last stand, the loyal Old Guard, the final vanishing remnant of the old-fashioned American dry-fly purists. At first glance it seems strange that this group, more than any other, should exemplify the classic tradition of the dry fly. These are stern and hardy men, unfashionable, contemptuous of innovations, indifferent to foibles; enemies of pretense, averse to strangers, woman-haters; reading no fishing magazines or books—they already know how to fish; immune to British prestige, unknown to Abercrombie's or the Crossroads of Sports, contemptuous of Halford.

But these are the *American* purists. Not for them the long leaders and 4x points, the stream entomology, the tortured science of line calibers and rod action, the elaborate long casting to a rise in still water. Here, as nowhere else, there is exemplified the pure gospel of American dry fishing, just as its prophet George La Branche engraved it on the stone tablets of *The Dry Fly and Fast Water;* as Fred White saw it demonstrated by Theodore Gordon; as Chancellor Levison and Les Petrie and the youthful Guy Jenkins and all our members who grew up in the great tradition practiced it—the gospel that it doesn't matter what tackle or what fly you use, it's how and where you use it that counts; the gospel of fishing the water rather than fishing the rise, and covering the broken water rather than the smooth. Every inch of the Brooklyn water is broken, or at least ruffled, at normal tides; every inch of it is fished by the members with the dry fly. And with the dry fly only. Scotty Conover assured the present writer that he had not fished a wet fly in more than thirty years, and he is typical.

Here then is that echo of the Golden Age, that tiny angling Eden which has survived as the Brooklyn Fly Fishers. Would that it were timeless—but its end is early written. Not too many years hence the adjacent waters will be owned by estates instead of individuals, and when they are sold in settlement, the state, that greedy grabber of dead men's water, will surely get them. With state open water at either end of its unguarded stretch of river, hikers swarming over its acres and cars churning the dust, the club will see its end inevitable. It will sell out to the state, which will dredge the Home Pool for swimming and put a hot-dog stand in the cabin.

The lotus eaters will die of remembrance.

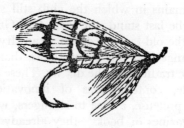

Murder

SPARSE GREY HACKLE

"If fishing interferes with your business, give up your business," any angler will tell you, citing instances of men who have lost health and even life through failure to take a little recreation, and reminding you that "the trout do not rise in Greenwood Cemetery," so you had better do your fishing while you are still able. But you will search far to find a fisherman to admit that a taste for fishing, like a taste for liquor, must be governed lest it come to possess its possessor; that an excess of fishing can cause as many tragedies of lost purpose, earning power and position as an excess of liquor. This is the story of a man who finally decided between his business and his fishing, and of how his decision was brought about by the murder of a trout.

Fishing was not a pastime with my friend John but an obsession—a common condition, for typically your successful fisherman is not really enjoying a recreation, but rather taking refuge from the realities of life in an absorbing fantasy in which he grimly if subconsciously re-enacts in miniature the unceasing struggle of primitive man for existence. Indeed, it is that which makes him successful, for it gives him that last measure of fierce concentration, that final moment of unyielding patience which in angling so often make the difference between fish and no fish.

John was that kind of fisherman, more so than any other I ever knew. Waking or sleeping, his mind ran constantly on the trout and its taking, and back in 1932 I often wondered whether he could keep on indefinitely doing business with the surface of his mind and fishing

374

with the rest of his mental processes—wondered, and feared that he could not. So when he called me one spring day and said, "I'm tired of sitting here and watching a corporation die; let's go fishing," I know that he was not discouraged with his business so much as he was impatient with its restraint. But I went with him, for maybe I'm a bit obsessed myself.

That day together on the river was like a thousand other pages from the book of any angler's memories. There was the clasp and pull of cold, hurrying water on our legs, the hours of rhythmic casting, and the steady somnambulistic shuffling which characterizes steelworkers aloft and fly fishermen in fast water. Occasionally our heads were bent together over a fly box; at intervals our pipes wreathed smoke, and from time to time a brief remark broke the silence. We were fishing "pool and pool" together, each as he finished walking around the other to a new spot above him.

Late afternoon found me in the second pool below the dam, throwing a long line up the still water. There was a fish rising to some insect so small that I could not detect it, so I was using a tiny gray fly on a long leader with a 5x point. John came by and went up to the dam pool and I lost interest in my refractory fish and walked up to watch, for there was always a chance of a good fish there. I stopped at a safe distance and sat down on a rock with my leader trailing to keep it wet, while John systematically covered the tail of the pool until he was satisfied that there were no fish there to dart ahead and give the alarm, and then stepped into it.

As he did so his body became tense, his posture that of a man who stalks his enemy. With aching slowness and infinite craft he began to inch up the pool and as he went his knees bent more and more until he was crouching. Finally, with his rod low to the water and one hand supporting himself on the bottom of the stream, he crept to a casting position and knelt in mid-current with water lapping under his elbows, his left sleeve dripping unheeded as he allowed the current to straighten his line behind him. I saw that he was using the same leader as mine but with a large No. 12 fly.

"John, using 5x?" I breathed. Without turning his head he nodded almost imperceptibly.

"Better break off and reknot," I counseled softly, but he ignored the suggestion. I spoke from experience. Drawn 5x gut is almost as fine as a human hair, and we both knew that it chafes easily where it is tied to a fly as heavy as No. 12, so that it is necessary to make the fastening in a different spot at frequent intervals in order to avoid breaking it.

I kept silence and watched John. With his rod almost parallel to the water he picked up his fly from behind him with a light twitch and then false-cast to dry it. He was a good caster; it neither touched the surface nor rose far above it as he whipped it back and forth.

Now he began lengthening his line until finally, at the end of each forward cast, his fly hovered for an instant above a miniature eddy between the main current and a hand's breadth of still water which clung to the bank. And then I noticed what he had seen when he entered the pool—the sudden slight dimple denoting the feeding of a big fish on the surface.

The line came back with a subtle change from the wide-sweeping false casts, straightened with decision and swept forward in a tight roll. It straightened again and then checked suddenly. The fly swept round as a little elbow formed in the leader, and settled on the rim of the eddy with a loop of slack upstream of it. It started to circle, then disappeared in a sudden dimple and I could hear a faint sucking sound.

It seemed as if John would never strike although his pause must have been but momentary. Then his long line tightened—he had out fifty feet—as he drew it back with his left hand and gently raised the rod tip with his right. There was slight pause and then the line began to run out slowly.

Rigid as a statue, with the water piling a little wave against the brown waders at his waist, he continued to kneel there while the yellow line slid almost unchecked through his left hand. His lips moved.

"A big one," he murmured. "The leader will never hold him if he gets started. I should have changed it."

The tip of the upright rod remained slightly bent as the fish moved into the circling currents created by the spillway at the right side of the dam. John took line gently and the rod maintained its bend. Now the fish was under the spillway and must have dived down with the descending stream, for I saw a couple of feet of line slide suddenly through John's hand. The circling water got its impetus here and this was naturally the fastest part of the eddy.

The fish came rapidly toward us, riding with the quickened water, and John retrieved line. Would the fish follow the current around again, or would it leave it and run down past us? The resilient rod tip straightened as the pressure was eased. The big trout passed along the downstream edge of the eddy and swung over the bank to follow it round again, repeated its performance at the spillway, and again refused to leave the eddy. It was troubled and perplexed by the strange hampering of its progress but it was not alarmed, for it was not aware of our presence or even of the fact that it was hooked, and the restraint on it had not been enough to arouse its full resistance.

Every experienced angler will understand that last statement. The pull of a game fish, up to the full limit of its strength, seems to be in proportion to the resistance which it encounters. As I watched the leader slowly cutting the water, I recalled that often I had hooked a trout and immediately given slack, whereupon invariably it had moved quietly and aimlessly about, soon coming to rest as if it had no realization that it was hooked.

I realized now that John intended to get the "fight" out of his fish at a rate slow enough not to endanger his leader. His task was to keep from arousing the fish to a resistance greater than the presumably weakened 5x gut would withstand. It seemed as if it were hopeless, for the big trout continued to circle the eddy, swimming deep and strongly against the rod's light tension, which relaxed only when the fish passed the gateway of the stream below. Around and around it went, and then at last it left the eddy. Yet it did not dart into the outflowing current but headed into deep water close to the far bank. I held my breath, for over there was a tangle of roots, and I could imagine what a labyrinth they must make under the surface. Ah, it was moving toward the roots! Now what would John do—hold the fish hard and break off; check it and arouse its fury; or perhaps splash a stone in front of it to turn it back?

He did none of these but instead slackened off until his line sagged in a catenary curve. The fish kept on, and I could see the leader draw on the surface as it swam into the mass of roots. Now John dropped his rod flat to the water and delicately drew on the line until the tip barely flexed, moving it almost imperceptibly several times to feel whether his leader had fouled on a root. Then he lapsed into immobility.

I glanced at my wrist watch, slowly bent my head until I could light my cold pipe without raising my hand, and then relaxed on my rock. The smoke drifted lazily upstream, the separate puffs merging into a thin haze which dissipated itself imperceptibly. A bird moved on the bank. But the only really living thing was the stream, which rippled a bit as it divided around John's body and continually moved a loop of his yellow line in the disturbed current below him.

When the trout finally swam quietly back out of the roots, my watch showed that it had been in there almost an hour and a quarter. John slackened the line and released a breath which he seemed to have been holding all that while, and the fish re-entered the eddy to resume its interminable circling. The sun, which had been in my face, dropped behind a tree, and I noted how the shadows had lengthened. Then the big fish showed itself for the first time, its huge dorsal fin appearing as it rose toward the surface and the lobe of its great tail as it turned down again; it seemed to be two feet long.

Again its tail swirled under the surface, puddling the water as it swam slowly and deliberately, and then I thought that we would lose the fish, for as it came around to the downstream side of the eddy it wallowed an instant and then headed toward us. Instantly John relaxed the rod until the line hung limp and from the side of his mouth he hissed, "Steady!"

Down the stream, passing John so closely that he could have hit it with his tip, drifted a long dark bulk, oaring along deliberately with its powerful tail in the smooth current. I could see the gray fly in the corner of its mouth and the leader hanging in a curve under its belly, then the yellow line floating behind. In a moment he felt of the fish again, determined that it was no longer moving, and resumed his light pressure, causing it to swim around aimlessly in the still water below us. The sun was half below the horizon now and the shadows slanting down over the river covered us. In the cool, diffused light the lines on John's face from nostril to mouth were deeply cut and the crafty folds at the outer corners of his lids hooded his eyes. His rod hand shook with a fine tremor.

The fish broke, wallowing, but John instantly dropped his rod flat to the water and slipped a little line. The fish wallowed again, then swam more slowly in a large circle. It was moving just under the surface now, its mouth open and its back breaking water every few feet, and it seemed to be half turned on its side. Still John did not move except for the small gestures of taking or giving line, raising or lowering his tip.

It was in the ruddy afterglow that the fish finally came to the top, beating its tail in a subdued rhythm. Bent double, I crept ashore and then ran through the brush to the edge of the still water downstream of the fish, which now was broad on its side. Stretching myself prone on the bank, I extended my net at arm's length and held it flat on the bottom in a foot of water.

John began to slip out line slowly, the now beaten trout moving feebly as the slow current carried it down. Now it was opposite me and I nodded a signal to John. He moved his tip toward my bank and cautiously checked the line. The current swung the trout toward me and it passed over my net.

I raised the rim quietly and slowly, and the next instant the trout was doubled up in my deep-bellied net and I was holding the top shut with both hands while the fish, galvanized into a furious flurry, splashed water in my face as I strove to get my feet under me.

John picked his way slowly down the still water, reeling up as he came, stumbling and slipping on the stones like an utterly weary man. I killed the trout with my pliers and laid it on the grass as he came up beside me and stood watching it with bent head and sagging shoulders for a long time.

"To die like that!" he said as if thinking aloud. "Murdered—nagged to death; he never knew he was fighting for his life until he was in the net. He had strength and courage enough to beat the pair of us but we robbed him a little at a time until we got him where we wanted him. And then knocked him on the head. I wish you had let him go."

The twilight fishing, our favorite time, was upon us but he started for the car and I did not demur. We began to take off our wet shoes and waders.

"That's just what this depression is doing to me!" John burst out suddenly as he struggled with a shoelace. "Niggling me to death! And I'm up here fishing, taking two days off in the middle of the week, instead of doing something about it. Come on; hurry up. I'm going to catch the midnight to Pittsburgh; I know where I can get a contract."

And sure enough he did.

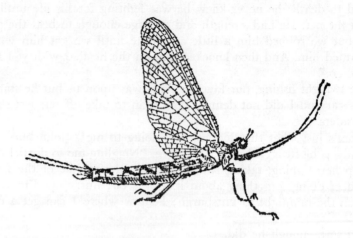

Black Salmon

ARTHUR TRAIN

Arthur Train hoaxed the book world a few years ago in creating Mr. Tutt, angler and lawyer extraordinary. "Black Salmon" is one of his best angling tales, and as authentic as Blackstone.

DURBAN NEW BRUNSWICK CANADA

SALMON RUN DOWNSTREAM JUST STARTING IN NIPSICODIAC STOP BETTER
HUMP IT

ANGUS OGILVY

Mr. Tutt handed the telegram to Minerva Wiggin.

"I'm off !"

"But this is only April," she protested. "Besides, salmon run upstream in spring, not down."

"Not always. In some rivers they get trapped by the ice and can't get back to the ocean. When it breaks up the following spring, they bolt for the sea—'black salmon' they call 'em."

"There's something queer about the whole business," remarked the chief clerk. "Doesn't the Canadian law prohibit salmon fishing until June?"

"In most rivers, but not in the Nipsi. For some reason—political, I fancy—it's an exception. Not many fishermen know about it, luckily."

"You'll freeze to death in the woods this time of year," she warned him.

"My dear Minerva," he answered patiently, "I never went on a fishing trip yet that I didn't have a good time. Se be a good girl and wire Angus to engage a cook and meet the Halifax Express tomorrow afternoon. Don't worry. I'll catch something."

She made a face at him. "Pneumonia, probably."

The spring had been well advanced in New York, but Mr. Tutt stepped out of the sleeper at Durban, New Brunswick, into the depth of the Canadian winter.

"We had quite a warm spell last fortnight," said Angus, greeting him on the station platform. "Enough to start the ice in the Nipsi, but it looks now as if we were in for more cold weather."

"Did you hire a cook?"

"Yes, but I had a tough time locatin' one. Most of the men are off in the lumber camps or loggin' it on the river. But I found a feller finally, and paid him something in advance. Maybe that was a mistake. Anyhow, he's promised to meet us at the train tomorrow morning. You better buy yourself some warm clothes."

"I certainly had!" agreed Mr. Tutt, who was already half frozen. "If you'll carry those things to the George, I'll go over to the store and reoutfit myself."

Mr. Tutt, having purchased a heavy mackinaw and sweater, thick woolen cap and high-laced boots, walked back to the little hotel. Lugging his rod case, he followed the clerk to the sagging corridor above the office.

"Here, Martha!" called the clerk into the darkness beneath the stairs. "Hot water for Number Nine!"

The lawyer stacked his luggage, lit a stogie and looked about him. The room was clean, but the rug was full of holes, the wallpaper discolored and hanging in strips, the ceiling mapped with islands, coast lines and inland seas. Thank heaven he'd have to stay there only one night!

There was a step in the hall outside, a light tap, and an elderly woman in spotless calico entered, carrying a steaming pitcher.

"I've brought you some hot water," she smiled. Mr. Tutt withdrew his hand from his trousers pocket, where he had automatically thrust it. One couldn't offer a dime to a woman like that. She seemed to be so glad that she could bring him his hot water.

"Thank you! I need it."

"Mr. McCrea planned last summer to put runnin' water in all the rooms," she apologized, placing the pitcher beside the washstand. "But he says now the trade don't warrant it."

Her voice was deep-throated, soft and clear, with a faint Scotch burr; her face, of an unusual dignity, was made almost beautiful by her smile.

"Is there anything you want?"

She was like a considerate and interested hostess. She did not once call him "sir."

"Let me see!" deliberated Mr. Tutt, wishing that there was. "Do you suppose I could find anyone to sew on this button?"

"Yes, indeed! Let me have it, please."

"I'll have to sit here until it comes back."

"It won't take me a minute."

Mr. Tutt shed his old Prince Albert and handed it to her. Not since his boyhood had he seen a woman quite like her. One didn't find them in cities. He had rarely seen a face that held more appeal for him. Character was written all over it. A chambermaid in this third-class hotel, he perceived that she was a valiant soul. One who had suffered, yet retained her faith in what was good.

"There!" she said, giving him back his coat. "It won't come off again in a hurry. Do you need anything else?"

"Perhaps you can tell me where Doctor Blake lives?"

"Certainly I can. You go right down Queen Street. Doctor Blake's is the fourth house on the right." She glanced at the washstand. "I'll fetch you a fresh cake of soap."

"Do you come from around here?" he asked in his customarily friendly tone.

"I'm a 'Bluenose,' " she laughed. "I was born in Nova Scotia."

"Worked here long?"

"Only about a week."

There was no reproof in the brevity of her reply, but there was obviously no reason for her to amplify it.

"Well," she said after a moment, "I must be going back to my work. I hope you enjoy Durban. It's a nice place."

"I'm sure it is. Anyhow, it has nice people in it."

Outside the door, she paused.

"If you want anything, just call 'Martha,' " she said.

Ten minutes later, when Mr. Tutt went out to pay his call, he found Martha on her hands and knees beside a pail of soapsuds, scrubbing the grimy little office.

"Martha?" returned Doctor Blake to the old man's question. "You must mean Martha MacDonald. I heard she'd gone over to the George to work. What about her?"

"Isn't she a person of unusual refinement to find drudging in such a—if you'll pardon the word—dump?"

The doctor laughed.

"Go as far as you like about the George, except to ask me to eat there! Yes, Martha is an unusual person. Quite a wonderful character, in fact. She's had a tough break all her life."

"Tell me about her."

"Her story is simple enough. She's of Scotch stock, from Down East somewhere. As a mere girl she married a man who turned out to be a drunkard; left him to become a nursemaid in Toronto; then, about thirty years ago, she came here to work for John Mack."

"And who's John Mack?"

Doctor Blake stuffed his pipe.

"Old John's another unusual character. As a young fellow he was the most beautiful human being I ever saw; the best woodsman and lumberjack on the river. At about forty he decided to settle down, married a Durban girl and got a job as express agent. His wife died giving birth to their first child—a boy. There was no one to look after it. Martha's a sort of distant cousin of John's. He heard that she was working in Toronto and asked her to come and keep house for him. She's been here ever since."

"But where does her hard luck come in?"

"Because she gave her life to this kid, nursed him like a mother, sacrificed her youth—for nothing. He turned out a bum, always in trouble. Every once in a while he'd stage a reform, and Martha and John, between 'em, would give him a fresh start. But he always tricked 'em somehow. Finally, after he'd been sent to jail a couple of times, the old man kicked him out. About two years ago, John contracted a fatal illness. He knew his number was up, and, realizing what Martha had meant to him all these years, he made over his life insurance policy to her. It's for ten thousand dollars, fully paid up."

"That was pretty decent of him."

"Little enough in return for her lifetime of devotion. Martha stripped herself of most of her own savings to get Lem out of his difficulties and put him back on his feet, from time to time; and after John's operation and his wages had stopped, she supplemented his tiny pension, paying for doctors, medicines and household expenses until she had nothing left. She adores him. He's been the real love of her life, I guess, but being a married woman—her husband died only about six months ago—there's been no suggestion of romance between them. Recently, John's illness took a turn for the worse, and, as often happens in such cases, he passed through a depression during which he became so irritable, at times even abusive, that she could stand it no longer, secured a village girl to act in her place and left the house.

Not having a penny to her name, she had to take any job she could get, which happened to be chambermaid at the George."

"I understand now what you mean by her having had a tough break," said Mr. Tutt.

It was Martha, fully and crisply dressed, who awoke the old lawyer before daylight next morning and, a few minutes later, brought him a tray of hot rolls, coffee, eggs and bacon which she had cooked herself.

"Be sure to keep warm," she urged, as she let him out into the darkness. "I'll keep an eye on your belongings while you're away. I hope you have good luck."

"I'll save a salmon for you," promised Mr. Tutt.

The Whooper was panting beside the platform, its overheated smoking car already crowded with lumberjacks going back to camp after the weekend, the air foul with the fumes of whisky and bad tobacco. A series of snorts, followed by a terrific jerk, and the little train started. Angus hopped on and assisted another man, obviously the worse for liquor, up the steps. The guide's face was dour as he entered.

"All set!" he growled. "This is Lem Mack, our cook. . . . Say howdy to Mr. Tutt, Lem."

The man, without replying, collapsed into a seat and closed his eyes.

"He'll be all right," remarked Angus. "He was on a binge all yesterday. I had to drag him out of bed and help him on with his clothes to get him here at all."

"Do you know anything about him?"

"I don't know any of these hairy apes from around here. They say he comes of good people. He was all I could get."

Angus' "hairy ape" lay there, snoring, a trickle of tobacco juice meandering across his unshaven chin. So this was the swine that old Martha had sacrificed her youth and savings for!

They rode on in the fetid atmosphere without speaking. Those of the lumberjacks who were not playing Forty-five were either singing or sleeping. There were a few short-lived fights. Suddenly the kerosene lamps paled in their haze of smoke; the sky above the racketing pine and spruce tops turned yellow; day broke through the frosted windows. Some hours later, the Whooper uttered a prolonged wail, and, rattling over a trestle, came to a standstill on an embankment above a swift molasses-colored stream.

Angus took the sleeping man by the shoulders and shook him.

"Wake up! We're 'most there!" he ordered.

Mack sat up and wiped his mouth with the back of his fist. "Take your damn hands off me!" he snarled, getting slowly to his feet.

The crew unloaded the two canoes, the engine coughed, there was a succession of jerks, a whistle, and the three men were left alone in a white and silent world. Launching the canoes, they divided the dunnage between them. With the old man sitting in the bow of the first, Angus took the paddle in the stern, leaving the cook to follow in the second and smaller one. The stillness was unbroken save by the dip of the paddles and the snap of the ice panes as their wake reached the shore. No hawk hung suspended overhead; no beaver slapped the water in warning of their approach; no kingfisher dipped ahead of them, an avant-courier. There was no indication of life in this vacuum of sound and sight. Yet Mr. Tutt knew that beneath the skim along the snow-covered banks and motionless upon the bottom of the shallows were lying hundreds of great fish, caught the preceding autumn by the sudden forming of the ice which had turned the sand bars into ramparts, hermetically sealed the pools, closed the mouths of the brooks where they had been spawning, and held them prisoners, rationless, until the spring.

They swept on down the river. The sun had slipped under a bank of cloud and a knifelike wind had come up. Mr. Tutt thrust his mittened hands deep into his pockets and wiggled his old toes. Gad! It was cold! The cook had fallen a quarter mile behind. At ten o'clock, when they stopped to "bile," Angus had already got the fire going, long before he overtook them. It was clear that he was in a recalcitrant mood. Grudgingly he dug out the bacon and eggs, and squatted down without speaking, with the frying pan in his hand.

"How much farther are you guys goin'?" he growled at length. "I didn't sign up for no polar expedition!"

"To the Schoolhouse."

"That's forty miles! There won't be time to make camp before dark. Besides, it's goin' to snow. We better stay here," he rasped.

"I shall decide where to fish," replied Mr. Tutt curtly.

They paddled on under a leaden sky. Presently it began to snow. The great flakes came floating down like feathers, melting in the black water, but accumulating in a heavy blanket upon the canoes and dunnage. It was four o'clock when the Schoolhouse—a wrecked shanty without doors or windows, reeling drunkenly at the edge of what had once been a clearing—came into view. The cook was nowhere to be seen. Angus carried their paraphernalia up the bank and piled it inside, while Mr. Tutt, standing half congealed amid broken glass and the filth left behind by porcupines, set up his rod and rigged it, putting on a huge flamingo fly he had seen in a window in Durban. Then they pushed off into the blinding snow.

"They'll be in midstream," said Angus. "The best place is on the other side of the bend."

He dropped the killick and steadied the canoe with his paddle blade while Mr. Tutt, with numb fingers and the wet flakes stinging his cheeks, made a short cast preliminary to getting out a full line. The fly had no sooner touched the water than two black shiny backs rose on either side of it, and, with a tug that nearly tore the rod from his hands, the reel began to scream. Mr. Tutt braced the rod against his old belly and held on for dear life.

"We can't see to follow!" warned Angus. "Give him all you've got!"

Mr. Tutt lifted the rod with all his strength. Unexpectedly, the big fish broke behind them. The old man dropped his tip, swung about in what he thought the right direction and reeled in the slack as fast as he could. Again the salmon broke—this time downstream. There was no way to tell, in that white dizziness, where it was. This time, when he reeled in his line, the salmon even more unexpectedly came with it, towing straight for the canoe.

"Look out! He'll break your rod!" yelled Angus. "He's ducked under the bow!"

Mr. Tutt was nearly hysterical. It was exciting enough to hook a salmon in a driving snowstorm—he had never heard of its being done before—but what should one do when a fish you couldn't see decided to rush into a clinch, overrunning your line? Where was the brute? With the line slack, Mr. Tutt reeled and reeled. The salmon must be somewhere! Suddenly the canoe swerved and tipped. The line, tangled around the bow, had brought the salmon up short, midway between bow and stern. Fortunately, the leader held, and Angus leaned over, gaffed it and heaved it in.

"Twenty pounds," he estimated. "Would weigh thirty-four in summer."

It was a silver fish with only a suspicion of black along its dorsal, lean as a race horse, hard and clean. The fly was unharmed; Mr. Tutt cast again, and once more it was seized as soon as it reached the surface. For an hour he forgot cold, snow, wind and wet in the greatest fishing of his life. Only when he could no longer see the shore did he reel in. Black salmon? What of it! They could fight all right! All the same, a warm tent and a hot supper would seem pretty good!

They rounded the point, but no welcoming beam came from the direction of the Schoolhouse. There was no sign of a canoe anywhere. The cook should have been there an hour ago.

"The so-and-so must ha' quit on us!" Angus spat wrathfully as they grounded.

"You mean he's gone back?" asked Mr. Tutt incredulously.

"Just that! Wait until I meet him in Durban! I'll knock the lights out of the hairy ape!"

Ripping a couple of boards off the shanty, they scraped clear a spot for the tent, pegged it down and unrolled their blankets. Their stove had gone back with the cook, but they tore up part of the floor, built a fire in the opening and heated some beans and bacon.

The old man awoke at daylight with a sore throat and a bad cold in the head. It was still snowing. Angus had patched the windward side of the cabin with planks and they managed to eat breakfast in a fair degree of comfort.

The black salmon were as insatiable as ever, but after a couple of hours on the river, Mr. Tutt, who had developed a splitting headache, decided that he had had enough.

"How far is it to the nearest settlement?" he asked when they stopped to "bile."

"Ste. Marie des Isles—sixty-five miles. If we move right along, we ought to make it by tomorrow night."

"And if we turn back?"

"It will take us even longer and we might miss the Whooper at the bridge."

"Let's go on," said Mr. Tutt weakly.

They camped at Burnt Hill, about forty miles above Ste. Marie des Isles, where there was a cooking shack used by summer sportsmen. Mr. Tutt ached all over, he had a sharp pain in his chest and was running a temperature. Next morning Angus bundled him in blankets, propped him against the tent and, realizing that he had a sick man on his hands, paddled so furiously that they reached the settlement in time to catch the evening train back to Durban. It was after midnight when they arrived at the George. Martha and Angus. after sending for the doctor, managed between them to get the old man to bed.

"Pneumonia," said Blake shortly, finding the patient's temperature to be 105 degrees. "You'll stay right here until you get well. You'll need a good nurse too. Shall I send for a girl from the hospital or . . ." He looked at Martha.

"Please, doctor. Let me take care of him."

"Well, which shall it be?" asked Blake. "No doubt I can arrange with the proprietor—"

Mr. Tutt's head was whirling. Through his blurred vision he saw the kindly face of the old nurse. Next to Minerva Wiggin, she was the one woman that he wanted near him.

"I—want—Martha," he whispered.

He lay there cursing himself for an old fool. Why had he attempted any such expedition at his age? Why reverse the order of nature? Salmon were intended to be caught in June, not April! Was he going to die, he wondered. Martha had turned down the night light and stolen away to her cubbyhole under the stairs. He tossed from side to side, fighting the fever, bells ringing in his ears, voices.

The sounds grew louder and more distinct. They seemed to be coming through the partition of the wall from the next room. Was he merely imagining that clink of glass, that coarse laughter, those curses? He raised himself on his elbow and listened.

"It'll be a cinch," said a rasping familiar voice. "The old bird's nearly cuckoo, anyway. He'll do anything we ask."

"I can swear he's competent," commented another. "But you'll need two other witnesses."

"What's the matter with Doctor Kelly and Ed here?"

"They're all right!" There was a gurgling sound, as from a bottle. "Well, boys! Here's luck!"

Mack! Mr. Tutt relapsed upon the pillow. What deviltry could he be up to now? He tried to concentrate, but without avail. Who was the old bird? Tomorrow he'd find out—do something about it! But when tomorrow came, Mr. Tutt had become delirious.

For a week Mr. Tutt hung between life and death. Then, largely owing to Martha's expert nursing, the fever broke and he passed into a profound slumber from which he did not awake for thirty-six hours. When he opened his eyes, Minerva Wiggin was bending over him.

"Minerva! How did you get here?" he asked faintly. "I thought Martha was taking care of me."

"She was, and she saved your life. But you're all right now and I've come to take her place. Drink this, like a good boy, and then turn over and go to sleep again."

The next time he came to himself, Doctor Blake was sitting by the window.

"You old rascal!" he grunted. "Think twice before you go salmon fishing again in winter!"

"I'll think twice about who I take with me! That damned Mack—"

"He told everyone you sent him back!"

"He lies! By the way—" Mr. Tutt sat up—"I heard him plotting something the night I got here. He and some other men were in the next room, drinking and talking about witnesses. It may have been an illusion."

Doctor Blake shook his head.

"It was no illusion. They got into old John's house while his attendant was out and induced him to make a will leaving everything he had to Lem. The irony of it is that he passed out of that phase of his illness soon after, regretted what he'd done and sent for Martha to return. That's why she isn't here."

"But she still has the life insurance?"

"No. He reappointed it to Lem by the will, which is safely locked up in Lawyer Quinlan's deposit vault."

Mr. Tutt started to get out of bed.

"No, you don't!" Doctor Blake forced him back. "There's nothing to be done—old John is dying. The will can't be obtained for cancellation by destruction. He's too feeble to make a new one and, if he did, there'd be a serious question as to his competency—a contest anyway —and Martha has no money to litigate."

"How long have I got to stay here, doctor?"

"You shan't put your foot to the floor for a couple of days at least."

"How long can old John last?"

"Perhaps a week."

"Where's the nearest law library?"

"Across the street, at Weld and Potter's."

Mr. Tutt turned to Miss Wiggin.

"Minerva," he ordered. "Go get me the *Revised Statutes of New Brunswick.*"

Mr. Tutt proved a refractory patient. He spent the first day of his convalescence in bed, smoking innumerable stogies and perusing the volumes procured for him by Miss Wiggin; but on the second, in defiance of the doctor's orders, he insisted on getting dressed and sending for Martha.

"If you weren't so tough, you'd have been dead long ago," grinned Doctor Blake the next morning. "Imagine your talking to that old woman for three hours when you ought to have been resting quietly in bed."

"I'm going to return her call this afternoon."

"Over my dead body!"

"How long is old John likely to live?"

"He's going fast. His mind is perfectly clear, but he has no strength. He won't last over forty-eight hours."

"That settles it," declared Mr. Tutt. "I must see him this afternoon."

Muffled from head to foot, and assisted by Doctor Blake and Miss Wiggin, Mr. Tutt tottered over to John Mack's little house. Martha opened the door for them, her sleeves rolled to her elbows. The fine white texture of her arms was in curious contrast to the cracked hands and rough nails. For the first time she seemed depressed in spite of her attempt to smile.

Martha went back to the kitchen and Doctor Blake led the way upstairs to John Mack's bedroom. The sunlight fell full upon the emaciated form of the dying riverman and turned his waxen cheeks to alabaster. His hands lay folded upon his bosom and the white hair surrounding his sunken features upon the pillow gave him an almost saintlike appearance.

"I've brought a visitor to see you, John," said Blake. "This is Mr. Tutt, an old friend of mine. He wants to talk to you about Martha."

The thin blue lips quivered, the faded eyes lighted.

"Yes," came in a whisper. "Martha."

Mr. Tutt sat down by the bed.

"Martha is a very fine woman," he said gently. "She has served you for over thirty years. She is devoted to you."

"Yes. Yes."

Mr. Tutt bent closer.

"I understand you tried to reward her, but that something has happened to interfere with your plans."

Tears gathered in the old man's eyes.

"Has it occurred to you that one way to show your gratitude would be to give her your name—to marry her?"

The magazine in Doctor Blake's hand dropped to the floor. Miss Wiggin gasped.

The look of surprise that fluttered over the lumberman's face was succeeded by one of deeply realized satisfaction.

"I'd—like—to—marry—Martha."

"Very well!" exclaimed Mr. Tutt. "The Reverend McCook is waiting across the street. Doctor Blake can act as your best man. . . . Minerva, ask Martha to come upstairs!"

Ten minutes later, John Mack and Martha MacDonald having been made man and wife, the little party returned to the hotel. A first-class fight was in progress outside. Angus Ogilvy was engaged in knocking the lights out of Lem Mack, as promised, and he was doing it not only to the Queen's taste but to that of most of the male population of Durban. Strangely enough, the sheriff, who was among the gallery of spectators, made no effort to separate the combatants. A final hook to the jaw sent Mack spinning against a pile of coal, where he remained, prostrate and bleeding.

"Well, that's something!" said Mr. Tutt, and he allowed himself to be put to bed.

John Mack died forty-eight hours later. When Lawyer Quinlan appeared at the office of the registrar to file an application for the probate of the will, he was astounded to find that a caveat had been lodged, requiring the testament to be proved "in solemn form," together with notice that the contestants were prepared to appear on twenty-four hours' notice. He was even more disgruntled when, having secured an appointment from the probate judge to make his proof the following morning, he discovered Mr. Tutt, together with Doctor Blake, Martha, now neatly dressed in black, and Mr. Montrose, distinguished local K. C., gathered before the bench in the adjoining courtroom.

Lawyer Quinlan, knowing that, for once at least in his professional existence, everything had been clean and aboveboard, felt the strength of ten because his heart was pure, and for the moment was undismayed. The probate judge, a kindly-looking grayhead, entered and took his seat under a wooden canopy bearing the British coat of arms. There were no other cases, and Quinlan, as solicitor for the executors, promptly offered the will of John Mack for probate.

"I see that a caveat has been filed, Mr. Quinlan," remarked the judge, lifting a paper. . . . "Do you represent the contestants, Mr. Montrose?"

"I do, Your Honor," answered the K. C., arising.

"What does the estate consist of, Mr. Quinlan?"

"A house, here in Durban, assessed at thiry-five hundred dollars and mortgaged for three thousand, a few pieces of furniture, and a paid-up life insurance policy for ten thousand dollars. The equity in the realty isn't worth more than five hundred dollars and there are debts of at least four hundred."

The judge nodded.

"So Mr. Mack's life insurance is practically all there is?"

"Exactly, Your Honor."

"Is there any question as to testamentary capacity, Mr. Montrose?" asked the judge.

The K. C. looked at Mr. Tutt.

"None whatever, Your Honor."

"Or undue influence?"

"We prefer to await proof of execution."

"What in hell—" whispered Mack.

"Keep still!" ordered Quinlan, who was getting jittery. "They ain't got anything on us!"

"Proceed with the proof."

The solicitor stepped forward.

"I drew the will and superintended its execution. Will Your Honor grant me leave to act as a witness?"

The judge nodded.

"I apprehend there will be no objection."

Quinlan took up the Bible, and the registrar administered the oath.

"On the morning of April twenty-seventh," testified the solicitor, "I attended the late John Mack at his home, where he was confined to his bed. With me were Doctor Kelly, Mr. Edward Murphy and Mr. Lemuel Mack, here. Doctor Kelly engaged the testator in conversation in order to determine his mental condition. I asked him if he wished to make a will, whether this paper now offered for probate represented his wishes, and whether he desired the gentlemen with me to act as witnesses. He signified that he did. I then handed him a pen and he subscribed his name. After reading the attestation clause aloud to him, I signed, together with Doctor Kelly and Mr. Murphy."

"And, in your opinion, was Mr. Mack of sound mind and disposing memory?"

"Beyond any question!"

"Do you wish to cross-examine, Mr. Montrose?"

The K. C. got up.

"If Your Honor please. I ask leave to introduce Mr. Ephraim Tutt, of New York, an eminent member of the bar of that state. He is even more familiar with the facts than I am. I move that he be accorded the privilege of interrogating the witnesses."

"We all know Mr. Tutt," the judge smiled. "If he's as good a lawyer as he is a fisherman, I'll be glad to hear him."

He bowed; Montrose, K. C., bowed; Mr. Tutt arose rather weakly and bowed.

For an instant, his eyes sought the entrance to the courtroom. Then he said: "While Lemuel Mack is not a witness, I should like to examine him."

"That is rather out of order, Mr. Tutt. Are you prepared to concede the technical fulfillment of the legal requirements for execution?"

"Yes, Your Honor. We make no point as to that. I also concede that in calling this witness, we shall make him our own."

"Then let him be sworn."

The former cook, exhibiting an unprepossessing pair of blackened eyes, stumbled forward. The judge studied his disfigured appearance with interest. He knew a thing or two himself about Lem.

"How old are you, Mr. Mack?" asked Mr. Tutt.

"Thirty."

"You are the only child of the testator?"

"Yes."

"What do you do for a living?"

" 'Most anything that comes along."

"How many times have you been in jail?"

The witness scowled.

"What business is that of yours?"

"Answer the question!" interrupted the judge.

"Twice."

"For stealing?"

"Once for larceny, once for assault."

"Do you know this lady here beside me?"

"Sure."

"Who is she?"

Mack shrugged contemptuously. "Martha MacDonald. She was our cook, did general housework."

"She was also the only mother you had?"

"My mother died when I was born."

"Martha brought you up, didn't she? Taught you your lessons, pulled you out of scrapes, slaved for you, get you what jobs she could, tried to make a man of you?"

"I object!" snapped Quinlan. "He's attacking his own witness!"

"Technically, yes," ruled His Honor. "But I'll allow it."

The witness did not answer.

"For thirty years," continued Mr. Tutt, "Martha cooked, washed, cleaned, mended, and when your father fell ill, three years ago, tended him day and night?"

"She lived in the house and was paid for it."

"You know, don't you, that she spent all her savings to pay your debts and to procure doctors and medicines for your father?"

"She always seemed to have plenty of money."

"You are aware that, when her savings were exhausted, she even went out and did washing by the day to earn enough to keep your father alive?"

"I don't know anything about it."

Mr. Tutt paused again, glanced toward the door and proceeded: "Five years ago, your father kicked you out of the house, didn't he?"

"I got out."

"Now, how long was it before you saw him to speak to him again?"

"Not until about three weeks ago, I guess."

"That was when, owing to some phase of his illness, he became so crotchety that Martha, who was nursing him, could stand it no longer, engaged someone to look after him and went to work at the hotel?"

"I know she left."

"And you took advantage of her absence to sneak back and re-instate yourself in your father's favor?"

"I object!" shouted Quinlan.

"Oh, I'll give Mr. Tutt some leeway," replied His Honor. "I find this story quite engrossing. It seems to have what, I believe, is sometimes referred to as 'human interest.'"

"And during this period, which lasted less than a week, you induced him to make a will leaving everything to you?"

"I didn't induce him! He wanted to!"

"Oh, he did? Didn't you tell Mr. Quinlan what to put in the will?"

"My father told me first."

"Did you know what property he owned?"

"Sure."

"Did you know that he had appointed his ten-thousand-dollar life insurance—his only asset of value—to Martha in recognition of her thirty years' devotion?"

"He said he was sorry he'd done it."

"So the chief purpose of the will was to alter the appointment of the policy to yourself?"

"One of the purposes."

"Did you not know that your father had made the original appointment to Martha, partly to reimburse her for the money she had expended for you and for him?"

"I didn't know anything about it."

Mr. Tutt lowered his voice: "Didn't you think it was a dastardly thing to take advantage of his condition to jockey her out of her inheritance and to deprive her of support in her old age?"

"I object to this!" cried Quinlan. "A man has a right to dispose of his property as he sees fit. My client is his own son; this woman is only—"

"His wife!" finished Mr. Tutt dramatically.

"His wife!" ejaculated judge and solicitor in chorus.

Mr. Tutt turned and beckoned to a messenger from the local post office, who had entered during the debate and was standing by the door with an envelope in his hand.

Tearing it open and removing a formal-looking document the old lawyer said: "Justice sometimes triumphs in unexpected ways. John Mack and Martha MacDonald were married five days ago by the Reverend McCook, acting under a special license issued in accordance with the New Brunswick Marriage Act. Rather than call witnesses to the ceremony, I have taken the precaution of obtaining an official certificate thereof from the Vital Statistics Department for this province at Fredericton. It has just been delivered and I offer it in evidence. Since I was present at the wedding, I can testify that the John Mack mentioned therein is the same John Mack whose will is now being offered for probate."

There was no sound in the courtroom. The witness and the solicitor both gaped helplessly at the judge.

"But, Your Honor," finally protested the latter, "John Mack wasn't competent to get married! He was practically non compos!"

"Non compos?" retorted the judge. "When you claim he was competent to make a will just a few days before that? You can't have your cake and eat it, Mr. Quinlan!"

"I shall bring an action to have the marriage declared invalid!" threatened the solicitor.

"My learned friend overlooks the fact that, under the laws of Canada and of this province, a marriage in legal form is not subject to question save at the instance of one of the parties," commented Mr. Tutt quietly. "I move that this application for the probate of the document submitted as the last will and testament of John Mack be denied."

"Have you any reasons to advance why I should not grant the motion?" inquired the judge of the crestfallen solicitor.

Receiving no answer, he continued:

"Under the laws of the province of New Brunswick, a will not made in contemplation of marriage is revoked by the subsequent marriage of the testator. This document, while it may have been a valid will when executed, not being made in contemplation of marriage, was revoked by the testator's subsequent marriage to Martha MacDonald. This situation regarding the assignment of his insurance policy remains as if that will had never been made. Hence, the appointment of the policy previously made in favor of Martha MacDonald, now Martha Mack, still stands. The application for probate of the document submitted as the will of John Mack will be refused, the applicant to pay the costs of the respondent, fixed at one hundred dollars. Since no valid will exists, I am prepared to consider an application by the widow for administration of the estate. . . . Have you the necessary inventories and affidavits, Mr. Montrose? If so, in view of the unusual facts which have come out at this trial, I shall be pleased also to entertain an application to dispense with a bond for the administratrix. If there is nothing else before me, this court stands adjourned. . . . Glad to have met you, Mr. Tutt!"

Once the excitement was over, the old man was beginning to feel very shaky. Doctor Blake and Mr. Montrose each took an arm as he dragged himself out of the courthouse.

"And now, old stravagler, you'll go straight back to bed again!" ordered Blake.

"I don't object," he admitted, "so long as I've got two such good nurses to look after me. . . . I told you I always caught something when I went fishing, Minerva."

"Yes, and I told you what it would be!" she returned.

"I'll look after him," said Martha Mack. . . . "Oh, Mr. Tutt, how can I ever thank you!"

"It's fifty-fifty, my dear," he answered. "I owe you my life! Come to think of it, I owe you a black salmon too."

In Defense
of Worms

F. F. VAN DE WATER

Despite the great swelling of the ranks of fly fishermen there are dedicated anglers who will insist that the worm fisherman needs no defense or apology. It is probable that F. F. Van de Water had this in mind when he wrote "In Defense of Worms."

I N THE LONG, long ago, when Calvin Coolidge ruled in the land and newspapermen still were unguilded, the editor of the sheet on which I worked sent his best feature writer to interview the President of the United States. The assignment had nothing to do with problems, domestic or international. It was to produce one of those homey stories which remind their readers, usually needlessly, that great men are composed of substances common to us all.

"Straight human-interest stuff," the editor said. "Keep it warm and intimate, if possible. Get him to tell you what he likes to eat and wear and read and see in the theater. His hobbies, if he has any; his dogs and the other pets they've sent him; his outdoor interests, fishing and —no, you better lay off fishing. I understand he's grown rather sensitive about his fishing since all that stink was raised because he uses worms."

Those were the editor's instructions. I heard them delivered to my friend, the feature writer, and I still recall the disappointment and sense of betrayal that oppressed me, for in that ancient time I still was a worm fisherman myself. If the editor spoke truth and the nation's chief executive were ashamed of using worms for bait, the humble of the fishing world, the entered apprentices in the Brotherhood of Peter, were being deserted by their leader.

It was about this time, according to Thomas Sugrue's *Startling of the White House*, that Mr. Coolidge's bodyguard, a fishing purist, weaned him away from worms forever. Just for a handful of trout flies he left us. It may have been the Presidential example that started me on my climb from angling ignominy—if ignominy it be.

I have worked my way up to the fringes of angling aristocracy by never using worms any more—or hardly ever—though I still am a better fisherman with such bait then ever I shall be with a fly. I commonly employ the latter, just the same. Postmaturity has furnished me with too many troubles for me willingly to undergo the additional anguish a worm user must suffer when a purist is around —embarrassment, sulky defiance, and a sense of treachery, all horridly emulsified and endured under the contemptuously pitying regard of his betters.

Yet though I am practically a reformed character and have come up in the world, I can find in myself little of the climber's usual itch to defame his origin. Instead of detestation, I discover in my heart, when I look back at my former abject position in the fishing hierarchy, a reprehensible wistfulness and a sneaking regret. After all fish prefer worms; why should not I?

I profess to scorn worm fishing because so many authorities have told me I must. Morality of all varieties is, after all, only the voice of the majority, or even a minority devoted to noise. A messiah frequently is he who can yell loudest and longest. Decalogues and decibels have more in common than most people suppose.

Reformation has done its worst for me. I turned from worms to flies in a spirit of snobbery, in the hope of being considered by my fellow anglers as something a little better than hopelessly plebeian. I normally fish with flies now, partly from habit, partly because I have grown to enjoy it, but that enjoyment has not blinded me to the unfair scorn visited upon the lowly. I wish a prophet might rise among them. There is much to be said for worm fishing and worm fishermen.

It never is. The practitioners of this discredited art are a humble, inarticulate folk. They are among the meek who, year by year, enjoy increasingly less prospect of ever inheriting the earth. They do not proselyte; they do not preach. They only want to have their fun in their own simple way, which, on some counts, gives them their warrant to scorn the angling purists.

The scorn, however, always is upon patrician faces.

"What are you using? Oh, worms! Well!"

Thereupon the malefactor flinches and retires into himself like a box turtle. Fly fishing is a needless complexity, an affectation, a vanity. The worm fisherman knows it, yet he shudders and tries to hide the tomato can.

The world is overstocked with persons who identify efficiency with complication. Ethics and culture and sport are ruled by them. Yearly, government manages to make an income tax return still more unintelligible. Religion becomes inextricably entangled with philosophy and anthropology. The mild game of whist has grown into the ordeal of contract bridge. Golf and tennis have become professions; baseball and football teams are corporations with boards of directors.

The very implements of a once so happy and impromptu enterprise as trout fishing have multiplied like Hindus. From pole, line, hook— and a can of worms—we have progressed, if that be the word, to the jointed and delicately balanced wand of split bamboo, the reel built with watchmaker precision, the enameled line, the cobwebby leader, and the miniature millinery ornament at its terminus. We aren't stopping there.

Complicators are the enemies of democracy. No sooner does the rank and file begin to overtake them than they proceed to make things more difficult still. Generations of experience had made most fishermen familiar with the wet fly and its manipulation. Anglers that the purists could scorn were growing fewer every year. Wherefore, the illuminati took thought to themselves and dry-fly fishing was born, with a new technique and a vast increase in the number of requisite implements: tapered lines and leaders, lures that are handled with tweezers, grease tins, waterproofing squirt guns, scissors, magnifying glasses, fly boxes instead of books, and, created by these, an air of hauteur toward the fisherman who doesn't use such gadgets.

Far away and long ago are the tranquil idylls in which Piscator, master of the angle, taught his pupil, Venator, the art of catching trout. Walton discussed artificial flies—but he took his fish on worms.

We have come a great distance since then, and mostly in the wrong direction.

The worm fisherman's the pristine art and he the happier man, if he only dared proclaim it. He is too shamed by general disparagement to take his own part. He never even announces his reverence for the worm, planted in earth by a benevolent deity for obvious twin purposes—to supply bait and to provide that anyone who wants to go fishing must work for the privilege by a little healthful digging. Truly, if he dared look up, the worm fisherman would find that the Lord was on his side.

He is the fortunate man, if fly fishermen would only permit him to believe it. The angler who purchases his lures from a languid sporting-goods clerk forgoes part of the adventure, misses the opening chapters of the romance, never hears the first movement of the symphony. The redolent manure heap behind the barn; the rusty potato fork plunged into the rich and quivering earth; the revelation of pink-and-brown divinely ordained bait among the shattered clods; the ecstasy over the bluely glistening night crawler, lure for a two-pounder at least; the growing Laocoon lump in the bottom of the tomato can—all these I renounced when I took up fly fishing and removed myself a still further step from reality.

I look back sometimes now to the days of my unenlightenment with a poignant feeling hard to distinguish from nostalgia. I never shall be a deft fly fisherman. I was pretty good with worms. There is a smug sense of rectitude, a consciousness of being among the elect, in casting a Coachman, however ineptly. There is more good, wholesomely vulgar enjoyment in worm fishing. And now and then, of you are angling in the company of a purist, you can derive a deal of belly-shaking, more or less politely stifled laughter out of the enterprise, too.

It was shortly after my reformation that Izaak, who largely wrought it, and I went fishing in Canada together. Izaak would no more take worms with him on such an enterprise than he would pack a boa constrictor. With the zeal of the lately converted, I limited my own lures to the contents of my new and overstuffed fly book. Thus chastely and exclusively equipped, we plunged into the Quebec bush, but Satan himself came also. He bore the not particularly diabolical name of Adélard and professed to be our guide. Among the equipment Adélard had brought along for our guidance was a pail of worms.

The miscreant, confronting Izaak's open scorn and my hurriedly concealed relief, explaining that it had been a cold spring, the water was high, and trout were not rising with enthusiasm to flies. The worms were merely an insurance that we should catch fish. After all, we had to eat. If fly-fishing gentlemen failed to supply enough trout for the frying pan, Adélard would have to get them himself. On worms.

I was then, as I have said, a recent convert, with the stain and aroma of iniquity still adhering to my hide. Though Izaak, observing the preliminary signs of backsliding, exhorted me and continually predicted that within another few moments trout would be rising to our flies all over the river, he was a better exhorter than prophet. The fish he caught were few; the fish I caught were none at all.

By noon of the first day, virtue had completely run out of me. When we went back to the river after dinner, I took the worm bucket with me. Izaak's stiff and scandalized air bothered me less than he had hoped. It added, I discovered finally, a piquant flavor to my fishing.

Izaak scuttered along the riverbank like a sandpiper, working himself into a lather while he whipped swirls and eddies. He slipped and floundered and grew extremely hot but remained faithful to his trust. One by one, he employed every type of fly his considerable album contained, including besides the tried and conventional, a number that had been invented during the previous winter by some obviously color-blind artisan.

I sat on a rock in the shade. The river laid tributes of foam at my feet and the pool before me was amber-colored and deep. Each time Izaak changed his fly, I caught a trout. I grew inured to his exasperated stare. In time, I began to enjoy it. I had not been so far withdrawn from the pit that slipping back into it again could fail to be a qualified homecoming. I discovered that in spite of Izaak's disapproval—perhaps because of it—I was having an unregenerately good time.

After a while, as Izaak and I plied our flies and our worms, I forgot entirely the sneaky sense of iniquity that so often accompanies me when I am doing what I really want to do, and, watching Izaak, I began to chuckle. Nothing is more amusing to the heathen than the sight of his missionary rapidly growing demented through the futile practice of his own dogmas.

Izaak, having wearied of displaying his wares to whatever unappreciated trout lay downstream, plodded past and began to whip the pool above me, a lovely, fir-shaded stretch of water. I caught another fish and turned to watch my companion. His color was high, his breathing came hard, and he had stopped talking to me, but his angling deportment was, as always, eminently correct.

All fly fishermen approach a stream with a smug consciousness of rectitude. Among worm fishermen, they continually wear the satisfied air of the one correctly dressed man in the ballroom. They may endure unnecessary discomforts, they may look downright comic, but still they are upholding The Law.

It was borne in upon me that Izaak did look comic. Above and behind him the stooping branches were thick. My friend's casts were beautifully fluent—when he completed them. When he didn't he laid down his rod and climbed still another tree to disengage his snagged fly. At least half the time, Izaak was ascending or descending. Had he lingered beside the river for a year or so, he would have become almost completely arboreal.

In ten yards of horizontal progress, Izaak accomplished at least a hundred vertically. I dearly longed for a picture of him, hung in mid-air in a slothlike posture, reaching far out to free his fly, with his clothing awry and bark-powdered, with fir needles down his neck and lichens in his hair. Merely to carry such a photograph in my fishing coat would have armored me against a deal of scorn.

While Izaak went up and came down with the frequency of an office building elevator, I sat on my rock and, when I had looked and laughed my fill, rebaited my hook and lowered into depths pregnant with mystery a violently gesticulating worm. I remember thinking that my way of fishing was eminently fairer than my friend's. If a trout stole my worm, he got a free dinner. If I got the trout, he had thrown him-self away for at least a possible gain, not for vanity of silk and feathers he wouldn't have eaten on a bet.

I, a temporarily shameless recidivist, found myself comparing the romance and suspense of worm fishing and fly fishing to the latter's detriment. Into the current plopped my worm and vanished. Only the telegraphic line told me what went on in the depths. The twitching that ran from my fingers, up my arm, and into my heart might signal a two-pounder or a four-incher. You never knew.

Fly fishing, I thought defiantly, plumbed no such cryptic and excit-ing depths. It was a barely subsurface, superficial enterprise. More often than not, you could tell the general dimensions of a fish by his rise. The art that the purists extolled actually was a flat-toned pro-ceeding, no more akin to the profundities of worm fishing than free verse was related to *The Iliad*.

With worms, too, you played more fairly with the trout. You offered him what he wanted most. You bet a worm and he wagered himself. If the trout lost, he usually had had the worm, or most of it, not just a mouthful of deceptions to add bitterness to surrender. Fly fishing, comparatively, was a cheap fraud in which the victim staked his all against an utterly inedible jigger that looked like something it wasn't. The trout could not possibly gain anything; he could lose everything on nothing more estimable than vanity. The sole deathbed comfort he possibly could derive was the knowledge he had been hooked by a purist. It was easy to understand why a politician might come to prefer flies.

Izaak came down out of still another tree and I netted and released one more trout. He looked toward me and his lips moved, but the tumult of the rapids chastely hid what he was saying. I felt this was a time for me to hold my peace, if our friendship and maybe one of us in the bargain were not to perish here in the Quebec bush, though I should have liked to have told someone what I had been thinking.

I had been reflecting on the unspectacular skill that worm fishing requires. We, despised by the purists, had our own uncelebrated art. It was not the well-knit co-ordination and grace the fly fisherman had to possess but a more sedate and, I thought, more appropriate knowledge. The illuminati concerned themselves largely with the atmosphere and the knack of casting a light lure through it. A worm fisherman's lore was aquatic. His knowledge was not of air, but of the water itself, its current, its clarity, the probable position of invisible eddies, snags, boulders.

A purist could try vainly four times and on the fifth essay put his fly where he wanted it without materially discommoding himself or the fish. His lowly brother, baiting his hook with a worm, embarked on a graver and weightier enterprise. He was sending forth an argosy that must be launched with a wisdom greater than mere skill.

He must consider the water and how it moved, the fish and what they probably were thinking. He must be stream-minded and fish-minded, and the more nearly he achieved this harmony with nature the better his chances. The fly fisherman had to be clever; the worm user, profound.

I didn't say it. I didn't even fish any more for the moment. I let my worm drag in the water and watched Izaak. Between him and me, the river came over its rapids with a pleasant sound and a flashing white, like a girl running downstairs. In the upstream pool Izaak still fished. His face was redder but he was too far away for me to see its expression clearly, which I regretted.

In Izaak, passion deep-rooted was warring with standards almost as firmly planted. All afternoon long, he had been faithful to the code; all afternoon long, he had cast with enviable grace; and all afternoon, I had been taking fish on Adélard's lowly worms while no single trout had tasted the sophisticated fare Izaak had set before them.

My friend's morals are admirably durable, but they had been strained for hours. Even the most saintly can hold to his creed for just so long while, right under his nose, the sinful repeatedly are rewarded.

A trout had attached himself to my trailing worm. I brought him to net, disengaged him, and with wetted hands slipped him back into the pool. Someone stood behind me. It was Izaak and he had the grimly defiant look that Benedict Arnold and Iscariot must have worn.

"Worms," he said and swallowed audibly. "Give me some worms."

I complied mutely. This plainly was no time for jest or light comment. Izaak stalked back to his pool and baited up. While I watched him, a trout stole my worm. I did not replace it. Izaak was dabbling about, inexpertly and without profit. He had stopped being comic and had become pitiful. Few things are more pathetic than the traitor who has won no gain from his treachery. I rose and went toward him with some apprehension.

"Look," I ventured. "You've fished this pool into suds. Probably there are no fish in it. I know there are plenty in mine. Go down there, catch a trout, and change your luck."

He obeyed without a word. For a space, I watched him fish clumsily, persistently, vainly. Then, at hazard, I dropped my own worm into the pool Izaak had deserted and fought and finally netted the largest trout we had seen that day.

We went back to camp after that. Neither of us said anything on the way.

I fish almost exclusively with a fly now from preference commingled with a deal of cowardice. I am getting to the age when one holds desperately fast to what small advances he has made in life. It will be bad enough for my heirs to list my other delinquencies without adding that, to the very last, I had been a worm fisherman.

I have done my best for years now to comport myself correctly while trout fishing, yet I lag a humiliating distance behind the anointed. Their tight and arrogant organization is still dedicated to further complication of existence. It continues intent on putting all possible distance between itself and me.

Now that I have begun to use dry flies, my betters are extolling the intricate advantages of nymph fishing. I shall never catch up with them as they move onward toward some new height of formalism. There are moments when I almost would say, "Let them climb," and, myself, turn back. There is nothing but a snobbish assurance of conformity in following them further. Nevertheless, I plod on, a long way behind, though I wonder increasingly whether the ascent is worth the effort.

Down in the valley we have deserted dwell the unaspiring, comfortable folk of the world—and their worms. Left to themselves, they would be happier. Joy, to them, does not consist in calling attention to how high they have scrambled. Their accomplishments are too elementarily satisfactory to demand the spice of applause.

Worm fishermen allow the brethren of the fly to proclaim each new tenet of complication as shrilly and insistently as they please. They will, anyway, with or without permission. They will hold that dry flies are better than wet and nymphs more estimable than either; that contract bridge is superior to poker; that Van Gogh surpasses Norman Rockwell; psychiatry excels prayer; Stravinsky outweighs Kern; and communism is more to be desired than free enterprise.

"Let them," the unenlightened should say. "We have our worms."

If they voiced that defiance louder and oftener, there would be less to fear. The complicators have continued their erudite propaganda that ensnared and subdued both Calvin Coolidge and me. No President since my fellow sufferer, as far as I am aware, has had the temerity to fish with worms.

In my mutinous moments, I think this a pity. More voters than anyone thinks would support a Worms-for-Angling ticket. There are worse political slogans.

Old Poacher's
Return

HOWARD T. WALDON

Many readers of Big Stony *expressed the wish that Howard T. Waldon would devote less time to fishing and more to writing other volumes in the same vein. Almost any angler knows a Lank Starbuck. His kind are always hovering on the margins of posted waters.*

THE LONG train curved out of the gorge of the Big Stony and swooped across the expanse of the meadow. From his window in the rear coach Lank could see the leaning locomotive, far ahead, rush upon the widening landscape. He could see the churning piston and three revolving drivers and, far beyond that, 'way down the sweep of the rails, a little cluster of buildings. Now a white plume trailed from the locomotive's whistle and its low and distant wail came back to him: Number One's warning for the crossing at Stony Forks. He unlimbered his long body from the low plush seat, took down his black felt hat and his old black suitcase from the rack above and lunged up the car aisle to the door. The train ground to a reluctant and patronizing halt, complaining in all its journals and underparts.

Lank Starbuck got off. The train sighed again through its dusty length and labored away, straining up the narrowing valley, leaving him there absurdly alone in the wide and brilliant afternoon.

In odd moments during the past five years of his exile Lank Starbuck had contemplated cheering at precisely this point. But now that the time was at hand he couldn't cheer, any more than he could have cheered inside a church. There was a solemnity in this country peace which he either had forgotten or had never known until now. It smote him like a silent wave; it washed over his gaunt and tired frame, hushing the little surge of his superficial gladness. It was like a benediction to the infinite fatigue of his spirit. Lank Starbuck was a religious man in his own way; he stood there for a moment with his head bowed, and his lips moved faintly with his thoughts.

Then he looked up and around him, drinking in the immediate and familiar scene with his eyes as if he were slaking a great thirst. He saw with relief that the village of Stony Forks had suffered no vital change since he had left it. Its physical shapes were intact: the little white depot, the general store, the post office and the quick lunch. The feed mill stood apart on its siding, and the two freight cars basking by its platform might have been the same cars that had been there one May morning, five years ago, when he had boarded the train for New York. It was all there, drowsing in the sun as of old. It seemed insulated against time. The years had blown by, high over the little village, but only the echoes of their tumult had drifted down to register faintly on the surface of its slumberous and immemorial peace.

The leafy tunnel of Oak Street drew away, north, from the bright corner; the road he would take to his home crossed the tracks, slanted south over the broad meadow to the Forks bridge, and made a long ascending turn around the base of a knoll to the westward.

Lank had an impulse to follow that road at once. Then he thought better of it. He couldn't get away unseen: Dave Strouthers, the station agent, had no doubt seen him already. Dave saw everyone who got off Number One at the Forks. And Dave would have it over half the country in no time. . . . His movements would be suspect, anyway—as they had always been at just this season of the year, when trout were feeding—but they would be less so if he made known promptly and openly his return to the Forks.

He went into the station and hailed Dave Strouthers, agent there since time out of mind. Dave looked up from the ticking of his telegraph key. "Well, bless me 'f 'tain't Lank," he said, as if surprised. That sly and knowing look, familiar to Lank Starbuck, crept into his eyes. Everyone who knew Lank looked at him with just that expression between the fifteenth of April and the thirty-first of July and, not

infrequently, before and after those dates. He had missed it during his
five years in the city and it was good to get back to it again. He felt
at last that he was home, restored to his proper sphere where his
genius was recognized. "Don't be actin' startled, Dave," he said. "You
saw me climb off of Number One."

"Didn't recognize ye, though. I'd as soon of looked for the Dook
o' Windsor to get off of Number One as for you. God Almighty, we
been mournin' ye for lost around here. The country's poor have become resigned to troutless Fridays." Dave poked among some freight
waybills and express receipts on his desk and added, as if talking to
himself: "An' the fishin' club members been celebratin' their release
from the dep-ry-dations of the past. . . . How ye been, Lank?"

"Older'n I was, Dave."

"You better take care of yourself—at your age. They tell me the
stream's still cold as a spring brook. Mark Herring, he's down with
rheumatism—fishin' up above the Rattlesnake two weeks ago. You
won't bother it none up thataway, though, I guess—eh?"

Dave accompanied his question with a wink. But Lank needed no
such accent on the implication of Dave's words. The Rattlesnake was
a small feeder brook that emptied into the Little Stony a mile above
the Forks. Up there it was public water. Below the Forks, for three
miles, the Big Stony was leased to and posted by the March Brown
Fly Fishing Club and rather closely patrolled by the deputized guard
of that organization. Those three miles, approximately, had been his
favorite fishing water, club or no club, and would be until the day he
died. Dave Strouthers knew that, as did everyone else in Forks Town-
ship. Yet it was a subject never openly discussed with Lank himself.
It could be hinted at, Dave was hinting at it now. Such innuendo was
within the bounds of good manners, indeed it was considered a complimentary recognition of Lank Starbuck's exploits; but the tight little
code of the amenities in Stony Forks permitted no trespassing beyond
the line of inference. . . .

Lank Starbuck crossed the stretch of cinders behind the depot and
entered Caleb Wilson's general store. Caleb boomed at him from the
redolent cool shade in the rear.

"Saw ye comin', Lank—the last of all critters I expected to see.
Want some Number Four Sproats, I expect, eh? Or hev ye turned
purist after all this time in the big city? How the hell are ye, anyhow?
Good time, down there? Ketch any trout in the East River?"

"Full o' questions as always, ain't ye? Well, 'no' is the answer to
all of 'em, I guess."

"No hooks, eh? I've damn near went out of business sence you
ain't been here t'buy hooks in the springtime. You never been much
of a fly fisherman."

"I've never been one to let sentiment interfere with what a trout needs."

"What about spinners—or an ar-ty-ficial mouse? I hear there's some big browns feedin' below the bridge, nights."

"Who said I was amin' t'fish below the bridge?"

"Wait, now. I was goin' to add that maybe them big browns'd run upstream, some."

"Nope. I just don't want any tackle, right now. For one thing, I'm short of money. For another, I'm seventy-two next month—and Dave Strouthers tells me the water's colder'n all get out. I'm a mite oncertain about my fishin' this year, Caleb."

"Shucks. Your credit was alway sound in this here tradin' post an' I'm still willin' to extend ye a line. I'll sell ye a pair o' boots that'll keep the misery out'n your legs—nothin' down and a dollar a month. How 'bout it?"

"No thanks. I'm walkin' up home an' I don't want t'be burdened with luggin' boots additional t'all the baggage I've got with me now."

"I'll drive ye up, boots an' all—if you'll wait'll my boy gets back with the truck."

"Nope. Much obliged. . . . Thad might've met me. But I guess Thad's too busy, gettin' seed in."

"Thad ain't farmin' this spring."

"He ain't?"

"No. Thad ain't turned a furrow. Sold out his stock, chickens, implements—the whole works—'bout a week ago."

"Well I'll be damned."

"Didn't ye know? Didn't your own son ever write to ye?"

"Practickly never. But then, Thad ain't much of a hand to write."

"Does he know ye're comin' home?"

"Guess so. I wrote him t'that effect. . . . Thad ain't farmin', eh. Well I'll be damned. What is he doin'?"

"Don't know. Don't anybody know. 'Course it's only a week sense he sold out all his stuff—and whatever he's doin', it ain't had time to infiltrate into Stony Forks society. If he had a wife, now, the womanfolks'd git hold o' the lowdown on Thad's doin's. But he don't have ary wife."

"No. He's got his points, but . . . 'Tween you an' me Caleb—an' maybe I hadn't ought t'say it about my own son—no sensible female's likely t'take up with Thad."

" 'Twon't get any further'n you an' me, Langtry." There were moments when Caleb took the trouble to pronounce Lank's given name. "I don't know—I can't figure that boy. He's smart enough, in a way. He's been a good customer o' mine an' paid his bills when due. I don't know what 'tis about him." In his heart Caleb despised Thad Starbuck, without quite knowing why.

Lank was leaning against the counter, his long legs stretched out before him, gazing down at his shoes. "I know what 'tis," he said, studiedly. "It's his lack o' visible vices. It's his damned petty morality."

Caleb didn't reply. There was no need to embellish Lank's stark and truthful utterance. Lank was a shrewd devil—he could find words for things. He could bring a thing out of the fog in the back of your brain and show it to you clearly, just with a couple of words. . . . Thad's lack of visible vices. Lank was right, by God. Why, Thad wouldn't even swear. If he banged his thumb with a hammer he wouldn't say "Damn it to hell" like any good Christian man. He'd say "Jupiter!" or "Thunderation!" Lank had seen that much. But Lank was fond of his only child and maybe he hadn't seen what Caleb had always suspected: that somewhere, hidden among Thad's visible small virtues, was the shadow of a great vice which would one day take form. Thad's Jupiters and Thunderations kept in some poison which a good oath would have let out into clean air.

It was a half mile from the town to Forks bridge, an easy half mile, gently down-sloping across the wide area of the meadow. Lank took it in his stride, his suitcase hoisted on his shoulder. A sharp inner compulsion acted perhaps as a propelling force. For now that he was on the road at last, his social obligations paid off at the village, he was aware of an active and acute desire to see the Big Stony again at the bridge.

As he approached the bridge he could smell the stream. He could smell the cool damp of the wash of fresh water over stones, the wet leaf mold of the shady banks where new ferns and fat-leafed skunk cabbages stood moist and supple with their sap, amid violets and dog-tooth. He smelled May and trout fishing, for the first time in five years. It brought a catch in his throat, like the sudden evocation of an ancient and poignant memory. . . . And now he could hear the stream: the eternal soft voice of truth, the voice from which his youth and manhood had drawn fortitude and peace and a trust in the verity of God.

Then he saw it. He took the bag from his shoulder and put it down on the bridge, and stood leaning on the log rail, gazing down at the familiar features. The long and constant riffle, stream-wide and shallow, ran out from under the bridge, sloping easily into a black and rock-hemmed pool two hundred feet downstream. At the lip of the pool the water narrowed a little and poured like curved glass over a solid rock bottom, smooth as a floor, and disappeared to the right in the green gloom of the woods.

He gazed at it all, in a reverie, for several minutes. His gray angu-

lar face bowed again, over the rail, and his lips again were murmur-
ous with his thoughts.

The reverent moment passed, his head straightened from his little
communion with his God, and into his eyes came a keen appraising
scrutiny. Lank Starbuck knew, definitely now, that he was going to
fish that water—tonight. It was right, if ever he had seen it right.
Its color, its pitch, and something else—some quality which even
Lank could not define though he could sense it—spoke trout to him
in words he could not possibly misunderstand. It might not have been
just so, yesterday; it might not be just so tomorrow. But now—it was.
It had the once-in-a-season bloom, the transitory peak of sheer perfection. And while that held he was bound by every dictate of his
conscience to avail himself of the gift.

But he was in a dangerous spot, a place where, if he were seen, he
would be suspected at once. Two signs—one on either bank—faced
the bridge squarely from the downstream side:

PLEASE KEEP OFF
POACHERS AND TRESPASSERS
WILL BE PROSECUTED
March Brown
Fly Fishing Club

It was a nice polite sign, not hard-boiled like some others he had
fished under. But it had teeth. Lank Starbuck had never felt them
but he knew others who had.

One thing more he wanted to do—feel the temperature of the
water. He crossed over to the other side of the bridge and went down
to the stream. There were no signs here; upstream from the road the
water was public. The fork was in sight immediately above, where
the Little Stony poured in its tribute from the north. It was pretty
water but it did not tempt him now. . . . He dipped his fingers in
the stream. It was cold—no doubt about that. It was damned cold for
this late in May. On one count, that pleased him: it gave validity to
his preference for nightwalkers. On another, it did not. For he was
pretty sure he'd have to wade wet.

He was on his way again. Another half mile stretched before him
to his house, all of it upgrade. About midway of this distance Lank
put the bag down and rested a few minutes, his thoughts and his
eagerness preventing any great preoccupation with his fatigue. Already he was planning tonight's foray, considering his old lines of
ingress to the stream and his old strategic routes of withdrawal. After
five years he would perhaps be at a disadvantage. His once smooth
technique might be rusty from disuse. Certain old paths and hideouts
and places for secreting tackle or trout might not likely be there any

more. The club guard likely had altered his schedule. Perhaps there were two guards now. The thing would need all of his old-time cunning. Despite his long absence from the stream he had no great doubt of his fishing skill. In the five years' famine he had kept fishing alive in his mind and his spirit. He had thought of the feel of the rod in his hand and the pull of Big Stony's currents on his line; night after night, in that mean little city room, he had wooed sleep by imagining himself back on the stream, by conjuring up in his brain a detailed tableau of another secret raid upon those forbidden waters. In his heart he had kept alive Big Stony's riffles and pools and back eddies, its snags and stones, the endless diversity of its action as he had known it of old in all of its sunlit and shady stretches and as, in more recent years, he had seen it by moonlight or felt it in the total dark. It wouldn't be strange to him, now, any more than his wife's dear face would be strange if he could see it again after the same length of time.

He sensed the change upon the little farm as he came around the last bend of the road and saw the white small house a hundred yards ahead. At this point always, in the spring of the year, he could see his Holsteins knee-deep in the timothy and clover beyond his line fence. But now the gate was open upon a wide and cowless field. Burdocks and daisies were a spreading rash on the velvet green breast of his old east pasture. The little margin along the road, between the road and the fence, had been newly and neatly mown. That was like Thad, he reflected: neat where he thought neatness would show.

He could smell the emptiness, the abandonment of the place. The barn was innocent of any sign of animal life. A ghostly odor of cows lurked in odd corners, but it might have been only imagined. The combined reek of a disinfectant and of crankcase oil was too real to be thus haunted. A rubber tire hung from one of his old cow stanchions. No thumping of hoofs came from the horse stall. The silo was open at the bottom, bright with sun on its clean-swept cement floor. The poultry yards were unpeopled and already rank with pigweed.

Complete silence where complete silence ought never to be. It struck Lank with a slow and cumulative force.

He went up the path to the kitchen and found the door locked. He had a key, though, and he applied it, wondering for an instant if the lock had been changed in the general upheaval. But his key went home and turned the bolt and Lank Starbuck entered.

The kitchen was neat in a man's way of being neat. His wife— Thad's mother—would have had flowers around and a bowl of fruit on the kitchen table, a fire in the stove and a pot of something stewing on it. The room would have delighted your eyes and your nostrils immediately you entered it. Thad's stove was studiously cold, and such of Thad's appurtenances as were hung on their proper hooks were strictly utilitarian. Well, Thad had always been businesslike, a better manager than his old man ever was. He shouldn't be unjust in his thoughts about his own son.

The house echoed with his footsteps. He looked into the neat front parlor, which smelled almost antiseptically clean, and looked away. The dining room had lost its heavy old table; the pine cupboard which Lank's father had built into one corner had been removed. In their venerable places were a bright golden-oak table and a glass-doored china closet. Chairs and a sideboard of the same cheap gleaming veneer stood precisely around the walls.

He went upstairs, sick with a queer nostalgia. To his immense relief he found his old room just as he had left it. It had the smell of a place long untenanted; it needed fresh air and the habitation of something human. Dust lay on every flat surface like new snow before footprints get into it. Thad had scrupulously cared for every other room in the house but this one. That was because Thad was indifferent to, not reverent of, the things of his father. Lank knew it, without defining the thought. His room had been closed to Thad and to Thad's guests, like an out-of-the-way closet where some foul and shameful thing is stored.

He opened the windows to the south and west, letting in the fresh air of the late afternoon. The dust could keep—for a while. He went to his closet and to a big chest inside it, like a hound going to a holed-up rabbit.

He dragged the chest out into the light of the window and raised its heavy lid. His stuff was all there, thank God. The sight of his old treasure, after his long time away, created an uproar in his blood. This kind of thing, this boyish thrill in the mere sight and feel of trout tackle, he had considered a deceased capacity, buried deep, deep, under the old years. He was a little embarrassed in the strange recurring glow. He took his rod out of its cloth case and velvet-covered form. It had been a beauty in its day, costing him just half of one month's milk check in that spring when his favorite Big Stony water had been taken over by the March Brown Club. He had chosen it because it was a specialized instrument for the sort of work he would have to do from then on: six short joints so that he could carry it, taken down, in his trouser leg. He had rewound it with his own hands, in his own scheme of colored silk, on that long-gone day when he had brought it home. He remembered how his wife had ransacked her sewing baskets for the precise shades of thread he had wanted; and how Thad, then twelve years old, has looked over his shoulder with a rapture he had prayed would live.

Lank Starbuck assembled the joints with his eager fingers, sighted along the rod's length as he'd sight along a gun barrel and rotated it slowly. It had had a little bow for years, from the pull of Big Stony on his heavy nightwalkers. But it had grown no worse in its long incarceration. He swished it back and forth in the room, happy in the response of the good old bamboo.

He took a quick inventory of the rest of his gear. A couple of level enameled lines, wound carefully around a cylindrical oatmeal container, were still good enough. A tin box held his reel, divorced of its click for professional reasons and well oiled in its cloth sack, the flat tobacco can he used for a bait box, two or three candle stubs for getting nightwalkers, a few large wet flies, a simple collection of spinners and half a dozen Number Four Sproat hooks, eyed. All O.K. His leaders, of course, were useless; but he drew from his pocket an envelope containing a few level six-footers, heavy-trout, bought in New York before leaving because their purchase in Caleb Wilson's would have started gossip. His folding net had been left assembled and the cords were still sound. He cut off the dead elastic thong, drew from another pocket a five-foot length of new black elastic and attached it in a big hoop.

That left only his boots. Greatly patched and brittle with age, they were beyond further repair. Well, he'd wade wet, as he had expected. It wouldn't be the first time.

Working fast, and with something of his old smooth mastery of detail, he fetched two rubber bands and two short lengths of string. He took down the rod, placed all the joints side by side, lashed them together lightly at one end with a piece of string with a bowline loop left on it, and at the other end with a rubber band. The handle and folding frame of his landing net were similarly tied. The joints of the rod would of course go into one leg of his trousers, the landing net in the other, with the loops of string around his suspender thong, on either side, preventing rod and net from dropping while allowing them freedom to swing, inside his pants, with his stride. He stowed the velvet form and cloth case in the chest. He knotted a hook on the end of each of three leaders, coiled them around his hand and folded them separately, into a big handkerchief. He wound the better of the two lengths of line on his reel, and he was ready. Then he thought, with a little reminiscent smile, of the defiant notes he used to leave on the stream. Well, just in case, he'd take a pencil and a piece of paper— in an upper pocket where they wouldn't get wet.

The sun was lower in the west window. An oriole, in one of Lank's old apple trees, was a brilliant recurrent sound against the fundamental stillness of the late afternoon.

As yet, no Thad. Lank arranged his gear carefully for an immediate getaway—all of it except the folded handkerchief of leaders. This he took downstairs to the kitchen and soaked under the tap at the sink.

An inspection of Thad's larder revealed, among other things, bacon and eggs and coffee. Lank kindled a quick fire in the stove with light wood. . . .

His supper consumed and the utensils washed, he went back to his room and changed into his fishing clothes, his old corduroy pants, a blue flannel shirt and a blue denim work jacket of many pockets. He stowed the tied rod joints in his right pants leg, the net in the left, and pocketed the rest of his gear, amused a little at the realization that he remembered to a T his old system of certain pockets for certain items. He deliberated a moment over the flies and spinners, then made a decision for the exclusive use of worms. He patted his pockets and pants legs in a final checkup, and went below. If Thad didn't want to come home, he needn't. The hours of fishing waited for no man.

Outside, the sun was already under the ridge to the west and the world was blue and quiet with the dusk. The song of a wood thrush in the old orchard was a smelting of bright silver in the twilight. The gentle contours of his ancient acres heaved and dipped away, blurred in the soft wash of the fading light. The wall of the distant woods stood vague and motionless, curving out to the road ahead of him. A cottontail sat in the roadside dust and loped easily off at his approach, a close and distinct accent to the blended masses of the dusk. A star was suddenly coined in the high east straight ahead.

He came cautiously to the left turn where the road heads north, verging into its down-slope to the Big Stony. He listened for cars, horses, men: any traffic which might be abroad and to which, likely, he would be suspect if seen headed toward the stream—particularly if such traffic should happen to be the club guard himself, Foster Prentiss. A decent enough man, if you stayed off the club property, though of course a lackey and bound by the lackey's point of view. Lank wondered if Foster still kept to his old schedule. If so, he would be on the prowl, this time of the evening, in his Ford.

He should have passed here half an hour back and he would pass again in another half hour.

He hated himself for the slight nervousness which possessed him. But he was long unaccustomed to secrecy; his old inurement to the skulking philosophy of all hunted things had slipped from him in his five upright and dismal years in the city.

Feeling like a target for some ambushing fire, he made the turn and proceeded north along the sloping road. The old keenness for fishing was rising in him, too, along with his little fear. He was eager to the quick to feel the press of the water again, the weight of a brown trout on the far end of his line. He would get over that dread of detection. One or two more raids and he'd be immune again. The old confidence would return. He would continue to practice stealth, but fear would be no part of it. It never had.

The verdict calmed him. And there, just ahead, was his old cut-off, now almost invisible to any casual or unsuspecting eye. He veered into it from the open road. The dark woods and a warm flood of reassurance engulfed him. The little path looked the same as it always had. Under his feet he felt its firm friendly texture.

The long twilight thickened almost imperceptibly. Even here under the tall hardwoods the dark would not be complete, he knew, for half an hour. He had ample time but he must not waste any.

The path sloped down, northeastward, to the stream. In a moment he saw the glint of water, an area of a quiet pool through the trees ahead, and heard the murmur of the riffle above it. He stopped, tense as a panther, peering into the empty and silent radiating aisles. Then he took his rod out of his trouser leg, removed its string and rubber-band lashings, assembled it, attached the clickless reel, threaded the line quickly through the guides, looped on a leader, drew the hook back to the handle and inserted it in the cork grip. He removed the landing net from the other trouser leg and undid the string lashing but left the rubber band on.

Thus prepared, Lank Starbuck disappeared around a mass of rho-dodendron to his left. In a minute he returned, empty-handed, and started back up the path.

Back to the road, up to the southward fork, a quarter mile over the hill and a few steps through a strip of wood lot brought him out, in less than ten minutes, upon the cropped surface of a golf club fairway. Going in that direction, away from the stream and unencumbered with even the indication of a fishing rod, he was above suspicion.

The darkness was not quite whole but it would do, he thought. He took a candle stub from his pocket and lit it. Bending close to the earth and holding the candle low, he proceeded slowly along the edge of the grass, giving a five-foot-wide strip of turf a microscopic scrutiny. Fifty yards of the fairway yielded to his flat tobacco tin a dozen fat nightwalkers. He doused his candle and hurried back.

It was dark now, and he felt his way into the cutoff, proceeding with extreme caution down the little path. Coming up to the place where he had assembled his rod, a thin vein of apprehension threaded the almost solid structure of his confidence. Things had gone too smoothly, perhaps, and it were well to keep his guards up, to take nothing for granted.

He stopped, suddenly, to decide whether his imagination or his physical ear had heard that voice in the darkness ahead. It came again. . . . No imagination about that. It was a voice. Two voices. Lank knew, even, whose voices they were. Mr. Stokes and that college professor—Lank couldn't recall his name—who was by all odds the best fisherman among the members of the March Brown Club.

Lank knew where they were sitting, too, and at the thought of it he chuckled quietly to himself. But he would have to wait until they left—and get himself hidden at once. They wouldn't come up his path; there was an easier one, a little to the left, which Lank had avoided because it was the usual exit of fishermen. But they would come near his path, and they'd have a flashlight.

Testing each footstep before giving it his weight, he eased his way twenty feet into the woods to the right.

Stokes was a good fisherman but that professor was a better man with a fly than any Lank had ever watched. Both, he knew, had been fishing flies this evening—they always fished flies unless the stream was over its banks, and then, usually, they didn't fish at all. They embraced some queer artificial faiths; they were full of strange codes of self-denial. When the night came on and the chance of snagging into a big brown was really good, they were coming off the stream instead of getting into it.

They had come off the stream now, and were resting a minute; he knew that, even without their words to inform him. Well, that was all to the good. There was at least one big trout down there who was not interested in flies tonight. In the back of his head where he kept his gallery of mental slides Lank saw the dark two-foot-long form, a sinister shadow, cruise into the shoals on the night prowl for its prey. None of your little flies—that fish wanted a dinner. A big streamer, presented in just the right way, would perhaps take him but no other fly would. A six- or eight-inch chub would be ideal. But the night-walker, he thought, would do. He could divert that fish, momentarily, the way he'd offer the worm. . . . And almost certainly that trout had not been frightened by the fly fishermen. Stokes was a quiet careful angler and the Professor didn't disturb the water he fished any more than a ghost would.

Yes, his luck was holding. But he must not relax for a second. His vigilance was, and always had been, the secret of his success.

Crouched there in the brush he thought briefly of himself, looked objectively at himself as a poacher, as a man outside the law. The free and open water above the bridge had offered the legal way of safety, and most of his fishing acquaintances around Stony Forks had followed it. But his gnarled old pride had been too deep-rooted to let him confine his fishing there. His best sport, the best moments of his life, had been sneaked, in a sense stolen, from other men. On that point—on all points that touched his fishing—his conscience was clear. If he had had to skulk from the sight of men he had never been furtive from the bright eye of his God. He had not the least remorse over the numbers he had taken, upon occasions, in excess of both club and state limits. On the public water above the bridge, on those rare times when he had fished it, he had respected the closed season and the state bag limit, simply because that water was the property of other plain men, his friends. But from his forays below the bridge Lank Starbuck had distributed club trout among the needy people of the countryside —as many as twenty in a single day—in all months from March to October inclusive. And he was aware that the club members knew it; had known it for years. The only cardinal sin was waste: a trout killed but not eaten. And the only cardinal error was to let himself be caught. As yet he was guilty of neither.

Mr. Stokes and the Professor were coming up their path. Their flashlight made jerky silhouettes of the intricate patterns of the woods. Lank drew into himself, into the intimate earth and the undergrowth, like a grouse before a bird dog, as they went by in the woods to the left. In a minute their voices were no longer audible to him. He stayed under cover a minute more. Then he felt his way back to his path and followed it down a little distance toward the stream. He diverged from it again, left, where he had turned off earlier in the evening. Under his mounting anticipation he was aware, for the first time tonight, of the fatigue of his body. He came up to the hollow log on which Stokes and the Professor had been sitting. Reaching into the butt end of the log he drew out his assembled rod and his landing net.

The cold water shocked him at first. In five years he must have forgotten how cold the Big Stony could feel. It took his breath but he went resolutely in. It would recognize him after a while and warm up to him, like a woman with a stranger. It always had. He smiled a little bitterly at the thought; it might not still be so. He was older and he felt the cold more. . . . He remembered the lay of the bottom at this point. It would have changed some, but he relied upon its not having changed greatly in his years away. He waded quietly and steadily out; at this pitch of water it should grow deeper and stronger gradually until it reached his thighs, then level off in midstream and shoal again to his knees on the far side. It did.

This was the point he wanted, ten feet out from the north bank. The deep run eased its pressure here, flattened and widened below him over a broad, pebble-bottomed, rippling shallow. The encroaching trees gave way from this expanse. Above him was the night sky, luminous already with the prescience of moonrise.

He let the big worm go down into that shallow drift below. The whole of the Big Stony held no better night-feeding ground for big fish. There was depth below it and depth above, day hideouts for the large browns, and between them this two-hundred-foot shoal for the night range. The guard appreciated the strategic importance of this place—called the Poacher's Pocket by the March Brown members—and gave it extra vigilance on his rounds. For a trespasser it was the most dangerous water of the club preserve. He would go down it easily with fifty-foot roll casts across stream, letting the current effect the wide arc of his bait, downstream and back to his side. He'd let the worm hang in the gentle flow a moment and then ease it back and let it drift again. With the moon up he'd stay in this stretch only long enough to hook a fish, then he'd play it into the dark water below.

His heart pumped a little against the biting chill of the water. Or maybe it was in remembrance—and in immediate anticipation—of the feel of a big brown trout's strike in the dark.

For that would come to him again, in these next few minutes. Without sentiment now, he could appraise the value of that simple thing, that moment just preceding and containing the strike. He could look at it in relation to the sum of his life and see its constancy and its truth. It had survived because it was fit and honest and pure, along with a handful of little memories and beliefs—such plain things as pride and love and his hardy faith in his son, and the clear quiet memory of his wife. Standing there in the night and the stream, just before moonrise gave back to Lank Starbuck the familiar identities of his ancient haunts, the deep vessel of his years evaporated at last and left this simple residue of its vain ebullition.

Returning from his professional rounds, Thaddeus Starbuck warped his shiny roadster into the end of the cow barn. He shut off the ignition and lights, jumped out and slammed the door behind him in virtually a single motion. Standing there in the barn door he surveyed his property—as he liked to think of it—in the early moonlight. Several nicely groomed conclusions came out for encores in the forefront of his brain. He visualized it as it would be when at last his industry and thrift had shaped it according to his dream. With the old barn torn down and a hollow-tile fireproof garage erected in its place, with the chicken houses out of the way and a neat cement path instead of the old rickety flagstones going up to the house, the place would reflect the fact of his success.

He glanced up at the house and was relieved to see it completely dark. The old man had not come, then, after all. Thad had guessed that it was mostly talk, and that it would subside if he ignored it.

Congratulating himself on his judgment of men in general and of his father in particular, he walked up the path. His gait was at once springy with his twenty-nine years and conscious of the new dignity attaching to him. He let himself in at the kitchen door and snapped on the light.

Quick chagrin tightened his apple face at the flick of the switch. For he smelled, now, the evidence of his father's arrival, the remains of the recent fire, the bacon and eggs.

For all his full-bodied roundness Thad Starbuck had the instincts of a ferret, and they had sharpened in the recent days of his new employment. His khaki-clad and putteed figure stood still for a moment, then abruptly marched upstairs and entered the old man's room.

He saw the chest first, where Lank had left it, and it was all he needed to see. But as a routine confirmation, as a detail of a thorough-going professional job, he raised the lid of the chest to make certain that the old man's rod and gear were not there. . . . If only he had acted upon his impulse, this very morning, and done away with his father's rod and tackle while still there was time.

No emotional conflict whatever stirred in Thad. In that moment, looking down at the evidence, he was conscious only of his duty to his employer. In a later moment, when well launched on his course, a little question was to disturb him. Thad needed an interval of time in which to grasp the implications of a given set of circumstances. He was the ideal policeman in that respect. Duty spoke to him with a peremptory voice, crowding out of his ears the little whisperings of conscience which other men may know at such times. Hearing the voice now, he acted without question. He patted the badge on his chest and the gun in his holster without looking at them. He had formed that habit in his short time on the new job—to make sure, always, that the badge and gun were there.

The ways of the father's poachings and trespassings were familiar of old to the son; and just now this knowledge gave Thad the advantage of which he delighted to avail himself. He backed the car out of the barn, turned it quickly and was off down the road in pursuit. He went by his father's old cutoff slowly, looking it over in the moonlight and in the light of his headlamps, but not stopping. He kept on across Forks bridge, parked the car just beyond, and made his way on foot along an easily traveled wagon road, his beat on the north bank of the stream. His father had had many points of entry but Thad remembered the one he had liked best, and he thought the old man would use it now, on his first attempt in five years. That single two-hundred-foot stretch might take two hours of his father's fishing, if no strike rewarded him. Then he, Thad, had plenty of time. It was not long after nightfall and he knew the old man could not have started until the dark was complete, for Mr. Stokes and Professor Kent had been on this very point of the stream at dusk—

He felt a quick pang of something akin to dismay. Had they apprehended his father? . . . It subsided. Of course not—the old fox was not to be snared that way. . . . But it thinned out into a dull misgiving, the first of two which were to nag him briefly. It brought to him, in due time, the realization that his arrest of his father might be embarrassing to himself. Conceivably it might cost him the job as club guard—which he had applied for and obtained after the recent death of Foster Prentiss—for his employment by the club, he suspected, was partly predicated upon his own statement that his father probably would not return to Stony Forks. Thinking of that declaration to the club members he recalled that it seemingly had caused Dr. Hatch to wink at Mr. Harlow and to mutter something about "preferring his ghosts unlaid," to which Harlow had replied, "That's one ghost who can't be laid." But he hadn't understood at all. The club members, particularly Hatch, were always saying things which made no sense to him. He stopped in the trail to ponder his problem and as he stood there in the sifted moonlight the alternative dawned on him, giving him slowly the solution. For he certainly could not take a chance on not arresting his father. If he let him go, tonight, the old man might be at it again tomorrow night or the night after. Someone might see him, eventually, and it would come out. "No," he said, half aloud, "I've got to take him quietly, without any fuss."

And then that other misgiving made signs at him. Suppose you can't, it said. Suppose the old man got tough about it? He was capable of it; he had gotten tough with other men before. Thad recognized, without understanding, his father's contempt for uniforms and badges, for any authority which sought to shackle the dictates of his private convictions.

He patted the gun holster and went ahead. A minute's walk brought him to the long flat where he expected to see the old man. In the flood of moonlight he should be distinctly visible to Thad, looking for him. To other eyes he might be another of the several boulders ranged about, on shore and in the water. The old man could be companion to the rocks, almost as motionless as they. Thad strained his eyes at the moon-flushed expanse of open stream, focusing intently upon each boulder and the in-between spaces of water. There was no slightest movement, no sound except what the stream and the woods made in the nights of May. He crept quietly to the water's edge, took out his flashlight and sprayed its beam over all of the water within its range. His father was not there.

Thad returned to the wagon road and followed it quickly and quietly downstream. There was another point, and he didn't think it would fail him.

There it was—there it was, at last. He knew he should not have to wait much longer. That immemorial pull, that age-old signal of the big brown . . . Again.

Lank Starbuck struck. He put his rod high and gave out line grudgingly with his left hand. The trout took it from the clickless reel—out, 'way out—seventy-five, a hundred feet. Lank braked the fish gently and went down stream with him, into deepening water, snubbing him, wondering if the old line would hold. This fellow was big—as big as any he'd ever known. Five pounds, if an ounce. The strain seemed insupportable but he must turn now, with most of the line gone and deep water ahead. He held his breath in the long moment of crisis; then, as the great fish turned and raced upstream, winning yards of slack, he murmured a prayer of thanks. And now he stripped in line like a man possessed, and as the fish came opposite and bored past, upstream, he fed it out with added pressure. He forgot the ice-cold band where the water level girdled his thighs; he forgot everything in the waxing conviction of his mastery. He was licking the biggest trout that had ever grabbed his bait. He had known that something big would be in this shoal tonight—he had known it, this afternoon, when first he had seen Big Stony from the Forks bridge—but this monster was beyond his wildest hope. And he was beating it down, for all its size—his first feel of a fish in five years.

A half hour passed. The tempo of the battle had slowed almost to a halt. Lank had worked the fish down near the narrow tree-arched water, to land him out of the moonlight, out of sight of any prowling guard. And now in the last stages of the struggle the old man stood still, fighting his tiring adversary direct from the reel. The rushes of the great fish had become feeble; his last leap had long since been essayed; he was surging heavily near the surface now, fighting a losing and exhausted fight against the old iron of the wrist at the other end. Lank's droning monologue, always a part of his battles with large trout, died to the merest whisper as the strength faded from his antagonist, and now it had almost ceased.

"Easy—easy, now. Easy—easy, now," he kept repeating, and that was all there was left of it. He was bringing in that mammoth brown trout, slowly and with exquisite care. "Easy. . . . Easy. . . . Over the net. . . . Easy."

Slowly over the net and out.

So far, he had won. But his victory was never complete until he had retired safely from the stream. It looked simple, at this moment—go ashore back there in the open, knife his fish, write his note and hang it on a bush, and return via the wagon trail to the road and home. But that was against all the ancient tenets of his strategic code.

Guards liked that spot too well. It was easy for them to wait there and nail you with a big fish as you came out. Retracing his steps to his point of entrance would be risky, too, now that the moon was up, and even if he wasn't seen he might be heard. Wading upstream was noisy. There was another way, harder, but safe. It meant wading a hundred yards downstream, most of it up to his waist, and crawling out to high ground through a rift in the rhododendron jungle, and curving a course through the woods to home, avoiding roads. He hoped that little exit was still as it used to be.

The big trout was half out of his net, head down, gulping air with its convulsive, exhausted gills, full of a spasmodic dying power. Lank gripped one hand around the net cord above the protruding tail, held it high to avoid splashing and started downstream.

Immediately, he was glad he had followed his rule and not gone ashore. Footsteps came to him distinctly from the path on his side, approaching him from upriver. He had a quick impulse to crouch, but his old experience contradicted it in time and he proceeded as rapidly as he could without splashing, gaining the end of the wide and open stretch of water and entering the deep narrow run under the dark trees. He was out of the moonlight just in time. The footsteps ceased behind him, and in the stillness he kept going, feeling his way in the deeper water. In a moment he was aware of a ghostly illumination moving under the trees. Instinctively he stood still; then, as it dawned on him that he was out of range, he turned his head and saw the point of the flashlight and the beam searching out the surface behind him.

He kept on. The water was an icy belt around his waistline, making him gasp audibly. His escape could not be effected on the other side; the Deeps started just below and the Big Stony for a quarter mile down was too deep and fast to wade across. But he felt safe. The guard had made a routine search of that part of the stream where searching was easy and would follow the path down to the next place where it came out upon open water, well below Lank's exit. By that time Lank would have vanished behind him. He smiled a little in the darkness and looked back. The light had gone.

After the guard went by he'd write his note and leave it on the trail. Not here—it might give away this useful exit. In his mind he had it all nicely worded: "A five-pounder Mr. Stokes and the Professor missed. Poacher's Pocket, moonrise May 18."

The trout struggled and lunged once or twice in the net. Holding that heavy fish high was making his arm ache. The freezing girdle at his waist had slipped on inch or two down but the cold was beginning to paralyze his legs and the chill rose like a mist up into his chest. But he'd be all right if he could get out in a minute—if the guard would hurry and get below him. The walk home on dry land would warm him up. God Almighty, he hoped Thad would have a fire in the stove.

Groping along under the high bank, in what little moonlight sifted through the trees, he came at last to his old outlet. A four-foot boulder here, just offshore, and a great leaning sycamore identified the spot. That tree had almost collapsed in the years since he had last seen it; it leaned now precariously, half its roots heaved up the earth. His little path, negotiable only on hands and knees, went up the bank from this point, joining the wagon trail above.

He worked up between the big rock and the bank. He would go quietly ashore and sit down by the sycamore's upthrust roots to wait. If he could kill his fish quickly he'd be saved a lot of trouble. Drowning would be difficult with a fish so large, sure to make a splashing loud enough for the guard to hear, and would risk losing the trout. As he came up to the steep bank, still knee-deep in water, he put his rod down and reached for his knife. Operating entirely by the sense of touch he pressed the long blade deep where the back of the head and body joined. The great fish welled up against the strength of his left hand and wrist, and lay still. Lank transferred it quickly to the big back pocket of his jumper and buttoned it in. The tail end protruded several inches out the right side. And at that moment the expected footsteps were on the trail above him, approaching.

The flashlight could pick him out here, for keen eyes, despite the underbrush. He took up his rod again and crouched low behind the high bank. The water, circling his waist, took his breath in a gasp that might have been audible up there on the trail. But the guard's footsteps didn't miss a beat. They came on fast—they would go beyond in a minute. His luck was holding; he had gotten the trout and killed it in time.

That regular, almost measured tread halted abruptly above him, where his little path came out on top of the rise. Lank Starbuck's eyes, squinting over the rim of the bank, saw the light go on again. He ducked below the edge, sinking a little deeper into the water, and immediately the beam shot down the path, flooding the area of stream behind him. In the tense stillness the water flowed into the circle of light, crossed it and disappeared in the darkness downstream. The light veered a little and came back to its focus; and above him were renewed footfalls and the rustle of underbrush. The guard was coming down the path.

Lank Starbuck, half submerged, pressed into the wet earth of the bank. In the intense cold his breathing was quick and labored, but it wouldn't be heard until the guard finished fighting the brush and stood still on the bank above him. In those few seconds, noisy with the guard's progress, he took the deep loud gulps of air his lungs were crying for. With the full intake of breath he regained a measure of mental poise, and the reality of the situation seeped into his underlying disbelief of the whole affair. He knew he had not been seen and it was not possible that any club guard could have anticipated his exit here. Foster Prentiss had never known of his use of this place, nor had any other living man—so far as he could remember.

Yet, here was the guard coming right at him with a light. In a minute more he'd be seen, arrested. In the darkness and the cold and the ebbing of his strength, that was clear. He had a minute, at most, for a getaway or a fight.

There had been a time when he'd have stood and fought. He considered it now, but so briefly that it was only like a faint irrelevant reminder that once he, Lank Starbuck, had been young and strong. . . . Let it pass. Age and exhaustion had him now, and the cold water.

The flashlight beam, brilliant directly above him, flickered once and died. In the ensuing smother of the dark Lank heard the man stop still in his thrashing down the path and say "Jupiter!"

There was no other voice like it anywhere in the world. And no man on earth but Thad, his own son, would have said "Jupiter" in just that situation.

Thad, his son . . . His crazy crowding thoughts had a kind of core, a central, master thought about which all the loose tag ends of related notions revolved. Thad was a gamekeeper, a servant. His own son, reared in the wide freedom of his farm and brought up to be, above all else, proud, had hired out as a lackey to other men, had put the cheap delegated authority of a uniform and a badge above the will of his individual soul. The conviction carried a deep hurt to the old man, a sense of some fatal omission of his own, never recognized until now, some dereliction in his training of the secret and quiet boy. The old years came back at him again, full of too much reliance on inherited pride, too little awareness of the slow erosion of the spirit in that way of life which had been his and Thad's.

And yes, he remembered now: 'way back in the past he had told Thad of this hidden path, this secret outlet. And Thad had stored that bit of knowledge through the years and uncovered it tonight for this bright, vindictive employment. Lank Starbuck knew, with a deep wounding insight that was not surprise but an ancient buried awareness, that Thad had followed him from home to arrest him. All men had their scales of loyalties, and now in this moment he knew how Thad's was graduated.

But he wouldn't be taken. He had never been, and he wouldn't be now. If there could be, still, a conflict of allegiance in his son's heart he could eliminate it for Thad by removing the cause. He could go, now, with his record and his conscience whole. The revealing moments of his life, when the truths had come out, had ever been dark moments; and here at last, in the old dark setting, was the final apocalypse. His time had run out. He had come up short upon the end and it looked all right to him. He had no reason, any more, to stay. The knowledge came into his mind, easily and without shock, that tomorrow's dawn had no meaning for him, nor all the dawns to follow. He knew all that they had to tell; his eyes were satiate with the procession of their beauty and his heart understood their ultimate message. Let the young, quick eyes have them now, the eyes vulnerable to their wonders as his own once had been.

He saw reason and comfort in the prospect, beauty and peace and the fair proportions of any fitting thing. The Deeps of the Big Stony could have him now, and the pure record of his poaching. . . . Sink into it low, quiet—push offshore easy, into the strong deep current, and keep down. Never mind the long breath—it couldn't be taken anyway.

Thomasheen James and the Absent-Minded Professor

MAURICE WALSH

Maurice Walsh is one of the most prolific of writers, but rarely does he complete a best seller without working in a chapter or two on some form of fishing. His short stories involving one Thomasheen James have a mixture of humor and pathos that give them broad appeal. This one has always seemed to the editor Walsh's crowning effort.

YOU ARE certainly going to miss that bus," my wife warned me. "Blazes! If you left those confounded fishing boots—"

"On the summerhouse floor where Thomasheen James dropped them? Ah! here they are. Run and you might catch it. Shall I ask some friends in for a salmon supper?"

"Fine! I'll buy you one on the way back," I shouted from the hall.

I banged the door, swished round the end of the privet hedge, and was brought up all-standing by Thomasheen James's wheelbarrow dead in the middle of the path. Thomasheen James himself, my-man-of-no-work, sat on the tail end smoking one of my old pipes. There was nothing in the barrow but his yard sweeping brush.

"Cripers!" he exclaimed. "Is the house on fire?"

"You and your damned barrow!" I exploded, rubbing my shin as I hobbled down the drive. He was already trotting at my side.

"Gi'e me them waders and the creel, if 'tis the nine-forty you're after."

He ambled down the hill ahead of me toward the bus stop at the road junction, and mocked me over his shoulder.

"Surely-to-glory! You don't fancy yourself to catch nothin' a day like this—not even the bus maybe?"

"Perfect fishing weather."

"So it always is—in the morning. You'll have a different tune at the end o' the day—like most fishermen ever I knew."

"Fat lot you know about fishermen!"

"The fill of a book, only you couldn't print most of it. Run now! Run like hell! Here she comes."

The driver of the bus saw us coming and obligingly waited; and Thomasheen James and I bundled on the platform shoulder to shoulder.

"That's our first catch o' the day—an' our biggest be far," said Thomasheen James complacently.

"Put down that tackle and get off," I ordered, the bus beginning to move. "If that lawn is not cut—"

"Aisy—aisy! the week is long. It'll be cut."

He stowed waders and creel carefully in a corner and sat down opposite me.

"Where are you going?" I demanded.

"Fishin'. But not a sprat—and mind I told you."

The conductor, an old friend, was at my side.

"One to Tober Bridge, Michael—one!" I said.

Thomasheen James looked at me, half challenge, half appeal in his eye.

"Have a heart an' start the day dacent!—Better make it two, Mick."

I nodded to the conductor. Thomasheen James was bent on coming with me, and he knew that I would not repudiate him in public. Moreover, he was good company.

"Our bit of a joke over," he said, "we'll have a smoke to ourselves," and borrowed my pouch.

I sat contemplating the lean, wiry, red-haired indestructibility of the man. He was a freer man than I was. At the loss of all respectability, at the loss of many things much more valuable than respectability, he had achieved his own freedom. He carried freedom under his hat, which was an old hat of mine. He was not my chattel; he was never legally in my employment; he was in receipt of no fixed wage and had not yet suggested one; but we tolerated each other outside the barrier of class consciousness, and were implicit partners in a consideration of certain aspects of his own venality.

As I sat there looking at him I realized how much talent he had misused in seeking to avoid the unavoidable, all the vain and daring exploits he had just failed to pull off because of the one final, inevitable false move that had brought the shadow of Nemesis but never the complete vengeance; and there and then I realized that I was only one of a long succession, and that some day I too would throw him out on his ear to be a menace to some other member of what we call our social organization. And then I had a feeling of dismay. Had he at last perfected his technique to the management of a final and unescapable victim? And was I that victim? I swore.

"Damn! I wish I had never set eyes on your subhuman façade."

"Don't be blaspheemious," said Thomasheen James, startled out of a daydream. "Me what?"

"Your face."

"You never took your eyes off it the last half hour. The next stop is Tober Bridge."

He possessed himself of waders and creel, I took the rods, and we dismounted above the strong flow of the Owenbride River. We leaned over the parapet of the high three-arched bridge and looked far down at the water running strong and sternly in its gorge over smooth shelves sloping from a long cascade higher up. A little of the early sanguine mood of the angler faded in me.

"I told you so," said Thomasheen James exasperatingly. "Look at it! You could see the head of a pin in the bottom of any dam' pool."

"But the sky is just right," I persisted, "and a nice breeze to riffle the water. A twenty-pounder at least—maybe two."

"Live horse, and you'll get grass," quoted Thomasheen James. "Where do we make a start to commence with?"

"A mile up—Cloona Reach."

"Hell's blazes!" His eyes lit. "Is it poachin' we are?"

"Certainly not. I have a day's permit from Colonel Sandys to fish his lower reaches."

"And oughtn't that be a warnin' to you. That ould divil wouldn't give his own mother a day's fishin' an' the fish takin'.'"

"That's a straight libel on a gentleman you don't even know," I said angrily.

"Don't I? The same ould dugout lost me the best job ever I had—an' may the divil melt him!"

"Oh! So you know him?"

"We have cause to remimber each other," he said with restraint. He lifted the lid of the creel and looked inside. "We have lashin's o' sangwiches anyway, but they'll be dry atin'."

"Plenty of water to wash them down."

"River water! That's no safe drink for a human man without 'tis polluted be a drop o' good whisky—half an' half an' plenty o' water. You'll have that bit of a tin flask in your poacher's pocket?"

I had, but I did not tell him so.

Thereafter we went fishing. And I did fish. And Thomasheen James proved himself a true prophet. The breeze was propitiously in the southwest; the sky was perfect, sheeting and shining with a warm smurr of rain every half hour; but the water was all wrong. The water was clear and low and just one degree chilly with the melting of the last wisps of snow in the hill chorries; and in the stiffest riffle I could catch the glint of the Blue Palmer fly I was using. I rose not a single fish.

But the salmon were there. They were there in every pool. They came out of the water playfully—sometimes over my very cast—in a clear silver smacking curve, but never in that porpoiselike head-and-tail rise that betokens a fish ready to take. Once I hooked a playing fish in the back fin and had a furious ten seconds before the hook tore free. And that was all.

But, notwithstanding, the day was a pleasant one and passed quickly. There is more to angling than the mere catching of fish; otherwise, who would be an angler? The weather had turned definitely toward summer, and the air was all balm; the larks were soaring and singing, and the river curved and fell and sang, and smoothed itself out into shining reaches below tall banks of fresh-foliaged trees; the pastures were bright green round patches of brown tillage; and, behind all, the moors swept upward into the flowing curves of the great hills of Wicklow, where cloud shadows running smoothly made the sunlight seem more brilliant.

It was good to loiter along the head of a bank looking over a hopeful pool; to pause, while one filled a pipe, and consider the best way of covering all the likely spots; to put oneself in the salmon's skin and choose the exactly appealing fly; and then to work down the pool yard by yard, hope never dying until the final cast into the tail riffle. One might say a few choice words then, sit on a boulder, try a small taste from the tin flask that was really silver, relight one's pipe, and discuss with Thomasheen James the possibilities of another fly.

My henchman astonished me with his knowledge of flies and fish. He would sit on his heels at my side turning over the felts of my old-fashioned leather book and wonder why, "in the name o' hell," I had cluttered it up with as "infayriour a collection of flies as I ever put eyes on."

"There now is a Orange Grouse that might do the trick for us if it was only two sizes smaller; and this Scottie, the Green Highlander, we could be after tryin' in the next bit of a shower; but when all is said and done, gi'e me a Spring Blue—number one—with a touch of yalla in the hackle to timpt a suspicious fish on a day like this—an' dam' the one in your whole selection."

We did tempt the fish with every possible and same impossible lures, but no fish fell. Shortly after midday the sky began to clear, and by the time we reached the head of our water no cloud marred the fragile spring blue; the breeze died away, every pool became as flat as a mirror, and the sun was as warm as in early June.

"Go on wastin' your rasher an' eggs if you have a mind," said Thomasheen James, "but if you're after that fish your missus wants 'tisn't with no rod and line you'll get it."

"I know no other way."

"Do you tell me that? What about that time in the Big War when I was out fightin' for your investmints and you away up in Bonnie Scotland?"

The only fighting Thomasheen James had done in the war was with his fellow stokers in the bowels of a transport ship of the Mediterranean Fleet.

"You haven't a stick of dynamite about you?" I suggested.

"No then. But this minit I have a stomach an' it glued to me backbone with imptyness."

So we sat on a green bank in the gentle warmth, our feet on dry gravel, and munched sandwiches. Above us a swinging footbridge spanned the water to a fine spread of parkland clumped with lindens and grazed on by deerlike Jersey cows; and at the head of the park a white square house with a Greek portico slept in the sun. I noticed that Thomasheen James kept a wary eye lifting toward that white house.

"That is Colonel Sandys' place," I told him.

"I know it. Is he at home?" he inquired with interest.

"I think so. He lost you the best job you ever had?" I hinted. "But all your jobs were best ones."

"I can't say that on the present occasion," he riposted.

"What job did you lose?"

"A good job."

"No sweat on your brow?"

"It was the reesponsibility," said Thomasheen James.

"All right! Tell me about it."

"There might be libel in it."

"There will be. Go on!"

He finished his sandwiches, looked at me with a calculating eye, and gestured widely toward the silver flask. I uncorked it consideringly and Thomasheen James brightened.

"A reesponsible job! I was the guide, guardian, an' gineral recuperator of a professor out of the univarsity."

"He never survived all that?"

"I didn't. I won't be tellin' you his name, an' if I did you wouldn't make nothin' of it, not movin' in thim advanced circles. I mind the evenin' well. I was after footin' it all the way up from Maryborough—"

"Where the jail is?"

"Do you want to gloat over me misfortunes or don't you?"

"All right—all right! Say when, man!"

"The cup'll tell you when," said Thomasheen James.

II

I was a young, strong, hardy butt of a boy thim days (began Thomasheen James), an' the longest cir-circuitest road couldn't knock a feather out o' me. I had done me twenty mile up from Ard-na-Righ, an' was makin' for the Vincent de Paul night shelter, me bein' without as much as a ha'penny to bless meself with. I had come in be the borders o' the City, when I overhauled an ould fella progressin' vagariously in front o' me. 'Twasn't the length of the street that was troublin' him but the breadth of it, for he was tackin' by an' large from sidewalk to road an' back again like a hooker in a head wind. A fine summer evenin' at the back o' ten, an' he navigatin' his way home after bein' thrown out of a pub somewhere. A short stub of a thick-built man in a good loose flannel suit, an' a floppy panama hat on the back of his poll.

As I came up behind him he intercepted a white lamppost and set back two steps, liftin' his hat most polite an' " 'Scuse me, madam," says he. Then he set back two more steps with no intintion an' collided on me chest. At that he faced round, swayin' on his props, an' speculated me out of an eye like a dead herrin'. A red-jowled ould buffer with a bush o' white hair, an' I saw at wanst, be his gineral appearance, that he was no customary soak, only an ould gintleman vitiated by an intermittent occasion.

"You red-skull of a prooletarian," says he, stern but scatterin', "would you assult a illustr'ous visitor to this i'noble city? But, behould!" says he, "you will find no plunder on me carcase, for I have shared me last pasedo with thirsty brothers. Begone, vartlet!"

An' he made wan almighty swipe at me with the panama hat, an' took two full circles out into the middle o' the road. I was just in time to snake him off the raddiator of a bus, an' I propped him secure aginst the lamppost; an' he up an' apologized for beltin' me so outrageous hard. He hadn't touched me within a foot.

"Do you live hereabouts, sir?" says I to him.

"Far an' far from here, me inquirin' fri'nd," says he, sad. "A city where the unbeliever trimbles and if he don't trimble we makes him trimble. Behould," says he, "a citizen of the great accidental city o' Dublin."

"Dammit!" says I. "This is Dublin."

"Dublin!" He straightened off the post. "So this is Dublin! I know it from the mountains to the sea, but this mean street I have not seen before."

"Might I be bould to ask, sir," says I, coaxin' an' wonderin', "whereabouts in Dublin you pound your ear?"

"Ah!" says he; "the jargon o' the west! Crumlin!" says he. "Crumlin! where the boorjoo percreate theirselves in gimcrack simidetachable villa residences." That was true for him.

I was proppin' him up in the heart o' Crumlin that very minit.

"Whereabouts in Crumlin, sir?" I puts to him.

"I have it!" says he. "Six—three-six-seven! Yes, three-six-seven, Dunover Avenue, Crumlin, South Dublin, in Ireland."

Dunover Avenue—one o' them new roads a mile long—it was only round two corners from us.

I anchored him be one arm. "Let us see if we can locate the place, sir," says I, haulin' at him.

He brewed that in his mind, houldin' aginst me. "Very well, aborogeen!" says he then. "Let me assist your errin' steps. The members o' me hareem awaits me long—her name is Mary."

An' he started to sing. Well, sir, we went perambulatin' round two corners an' up Dunover Avenue, me eye liftin' for number three-six-seven; an' when we came to it I steered him across a bit of a lawn into a imitation of a porch.

"Here we are, sir!" says I.

"A remarkable feet of exploration!" says he. "Alas! this place looks mean an' strange after all these years." He shook hands with me. "Thanks for the use of your carpet, Harroon-all-rascal," says he. "Further larges I cannot bestow at time o' goin' to press. Call round in your next voyage."

He aimed his finger at the bull's eye o' the bell push an' scored only an outer.

"Show me the keyhole," says he, "an' I'll find the door meself."

So I propped him aginst the door, pressed the bell hard, an' made off down the path; for I was feart the lady he called Mary might be that sort o' woman to blame me for the biled condition of her sultan. All the same, I watched him round the corner of a lonicera hedge.

The door opened an' he fell in on the bosom of a thin woman—I knew she'd be thin—and the both o' them went back into the passage, an' I heard the clatter o' furniture an' the wallop o' chinaware on the floor, an' a screech to wake the dead, and another screech on top of it, and the bellow of a man's voice behind all. An' before I could wink twice, me ould gint comes propellin' through the door in a flyin' jump. Boys, oh boys! He had his feet under him, I tell you, and came scatterin' down the path like a tarrier dog, his hat in a ball in his fist, an' never a halt out of him till he hit the railin's on the other side o' the road. I wint across an' recovered him.

"Lids o' hell!" says he. "The city has fallen to the infidell. I seems to reco'nize you, stranger."

"Was it three-six-seven at all?" says I, havin' me suspicions.

"Six-three-seven—what else?" says he.

I near moidered me brain calculatin' the way you could mix thim figures to a strange result. Eleven, maybe? Six, is it? Anyways it looked like I had a job before me, but whin I start a thing I finish it, an' he was a dacent-like ould buffer even if he hadn't a make in his pocket. I was actin' out o' pure tinderness o' heart, and I'm drawin' your attention to the same.

So we wint tackin' by an' large up the devous long road, an', as luck would have it, struck the right house the third time o' askin'. Six-three-seven it was all right. Well I remimber it. As soon as we got inside the gate he leaned down from the anchor I had on him an' extricated a plant, root an' branch, out of a flower bed along be the path.

"Consider that!" says he, holdin' it under me nose. "That," says he, "is a akwilleesio of the genius that runs in uncles."

" 'Tis what I call a columbine," says I, and so it was.

" 'Zackly!" says he. "From columbus, a dove—see the five o' them in each hand. My wife, Mary, paid ten shillin's a dozen for them, an' they are the apples of her lustry eye."

It was a stout dame—not thin—that opened the door to us this time. A plumpish, good-lookin', fresh-complexioned woman, and white in the red of her chair.

"Oh, John—me poor Johnny!" says she, partly in distress, but mostly relieved-kind.

"My dear," says he, makin' a bow and near buttin' her in the lower curve, "I brought you home a small gift." And he presented her with the columbine.

"How nice! Thank you, darlin'," says she, humorin' him, an' there was not a bit o' suspicion in the inquirin' eye she threw at me.

" 'Tis how we lost our way, ma'am," I tells her, "an' we sailin' home from foreign parts—Stamboul, I'm thinkin'."

"I know—I know," says she, noddin', an' a kindly grip on her rambler. "Thank you very much."

I knew then that this was not the first an' only time he had been discanted on his own doorstep after varous pre-pergrinations at the other side of a coupla shots o' malt liquor.

He shook me hand in fare-you-well, an' says he:

"You will have to dispose of me services now, me good man. Try an' navigate under your own steam. Strong drink is ragin' in you."

And there I left them, and asked for nothin'. But when I got as far as the gate the ould lady hailed at me an' came down the path.

"For your trouble, and I hope you don't mind," says she, her hand out. "I am very grateful to you for bringing me husband home."

A whole half dollar it was, an' I was able to sleep in clane sheets that night in the Iveagh Home.

Yes, sir! I liked them two—especially the ould lady—from me first survy. She had a pleasant eye and a ginerous line to her mouth. An' durin' the watches o' the night I consaived the polite notion of payin' me respecks next mornin' to inquire if the ould explorer had recovered from his jaunt in lands beyont the main.

I did it, bright an' airly, and there he was as spry as a trout, and him just settin' off for a day's fishin' in the Tolka River; an', when I sort o' interposed that it might be impert'nance on my side if I trailed along carryin' the bag, the good woman imbraced the offer an' meself at the same time, for she hadn't a ha'porth o' faith in her ould woolgatherer an' him out of her line o' sight. So off I wint with him, and I dunno if he knew I was there most o' the time.

That's the way it began, an', to make a long story short, in less than no time at all I was an institution. Becripers, ay! I was instigated as full-time retriever of the professor, an' me indispinsibility was as strong as a mountain.

A professor—that's what he was. A professor o' echo-nomics in the univarsity. Mind you, for nine months o' the year, he was a rock in the ocean aginst the timptation of a thirsty windpipe, lecturin' his bits o' false doctrine twice a day an' takin' the bus home to his wife reg'lar as clockwork, a bundle o' books in his oxter an' his pipe in his gob—an' nothin' in the pipe as often as not. It was only in the long vaycation that he was accustomed to dive intermittently off the deep end. He had nothin' to do, and in the garden he was as fatal as a sow in a patch o' spuds; but let him go out his walk alone, a few bob in his pocket, and he'd gradually circulate himself into a pub somewhere; an' after a second drink he lost his dimensions lock, stock, and barrel, an' found himself navigatin' his way home from some outrageous foreign clime—China or Peru or Pennsylvania, or some such consarned place.

Sober and head-sore he regretted his little proclivities, and be way of avoidin' the occasion o' sin he'd arm himself with a trout rod and lose himself in the wilderness o' the country. Lose himself is right. For he would go wanderin' up the riverside, droppin' in a baited hook here and there, dramin' a bit, readin' a book, an' wanderin' on again; and at the heel o' the day he might find himself ten miles from home, an' the points o' the compass twisted contrairy. More'n wance he came back in the tail of a turf cart next mornin's dawn. As absent-minded a block o' l'arnin' as ever drew breath, an' him by way of an expert to l'arn youth the legal way of extractin' the spondulicks out of another man's pocket accordin' to the rules laid down be Church and State.

I reg'lated all his trapesin's. Two or, sometimes, three mornin's a week we used set off for the country an' enj'y life on the loose foot betune stated hours, a dollar in me pocket—mind you that—aginst the misfortunes o' the day, a thermos flask o' coffee, and a pile of sangwiches in the fishin' bag; and before the fall o' night I had him restored safe an' sober to six-three-seven Dunover Avenue, an' a hot meal waitin' for me in the kitchen. The ould lady was as contint as a clockin' hen on a chinee egg, an' in no time at all was callin' me Tommy, an' consultin' me knowledge on this an' that about the house an' garden. Thim was the days.

Fishin'! We busted no records one way or another. He was a bait fisher, an' I can see your nose curlin' at the mention. He said that fly fishin' was plain cheatery; and what else is it? "If a trout," says he, "can induce a juicy worm off me hook I congratulate it an' supply another, but if it fails, then its want o' circumspection ends up in me wife's frying-pan." Many's the trout we fed in the Tolka River that summer, and I heerd anglers remark that the trout was runnin' bigger than any season yet. There was one big bull of a cannibal in the Mull Pot off the Navan road, an' he imbibed half a cannister o' worms off us reg'lar, till one day I took the rod meself an' baited a stuart tackle with a felonious brander worm, an' I set that fella danglin' in a holly bush six feet out o' the water.

We had a elegant summer, I warrant you. The professor was a respected man, an' known far an' wide for his l'arnin'; an' most o' the neighborin' fishin' proprietors, knowin' his little fault an' his harmlessness among the trout, gave him a free permit to fish where and when he liked. We tried the Tolka an' the Dodder, the King's River an' the Liffey, and this here Owenbride, an' began all over again. I used provide ourselves with a strickly limited number o' bottles o' beer at the start o' the day an' distribute them judicially betune us so as not to

cumulate any bad effects; and we used daunder along the banks, fishin'
when we had a mind, havin' a snooze to ourselves in the heat o' the
day, an' wakin' up to argyfy the affairs of the nation an' the ingenuity
of the civilized man to contribute to himself what belonged to widows
an' orphans.

I used have to watch him like a hawk, for when he was discoorsin'
away an' his pipe empty he would fill it often as not out o' the worm
tin; an' wanst, when he broke his line an' was for splicin' it, he found
it convaniant to hould the worm in his teeth. We caught fish sometimes
as well, for, when the conditions was suitable an' no interlopers about,
I used handle the rod an' bag a coupla trout to ameliate the ould lady,
tellin' her how himself caught 'em, an' if she didn't believe me, he did.
That's the sort o' gluggerhead he was. Mind you, me dacent man,
catchin' trout with a worm in low water is no mug's game. You have
to fish agin the strame, and keep the bait on a nice line, an'— All right
—all right! Amn't I workin' up to me denoomong?

Yes, sir! We was the completest combination of bullheaded brain
an' plain intelleck you ever heard tell of. He was the grandest talker
that ever ran his tongue round words with as many j'ints as a earwig,
an' me vocab'lary hasn't never recovered from contack with him.
Meself in them days had a nice balance to me tongue, an' a disputatious
way of interspersin' any argyment to bring him up all standin', so that
he'd have to go back to what he called his first principles an' build up
his conclusion again, storey be storey, an' me ready to clout it down
before he had the roof on. 'Tis he made a Communist out of me agin
his will.

"You donkey!" says he. " 'Tisn't money great men want but power
with a big P."

"Give me the money for a start," says I back.

"You poor dumb idiot!" he comes at me as if I was one of his stu-
dents—he had a hot flare o' temper. "Are you not cognizing of the fact
that if all the ready wealth o' the world was shared out, your share
would be exackly one pound eleven shillings and seven point nine circu-
latin' pence per week? Therefore aggregation of capital is not only—"

"Wait!" says I. "Wait there! Gi'e me one pound eleven every Saturday night, an' you can circulate the odd coppers into your own pocket.
I wouldn't call the Queen me aunt."

From that time on I was a convicted Communist. Aisy now—aisy! I
am comin' to the heart of it.

It was right here on the Owenbride that misfortune inflicted
on me the loss of the best job I ever had. Maybe I was growin' careless,
an' did not reconter me surroundin's as I ought. A day early in September, a gran' salubrious day with the corn stooks yalla in the field back
of us. I should ha' looked closer at the same bloody stooks. You know

the third pool we fished comin' up, the one where, be awkwardness, you broke a barb on the back cast. The Corrig Pool—that's it! All flat slabs o' rock above an' below water. 'Twas there that disaster conteracted us.

Me bould professor was sittin' on a lump o' rock, his back agin another lump, half dozin' or deep thinkin'—I couldn't tell which—his eyes shut an' his mouth makin' small puffs as if his pipe was still in his teeth, which it wasn't, havin' fallen betune his knees. He had just polished off four sangwiches an' enclosed himself round a quart o' beer, and the food an' drink was curlin' happy inside of him.

Meself was reclinin' on me stomach, me jaw over the edge of a rock, and the deep water a foot below me nose. The Corrig is a tarnation deep hole at that place, an' I couldn't make out the bottom; but, look you! a matter o' four foot down there was a convaniant flat shelf stickin' out, an' restin' on that was as nice a cock salmon as ever waved a fluke, all of fifteen pounds I would say, with blue showlders on him like a Berkshire pig. His nose was agin the rock, an' his flukes gave a waggle now an' then, an' when that happened I could see the beak on his bottom jaw an' the white o' his belly. A clane-run cock fish takin' a rest after the batter up the rapids before goin' on up to the spawnin' redds. Whisper! I saw a fish in the identic same place today—a bigger fish, all of eighteen. Four foot deep only, an' there's that telescope gaff o' yours in the creel— Very fine! Very fine! I wish your wife heard you denyin' the sartinty of a fish supper!

I lay flat watchin' that salmon, an' after a time I turned me head an' cogitated the professor. He was real sleepin' at last, his mouth open— and did I wake him? No, sir! I was too busy resistin' timptation, but it was too strong for me. It always is unless it is as wake as skim milk, an' then 'tis only a timptation you wouldn't give a dam' for. I fell—half a minute I lasted good.

I twisted the long-handled gaff we had sideways an' slipped the hook under water well behind the fish. If all tales be true you are fam'lar wi' the artifice o' gettin' a gaff under a salmon's navle. Slow an' a little at a time like the minit hand of a clock, an' then sudden an' fast like a flash o' sheet lightnin'—or you'll find yourself head over heels in deep water an' your belly full of it if you can't swim.

I didn't go into that deep hole, not be a jugful. When I was good an' ready I let that purty fella have it, an' brought him leppin' out o' the water an' over me head an' wallopin' aginst the professor's shins six foot back. I didn't mean to do that, for I didn't want to wake him up till I was ready to explain the way he caught that fish from the butt of a rod. I'd often noticed that after a snooze on a quart o' ale his mimory went all lopsided, an' he was liable to accept the conclusion with no laist notion o' the predispositions. Anyways, I waked him up, and he bumped his head on the rock, an' while he was rubbin' the place, his eyes shut, I reduced the salmon with a kick in the poll.

"Why, Tommy!" says he, his eyes open agin. "That's a nice salmo sailer we caught."

An' there, at that misfortunate minit, a voice spoke pleasantly from the rocks above us.

"Thanks, me good fellow. My fish!"

Yes, it was! Who else? Colonel Sandys himself. I knew him fine though the professor didn't, we havin' got the trout permit from his agent, Dan O'Shane. The ould fire-eater came down off the rocks bitin' his mustache, an' his eyes like a lump o' ice. An' the bottom o' me heart fell out.

"I needed a fish too," says he aisily, but it was the aisyness of a hangin' judge, the black cap already on his head.

The bould professor was on his props, blinkin' hard an' tryin' to remimber.

"Did you catch this fish, my man?" says he, his voice sternin', for when he was lit up be a quart he'd back down from no son of a gun.

"This scoundrel o' yours saved me the trouble," says the colonel.

The professor was tryin' his dam'dest to recall the past.

"Tommy," says he, "was it me or you caught this fish?"

A man has to be bould at the right occasion, an' two agin wan is no handicap in or out o' court.

"Betune us we did it, sir," says I, bould as brass. "Twenty-two minutes you had him on when I gaffed him nate as ninepence."

And he faced the colonel.

"Fella! I have a permit to fish this stream from Mr. O'Shane," says he. "How dare you claim my catch?"

"Not only do I claim it," says the other, houldin' himself in, "but I possess it as well." And he bent down to take a purchase on the tail o' the fish.

"I shall report this disgraceful insult," bawled the professor. "But manetime I insist on me rights."

He was always discoorsin' me on what he called the rights o' property, an' becripers! he could act on it as well. Do you know what he did? You don't! He up and gave the bendin' soger man a knee in the short ribs that made him grunt an' yelp an' drop the fish to hould on to his liver. An' there an' then me gallant professor took a stranglehold o' the salmon, both hands round the tail, an' says he:

"Your fish, you ruffian!"

At that the soger boy saw red murdher.

"Outrag'ous!" he yelled. "Put that fish down, you blind ould addlepate!" And in with him at the professor.

That was a error in ticktacks. I was tellin' you the way the ould boy clouted me with his panama our first renconter. But it wasn't no wisp of a hat he had in his hand this time. No, sir! He was a strong-built butt of a man, an' he swung fifteen pounds o' dead salmon like a champeen throwin' a hammer. Chroosht! right under the ear with a clap o' ten wet towels rolled into wan.

The colonel had no control of himself. He went sideways like a paper flappin' the wind, tangled himself in his own legs, tee-totthered on the edge of the rock, an' yellin' blue hell went behind-foremost into deep water. It was the same as if you exploded a stick o' dynamite.

"Oh, murdher!" says I. "This puts the lid on it."

The colonel, poor fella, came up once an' sputtered, an' down with him agin; an' when he came up a second time I retrieved him with the gaff in the bellyband of his trousers. But to make sure of his discretion I be way of accident let his head under a third time before extrackin' him out on the bank.

There was no more fight left in him than a drownded rat. Dammit! he hadn't wind enough in his carcase to thank me for savin' his life. But what's the use o' boastin'? Our victory was only temp'ry, an' before we could plan a retreat we was impounded be a irruption o' three water bailiffs lyin' in ambush among the corn stooks. We was reduced be numbers.

What more is there to tell? I am never the one to draw out me agony. That was the end o' the best job I ever had. Oh well! if you want to know. The professor had powerful fri'nds, an' influence was employed above an' below ground to keep the case out o' court. But I might as well be in jail, for I was thrown out on me ear for that wan small single lapse o' discreetness. That's it all for you now!

III

I looked out across the river and thought aloud.

"If this professor of yours fished only for trout and with bait, why the presence of a long-handled gaff?"

"Dam' well I know the suspicion you have in your mind," said Thomasheen James regretfully. "But if you saw the ould fool tangle his cast on top of a tree or twist it round a stone in slack water you'd know the binifit of a long-handled gaff to extricate him. Maybe you don't believe me—?"

"Not a word. How many salmon did you lift out of the river that season?"

"Go to—" He lifted to his feet quickly. "Look! Who's that comin' across the field toward us?"

A man in white flannels was strolling down toward the swing-bridge from the white house across the park.

"That is Colonel Sandys," I told him.

"I thought as much. Do you think he'd be remimberin' my countenance?"

"If he does," I hinted, "I get no more free fishing."

"I wouldn't want to discommode you. I'll cut me hook an' wait for you at the bridge. Hould you him in confabulation."

He moved off down the bank at any easy slouch that did not look in the least like a strategic retiral.

Colonel Sandys crossed the bridge and came down to greet me. A tall lean man with a mustache startlingly white against a face burned brick under tropical suns, and a particularly decent man too, notwithstanding Thomasheen James's animadversion. He preserved his salmon reaches as conservatively as possible in a land of poachers, but was most generous in distributing permits amongst honest anglers.

We talked for a while, and he proposed that I take another day the following week when conditions might have improved. But as he talked his eyes kept turning speculatively downstream.

"That was your gillie?" he suggested at last, and I was ready with the reply.

"He sweeps the yard and garden path for me," I said.

"Oh, that's all right. In the distance he reminded me of a scoundrel that troubled us a good deal some seasons ago. An inveterate poacher, he used an old wool-gathering college lecturer as a cloak, and must have lifted an unconscionable number of fish out of the easy pools—with a gaff. We found salmon scales where no scales should be, set a watch on the water, and finally caught him red-handed."

He then gave me his version of that capture, and at no point did it agree with Thomasheen James's. The professor had not been implicated at all; Thomasheen James himself had wielded the poached salmon as a weapon, not on the colonel but on his bailiff; and it was Thomasheen James who had been soused to cool his violence. I will not decide who was lying. Possibly both!

After the colonel's departure I set up my trout rod and fished the runs downward with a cast of minute, thin-hackled wet flies. The evening rise was on, and by some fair fishing I got half a dozen takable trout; and, as usual, I very nearly lost my bus. After the last minute I hurriedly bundled up my tackle, and it was only then that I noticed that I had lost my patent telescope gaff. There was no time to go back on my tracks, and all I could propose to do was to drop a note that night to the head water bailiff.

As I clambered, nearly breathless, out on the road Thomasheen James hailed me reproachfully from the porch of the Blacksmith Arms at the bridge corner.

"I hear her comin'. Dammit! why didn't you give yourself time to stand me wan pint?"

The bus came round the corner then, and I didn't waste time to curse him as I hurried to the stopping place. Thomasheen James was at my shoulder as I swung on. I stowed my tackle in a corner where there were two other fishing creels, but no sign of any fish, and took a vacant seat, back to the door. After a brief time Thomasheen James took the seat opposite.

"That's another dam' day over us, glory be," he said.

"If you've been drinking beer," I said, "I have a darn good mind not to pay your fare."

"I'll be astonished if you renage me," he said confidently.

And there one of the other anglers on the bus leaned forward and exclaimed warmly:

"My lord! Look at that, Tom! What a beauty!"

The man addressed as Tom looked behind my shoulder, and his mouth opened and shut. Then he stared at me.

"Sir," said he, "what marvel of a fly lured that beauty on a hellish day like this?"

I turned slowly and with discretion. Oddly enough, the first thing I noticed was the polished butt of my patent gaff projecting under the lid of the creel. But on top of the lid lay as shapely a salmon as ever came out of the famous Owenbride River. Its perfect shape denied pounds of its weight. I looked at it dumbly, and saw the gaff mark an inch above the vent. But Thomasheen James was not dumb.

"In the Corrig Pool," said he easily. "A Black Doctor with a grouse hackle on a number five Limerick bend. A summer fly, I know, but wasn't this like a summer day—an' how could the fish know else? A hen fish, eighteen pounds if an ounce, an' I gaffed him nate as ninepence after twenty-five lively minutes."

He looked at me with a calm eye.

"Have you the fare on you, sir? The conductor is waitin'."

"That's another best job lost," I said softly but grimly.

But I paid his fare.

"I can't lose what I haven't," said Thomasheen James.

The Fourth Day

Chapter VII—Observations of the
Salmon, with Directions how to fish
for him.

IZAAK WALTON and
CHARLES COTTON
[THE COMPLEAT ANGLER
London, 1653]

*Although recent literary unearthings may have
given rise to some doubt concerning the originality
of the efforts of Messrs. Walton and Cotton, "The
Fourth Day" provides us with a classic example of
the angling writing of the seventeenth century.*

THE SALMON is accounted the King of fresh-water fish, and is
ever bred in rivers relating to the sea; yet so high or far from
it, as admits of no tincture of salt, or brackishness. He is said
to breed or cast his spawn, in most rivers, in the month of August:

some say that then they dig a hole or grave in a safe place in the gravel, and there place their eggs or spawn, after the melter has done his natural office, and then hide it most cunningly, and cover it over with gravel and stones; and then leave it to their Creator's protection, who, by a gentle heat which He infuses into that cold element, makes it brood and beget life in the spawn, and to become Samlets early in the spring next following.

The Salmons having spent their appointed time, and done this natural duty, in the fresh waters, they then haste to the sea before winter, both the melter and spawner: but if they be stopped by flood-gates or weirs, or lost in the fresh waters, then those so left behind by degrees grow sick, and lean, and unseasonable, and kipper; that is to say, have bony gristles grow out of their lower chaps, not unlike a hawk's beak, which hinder their feeding; and, in time, such fish so left behind pine away and die. 'Tis observed that he may live thus one year from the sea; but he then grows insipid, and tasteless, and loses both his blood and strength, and pines and dies the second year. And 'tis noted, that those little Salmons called Skeggers, which abound in many rivers relating to the sea, are bred by such sick Salmons that might not go to the sea, and that though they abound, yet they never thrive to any considerable bigness.

But if the old Salmon gets to the sea, then that gristle which shows him to be kipper wears away, or is cast off, as the eagle is said to cast his bill, and he recovers his strength, and comes next summer to the same river, if it be possible, to enjoy the former pleasures that there possessed him: for, as one has wittily observed, he has, like some persons of honor and riches, which have both their winter and summer houses, the fresh rivers for summer, and the salt water for winter, to spend his life in; which is not, as Sir Francis Bacon hath observed in his "History of Life and Death," above ten years. And it is to be observed, that though the Salmon does grow big in the sea, yet he grows not fat but in fresh rivers; and it is observed, that the farther they get from the sea, they be both the fatter and better.

Next I shall tell you, that though they make very hard shift to get out of the fresh rivers into the sea, yet they will make harder shift to get out of the salt into the fresh rivers to spawn, or possess the pleasures that they have formerly found in them; to which end, they will force themselves through flood-gates or over weirs, or hedges, or stops in the water, even to a height beyond common belief. Gesner speaks of such places as are known to be above eight feet high above water. And our Camden mentions in his Britannia the like wonder to be in Pembrokeshire, where the river Tivy falls into the sea; and that the fall is so downright, and so high, that the people stand and wonder at the strength and sleight by which they see the Salmon use to get out of the sea into the said river: and the manner and height of the place is so notable, that it is known far by the name of the Salmon-Leap. Concerning which take this also out of Michael Drayton, my honest old friend, as he tells it you in his *Polyolbion*.

> And when the Salmon seeks a fresher stream to find,
> Which hither from the sea comes yearly by his kind;
> As he towards season grows, and stems the wat'ry tract
> Where Tivy, falling down, makes an high cataract,
> Forced by the rising rocks that there her course oppose,
> As though within her bounds they meant her to enclose,
> Here, when the laboring fish does at the foot arrive,
> And finds that by his strength he does but vainly strive;
> His tail takes in his mouth, and bending like a bow
> That's to full compass drawn, aloft himself doth throw,
> Then springing at his height, as doth a little wand,
> That, bended end to end, and started from man's hand,
> Far off itself doth cast; so does the Salmon vault:
> And if at first he fail, his second summersault
> He instantly essays; and, from his nimble ring
> Still yerking, never leaves until himself he fling
> Above the opposing stream.

Thus Michael Drayton tells you of this leap or summersault of the Salmon.

And, next I shall tell you, that it is observed by Gesner and others, that there is no better Salmon than in England; and that, though some of our northern counties have as fat and as large as the river Thames, yet none are of so excellent a taste.

And as I have told you that Sir Francis Bacon observes, the age of a Salmon exceeds not ten years, so let me next tell you, that his growth is very sudden: it is said, that, after he is got into the sea, he becomes, from a Samlet not so big as a Gudgeon, to be a Salmon, in as short a time as a gosling becomes to be a goose. Much of this has been observed, by tying a ribbon, or some known tape or thread, in the tail of some young Salmons, which have been taken in weirs as they have swimmed towards the salt water, and then, by taking a part of them again, with the known mark, at the same place, at their return from the sea, which is usually about six months after; and the like experiment hath been tried upon young swallows, who have, after six months' absence, been observed to return to the same chimney, there to make their nests and habitations for the summer following: which has inclined many to think, that every Salmon usually returns to the same river in which it was bred, as young pigeons taken out of the same dove-cote have also been observed to do.

And you are yet to observe further, that the he-Salmon is usually bigger than the Spawner; and that he is more kipper, and less able to endure a winter in the fresh water, than she is: yet she is, at that time of looking less kipper and better, as watery, and as bad meat.

And yet you are to observe that as there is no general rule without an exception, so there are some few rivers in this nation that have Trouts and Salmons in season in winter; as 'tis certain there be in the river Wye in Monmouthshire, where they be in season, as Camden observes, from September till April. But, my Scholar, the observation of this and many other things, I must in manners omit, because they will prove too large for our narrow compass of time; and therefore I shall next fall upon my direction how to fish for this Salmon.

And for that: first you shall observe that usually he stays not long in a place, as trouts will, but, as I said, covets still to go nearer the spring-head; and that he does not as the Trout, and many other fish, lie near the water-side, or banks, or roots of trees, but swims in the deep and broad parts of the water, and usually in the middle, and near the ground, and that there you are to fish for him; and that he is to be caught as the trout is, with a worm, a minnow, which some call a Penk, or with a fly.

And you are to observe, that he is very seldom observed to bite at a minnow, yet sometimes he will, and not usually at a fly, but more usually at a worm, and then most usually at a Lob or garden-worm, which should be well scoured, that is to say, keep seven or eight days in moss before you fish with them: and if you double your time of eight into sixteen, twenty, or more days, it is still the better; for the worms will still be clearer, tougher, and more lively, and continue so longer upon your hook. And they may be kept longer by keeping them cool and in fresh moss; and some advise to put camphire into it.

Note also, that many use to fish for a Salmon with a ring of wire on the top of their rod, through which the line may run to as great a length as is needful when he is hooked. And to that end, some use a wheel about the middle of their rod, or near their hand, which is to be observed better by seeing one of them, than by a large demonstration of words.

And now I shall tell you that which may be called a secret. I have been fishing with old Oliver Henley, now with God, a noted fisher both for Trout and Salmon, and have observed that he would usually take three or four worms out of his bag, and put them into a little box in his pocket, where he would usually let them continue half an hour or more before he would bait his hook with them; I have asked him his reason, and he has replied, "He did but pick the best out to be in readiness against he baited his hook the next time." But he has been observed, both by others and by myself, to catch more fish than I do or any other body that has ever gone a-fishing with him could do, and especially Salmons. And I have been told lately, by one of his most intimate and secret friends, that the box in which he put those worms was anointed with a drop, or two, or three, of the oil ot ivy-berries, made by expression or infusion; and told, that by the worms remaining in that box an hour, or like time, they had incorporated a kind of smell that was irresistibly attractive, enough to force any fish within the smell of them to bite. This I heard not long since from a friend, but have not tried it: yet I grant it probably, and refer my reader to Sir Francis Bacon's *Natural History,* where he proves fishes may hear, and doubtless, can more probably smell; and I am certain Gesner says the Otter can smell in the water, and I know not but that fish may do so too. 'Tis left for a lover of angling, or any that desires to improve that art, to try this conclusion.

I shall also impart two other experiments, but not tried by myself, which I will deliver in the same words that they were given me by an excellent angler and a very friend, in writing: he told me the latter was too good to be told, but in a learned language, lest it should be made common.

"Take the stinking oil drawn out of Polypody of the oak by a retort, mixed with turpentine and hive-honey, and annoint your bait therewith, and it will doubtless draw the fish to it."

The other is this: *"Vulnera Hererae grandissimae inflicta sudant Balsamun oleo gelato, albicantique persimile, odoris vero longe suavissimi."*

'Tis supremely sweet to any fish, and yet assafoetida may do the like.

But in these things I have no great faith, yet grant it probably; and have had from some chemical men, namely, from Sir George Hastings and others, an affirmation of them to be very advantageous: but no more of these, especially not in this place.

I might here, before I take my leave of the Salmon, tell you, that there is more than one sort of them, as namely, a Tecon, and another called in some places a Samlet, or by some, a Skegger: but these and others, which I forbear to name, may be fish of another kind, and differ, as we know a Herring and a pilcher do; which, I think, are as different as the rivers in which they breed, and must by me be left to the disquisitions of men of more leisure, and of greater abilities than I profess myself to have.

And lastly, I am to borrow so much of your promised patience, as to tell you that the Trout or Salmon, being in season, have at their first taking out of the water, which continues during life, their bodies adorned, the one with such red spots, and the other with such black or blackish spots, as give them such an addition of natural beauty as, I think, was never given to any woman by the artificial paint or patches in which they so much pride themselves in this age. And so I shall leave them both, and proceed to some observations on the pike. . . .

O Sir, doubt not but that Angling is an art; is it not an art to deceive a Trout with an artificial fly?

VENATOR. And now, good Master, proceed to your promised direction for making and ordering my artificial fly.

PISCATOR. My honest Scholar, I will do it, for it is a debt due unto you by my promise. And because you shall not think yourself more engaged to me than indeed you really are, I will freely give you such directions as were lately given to me by an ingenious Brother of the Angle, an honest man, and a most excellent fly-fisher.

You are to note, that there are twelve kinds of artificial-made Flies to angle with upon the top of the water. Note by the way, that the fittest season of using these is a blustering, a windy day, when the waters are so troubled that the natural fly cannot be seen, or rest upon them. The first is the Dun-fly, in March; the body is made of dun wool, the wings of the partridge's feathers. The second is another Dun-fly; the body of black wool, and the wings made of the black drake's feathers, and of the feathers under his tail. The third is the stone-fly in April, the body is made of black wool made yellow under the wings and under the tail, and so made with wings of the drake. The fourth is the Ruddy-fly, in the beginning of May; the feathers are the wings of the drake; with the feathers of a red capon also, which hang dangling on his sides next to the tail. The fifth is the yellow or greenish fly, in May likewise, the body made of yellow wool, and the wings made of the red cock's hackle or tail. The sixth is the Black-fly, in May also; the body made of black wool, and lapped about with the herle of a peacock's tail; the wings are made of the wings of a brown capon with his blue feathers in his head. The seventh is the Sad-yellow-fly in June; the body is made of black wool, with a yellow list on either side, and the wings taken off the wings of a buzzard, bound with black braked hemp. The eighth is the Moorish-fly; made with the body of duskish wool, and the wings made of the blackish mail of the drake. The ninth is the Tawny-fly, good until the middle of June; the body made of tawny wool, the wings made contrary one against the other, made of the whitish mail of the wild-drake. The tenth is the Wasp-fly, in July; the body made of black-wool, lapped about with yellow silk; the wings made of the feathers of the drake, or of the buzzard. The eleventh is the Shell-fly, good in mid-July; the body made of greenish wool, lapped about with the herle of a peacock's tail, and the wings made of the wings of the buzzard. The twelfth is the dark Drake-fly, good in August, the body made with black wool, lapped about with black silk, his wings made with the mail of the black-drake, with a black head. Thus have you a jury of the flies likely to betray and condemn all the Trouts in the river.

I shall next give you some other directions for fly-fishing, such as are given by Mr. Thomas Barker, a gentleman that hath spent much time in fishing; but I shall do it with a little variation.

First, let your rod be light, and very gentle: I take the best to be of two pieces. And let not your line exceed, especially for three or four links next to the hook—I say, not exceed three or four hairs at the most, though you may fish a little stronger above in the upper part of your line; but if you can attain to angle with one hair, you shall have more rises and catch more fish. Now you must be sure not to cumber yourself with too long a line, as most do. And before you begin to angle, cast to have the wind on your back, and the sun, if it shines, to be before you, and to fish down the stream; and carry the point or top of your rod downward, by which means the shadow of yourself, and rod too, will be the least offensive to the fish; for the sight of any shade amazes the fish, and spoils your sport, of which you must take a great care.

The Thames
at Halliford

J. P. WHEELDON

The English angler without "contacts" is rather restricted in both the extent and the variety of his fishing, but this situation was far more restrictive a hundred years ago than it is today. This may account for the popularity of J. P. Wheeldon's Angling Resorts near London *and similar pocket-size volumes that were available for one shilling and sixpence. Wheeldon, like many angling columnists of today, not only told his readers where the fishing was good and when, but how to get there and the best place to stay.*

ABOUT AUGUST, 1877, I had a capital day at Halliford Point with one of the Rosewells, an excellent fellow in every way as an attendant. Dull, cloudy weather and a sou'west wind set me again thinking as to the probabilities of another big day with the bream, so I determined upon trying them, and one morning found me en route for Waterloo. A hansom soon rattled me down to Friar Street, Blackfriars, a region wherein bone-crushing establishments and knackers' yards preponderate, reeking with smells, the very antipodes of Rimmel's establishment; but an excellent place wherefrom to lay up a store of "carrion" gentles, without which it is, perhaps, not wise to visit Halliford. I secured a capital lot of them, and as many liver gentles, fat, yellow fellows, for threepence as I should have obtained from any of the tackle shops for a shilling. With these, and a rare bag of scoured lobs, I felt pretty well fortified, and soon left the anything but ambrosial gales wafted down Friar Street behind, and found myself nicely in time for a glass of beer at the station, and the 2:35 for Shepperton.

Halliford is a quiet, sleepy little place, lying between Walton and Shepperton, and at present boasts of no nearer railway station than that at the latter place. On arriving at Shepperton, a broad country road, flanked on either side by tall hedges and pretty little cottage nooks, is seen in one's front, and some hundred yards from the station it sweeps round to the left, and the visitor, following the left hand round the road, will find that it leads him direct to the river, and to Stone's famous riverside hostelry. In front is Halliford Point, and some splendid deeps, where the plummet finds twelve, sixteen, and twenty feet of water. Here, in the autumn months, shoals of very heavy bream revel in the cool solitude; plenty of large barbel, and roach and dace are found in likely places to seek for such fish, together with jack, chub and perch. To the left hand the river sweeps round the point with a rapid stream, and widens out to a charming and expansive pool. I should fancy that in the winter time good jack and perch fishing might be had all round the bends of this part of the river, particularly round the stone walls that bound the gardens of the villas to the left of the stream, and paternostering round the old wooden piles and steps of the waterway to the gardens of some of the houses would, I am sure, be productive of many a good haul of ruddy-finned perch. Following the stream as it flows, the angler could not miss marking many glorious spots for the exercise of his craft, while the scenery is simply charming. An ait is passed, where the willows hang over the stream; all down the side of this little island is splendid chub water, and I marked many good fish rising at the insects dropping from the boughs as I went toward Walton the other day. Immediately opposite the tall chimney shaft seen to the right are the famous "Cowey Deeps," formerly a rare pitch for barbel, but now tenanted more, I think, by bream and roach. More sweetly pretty river scenery it would be hard to find than that up the whole of this reach to Walton Bridge, and if the angler can get the bream "on" at Cowey, there are some fish there that will try his skill and tackle, good as the latter may be.

Just opposite Stone's hotel there is a little island with some fine willows, and an ait with a thick growth of withies lies to the right. Between this island and the ait the punts lie moored, and upon my arrival I strolled down to the riverside to pump for information. First of all I wanted some tea and a bed for the night. The hotels were full, seemingly, and a man to whom I applied, and who was mopping out a punt, directed me to a Mrs. Searle, a private resident, who lives next door to Stone's. There I found beautifully clean accommodation, with every comfort that an angler could wish for. Then back again to my puntsman, whom I at the time didn't know, but who turned out to be yclept Alfred Trodd; and of a surety the fates were kind, for a better fisherman or more persevering man never handled a ryepeck.

"How are the bream feeding?" was my first interrogation on rejoining the man.

"Well, sir, I can't justly say as they're feeding well yet; we've done nothing to speak on, but two gents as was with me the other day got a few, small fish though mostly, but then they pricked and lost a goodish lot."

"Hum!" thought I, and pondered over this recital—and, "Yes, and where did you get them?"

"Why, it's up at the Chalk Hole they lies now, mostly, I think. The water's a bit too heavy just here," he added, indicating the deeps in front of us.

"Well, and how far up is the Chalk Hole?" I queried.

"Oh, maybe its better'n a mile, perhaps not so much."

Had he got anything to do? No, he hadn't. Well, then, "Get the punt ready and I'll be ready for you in ten minutes."

Then to the Lion for some beer, and soon after I am rocking on the bosom of the dear old Thames, while my puntsman with powerful stroke propels the flat-bottomed boat up stream. Keeping close in to the shore, so as to avoid the full strength of the current, many a goodly chub shoots out from the overhanging willows, and makes for deep water or sheltering weeds; and presently we pass Mr. Lindsay's handsome residence, with the lawn sloping down to the water's edge, and smooth and close-shaven. Many good "shops," as the fisherman terms his swim, are passed on the way up, and notably on the margin of the first meadow after passing "the point" above the entrance to the backwater, and many places look "perchy" in the extreme, but in summer it would be useless to attempt fishing from the bank, for the weeds are thick and dense, and mortally tough. Here, however, the punt swings round with the current, and I gather that we have reached "Chalk Hole," and begin to look about me.

So it proves, and presently, after dropping down the stream for a few yards, the ryepeck is plunged in, and the harsh grating noise proves, as it works its way into the river bed, that we are on a gravel bottom, and then as soon as the punt is fixed I unpack the tackle, while my attendant makes up some clay balls lined with lobs, throws in some handfuls of loose worms as high up the stream as he can, and behind the punt, where the stream will bring them down and suck them under us. "Chalk Hole" has a wonderfully level bed, and Trodd knows every inch of it, I am convinced; he suggested to me that if I plumbed, and allowed a foot from the depth close to the punt, I should get the extreme depth of the swim, no matter how far I traveled; and this I found out afterward was very nearly right. The plummet bumps on the gravel and registers twelve feet, while the current here is slow and steady. Just the place for big bream.

"Well, here's my first swim," thought I, and the float, after performing some curious gyrations in the eddies close to the punt, now rights itself and travels steadily down, the hook baited with the tail end of a lob. I used a long Nottingham float, shotted down to an inch from the surface, and carrying a fair quantity of lead, and it dips down every now and then as the extra bit on the bottom catches in a stone or other obstruction, very fine running tackle, drawn gut bottom and hook link, the water being very bright, and half expected every moment to see my float glide out of sight with that slow, uncertain movement so indicative of a heavy bream. No such luck, however; swim after swim succeeded with no result, and it was scarcely to be wondered at. It was a glorious evening, and delightfully cool after a hot, close day, and boats, those delights of the angler's heart (?), simply swarmed. Look which way one would there were boats, boats everywhere; presently the horrid shrill scream from the whistle of a steam launch sounded jarringly on the serenity of the evening stillness, and directly afterward the boat, loaded with its careless freight, and spite of my puntsman's warning shout to "ease up," rushed by at full speed, almost washing us adrift, its occupants seemingly delighted at our annoyance. What would Walton have said, could he have but seen the river in his day as it exists in ours? He would hardly have called angling now the "contemplative man's recreation."

"It's not an atom of use, Alfred," I ejaculated. "I'm afraid we must give it up. Pull the poles up, and drift in to the side amongst the willows, and then when some of these gentlemen have cleared away, we'll bait the hole for the morning."

"All right, sir," and two minutes afterward the punt was pushed into the side, and there we sat smoking, for an hour, until the gloaming deepened on the river reaches, and the evening mist settled over the flowery meadows. I say "we" sat smoking; I should rather have used the personal pronoun, for, wonder of wonders, my puntman didn't smoke, and was contented to sit quietly chatting until we got a clear stage for baiting the hole. This we did shortly afterward thoroughly, and then dropped down with the stream for home. Soon Halliford lights gleam bright through the rapidly increasing gloom, then the punt grates on the gravelly shallows and next moment is fast at the landing place.

Collecting my traps, I was soon on shore, and presently my man and I wended our way up to the Lion for a drop of "whisky warm," for the evening air was quite chilly.

"Lemon, Alfred?"

"If you please, sir."

"And now," I said, "I want to be off early in the morning. What time will you be ready?"

"Your time's mine, sir."

"Very well, then, say four sharp; it will be light then; and now, good night. I shall turn in at once."

It was pitch-dark when I awoke in the morning, and I lighted my candle, looked at my watch, and was out of bed like a rocket, when I found it was three-forty, and after a good wash crept down the creaking stairs, candle in one hand and rods in the other, quietly opened the side door, then blew my candle out and stepped into the garden, where the mignonette smelled deliciously. I could not see the river for fog, and couldn't see Trodd either until I got down to the punts.

There he was, however, sitting like a ghostly fisherman in the white mist, and with everything in apple-pie order.

"Good morning, Alfred. What do you think of it?"

"Why, I thinks we shall get some very good fish, sir," he replied, as he pushed the punt off, while I fitted up Gregory's little spinner, on the off chance of getting an early-rising perch or two.

"Glad to hear it," I said, as I cast the spinner out, and the top joint bent down as soon as the revolving bait caught the stream; then I had a pull at the whisky flask, and lit my pipe, to keep the river fog out while the punt forged ahead. No boats now, thank goodness. All around was quiet and silent as the grave, while the fog wreaths grew less dense as the light advanced.

"Quack, quack quack," sounded out like a clarion on the still morning air, and I just caught sight of three wild ducks that rose from the sedge, and then a tug at the spinner as we rounded the bend woke me up thoroughly, and soon a handsome perch, a pounder, was over the side and in the well, five minutes afterward I got another, and then a baby jack, which I carefully put back again, seemingly none the worse for the triangle through his nose.

"Well, here's Chalk Hole," thought I, as the well-remembered willow clumps hove in sight, and then the punt rounds, and is soon fixed, while I fit up a leger, baiting the hook with a bright lobworm. I had not been in a moment before the top bent, and then came a "tug" that meant business. The next instant I struck, to find myself fast in a "big-un' " of some sort, and he made my little rod bend with a vengeance as he sailed first one way, then another, then bored hard on the bottom, and then steamed away downstream with full pressure on, which I couldn't check too rudely, for the gut was fine, and had had but little time to soak. A good point I noticed at once about my puntman was that he never bothered me with needless advice. Some of them, the moment a decent fish is hooked, tease one to death with recommendations: "Keep your rod up, sir," "Mind the pole, sir," and so on, until it makes a nervous angler still more anxious and sickens even a good one. Another vicious dig for the bottom on the part of my fish, and then he yielded to the strain of the rod, and a great bream rolled his golden sides twelve yards away from the punt. Down he goes again, and I cannot help thinking of the description given of the bream by some writers, "a coward, and soon killed." Try them, that's all, with very fine tackle and in deep water, and one like the fellow I was playing will cause an alteration of opinion, I think. "Now, Alfred, he'll come," said I, as my friend showed himself once more, and with many a roll and pull at my wrist the big fellow nears the punt.

"Bravo! he's a beauty," and a beauty he was. Cleverly netted, as golden as a guinea, and shining in the morning light. He scaled fully four and a half pounds if an ounce, and rely upon it we "wetted both eyes" over him for good luck. I wanted to get the Nottingham tackle fitted up, so after my man had thrown in a couple of handfuls of lobs I gave him the leger rod, while I set to work. Almost directly, he hooked a fish, then gave me the rod to play him, while he ran the running line of my Nottingham rod through the rings. This fish was nothing like the first, and I made short work of him, then rebaited and put the rod down. I soon had the float tackle in working order, and got the right depth to an inch, and, baiting the hook with the tail end of a worm, began my first swim. The float traveled steadily down, the line being clear off the water. The rod point gradually raised, so as to keep the line as taut as possible. The float dips down, then recovers itself.

"Was it a bite?" No, something catching on the bottom. Another dip, a slight rise, and then the long quill slides slowly down out of sight. No mistake this time, and I strike, to be greeted with that delightful twang from the strained silk that at once tells the fisherman he's "home." This fellow fought gamely and well; and, considering that I had drawn gut only to play him with, that he had out twenty yards of line when he was first hooked, I could not take any liberties with him, and had to handle him very tenderly. He made a furious rush, and rattled the silk off the reel, as he did half a dozen times at least before he was netted. Thus the morning sped on, and I took fish as fast as I well could, up till eight o'clock; and many of them rare good ones. Then, to my utter disgust, a party of "gentlemen" who had been "camping out," and whom we had passed while they were snoring under canvas as we came down, quietly and deliberately pushed a punt across our swim, into the willows not six yards from where ours lay, and eight of them, undressing, plunged into the very pool wherein we were taking fish.

I knew it was useless to argue with them, and mere waste of time to make any comment upon their behavior, particularly to men who were so ignorant of common courtesy as these evidently were.

I consequently held my tongue, and told my attendant to put me on shore in order to get home to breakfast. Nothing would induce Alfred to leave his swim.

"No, sir," said he, "we haven't done with this yet; and we'll get a very fine show of fish before the day's out. I daresay you'll be good enough to tell my pardner, an' he'll see to my breakfast."

"Very well, I will," and then, as I expected a friend down by the first train, I pushed on up the towing path for home. I was just clearing up the last egg when my hostess ushered in my friend, and "Halloa, Uncle," I exclaimed, "come along; there's some tea left and an egg or two."

Breakfast, however, my friend declined, and was anxious to get on the water, so, obtaining a boat we rowed up the stream, bound again for Chalk Hole. My friend eagerly listened to my recital of the morning's sport, and when we got up to the punt, and he peeped into the well, his blue eyes danced with excitement as he saw the great golden-scaled fish rolling about, and floundering in the too shallow water.

He soon had a rod fitted up with Nottingham tackle, managed it excellently, and before his float had traveled down the reach many times he was fast in a good fish.

"Bravo," I exclaimed, as my friend, holding a big bream deliberately, yet firmly, turned him from midstream, where he seemed bent on going, and then kept him well under the springing rod, until, fairly tired out, he yielded to a gentle pull and, after an unwieldy plash or two, was netted. A bottle of Bass paid tribute to my friend's fish, and the foaming beer creamed up over our glasses, as we drank "Success to angling."

Then to it again, fishing, I mean, and "Uncle" got another and yet another, while I sat idle and couldn't get a fish. At two o'clock a boat was sent with our hot dinner. We landed, and under the shade of the pollards discussed an excellent steak-and-kidney pie, provided by the good old soul at our domicile, and stout ale from the Lion.

Then, spreading the mackintoshes on the grass, we lay on our backs and smoked, watching the hundreds of swallows hawking about in the clear, fresh atmosphere, and two jollier mortals lived not that day. After a final pipe, and a toothful of "the cratur" to keep the sun out of our eyes, we adjourned to the punt and the afternoon's fishing.

Considering that shoals of boats swarmed on the river we did wonders, at the end of the day had a splendid lot of fish, and thoroughly satisfied with the day, the fishing, and, more particularly with the excellence of our attendant, we left off at six, and caught the seven o'clock from Shepperton to Waterloo.

Chet McAusland
of Fraternity

BEN AMES WILLIAMS

*Ben Ames Williams varies the locale of his tales
from the piney woods of Maine to the jack pine of
the Deep South, but his great love of nature creeps
into all of them. His Maine stories, most of which
are laid in the little village of Fraternity, are treasured by many sportsmen even when, as in this
case, they are only incidentally about fishing.*

I DROVE down the hill from Hardscrabble Farm alone, for Chet
could not come with me. Yet my rod was in the car, and my fish
basket; and in a tin pail on the floor were worms fresh dug from
the rich soil under the sink spout. Save that Chet was not here beside
me, all was as it had been so many times before.

I drove down the hill through the village, past Will Bissell's store, where Chet and I had used to come in the evening for the mail; I crossed the bridge and reached the fork in the road. To the right was the way to the pond where Chet had liked to go when perch were biting, but I took the left-hand road toward North Fraternity.

And suddenly there lay on my left a thicket of alder and young birch and hemlock, and my memory stirred. Fifteen years ago, I came here one day with Chet and another, and what was now all a thicket was then open pasture save for some alders in the wet hole. The eager dogs went coursing through the cover and came to point; and a be- wilderingly large, loosely feathered brown bird flew over my head, visible for an instant through an opening among the alders. My gun exploded almost of its own accord—my heart was pounding so—and Chet cried robustly:

"Dead bird, Ben! . . . Fetch, Frenchy! . . . Give it to Ben, Frenchy, give it to Ben!" And when the bird lay in my palm, he came to say triumphantly: "Now, thar's your woodcock!"

It was my first. Since then I had killed others, with him beside me, quick with approval when the bird fell. But he would gun these covers with me no more.

I drove on, somewhat hurriedly, instinctively wishing to put mem- ory behind; but beyond the woodcock cover I came upon another scene. Here, one October day, Chet and I discovered three moose: a cow in the young birches on the left of the road, two yearlings in the pasture on the right. I alighted that day, and the yearlings posed obligingly for a moving-picture reel, while Chet restrained, in the car, the eager dogs.

But I did not linger here today; rather I pushed on, with my eyes upon the road before me, as though by thus looking straight ahead I might shut out the nodding, beckoning memories.

At the Ranch I swung into the narrow road through the swamp toward North Fraternity, where, when we drove home from the brooks at first dark, Chet always reminded me that a moose might dispute the way. But the road today was deserted and I emerged and passed the boggy pond at the lower end of the meadow and crossed the Bartlett stream. Chet one day took two good trout just below this same bridge. Every spot hereabouts had some association; for he and I had driven this way so many times together.

But now I drove alone.

I passed through North Fraternity and turned up the hill, and along the ridge, and so down toward Ring's. Where the old dance hall once had stood, I swung aside, along a dusty road and then into wheel tracks that were not even by courtesy a road. When the ruts cast the last pretense of decency aside, I left the car and went on afoot. My rod was in my hand, my basket on my hip, a bait can at my belt.

And so, alone, I came down to Ruffingham, where two brooks meet, and trout forgather, and where with Chet I had come so many and many a time. I had never come here alone before.

On the last knoll I stayed a moment to look out across the meadow spread before me, its green and level monotony spiced with tall elms and girded by dark woods. This was a prospect kind and pleasing to the eye; yet my eyes just now were blurred, and I shook my head and went on along the fisherman's trail, and toward the stream.

I came almost at once to the first brook, winding in wide loops through the tall young grass; and I paused to look into the deep water in the bend, and saw trout dart out of sight in their stronghold under the roots. I might have tempted them out again, but I went on, indolently, without pausing to fish. The sun was still high. They would be more eager, and so more vulnerable, in another hour; and in any case, there was no zeal in me.

Yet though I did not fish, I still followed the meanderings of the stream for half a mile or so; and then I paused, suddenly, like one who has but just remembered something forgotten, left behind.

That which thus brought me to a pause was no more than an old pile of boards, of uneven widths and thicknesses, laid up in an orderly arrangement with strips of smaller stuff between the courses to permit free passage of air and thus prevent decay. But these boards had by their aspect been here a long time, for they were weathered to an even gray.

In fact, my own memory of this particular pile ran back through a dozen years or so. The pile of boards stood on a low knoll near the upper end of the meadow, ten yards aside from the brook; and two old apple trees grew close by, and a clump of birch shoots sheltered the spot from the wind. Chet and I had in these years that were gone used the place as a landmark and a rendezvous.

"That pool in the first bend above the pile of boards," he used to say. Or: "I'll meet you at the pile of boards at dark."

So, when just now I saw the old heap of weathered lumber, I paused, almost expecting Chet to rise up from a seat under the apple trees, puffing his short pipe, to greet me.

"Well, Ben, how'd you make it? Do anything?"

But of course he did not thus appear. Yet the illusion was so strong —and so welcome—that I turned aside to stay a while, as though, if I waited, Chet might again, as he had so many times before, rejoin me there.

Down the long sweep of meadow, the tall elms, each a little apart from her sisters, lifted graceful crowns against the sky. Beside me in its deep-cut bed the brook slipped silently among the screening alders. The sun was sliding down the western sky, and lengthening shadows cast by the solitary elms reached out across the meadow like skirmishers to search the land. Behind them, in a little while, night would follow to make the world her own.

Once while I sat there I thought I saw Chet's small, stanch figure far downbrook, but it was only an old gray stump, or perhaps an alder stirring in the wind.

Memories will betray a man and take the strength from him; yet I remembered now so many old occasions. Chet and I sat together, upon a certain day, on this same pile of boards. It was high noon, the sun directly overhead, the trout indifferent; and we had come here to fill our pipes and wait the pleasure of the fishes. There was an old cellar hole—now not much more than a dimple in the ground—here close behind us, and I spoke of it, and Chet said:

"It was here the same as it is now, the first time ever I fished the meadow brooks. All growed up and tumbled in."

I asked who had lived here, and Chet did not know; and I said there were many such traces of a dead civilization on this countryside.

"I never see an old cellar hole," I suggested, "without wondering about the folks who built the house and cleared the land."

Chet was a moment silent, puffing at his pipe. He nodded then.

"That's so," he agreed, and he said reflectively: "I mind once when I was a boy in Frankfort. I was maybe eight or nine years old. That's sixty-odd years ago. A man come back to Frankfort on a visit. He'd lived around there when he was a boy, and fished the brooks there, and he wanted to go fishing again.

"So father and I took him; and when we come to the brook, we fixed to meet at noon, and father went by himself. But I stayed with this man to show him the holes, because the brook had changed since his time.

"And along toward noon—we'd done pretty good—we come to where we'd meet father. There was an old house there that was falling down. The barn was gone, nothing left of it, only a heap of lumber on the ground; and the back end of the house was sagging, and the windows boarded up.

"We set down there to wait for father; but this man, he kept looking at the old house. I guess he was well off, by the clothes he wore. He looked at the house, and we set there waiting, and he didn't talk.

"So by and by I see that he was crying!"

His words were simple and direct enough, yet they conveyed somehow a sense of keen and poignant sorrow. He went on:

"Tears rolling down his cheeks. It kind of scared me, to see a man cry. But he see me watching him, and he says: 'It's all right, boy! Don't mind me!'

"And I asked him if he was sick.

"So he said: 'No. The thing is, I was born in that old house there. In the front room. It was Mother and Father's room. And I grew up in that house, and I was married in it. Because the girl I married, her pa's house had got struck by lightning and burned down.' And he waited a minute, kind of swallowing hard, and he went on: 'And they're all dead now. Mother, and Father, and my wife, and the only baby we had. And I'm seventy-one years old!' "

Chet was silent for a moment, as though he were sobered by this thought as memories will sober a man. Then he said slowly: "I remember, when he said that, I thought he was awful old! Seventy-one. He died about five years after." And he added, with a chuckle at this good jest upon himself: "I thought he was as old as Methuselah; but I'm seventy-one my own self, now!"

And when he turned to the brook presently, I thought that, as though the memory of this incident had reminded him that his own remaining time was short, Chet fished with even more than his accustomed keen and tireless zest that day.

Last night at Hardscrabble, with the bright lamp sputtering at my elbow, I had leafed through a book of accounts which Chet kept long ago. The entries were haphazard and promiscuous, in their very disorder curiously like the man himself. He recorded hours of labor, at twenty-five cents the hour, hauling rock, harrowing, haying, plowing. He set down cash received in the winter of 1889 and 1890. Butter, during the fall of 1889, fetched a total of $6.60, at twenty cents the pound. Also, he picked some cranberries; he sold the labor of himself and oxen. Total cash receipts for the five winter months here recorded were $19.92.

There followed a schedule of small debts, a dollar here, two dollars there, each one marked paid; and I found a record of how he settled the estate of Mrs. Mac's mother. Bills paid amounted to $168.50. I wondered where he got the money for those payments.

"Mary and I had to wait seven years before we could marry," Chet himself had told me more than once. "I had my folks to take care of, and she had hers, and when they died there was debts to pay."

I read slowly, and the lamp was warm beside me, and now and then some entry brought to my mind a quick, vivid picture of the man. "July 31—helped A B put in two loads of hay." Chet had held, I remembered, the reputation of being the best man in town to stow a load of hay on the rack. I had seen him, erect and vigorous, receiving each forkful as it came up to him, placing, spreading, packing it down. And I remembered how someone once told me: "Chet's a clever hand to work when he's a mind to!"

Then suddenly, on a fresh page, two accounts of a different sort.

Game shot over dog Spot, Oct 1905, by C L Mc

Plaisted Cover	W	2	....	Par	1
Lawry	"	" 1	....	"	
Heal	"	" 2	....	"	
Ledge	"	" 2	....	"	
Dummy	"	" 1	....	"	
Knights	"	" 2	....	"	
Bean	"	" 1	....	"	
River	"		....	"	2
Alder Run	"		....	"	1
		11			4

SEASON OF 1906—GAME SHOT OVER MACK

Heal Cover	......	Woodcock 10	......	Partridge	0
Plaisted "	......	1	......		0
Ledges	......	1	......	missed	2
Dummy	......	2	......		0
Bean	......	1	......		1
O Fuller	......	0	......		3
River	......	1	......		1
Alder Run	......	0	......		1
W Burgess	......	2	......		0
		18			

That word "missed," written very small, brought a train of pictures of its own. So often, especially in these slower later years, I had heard Chet say:

"I had an easy shot, but I had my safety on."

Chet had always a certain talent with the pencil. I found evidences of it here. A sketch of a dog asleep, and written below: "Mack under the stove." The stove itself appeared as a chaos of stove legs, doors and lids, with a teakettle atop, the whole suspended above the sleeping dog so that not one line of the stove crossed or marred any part of Mack's portrait. Chet's interest was not in stoves, but in dogs.

There were other sketches. Two of them, one in profile and the other in full face, showed a large, fat, mustached man with his head elaborately bandaged. There must have been a story here, but Chet had never told it to me. I could not even guess who the man was, and how he came by his injuries. His portraits were superimposed upon a daily record of "eggs from about 70 hens" for the month of March, 1906, 705 eggs in all.

I found a double page of records of amounts owed by the town to individuals who had collected nests of the brown-tail moth. Twenty-three persons collected 143 nests, and Chet, who had apparently acted as agent of the town in the matter, attested the amount due each one, at five cents a nest. And one item read:

A B delivered 63 specimens of caterpillar nests, but only two were browntail nests. . . . 2. . . . . 10.

Chet had once told me of the enemy he made by that refusal to attest more than two of these nests as genuine; a story to be retold at some apt time.

I found the inventory and appraisal of a farm unnamed—perhaps Hardscrabble itself—and a record of $261.25 received in the fall of 1917 for apples.

Here, too, were pages of accounts of his work as a maker of tombstones. The old granite-cutting shed in the orchard was falling into ruin now.

Thus, out of the disorderly pages of the old ledger, there emerged, curiously vivid, a complete and perfect portrait of the man. My thoughts returned to it for a time today, while I stayed here beside the pile of boards, at the head of the meadow, waiting till the good dusk fishing should begin.

This was May and the world was in the spring of youth eternally renewed; the world was full of the stir of life, rich with beginnings. And yet I thought that just now, for me, the world was deeply empty, too; with an emptiness not easily to be repaired.

Yet not easily to be supported, either, and my throat was bitter with grief that he was gone. Then it occurred to me that Chet himself, since Mrs. Mac died, must have been lonely as I was lonely now. I remembered Mrs. Mac as I last saw her. She sat in the low rocking chair that had belonged to her mother, by the window in the dining room. Her dress was white; her small, knitted overvest stretched about her plump shoulders to fend off the October chill. Her cheeks were bright, and her eyes were twinkling; yet they were shining, too, that day.

I was about departing after a week of gunning. Mrs. Mac had been of late not so well, but her spirit was undimmed. I kissed her goodbye and said:

"And I'll see you in the spring, when the trout are biting."

She smiled and nodded. "I'll be better then," she agreed. "So's I can cook those trout for you."

But as I drove away, I knew, and I knew that she had known, that this was our goodbye.

I had thought much of Mrs. Mac during these few days that just now were gone. Mary Thurman she had been, and Chet courted her for seven years. He lived at that time a bachelor's existence on the farm, and she dwelt in the village down the hill, with old folks dependent on her whom, even for his sake, she could not leave, since theirs was the greater need. Chet lived alone save for his cows, and certain cats, and a dog. This dog was that great Job, Old Tantrybogus, whose fame still lingers in the land, whose deeds have been related heretofore. But Old Tantrybogus grew old in fact as well as name, and came to his happy end, and Chet's house on the hill was empty when he was gone.

It was when Job was gone that Mary Thurman came to him, to say: "Well, Chet, I guess you need me more than the old folks, now."

Memories are patchwork, put together haphazard and without pattern. The mind picks them out of the past as a monkey picks bits of shining glass out of a tray of dull and lifeless objects. Thus now the years were all one to me. From an incident of a dozen years ago, my thoughts might leap to a matter not twelve hours old.

Elder Rowley had said to me, on the morning of this very day:

"You know, I married Chet and Mrs. Mac. He gave me twenty dollars. It was the largest wedding fee I ever had, and I've been a minister near fifty years."

I knew as well as he just how large a fee this was for Chet to pay. The figure seemed to me deeply elequent of Chet's rapture on his wedding day.

He was past fifty at the time, Mary Thurman forty-nine. Call them old people, if you like; yet I had known them when they were older still, and they had worn no rust of age. They dwelt in a happy concord, curiously alike in their kindliness and generous trust of all the world, and alike in their scornful anger at every evil thing. I chuckled to remember so many matters which concerned them now.

Chet, like most men, was constitutionally unable to find his own belongings after Mrs. Mac had put them away—and this even though she bestowed them in the identical fit and proper places every time. When we were about to set out from the farm for a day's fishing or for hunting, he would always call:

"Mary, where's my pipe? . . . Mary, where's my shells? . . . Mary, where's my reel?"

And she would protest in an irritable tenderness: "Your reel's on the mantelshelf! I declare, Chet McAusland, you couldn't find a thing if it was near enough your nose to make you sneeze!"

I had sometimes thought Chet affected a blindness greater than the fact, for the pleasure it gave her to attend on him; I sometimes thought she did, in fact, conceal his pet belongings so that he must appeal to her.

And remembering how he had never been able to find his belongings while she was alive, I remembered another matter too. After Mrs. Mac was gone, Chet told me:

"Ever since she died, when I've been setting things straight around the house, I've kept finding things that she had put away. She'd always put them in places where she knew I'd find them, after she'd be gone. She knew she was going, fixed it so's it'd be easy for me; but she never said anything to me about it, never let on that she knew. That hurt me awful, Ben!"

But this was after she died. So long as she lived they were full happy together, and deeply so; yet lacking words to touch upon this matter openly. She chided him because he was always busy in the barn when he should have come to sit down to meals; she scolded him for tracking the barn into the house; she protested that her wood box was not filled, that her water tank was empty, that he went fishing when there was farming to be done, or gunning when there were apples to pick or roots to be dug. And he in his turn was forever complaining that she hid his dearest possessions so secretly away.

I had thought they never told their love; but a night or two ago, while I sought to put his possessions all in order, as he once had done for her, I had come upon a writing in his hand, in which her name appeared. The paper was one of those brown sheets in which parcels are sometimes wrapped. When Chet and I returned with full baskets from the brooks, he liked to lay our best fish upon such a sheet of brown paper and trace its silhouette. I have many such records.

He had used this sheet at some time for such a purpose. There were the outlines of half a dozen trout upon one side of it, with the penciled legend:

Caught in Ruffingham Meadow with Ben, between six and seven in the evening, June 3, 1929.

But on the reverse side Chet had written, in his laborious, small hand, with many interlineations and amendments here and there:

Suddenly just above me something gleamed and sparkled in the sunlight as it floated down the stream. When it reached the ripples just above me, it appeared to bow, and dip, whirl, careen and dance, and with every changing move, a gleam of light would flash from it.

A moment more, it moved in shadow, all its brilliancy had gone, and as I watched it in deeper water, as it slowly floated past, it was only a maple leaf that soon vanished around the bend. Then a thought occurred to me. How like human life is a floating leaf.

A few years ago, I am very sure the last time Mary and I ever walked down to the river. She always went there in early spring to gather blue violets and star flowers, and always insisted the best ones grew up near the spring. This day, she sat down on the ash stump, now fast going to decay, that the ship carpenters left just above the boat landing.

Even then, it tired her to walk, especially up-grade. She said,

"Chet I know there's blue violets near the spring. Can't you go and get some? I'll wait for you here."

As I walked along the path at the edge of the woods, I picked up an empty bait can the boys had left the summer before while fishing. And very near the place we once roasted chickens when Ben was here, I found a dense, rank growth of blue violets. I carefully inverted the can down over the thickest part, and cut, with my knife, deep into the black mold, close around the outer edge of the can. Then dug from the outside and took up the violets on a piece of earth that just filled the can.

How well I remember the pleased expression on her face, when she saw the can and its contents. And this is the compliment she gave me.

"Who but you, Chet, would have thought to do that?"

She set the can in the ground near the end of the walk and kept them in bloom for a long time. She'd look at them and say——

But the passage ended thus, unfinished; I was never to know what it was she used to say.

Chet wrote to me when she died:

"I never knew the meaning of life till she came to live at Hardscrabble Farm."

You no more need to summon memories than you need invite children to peer into the windows of an empty house. They come unbidden; forever alert to seize on opportunity. The sun was lower now, the shadows longer, the monitory breath of approaching night in the faintly stirring air. The level sun rays touched the meadow grasses; turned them from green to yellow, then to a warmer hue. Along the flank of the hill toward West Fraternity the crests of the trees were brushed with gold. The trunks of the tall elms were gray on their shadowed sides; they blushed beneath the bright glance of the sun. The southern sky was like a tinted shell, shading from rose at the horizon to deep and deeper blue.

Some fashion of snipe high above my head came tumbling down the ladder of the air with booming wings, and a black duck rose from the lower meadow and circled wide, quacking in an anxious fashion now and then. A great blue heron on slow-beating pinions drifted toward the pond, head tucked back upon its neck, like an alderman with a double chin, long legs trailing far behind. Something splashed in the silent brook. A frog, a muskrat, a trout. I was incurious. I had no appetite for fishing. I stayed here on the old pile of boards, and I thought how empty Chet's life had been when Mrs. Mac was gone; empty as in a fashion mine, too, had now become.

And I thought Chet was a valorous man. Death had for him no terrors at all. So many times during his long life he had bestowed it as a boon on helpless, suffering things. So he was not afraid of death. Rather, this death men fear had been of late the friend whose coming

he awaited. Yet he did wait full patiently, offering no least invitation
to this too dilatory friend. He might at any time have taken in his
loneliness the easy way. Instead, he dwelt courageously, and not day
by day, but with a steady eye upon tomorrow too.

There have been men not afraid to die, but Chet had not feared to
live, though living must have been for him a weary task and long.

When I could do so, after she died, I had come to him. There was
a store of talk in the man that needed spending; and it was all of Mrs.
Mac.

"She went the way her mother did," he said to me, as though this
would have pleased her. "I had been reading the paper to her till
she said she thought she could sleep a while. So I left the door open,
but I piled some magazines between her and the lamp to keep the
light out of her eyes. And she said to me:

"Chet, you go to bed yourself and get some sleep. What are we
going to do if anything happens to you?"

"And I told her I would, and she said: 'You take care of yourself.'

"And then, a minute after, I looked in at her and she was gone."

I remembered, as he spoke, that he had written me in these same
terms heretofore; and I remembered, too, how he began that letter
which announced her death who was his life.

"As for me, all is well with me!" Thus he began. The phrase was
alive with the dauntless spirit of the man.

It was October when she died; and for that long winter and for the
others that were to come, he had no companions in the house on the
hill save the dogs—first Mac and Buster, and then Hunter after Mac
was gone—and the cats which, at milking time, came trooping from
the shed. The house at Hardscrabble is small; the rooms are few, and
compact as corn kernels in a row. Yet I thought that unless some other
moved through these rooms beside you, they might well seem vast
and lonely spaces, when the snow lay deep outside. The small house
in which he dwelt alone must have been as lonely for him as this
meadow spread before my eyes was lonely now for me.

He was gone, but he had been here so many times in the years that
were done. A small, straight, sturdy, vigorous figure of a man, in
rubber boots to his knees, trousers always a little too large for him,
flannel shirt buttoned at the throat, and an old black coat and hat.
To watch him at his fishing was an inspiration. There was no one who
could approach the wary trout as easily as he. That ancient steel rod
of his could perform miracles denied to the most subtle bamboo. His
black silk line, the hook knotted directly on the line without benefit
of leader or snell, could present a dangling worm in most disarming
guise. The devices of the most skillful tackle maker he mistrusted and
despised. He used a small reel, once nickel-plated, all the color of old

brass now; and running line had cut deep grooves and channels in the frame of it, the soft silk by sheer persistence wearing a course across the brazen lip. His fish basket had been mended a dozen times a year for a dozen years; it was black with the blood of countless trout. And for every stream where he was used to fish, he knew in what pools the trout preferred to lie, and how best to approach them all unseen, and where to drop his line.

It was so terribly easy to imagine that I saw him now, far down the meadow, poised alertly by the stream side with rod extended at full arm's reach, his eye upon the loose and ready line. It was easy to imagine that I saw him; it was hard not to imagine so.

It was bitterly hard to remember that though I waited here by the old board pile for ever so long a time, yet he would not again come trudging up in those burdening boots of his.

Yet let my throat ache and my eyes sting as they would, the thing was pitilessly true. He would come this way no more.

I rose at last, submitting cravenly; I turned to go back to the waiting car. I would not fish here alone, with emptiness for only company.

Yet something once more made me pause, as I had paused when upon my first arrival I had come thus far. It was another memory which checked me; a word he one day said.

"If I just set and think," he confessed, "I miss her awful. But I don't set much. There's always bushes to cut, to give the blueberries a chance; and there's brush to burn. There's always the farming to do or the roots to dig. There's always the cow and the cats and dogs to feed. It keeps me busy enough, the most of the time, taking care of the farm. So all is well with me!"

Let one beloved depart, and let you keep the fine, full memory. He had kept hers so.

"I aim to go on just the same," he said. "Keep things the way she kept them, much as I can. I 'low she'd want it that way."

And I thought the healing routine of the days can thus wipe out the scars of grief, just as successive waves upon the beach smooth to a neat serenity and peace the sand disordered by careless children's play. I nodded at the thought, as though in assent to a spoken word from Chet himself.

And I seemed to hear his voice. "By George Harry, it's time the trout were taking. Time to try them now."

So I nicked a worm upon my hook as he had taught me, and turned toward the brook and let my bait drop in the deep pool in the exact spot Chet had showed me, years agone. The line moved off upstream; I struck, and lifted the fine fish clear.

A deep voice ran in my ears:

"Thar! That's as handsome a trout as ever I saw!"

So that I smiled and was near to laugh aloud; for all trout were handsome in Chet's eyes, regardless of length or other mathematical tests. I dropped the fish into my basket and returned to the brook again.

The fish at dusk today were ravenous! They came romping to my hook as puppies come boisterously to greet the returning master. It was almost as though they wished to reassure me; to promise that Chet would still come to keep with me here by the pile of boards our ancient rendezvous.

So when at early dark, with a heavy basket, I trudged back toward the car again, content was in me. I had had many such evenings here with the man himself, when the trout were biting. It had seemed to me a while ago that since he was gone such hours were lost to me forever. But I knew better now.

A thing gone, but well remembered, is not lost. Rather it becomes by a sort of compound interest more deeply to be treasured through the years.

The Redds

HENRY WILLIAMSON

Few angling writings have the moving simplicity
of Henry Williamson's Salar the Salmon. *The*
temptation to include the complete book was aug-
mented by the difficulty of selecting one representa-
tive portion of it. How many angling writers, hav-
ing turned the final page of this great book, must
have reflected, "I wish I could have written this."

IGH OVER the valley the last swallow was hurled in the wind
which streamed the leaves from the oaks and kept the tall
spruce of the hillsides swaying in slow weariness of gray
clouds of sky. By the river the bullock paths were pitted and sploshed
yellow, under alders dispread black and bare. Over the viaduct a
miniature train moved in silhouette, creeping across the sky, anti-

quated goods trucks on webbed wheels swept about by scattered stream.

From the top of the hill, reddish brown with larch and dark green with spruce plantations, came little reports flattened away by the wind, the first pheasant shoot of the year. Old Nog the heron was trying in vain to outfly the winds over the hill. Higher and higher they took him, turning and slanting and flapping without forward movement, scared by the reports of guns which he thought were all aimed at him. When a thousand feet high he gave up and swung round, and swept across the valley; but a report louder than the others, coming direct to him in a pocket of wind, made him tumble and turn and fly into the wind once more, determined to fish in future only in the wide safety of the estuary. Old Nog had made this resolution a hundred times before; he always forgot it when out of gunshot.

Within the river many salmon and sea trout were moving. The sluice at Steep Weir was gone; posts, doors, framework, weighing more than a ton, had been jostled to the sea, no more to the river in spate than a few twigs and leaves. Already barnacles were laying their eggs on the wood, beside the jelly sacks of river snails' eggs killed by the salt.

Every tide brought in more salmon, which reached Sawmills with their lice still alive, four days from the sea. The gravel of the river bed was stirred and shifted by a myriad changing weights of water pouring around and eddying from fish on the move. And by mid-November, when the river level was steady with fast water running clear as glass, the gravel was being cut up by the tails of female fish—from the Carrion Pit to the runners on the slopes of the moor, streamlets scarcely wider than the step of a boy, salmon were preparing to spawn.

Gralaks lay above the Fireplay Pool. The roe which had been growing within her all the summer was now one-fifth the weight of her body. She was full ripe, ready to drop her eggs. Three male fish, knowing this, were near her, waiting to shed their milt on the eggs. One of them was Salar.

Behind the three cock fish lay Garroo the cannibal trout. Behind Garroo lay two smaller trout who had tasted salmon eggs before. And lying close beside Gralaks was Grai, a salmon parr weighing two ounces, who had fallen in love with Gralaks with all the volume of his milt, which weighed one tenth of an ounce. Gralaks was aware of Grai; indeed she was pleased by his nearness. Grai knew the other fish were there because of Gralaks, but his feeling for her, especially when she lay and hid him, was stronger than his fear. Grai was determined that no other cock fish should lie beside Gralaks.

No other cock fish had yet noticed Grai.

At nightfall Gralaks moved slowly forward on the level shallows above the throat of the pool. At once Salar and his two rivals moved behind her. She turned on her right side and sinuated in an arrested swimming motion, lifting by suction a few stones, which fell back with the stream. Watched by Salar and the other cock fish, Gralaks settled into the slight furrow and thrust herself into it, to widen it.

During a pause in the digging Grai darted forward from beside Salar's left pectoral fin and took up his rightful place beside the mighty mistress of all sensation. The swift movement loosened a mistiness into the water behind the parr's tail.

The effect of this milt passing by the gills of the cock fish was one of action and turmoil. One turned and slipped over Salar, and with open mouth made as if to bite the salmon on the other side of Salar, who drove at him, also with open mouth. The three-sided chase rocked the water of the Fireplay.

All during the night, at intervals, Gralaks was digging the redd for spawning—sweeping the gravel sideways and scooping a pit in which she lay. Another hen fish was doing the same thing ten yards above her, and two more, each attended by one or more males, were working in the fast water between the tail of the Fireplay and a larger and deeper pool below. This was the Wheel Pool. It was wide and round. The stream entering it divided into two streams, one turning left-handed and continuing the main course of the river under overhanging oaks and past somber yews, the other turning to the right and running back under alders until it was slowed by meeting the main run again. Sticks borne on this flattened circle rode round and round sometimes for months, shut within the backwater.

A ridge of rock lay across the middle of the Wheel Pool, and under this rock, with other quiet fish, Trutta was lying. The quiet fish were salmon new from the sea, and unaffected by the movements of the red fish, which had come into the river months before. Their coats were still untarnished; they would not spawn until the end of January, when the redds of the spring fish which had spawned would be cut up again, and the eggs, dark-spotted with eyes, swept away.

The Wheel Pool was Trutta's pool. He had spawned in the run between the Wheel and the Fireplay seven times. On this his eighth visit from the sea, however, Trutta had not yet begun to share the general excitement. There was still a dark ring round his neck, although the black collar had gone. His kyp, which was immense, had grown sideways, and looked to Shiner, who at noon climbed one of the oaks to look down into the pool, like a reversed clay pipe held in the pug's jaws.

At night the stars were clear and large, frost-sharpened. Tufts of withering rushes and grasses and thistles were rimed with hoarfrost in the morning. Sunrise over the hill of fir plantations was a flush of pink and gold; a clear sky all day. Again night glowed with stars above a mist of frost settling on bracken and grass and branch. The water was colder, and fish did not move much.

Salar, lying behind Gralaks, saw the stars above him with the quietness of his other self. He became alert with the rumbling in the rock under him; and saw the water in front of him glow with fire, which gleamed on the back of Gralaks. High over the valley the train passed, puffing on the upgrade, dense steam hanging over its length, and the play of flames reflected from its engine cab.

For nearly a week the water ran colder, slower, clearer. On the first evening of December, the wind went round to the west, the water became warmer, and fish became active. Gralaks was now ready to lay her eggs. Nearly five thousand were in the cavity beside her shrunken stomach. Spawning began toward the end of the night. During the darkness Salar had been roving round the pools, swimming from Fireplay down the run into Wheel, questing under the ledge of rock and hollows under the bank of alders. But always he had returned in haste, to move behind the trough where Gralaks lay, beside one or another of his waiting rivals. Both pools were astir with restless fish.

At last the tail of Gralaks began to work more quickly, and immediately one of the cock fish moved up beside her and shouldered her from the pit she had dug. Grai the parr pressed himself beside a large flat yellow stone which had been exposed by the digging. So tiny was Grai that the cock fish did not even know he was there. Thrust off the redd, Gralaks swam forward her own length, and lay still, while Salar moved in beside the cock fish. Immediately this fish turned with a sweep of its porpoise-bitten tail and came at Salar with open mouth. Salar swung round to avoid the lunge and also to grip his rival across the wrist. The swirl lifted Grai to the trough again, to be behind the tail of Gralaks.

Heedless of the turmoil behind her, but thereby excited, Gralaks had turned on her right side, to bend head and body backward until her belly was curved palely like a water-sunk reflection of the young moon. She jerked and shook on her side, as though trying to touch the back of her neck with her tail. Eggs dribbled quickly from her, sinking with the current amidst gravel and sand and rolling into the trough.

The sight of the eggs and the taste of the water made Salar quiver; and as Gralaks moved backward, he moved forward, feeling as though he were being drawn from underneath by a lamprey of sweeter and sweeter sensation. His milt flowed from him in a mist, millions of invisible organisms wriggling in the water. Some of them found eggs, into the skins of which they bored, desperate for security. Those which were successful in finding the liquid within were lost in the creation of new life; the rest drifted away, to perish in water palely lighted by the star galaxy of night, whose mirrored fate was as their own.

For a few moments Salar lay in ecstasy on the redd, but his larger rival seized him by the tail and held him despite his violent lashings. Salar's head was downstream; the water was opening his gills, he could not breathe. The big fish swam upstream, to drown him. The water was beaten and the two bodies rolled over. The other fish which was attending Gralaks was a grilse of her own school, which she had led from the Island Race; and this fish, whose back was a marbled pattern of green and pink, followed the struggle and in his excitement bit the larger salmon across the tail. This made it lose hold of Salar, to dash downstream after the male grilse, to abandon the chase and to swing up again below the redd and lie there. Salar returned more slowly and lay behind it, and to one side. The grilse also returned, and the three fish lay there, at rest for the moment.

During the struggle and chase, Gralaks had laid again, and Grai had covered the eggs. He lay beside Gralaks, by her right pectoral fin which was wider than his own width. He was fatigued. Unknowingly he had given fertility to nine of the two hundred and thirty eggs which had trickled from Gralaks like a necklace of small amber beads strung on water.

After a rest, Grai moved away to the shelter of a stone. From the stone he moved to his lie under the bank, his spawning done for that year. Most of his milt had been lost six weeks before, when he had been caught on an artificial fly during the last day of the fishing season. The angler had held Grai in his hand, and the touch of un-wetted palm and fingers had been a scalding agony to the little fish writhing to escape. The fisherman had held the parr after he had worked the barb of the hook from the corner of Grai's mouth, to illustrate to his son, carrying the net, the difference in strength between a small trout and a parr of equal size and almost equal appearance. Holding Grai in his fist, he told the boy to observe the muscular strength. It was during that agony that Grai had shed most of his milt. It wetted the angler's hand, a chalk-white liquid, after the parr's release. That was in October; now it was three weeks before Christmas.

During the day following his first spawning, Grai rested himself; but the next night he was back again at the redd, lying behind the three great fish, of whom now he was wary and afraid. But when Garroo the cannibal trout moved up beside him, Grai left the Fire-play and went down to other redds below the Wheel Pool and the yew trees and waited behind a pair of sea trout spawning in fast water there. Grai was hungry. Scores of eggs he swallowed as they rolled down between the stones.

All the other parr and trout of the river were feeding on eggs, too. Biggest of the berry gatherers, as Shiner called them, was Garroo. Salar drove him many times from the redd of Gralaks. Shiner used to climb an alder beside the Fireplay, and in the clear water of sunlit noon he saw the fish there. Gralaks was almost hidden in the blur of the deeper water; behind her lay Salar, his red coat looking browny-purple under the water, then the larger and darker fish, with the bite out of its tail fin, and the smaller form of the male grilse. Behind the trio of square tails lay a big-headed black fish which was Garroo.

When the two larger cock fish turned inward to menace one another, Shiner knew the hen fish was about to lay again. While the two big salmon were chasing and counterchasing, the smaller fish moved up onto the redd; and at the same time Garroo thrust forward and turned on his side to suck the eggs into his mouth. Then the grilse would chase Garroo away, and move back to the redd. But Salar or the other cock fish, whichever returned first, drove the grilse off, and followed him downstream, while Garroo fled before the grilse. Shiner would see the wave of pursuit going round the bend.

A few moments later they would come back. The wan winter sunlight revealed every white and yellow and brown stone of the gravel over which Salar moved. Just behind him was the male grilse, and just behind the grilse was Garroo, his black jaw, scarred and misshapen, protruding as though with a leer at all such foolishness as spawning. Garroo's milt glands had long since shrunken in wicked old age.

A fortnight before Christmas the weather became cold again. The river was running low, many of its feeders on the moor being fringed with ice. The larger cock fish with the bitten tail could no longer get to the redd. Salar had to go past the stones and drift down to settle in the trough by the side of Gralaks. Even then, his back and tail fin were out of the water. While he was coming back tail first, the smaller grilse usually slithered over the heaped gravel and bit him across the wrist. Salar slashed the grilse away, and the movement scattered some of the eggs, which Garroo caught on the end of his kyp. Shiner, watching from the tree, heard a distinct snapping noise as each egg was sucked into the trout's mouth.

Another time, Shiner saw Salar chase Garroo round the pool, down the run into the Wheel Pool, and up again to the Fireplay, where the salmon caught the trout across the back and shook it, his head out of water. " 'Twas just like a terrier shaking an ould black rat," said Shiner.

As the days went on, Salar became heavy with weariness. Most of his milt was shed; in slow pulse after slow pulse his life's sweetness had been drawn from him, leaving with each emptiness a greater inflaming desire, which during the day lapped about the wasted body with dreams of an everlasting sea of rest; but when darkness came, and the water was ashine with stars, he felt himself running bright with the river, and sweetness returned to him on the redd beside Gralaks.

The time came when the last of the eggs were spawned and Gralaks was gone, dropping back to the Wheel Pool, where Trutta was lying.

Trutta was dark brown, and thin. He had fought to cover eggs of a clove-spotted sea trout, a handsome hen fish nearly as long as himself, but slimmer and younger, most pleasant to see and be near to; yet no milt had come from him. He had driven away all other sea trout; and had it not been for the little peal which were ever ready to shed their milt, none of the eggs of that female would have hatched ninety days later.

Trutta remained on guard, never sleeping, and no salmon, not even the forty-three-pounder who had arrived, a clean-run fish, in the last week of December, was allowed to approach his mate—as Trutta considered her. The hen fish laid her eggs, indifferent to the clashes about her; the nearness of the little peal, with their dark mother-of-pearl hues, gave her contentment.

When the last egg was gone from her, hidden under the stones of the redd, she drifted down the river and came to the shelter of the alder roots above Humpy Bridge.

She lay there, day after day, night after night, waiting for the rain and the spate which would take her down to the sea. Near her lay Gralaks. Kelt and graveling rested side by side, thin, discolored, empty of all feeling, patiently awaiting the rain.

End and Beginning

The colder the water, the greater its density. In the frosty nights of the year's end fish sank close to the rock and gravel of the pools, hardly moving. Those late-running salmon which had paired, and had not yet spawned, lay side by side in the fast water, which hid them although their back fins were above a broken and uneven surface. The fever smoldered in them, as they waited for the frost to go.

Sticks and ferns near the waterfalls and fast glides around rocks which were wetted by spray slowly became coated with ice. Under many of the alders long stems of brambles were trailing in the water.

These were cadets of the main root which during the past summer had set out to make their own lives. The exploring heads had put forth roots on finding water; these roots were spread long and white on the surface. As the water lipped them, so frost made a layer of ice on them. Soon the brambles were stretched straight, downstream, with a weight of ice on the ineffectual roots. When the ice club became too heavy, the bramble broke and was dragged away. Ice began to dull the sight of the river where it was least alive: at the edges of pools and by the bays in the bank trodden by cattle. The frost had brought down the last leaves of waterside trees, and these had caught, one behind another, against outstanding stones of the shallows. The water flow pressed them together in the shape of fir cones, scores and even hundreds of leaves wadded together, and beginning to decompose on their undersides. This gave a little warmth, which was sought by snails and shrimps. Frost put its blind gray seal around the cones of leaves; frost bound together the roots of rushes; frost sealed the trickling places of the river, and thickened the icicles under the falls. Water found new trickling places; these too were sealed. Rocks and snags lipped by water were given brittle gray collars, which became wider until they broke off and floated into eddies and were welded into the local ice, strengthening it.

The slow solidification of eddies and still stretches by the shallows made the runs faster. New eddies were formed in reaction, new ice affirmed their stillness.

Toward noon the sun in a clear sky melted the rime on bracken and grasses, and in the straying hoof marks of cattle and deer. Some of the gray sheets of ice cracked and were borne down, making the water colder. No fly hatched, no fish moved. The larger eels were in the Atlantic, journeying under the Gulf Stream, seeking by instinct the weed beds of the Sargasso. Smaller eels, the survivors of which would set forth the next autumn, were torpescent in holes and under stones. A large sheet of ice covering the stiller water of the Wheel Pool suddenly whimpered and cracked and tilted, then settled again on the slowly turning water.

The little heat of the sun was soon lost in a frost of gold and lengthening shadows. Ice floes which had stopped by the piers of Humpy Bridge were sealed to the stonework. The sun went down behind the trees, grass drooped again as rime grew white on its blades. Thin layers of water stroked the floes, thickening them. Gralaks lay in the deepest water, never moving.

Up in the Fireplay Pool Salar lay below the redd, as though guarding it. Clots of semiopaque, jellylike water passed him—a slush of ice. Rapidly within his body the germs of salmon pest were multiplying; and as they conquered the living tissue weakened by the long strain of waiting stagnant in the river, so the vegetable fungus strengthened its hold on that tissue. Other forms of life were claiming that which Salar had assembled and used for a racial purpose of which he knew nothing. Salar was nearly emptied of self. He lay behind the redd, awaiting the rhythm of desire and all pleasure, seeing the stars wavery bright as he had seen them in the lustihood of Atlantic nights.

The fungus grew rapidly in the cold water. Soon Salar's jaw was covered with cream-colored ruffs. The edges and center of his tail fin were corroded, too, and his skin, which had thickened and caused the scales to shrink since his return from the sea, was also patched with fungus where it had been bruised on the weirs, and by fighting.

One night when the Fireplay was covered with ice except for a narrow canal Salar saw many fish moving before him. One of them was Gralaks, leaping with silver coat, and returning to lie beside him. Salar drove at the other fish, for they would lure Gralaks from him. They fled from him, and vanished beyond the redd. Gralaks moved to the redd, and grew larger, until she was all the river which was streaming with stars along her flanks; she covered Salar, and was the river in spate and all the shining strength of ocean. But the fish came back, and were black, opening monstrous grampus mouths to crush him, and Salar fled down the river which now was all broken water to bruise him and a weir which was high as the stars. The weir was a flood of red water, and thundering about him; then it was gone, and he saw the redd before him.

It was a goods train passing over the viaduct.

Salar had hardly moved, except to roll over in the delirium of his sickness.

The ice began to thaw the next day, with the coming of the southwest wind. Its melting released oxygen into the water, and Salar was stimulated to leap from the pool, falling back in a formless splash. Shiner saw the leap; he saw the lean rusty-brown body, the prolonged misshapen head covered with creamy fungus, green slime on the gill covers and the blackened jaw with its great white hook twisted and tipped with yellow. Edges of all the fins were yellow, too, while a rosette was fixed to the side, spreading out from the scar of the lamprey wound.

"Poor old chap," said Shiner. "What you needs now is a nice li'l fresh, to take you down to the sea, to clean yourself."

The southwest was blowing, but it brought no rain. By the beginning of February the river was at low summer level again. The phantom of spent passion for which Salar had remained by the redd was gone from him; he lay now in the deeper Wheel Pool, under the shelf of rock beside Trutta. At night the two kelts moved up to the edge of the run where it broke over the shallow. Warmer water had delayed the growth of fungus, but the pest bacillus had spread through his body, heart, liver, and gut. Strips of his skin, which fungus had covered, had broken away, and he had no strength for regrowth.

In the still deeps of the pool a dim blue-gray length lay, the rival of Salar. Two more dead cock fish lay on their backs in the Fireplay. They had died while waiting by redds in the shallows above, and the stream had brought them down. Every pool in the Two Rivers held dead or dying male fish. The wind was now from the northeast, a barren wind of drouth, a dry cutting wind which made lambs on the moor huddle into their ewes, and drove all birds into the lower valleys and the estuary.

When Shiner next saw Salar, the kelt was lying at the edge of the Fireplay, in still water, over a silt of mud and buried sticks. Salar did not move as Shiner knelt down and stared at him. He did not see the man above him. Even when Shiner put a hand out and curved it under the kelt's body, as though to support it, there was no movement. Only when he lifted it did Salar come back from his farawayness of self, and feel a shock, and move off slowly into deep water.

"You must n't bide by the bank, midear," said Shiner. "That ould crane ban't like Shiner, you know. He'll give 'ee a dapp that won't do no one no good." Old Nog, passing in the sky, uttered a screech. "You bestways must wait where you be now, until the rain cometh, midear." The pale mask in the water moved forward. "That's right, midear. Shiner knoweth." And, talking to himself, the old man ambled away along the riverbank, peering into the water, seeing almost everything that happened.

Night after night was starless. Clouds passed over the valley from the west, driven by a high salt wind which ruffled the pools and scattered the packs of leaves on stones of the shallows. Plants of hornwort and celery began to spread on the gravel their first leaves of the year, and the crowfoot was lengthening green near them. The dipper sang its soliloquy of stones-and-water; the kingfisher lanced its cry under the leafless alders. On the top of a spruce higher than the railway viaduct a missel thrush sang to the flaming purple sunset.

With the last of the winter's night snow began to fall on the moor, molding itself thinly on the windward side of writhen beeches and thorns, falling thin and pale and shrinking to beads of water, but always falling, until the black places where turf had been cut were white, and clumps of moor grass were cowled in white with flakes falling thicker until all save water was white. In the morning it was a new world upon which the sun looked briefly before clouds hid it again in snow with which the wind whitely streamlined all things standing from the earth—pillars of the viaduct, trunks of trees, felled timber, plowshare left in an unfinished burrow, abandoned motor-cars, and sheep huddled under the hedges. Through the snow the otters romped, making a slide down the cattle break in the bank by the yew trees, whose portent dark loomed through night's glimmer.

When the moon rose in a clear sky the otters remained by their slide of trodden snow, sliding together and singly, violently and easily, into the water, whistling and talking and wrestling and splashing until sharp heads pointed up the pool, to the noise of a jumping fish. Salar had leaped, the second time in the New Year. A wild hope of a spate and the sea had stirred in him. Together the otters slipped into the water.

Trutta lay beside Salar. Wherever Salar had gone during the past month, Trutta had gone too, following the phosphoric gleam of the kelt's head and flank and tail. When Salar saw the swimming shapes of otters above him, he went wildly away downstream; but Trutta, sure of the deep water, turned with open mouth and swam up hard and bumped the larger otter. Then Trutta, his mouth still open, swam down and swam up again and again, following them round the pool. Shiner was hidden behind the oak tree, and saw what happened. The big pug bumped the otters again and again, until they were growling with rage and one of them ran out on the bank, standing up on its hind legs and "chittering." Then it either saw or smelled Shiner, for after that he neither heard nor saw them more.

But when Shiner returned the next day, he saw, lying on the gravel edge above the Fireplay, lapped by rising colored water of the thaw, a great head with twisted kyp joined to a backbone from which the flesh had been stripped, and a large tail fin frayed convex at the edges. The otters had returned, and driven Trutta into thin water where he was helpless; and when they had killed and left him, a fox, who while passing over the viaduct had heard the noises of splashing and growling, had crept down to the river with his vixen.

And a hundred yards below the Fireplay Shiner found a kelt with fungus on its head and tail and flank, lying on its side in water not deep enough to cover it. Salar had got so far with the last of his strength, and had died in the darkness.

The spate rose rapidly, and washed all away, to the sea which gives absolution, alike to the living and the dead.

In the gravel of the moorland stream the eggs were hatching, little fish breaking from confining skins to seek life, each one alone, save for the friend of all, the Spirit of the waters. And the star stream of heaven flowed westward, to far beyond the ocean where salmon moving from deep waters to the shallows of the islands leaped—eager for immortality.

The Visiting
Fire-Eater

PHILIP WYLIE

*In the field of angling fiction Philip Wylie has few
peers, and he has little competition when it comes
to fiction based on big-game fishing. "The Visiting
Fire-Eater" has been judged by many as one of his
really glowing efforts.*

T HINGS WERE FINE. Too fine, Crunch found himself thinking as
he pushed out into the bay. The weather was good; the fishing,
which provided his livelihood, was good; the *Poseidon,* on which
he was master, had been running like a sewing machine; Sari, his wife,
had money in the bank and three new dresses; young Bill was learning
to talk with a precocity that amazed everyone at the Gulf Stream
Dock; and now the *Trident* was ready for her maiden voyage.

As if he disbelieved the extent of his fortune, Crunch removed the
cover from the *Trident's* engine and gazed dubiously at it. Then, with
a surge of his shoulder, he spun the flywheel. There was a cough and

a purr. Crunch grinned, headed toward open water, and waved at the men on the dock. He pushed up the throttle and watched the rush of bubbles. Ten—maybe eleven knots. Plenty. He eased her down. The vessel moved almost without a ripple and the motor merely whispered.

"Boy!" he murmured. There was, evidently, no end to his luck.

He decided to cruise on down to the dock and let the other boatmen see what he and Desperate had created in their charterless days and free evenings. He steered toward the County Causeway. The shortest route lay between and among various cruisers and yachts lying at anchor. He headed toward them, and a fly fell into his ointment.

"Holy smoker!" The voice came clearly to his ears. "Look what's coming! Somebody's put a motor on a gangplank!"

Crunch grinned and waved. He saw a gentleman in a yachting cap hurry to the rail and stare. The gentleman's face became mirthful. "What you got there, sailor? A motorized boardwalk?"

"Prog boat," Crunch yelled back.

He notched up the gas and moved along the side of a sloop. Two young men were polishing her brightwork. They spied the *Trident* and chortled. "Hey!" one yelled. "Are you sinking? Or is it a submarine?"

Crunch was still grinning, but not quite so happily. He steered away from the sloop. It was true that the *Trident* looked funny. But not that funny, he thought. It was also true that there was no other craft like her. But a man with imagination ought to be able to guess her purpose.

She was sixteen feet long and six feet wide and she consisted principally of two wooden pontoons decked over with boards. There was a rail all around her except for the stern, where you got aboard. Forward were two stools and, between them, mounted on a universal joint above the rail, was an automobile headlight. She had a small inboard engine with a direct drive shaft that ran to a propeller between the pontoons. The pontoons were shovel-nosed and there was a covered live well between them, amidships. There were two benches aft. Outside the rails were brackets for harpoons and gigs. She carried a bucket of rope and also a sort of reel made of an old car wheel with the brake assembly rerigged for hand operation. She had only a foot of freeboard; she draw only ten inches; a man could walk all over her; she did look something like a motorized section of dock, but anybody ought to be able to tell that she was meant for night harpooning on the flats.

Nevertheless, as he approached the stern of the *Paloma* from Southampton, a crowd assembled there, and Crunch began to flush. He'd seen the houseboat before—coming in from cruises to the Keys. It belonged to a gaudy personage on Miami's Riviera named Terry Walm. Crunch had a great admiration for anything so beautiful, so costly, so seaworthy. It would be unpleasant to be made fun of by the *Paloma*'s company.

Laughter welled across the water, so Crunch turned the *Trident*. But, as a man will discover in a long life of hardship, it takes only a trifle to precipitate humiliation. For some reason, his motor conked. Tide and inertia carried him toward the people on the houseboat. He went to his engine with a profane annoyance that looked dignified at a distance.

"What is it?" somebody yelled. "A hatch cover?"

"It's a raft," a girl said, delightedly lifting her voice. "He's playing shipwreck! Ahoy, Robinson Crusoe!"

Crunch stared at his engine.

"Storm coming!" somebody else bawled. "Never mind, Sailor! We'll save you! Hey! Captain! Man the boats!"

Crunch found the trouble and fixed it. A loose connection. He looked up. The people on the *Paloma*'s stern were almost over his head. He grinned again, but their certainty that Crunch was a crackpot with some "invention" was so great that they observed neither the amiability nor the sensitiveness of his grin. Instead, a young man in white flannels who was holding a highball called, "I say, Skipper! Has she been christened yet?" Before Crunch could reply, the young man poured his drink onto the *Trident* and said, "I christen thee H.M.S. *Pancake!*"

Ice and watered whisky hit the deck and splashed Crunch. He did not grin any more. Quietly, he spun the flywheel. The motor started. He headed toward the causeway, under it, and across to the Gulf Stream Dock. His appearance there was a sign for another moment of hilarity, which died as soon as the skippers could clearly see the details of the *Trident*. Mr. Williams came down from the shore. "Crunch," he said, "I think you've got something there. Where you going to put it?"

"Under the dock—if you don't mind. We'll pay extra for the space . . ."

"Will she lie under it—at high tide?"

Desperate, who had assisted his skipper with lines, answered that. "We measured before we made her. Plenty of room!"

So the *Trident*, a distant relative of the *Poseidon*, was moored astern of that well-known ship—under the dock. When the operation had been completed, Crunch rejoined his mate. "I took a hell of a ribbing coming over," he said. "Especially from a lot of wise guys on the *Paloma*."

"You sound sore."

"Sure I'm sore! What's the matter with the *Trident*? Wait till we get her in action! But to hear those rich yahoos laugh, you'd think

I'd claimed the *Trident* would take the gold out of sea water—or that she worked by perpetual motion! They got my goat!"

"Well," Des replied, "skip it! I got a phone call while you were up at the shipyard. Long distance."

Crunch quickly shook off his indignation. "Yeah? Who?"

"Old Man McLaen. Remember him? The guy we took bone-fishing?"

The *Poseidon*'s master chuckled. "I sorta do. Is he coming down?"

"Not yet. Can't. Busy. But he's sending us a guy. Fellow named Cradbey."

"Hell of a name!"

"Important guy. A sportsman, McLaen said. Seems old Mac has some big deal about set with this guy—and the guy went cold. Then Mac got talking about Florida fishing—and this Cradbey wanted a whirl at it before goin' home. So Mac put him on a plane and phoned us. He's going to turn Cradbey over to us to soften him up. Then— when he gets enough fresh air, sunburn and fish, Mac comes down and closes the deal. See?"

Crunch smiled. "Sure. Nice of Mac to send us the business. But I hope they keep on biting! You say he's a fisherman?"

Des frowned. "Well . . . sportsman was the way Mac put it."

"And how long we got before this Cradbey goes wherever his home is?"

"About a week—and his home's England."

"England?"

"Yeah. He's flying back next Friday. I said he was English, didn't I?"

"No." Crunch's eyes were amused. "Of course, you didn't say he wasn't—"

"Sure. One of them what-do-you-call-'ems. Viscounts."

Crunch took a cigarette from his pocket without troubling to remove the package first. He stuck the cigarette between his lips. "Viscount, eh?" He struck a match. "Does a Viscount polish a duke's boots—or vice versa?"

"How in hell should I know!"

Crunch and Des were on hand at the airport that night to assist the Viscount in the matter of luggage, or in any other way. If old Mac wanted him taken care of, he'd be taken care of, viscount or not. The plane came shooting down out of the moonlight and the Viscount came shooting out of the plane. He was stocky, bald-headed, and a man of many words. He has a high, imperious voice. Worn high, Crunch said afterward, from overuse.

"Steward!" he said, as his foot touched Florida soil for the first time, "Please hurry up my baggage! It's deuced late and I'm tired!"

"I'm sorry," said the man he had addressed, "I'm the pilot."

"Then find me a steward, what?"

Des was staring. So was Crunch. "One of those," said the latter quietly. They went forward. "I'm Crunch Adams, of the *Poseidon*. You're Viscount Cradbey?"

The Englishman pivoted. There was a monocle in his eye. It flashed redly with a reflection from the field boundary lights. "I'm Cradbey," he said with vigor. "Adams? *Poseidon?* Oh. Yes—yes—yes! The boat! Splendid! I'm no seaman, you know. Never cared for the briny." To their surprise, he held out his hand. To their further surprise, it was not a lilylike palm, but firm. However, he turned back to the plane almost immediately and began crying for a steward.

He assembled his bags as if he were a collie herding sheep. In that same vociferous mood, he dispatched them to the car which had been sent for him by the Royal Caribbean Hotel. Crunch and Desperate tagged along in the noisy wake of the whole proceeding, but he said nothing until he was ensconced in the car. What he did say, then, was in part too British for understanding. The gist of it was that he would see them early the next morning, that he had the address of their boat in his pocket, that travel in America was a devilish pest, that there had been ten thousand flies in the airplane, that the country reminded him of the Siberian bogs, and that he trusted they'd catch a couple of tons of fish for his pains.

Crunch told Sari about it before they went to sleep.

"You've got to put up with it!" she said urgently. "Mr. McLaen's such a sweetheart—and he loves you two boys. He didn't do this just to throw some fishing your way. He did it because fishing is his idea of the best thing on earth a man can do."

"Yeah. I know it. But this oaf squeals like the fiddle in a hoe-down."

"Mac told Des he was a sportsman. What kind?"

"Some new kind," Crunch answered grimly. "We'll find out to-morrow. Let's get some sleep. I have a hunch I'll need to be rested tomorrow. Cool and Collected."

They found out about the Viscount's sporting laurels on the next day. It was no trouble at all to make the discovery. He showed up at six in a pair of disgracefully battered slacks, a mackintosh, and a felt hat that must have been handed down from father to son through many reigns. "Never fished!" he said before he was within what a normal man would consider earshot. "Strictly a game hunter! Africa! The Gobi! Hear it's exciting! Passionately fond of excitement! Set sail, Captain, what!"

"What ho," said Crunch laconically—and he turned away as he saw a suspicious gleam behind the monocle.

Des was steering. The Viscount was trolling. Crunch came up top-side.

"Can you fish with one of those things in your eye?" Des asked. "I been wondering."

Crunch shrugged. "Maybe it'll drop out. Maybe it'll chum up something."

"Barracuda might snap it up. Might choke on it." Des stared at the sky. "There's going to be a squall later this A.M."

From below, after a while, came the voice of their passenger. "Damn it, men! Nothing happened! Ten-fifteen! Flies out here, too! Whole deuced cockpit alive with 'em! Old McLaen call this excitin'?"

Crunch slid below. His picked up the insect spray gun. After a search he found the fly that had tormented his noble passenger. He killed it. Viscount Cradbey was staring first at one bait and then at the other. There was a flash of lightning. Thunder rolled. The black tumult pushed out over the sea. Its calm was ruffled by a brief press of wind.

"It's going to rain by and by," Crunch said. "Maybe you'd better come in under cover."

The man turned. He removed his eyeglass with all the signs of dis-may. "Come in? Stop fishin'?"

Crunch nodded.

"D'you mean you quit it because of a drop of rain?"

"Usually. The lightning slows down the fishing anyway."

The man from England stared. "Slows it down? Get slower than this? Can't be, Captain! Nothing from nothing equals nothing! Funny, what? Why, up the Saigon we'd sit in those damned native boats for days in a cloudburst waitin' for a shot! I won't melt, Captain! The Cradbeys have been waterproof for generations. Just pour me out a peg of Scotch, like a good fellow, and I'll give you Americans an object lesson in how to go after game!"

A contradictory character, Crunch thought. If he wanted to get wet, let him get wet. The *Poseidon* churned along on blue water that slowly turned purple. The shore disappeared in a gray sheet of rain. The intermittent puffs of wind became forceful. Des hopped below to get his sou'wester. The thunder rolled nearer. A head-splitting shaft of lightning hit the sea nearby and filled the air with ozone. Presently the rain came—moving toward them in a silvery sheet on a pock-marked front that reached and enveloped the boat. The sound was a liquid roar; the sea flattened out to a floor upon which billions of glass globules danced; wind felt through the rain, shifting and rear-ranging it; the *Poseidon* was closed off from everything but a small, opaque world of falling water. Water streamed from the Viscount, and he sat in it, muttering.

Crunch had pretty well abandoned hope for Mr. McLaen's deal.

And then his gloomy forebodings were interrupted. There came a voice—unexcited, not even very interested. "Isn't that some sort of something or other out yonder pecking at the bait?"

Crunch lifted his head. He stared. His feet hit the deck so hard they stung. "Marlin! Des!" he bellowed up into the rain. "White! On the port side!"

The marlin was there, rain or no rain, thunder or no thunder, following the bait as it slid through the bubbling calm, its rounded dorsal out of water and its bill batting. Crunch ran out in the cockpit. The rain soaked him to the skin.

"I suppose," the Viscount said calmly, "from what Old McLaen told me, the next time he hits it, I pull it loose from the bally outrig thing?"

Crunch glanced at him, at the fish, and nodded. "Now!"

But his passenger had already seen the strike and knocked out the line. He was speaking again, thoughtfully. "Count ten, eh? One, two, three, four, five, six, seven, eight, nine, ten. Strike—am I right?"

He struck. "Three times, isn't it? One, two, three."

He put the rod in the socket. The marlin was running fast out toward the open spaces.

"You hung him!" Crunch explained. "Perfect! Dandy!"

The Viscount let go of his whipping rod with one hand in order to adjust his eyeglass and stare at Crunch. "Nothing difficult about it, is there? Mac explained the thing most clearly. Jove. There he is. I keep a tight line—right?"

Crunch took a firm hold on a cleat. There are many men—old hands—who think that, pound for pound, a white marlin is the most powerful phrenetic and elusive species of scaly dynamite into which a hook may be driven. This was a big white. Ninety pounds, maybe. He was raging around on the rain-drenched ocean like a barrel of skyrockets.

And the Viscount was merely sitting there, peering. Occasionally, when the maniacal fish drove his nine silver feet toward the boat, he quickly wound in line. "Active, aren't they?" he said.

Crunch ground his teeth. "Active," he agreed.

Up above was Desperate, wearing the half-ecstatic, half-terrified look characteristic of him when there was a big one jitterbugging in the wake of the *Poseidon*. The white marlin landed flat after its last pinwheeling leap. Its forked tail quivered in the rain spray. It sounded.

"Pump him up now?" the passenger said inquiringly.

Crunch did not look at him. He just nodded.

The Viscount began on the fish. "Practiced up in Michigan," he said. "On a piano stool with a walking stick. Up slow and easy—eh?

Down quick—and crank! We used to fish like this in grab bags at Worlemshire Castle. When we were little nippers, you know. Magnet on a bit of string. Caught all sorts of things. Sweets, mostly."

Crunch stared at the man's back. Ought to be tossed overboard, he thought. We could go in and say he attacked us. Or that he fell over while we weren't looking. I'd have to tie an anchor on him first, though. He probably learned to swim—in the castle moat. That idea revived Crunch a little. He began to pray that the marlin would throw the hook.

It didn't. After forty minutes of heartbreaking effort, it quit, and came in almost belly up. The Viscount reeled easily. He was not panting. He was not anything, so far Crunch could see when he leaned over to boat the fish. In fact, after a blow had killed it, and it lay in the cockpit changing swiftly from delirious indigos to dull grays, the Englishman produced a dry handkerchief from underneath his mackintosh, wiped his monocle, and condescended to have a look.

"Somehow," he said, "all dead fish look more or less alike."

He walked over to the electric refrigerator and opened a can of ale. He poured it into a glass. He came back, while Crunch was putting a piece of canvas over the fish. It was too big to go in the box. "Poor old McLaen," he said almost to himself. "Calls that excitement, eh?" He chuckled. "Wonder what he'd do if he had only a single shell left and a pair of water buffalo came through the grass? Or how he'd feel about a herd of elephants wheeling, trampling his boy, coming on? Or even tigers, eh? If a man's on foot."

Crunch said nothing. There were bigger ones in the Gulf Stream—but none better.

The Viscount seemed to notice, in a vague way, that Crunch was downcast. He clapped him cheerily on the shoulder. "No criticism of you, old fellow!" he said. "Very clever to find one of these creatures! It's just that my definition of sport involves a spot of hazard, I guess. Risk and that sort of thing. I daresay a sedentary old duffer like Mac would find all this extremely stirrin'!"

Later in the day they ran into a school of king mackerel. The Britisher caught six—and gave it up. He was sleepy, he said. He took a nap. Crunch waved Des toward the shore and they went in. At the dock, Cradbey woke. He viewed with mild amusement the enthusiastic rush to see his fish. It was quite clear that he had a low opinion of this American sport. He refused to be photographed with his catch, and when Des suggested having the marlin mounted, he guffawed. "Can you imagine what Ponsley and Ashton and old Douglas would say if they saw that damned mackerel—marlin—among the heads in my den, eh?"

He was on the point of stepping ashore when he caught sight of the

Trident, moored under the dock. He stopped and peered. "Odd-looking thing. What is it?"

Crunch looked at the man coldly. "A prog boat."

"Prog?"

"For harpooning things. At night."

The Viscount snorted. "Confound it, man, jacking fish with a light is bad business! We'd hang a man for doing it to a deer!"

"There's a difference," said Crunch huskily, "between a deer and a shark."

"Shark?" The small man's monocle twinkled. "Harpoon sharks?" Now, that sounds interestin', young man! Why didn't you mention it? More in my line. I'd like to take a whack at it!"

The merest glimmer of hope shone across the dark panorama of Crunch's mind. A notion formed there—a notion no bigger than a minnow but capable of growth. He shrugged. "It would mean a trip down to the Keys. Pretty uncomfortable country. Mosquitoes, flies, coral snakes, and a few other things."

The Englishman's eyes, for the first time that day, were a little livelier than lumps of blue clay. "You don't say! Well, well! If you'll make the arrangements . . ."

After he had departed for the Royal Caribbean Hotel, Sari came down the dock. When she saw the white marlin, she smiled. She hurried toward her husband. "Crunch! How perfectly marvelous!"

Crunch stared at her and gave a burlesque. "Active creature—but all dead fish look alike, what? Interestin' sport—for cripples—I dare say!"

"He wasn't like that!"

Crunch grinned ruefully. "Sari, the guy is an icicle! He caught that marlin as if he were tying up his shoelace! Sportsman—baloney!"

"That's dreadful! What are you going to do? Mr. McLaen will be so disappointed!"

"We're going down to Key Amigo," Crunch said. "Tomorrow."

The pier at Camp Amigo extends into the Bay of Florida for about a hundred feet. At the shore end are comfortable log cabins with electric lights, hot showers, bar service, and beds of luxury brand. True, two coral snakes, which are beautiful but dangerous, had been found in the summer in the lounge. The scream of a panther could sometimes be heard in the dining room. And the chef had shot a crocodile, once, that was trying to tip over the garbage pails. But, by and large, the camp was an oasis of civilization in the wilderness.

It is a wilderness of nameless trees and unknown vines where a man cannot hack his way fifty feet an hour with a machete. It is a far more sinister wilderness of water—water that extends from the dock north toward the Everglades and west clear to the Dry Tortugas. Islands rise by the thousand in this water—islands covered with pines, with palms, with ferns, with raw jungle, islands a few yards square and islands forty miles long. Between them run labyrinthine tidal creeks which are often miles in length, and around them lie bays and lagoons, charted but untenanted.

In the water there is life—abundant and formidable. It is, for the most part, shallow water. Low tide bares wide acreages of weedy flats. High tide may cover with a scant ten feet of sea limitless gardens of coral and aquatic vegetation in which live monsters longer than elephants, bigger than lions, armed with shocking weapons which disappeared from the earth's surface aeons ago but survive still in the huge, horrid things under the waters of the earth. The pier at Amigo Key was a tiny outpost in that wild marine world.

There the *Poseidon* was moored. And there, on the next evening, as the sun was setting in a red-streaked, windless sky, Crunch pushed off the *Trident*. She was armed to the teeth, then, with five-pronged, hand-forged gigs on ten-foot shafts, a lily iron, a turtle peg, a plain harpoon, rope, an eighteen-inch lance, and a smooth-bore large-gauge gun that fired a soft lead slug. Crunch twisted the flywheel and the engine purred. He sat astern, steering toward the low-lying islands in the bay. His guest was perched on one of the stools forward, a gig in his hands, his eyes roaming over the scene.

They moved rapidly along the coast. An echelon of pelicans coasted down the twilight air toward a roost in the mangroves. A man-of-war hawk teetered and plunged for a last morsel before the coming of night. A bald eagle passed on whispering pinions. The lights of Camp Amigo vanished around a point on which dead tree trunks stood above the jungle. There was no one in sight, finally. No boats, no lights, only the opalescent water turning gray as the sun withdrew. The disappearance of its last faint bars left a flat, forlorn world that looked utterly silent.

Crunch throttled down the motor. His passenger had stiffened in unconscious reaction to the environment. He, also, sensed its primordial quality, its balefulness. It was a land not meant to be invaded, a land of quietude and teeth and poison. He looked back at Crunch and his smile showed whitely. He gestured with the long shaft in his hand. Crunch nodded in response and pointed. The man saw something dark and triangular moving slowly on the surface of the water.

"Shark." Crunch's voice seemed loud.

"Let's go!"

"Little one," Crunch replied casually.

He waited until he was in the exact spot and until the night had closed in, black and hostile. At a creek mouth, some fifty yards from the tangled arches of mangrove root, he touched a switch. The big electric light in the bow went on. The Viscount looked down, saw the transparent water and fishes in it, looked deeper, and gasped. He was no longer on a boat. He was, instead, floating in the air. From his seat he could see for a hundred feet ahead and forty on each side. Underneath him was a fairyland.

Lacy, lavender fans stood stiff in the water. Yellow "plants" without leaves grew high as a man among them. Coral, white as alabaster, lay on the sea floor in brain-shaped lumps and branched toward the surface like the horns of a herd of stags. Huge niggerheads rose like reefs under their pontoons. Waterplants with bulbous stems writhed in the slow current. There were grottoes, shelves of hard coral, sand pits where shells swirled like snowflakes. On the bottom, spiny black seas urchins moved tentatively, red starfish lay in waiting, rock lobsters half hid, shifting their hinged feelers lazily. Here and there were patches of sponge, moss, sea mats—in sulphur-yellow, scarlet, green, blue. And in and out through the caverns and the vegetation and the coral, swam fish of every imaginable color and pattern—black and silver individuals, darting purple schools.

"Jove!" the Viscount said.

Crunch did not answer. He kept his attention focused on the murky outer fringe of the light. He was looking for several things—mud swirls, gray ghosts in the peripheral gloom, the flash of an eye. The *Trident* crept along. Ahead, near the shore, there was a violent flurry and the dark water was whipped to foam.

"What's that?" The Englishman asked it quickly.

"Tarpon. They're chasing a school of bait up against the mangroves. Feeding."

The man, silhouetted against the light, nodded and looked down at the gardens in the sea. There came, from inland, a hoarse, choked cough. A grunt. He turned, "I won't ask about that," he said quietly. " 'Gator."

"Croc," Crunch answered.

"Didn't know you had 'em here!"

Crunch smiled a little. "Yes. Crocodiles are fairly common on the Keys."

"But, Lord, man, on a flat little thing like this—if one took a notion to swim out . . . ! Why! I've seen 'em on the Nile thirty feet long!"

"Never saw one that big here. But we have a gun—and a good motor."

The man nodded. Presently he said, "All right for me to spear one of these things? I'd like to try my aim."

"Shoot." Crunch came up and took the stool beside him then. He had auxiliary controls on a panel there. He watched his passenger sight at a crimson fish that was standing still in the brilliant light. The gig shot into the water.

"Missed!" said the man, with chagrin.

"There's some diffraction. You've got to compensate for it. Next time slide your spear down toward your fish—and jab. Can't let go. You'll begin to be able to judge the angle, that way."

There was another small fish, blue with yellow spots, a triangular fish with a sharp back, a flat belly, and two tiny horns. The man let the three-pronged spear slide toward it through the water until the tines were only inches behind it. Then he stabbed lightly. He hit the fish. They could see it tip sideways. But it swam away.

"Cowfish," Crunch said. "They have a skeleton on the outside. Good-eating meat inside, though. You didn't hit it hard enough. Try one of those crayfish."

The Viscount tried. A moment later he hauled his spear triumphantly out of the water. He had impaled a large lobsterlike animal that was flapping wildly and emitting a croaking noise. Crunch removed the crayfish, killed it, and dropped it into the live well. "You can have it for lunch," he said.

He started back toward the stern. The Viscount wheeled and grabbed his arm. "That thing, old man!"

"Hit it!" Crunch answered instantly.

The thing was diamond-shaped and about four feet long, not counting the tail that dragged behind it. Sand-colored and flat. A skate of some sort, the Viscount thought. He measured its course with his eye, poised himself, and drove in the spear. He could actually see the tines imbed themselves in the thing's back. The shock galvanized it. Like a boomerang coasting up on the air, it rose in a swift circle. The Viscount leaned over to see, and the shaft of his spear hit him sharply on the head. He slid off the stool and caught himself by grabbing the rail.

"Stupid!" he said. "The demned pole stuck up straight, eh? Here!"

Crunch was paying out line as the ray rushed through the night. The Viscount grabbed the rope. Crunch tilted up the light. They could see the ray leaping and shaling out on the water. Its efforts shook loose the head of the gig, but the line was made fast to both the metal and the wood, so it did not free itself. For a few minutes the Englishman hauled furiously on the line. The ray came closer, plunging and leaping. Crunch put the light on the *Trident*'s side and leaned over the rail. With a heave, he tossed the ray aboard. It lay on the deck, its edges rippling with efforts to swim, its tail threshing. The Englishman stepped toward it fascinatedly.

"Get back!" Crunch yelled.

He jumped. The ray's tail lashed at the deck in the spot where he had been. Crunch went around it gingerly and picked up the lance.

He thrust it home. The fish quivered. "Now," he said, "I'll show you why I hollered. See that long spine at the base of the tail? That's his stinger. It's poisonous. It would break off in your leg—a good six inches of it—and stay there, because it's barbed. That would be the end of our party tonight—and all others, for a few weeks."

"Well, well," said the Briton. His voice was bland, but Crunch detected a note of tension in it.

"We'll keep this guy," Crunch continued. "Trophy. Must go a hundred pounds, easy." He swung the light back on the water.

Cradbey went back to his post. He speared a snapper, which Crunch told him was difficult, inasmuch as they were quick. Then he missed a sea robin. Something amorphous and bright green next caught his eye. It was about a yard long. When he struck it, there was no answering quiver in the spear shaft. Instead, the thing vanished and in its place was an inky cloud.

"Octopus," Crunch said. "Little one."

"Hummmm."

Crunch was going to add that they didn't grow very large in that region. He decided to keep his counsel.

"There's a big fish!"

Crunch looked. It was big—for a barracuda. A five-footer, lying in very shallow water. Motionless, mean, and glittering, it floated there. He headed toward it. His passenger got ready. The barracuda looked with wicked, unblinking eyes into the light. Cradbey plunged. He could feel the spear go home—and he did not let go. It was a mistake. The 'cuda wrenched the spear from his hands, hurting his wrists, and shot under the boat. There was a crack as the shaft snapped, and the fish vanished in the night with the tines in its back.

Cradbey rubbed his wrists. "If I'd let go—let him take it on the line . . . ?"

Crunch shrugged. "He might have gone under the boat anyhow."

"Hate to think of a fish getting away with that in him!"

Crunch understood that feeling. This, however, was different. "He'll shake it, and heal—or else something will eat him in no time. Besides, I don't like 'cudas. I've seen a man with nothing left of his upper arm but the bare bone from one of those things."

"Hunh!" said the Viscount. "Wouldn't pay to fall overboard, eh?"

"In more ways than one, it wouldn't!"

The Englishman glanced down at the twelve short inches of freeboard. He stepped back a little from the edge. He peered through the thick night toward the shore. He noticed that they were heading into a wide opening that looked like a river mouth. He sat down and glued his eye to the marine wonderland which now seemed more hellish than fairylike. He began to feel a little excited. A ray came by, and he missed it. Then a shark, big and ghostly—but out of range. They chased it, but it put on a burst of speed and vanished.

Crunch steered, searching, hoping. He lighted a cigarette. And suddenly a ripple of cold fear ran down his spine. It was coming toward them. Dark—it looked black—and a good eighteen feet across. Its batlike "wings" propelled it. Its eyes shone. Its tremendous mouth opened and closed. Crunch had never before seen one that close to shore.

Of all the contrivances of nature for swooping and guzzling on the shoals, the manta is the most hideous. It is a ray, a giant ray that grows to weigh three or four thousand pounds. Usually peaceable, it is fierce and destructive when aroused. Harpoons and guns will not always stop it—and more than one small boat has been crushed in its "wings" or by its weight when it leaped and fell upon it. Crunch stared and gulped—and saw the Viscount reach for the lily iron.

He spoke in time. "No! Not that! Let it alone! We'd need a bigger boat and more men!"

There was a moment of suspended action. The awful fish swam into the light and turned and went away. The Englishman put down the iron. Crunch felt sweat leak down his back.

"The thing did look—dangerous," said the Englishman.

"It could be. They leap like the little one. Fall on the boat. They like to come up underneath you, too, when you have an iron in 'em. And the *Trident*'s only inch cedar."

Cradbey took out his handkerchief. He whipped it open in the cool air. He passed it across his brow. "Plenty of game," he said.

Crunch was pointing again. "But there—yonder! The lily iron!"

The Briton turned. "Shark?"

"Look!"

"Great heavens, man! It's got a sword!"

"Saw! We can give it a whirl, if you care to!"

"Do I!" He was standing. His iron was ready, pointing down across the square bow of the raft. The sawfish swam slowly along the edge of a bank. When the light touched him, he stopped for a moment, and then went on more rapidly. Crunch gunned the motors. The great fish turned toward deeper water. But Cradbey was getting closer. He had a clear view of the thing—its long, toothed beak oscillating, its tail waving. He could see small fish dodging under cover. He had no idea of what would happen. He threw.

The shaft of the harpoon stood quivering for a split second.

"Got him!" Crunch whispered.

Then the line was yanked from Cradbey's hands. It snapped tight on the automobile wheel which had been made into a reel. Crunch rushed forward and pushed on a lever. The wheel whizzed and in a minute the air was rank with the odor of hot brake lining. Far ahead the water went white as the fish's tail broached. The *Trident* was gathering speed. Presently the wheel stopped revolving. Ahead, the creek opened out. There was a bend and then another. The sawfish was pulling them steadily. Crunch tipped up the light. Cradbey could see far beyond its range, the dark, level horizon on the open sea. They were going straight for it.

"Is it safe to take this thing out there?"

"No!" Crunch answered. "Shall we cut him loose?"

"That's for you to say."

Crunch shook his head. "It's a question of whether or not you want to take the chance. I, for one, hate to cut off a fish——"

"Carry on!"

The fish slowed. They were several hundred yards from shore. The water was glass-clear and not deep. Six feet, perhaps. The bottom was grassy. Cradbey saw the line go slack. Crunch began to spin the wheel. "Here!" Cradbey said. "I can do that! You get to the engine!"

Crunch threw the *Trident* in reverse. But the sawfish was coming around fast. You could tell that by the slack. The Englishman was spinning the auto wheel, taking in line with all his might. For a small man, he had a great deal of power and endurance. They both heard again the sound of the broaching tail. Crunch tipped the light. He caught the blur of the fish a hundred feet away, as it cut in a circle around the boat. He pushed up the throttle and turned the rudders. The *Trident* was designed for sharp spinning. It swung to face the fish. Cradbey was not getting in the line fast enough with the auto wheel. He gave up and grabbed the rope, pulling it hand over hand. Crunch watched the fish. It charged up and over a submarine bank into very shallow water. It seemed extraordinarily violent for a member of its fairly sluggish breed. Then Crunch saw why: Under the bank, following hard on the bleeding fish, was a big shark. Cradbey got the line tight and heaved with all his might. The sawfish cut in close to the *Trident*. The shark lashed at it in the darkness.

There was a split second of furious complex action. The sawfish, trying to slash either at the boat or at the shark, reared out of water. Cradbey yanked again. The toothed blade came aboard, cutting right and left. The *Trident* heeled up. The shark broke water and its jaws snapped. The rail of the *Trident* went to smithereens. Pail, automobile wheel, rope, harpoons were ripped loose and tossed overboard. Cradbey lost his balance and slid down the deck. He teetered on the canted edge above the melee of blood, foam, saw and fins. Crunch hooked his leg around a rail stanchion, leaned, grabbed with his powerful right arm, and yanked the man bodily out of danger. The combat churned and gurgled astern. The *Trident* settled back level.

Crunch turned the light on the boat. In a moment, everything was quiet again. Not even the engine broke the stillness.

The Viscount spoke. His voice was level, even amused. "Thanks, old man!"

Crunch waved his hand. He had wanted passionately to show the Englishman a little excitement. Even a little danger. But not that much.

"Great sport! Another fish down there, what?"

"Yeah. Shark."

"Thought so. Heard his jaws snap. Rotten sound."

Crunch sat down and lighted a cigarette. The Englishman polished his monocle. Suddenly he stood still. "We're settling a bit, aren't we?"

Crunch nodded. He was digesting the thought that if Cradbey had been six inches farther across the deck—there might have been no Cradbey. "That sawfish holed one of our pontoons."

The Englishman sat down on the opposite bench. "I see," he said quietly. "Tough."

There was a splashing far out on the water. Perhaps the sawfish had escaped. Perhaps the shark was feasting. Perhaps some other voracious drama was being enacted. "We could shoot a few rounds," the Englishman suggested.

Crunch was still thinking about the narrowness of that moment on the water. He shrugged. "Useless." He assumed the Britisher was hoping for his sawfish.

Then it dawned on Crunch. The man from across the sea thought they were going to sink. He had suggested shooting as a signal for help. He didn't know that there were bulkheads in the pontoons. Bulkheads he and Des had carefully built against just such accidents as a fish charging, or a sharp rock. The Englishman assumed that when the *Trident* went down a shark or a barracuda, or perhaps a manta, would come shooting through that limpid, murderous water, and they'd yell once or twice, and that would be finis.

For a moment Crunch felt his flesh creep and tingle. That was what they'd meant when they talked about the British. He wondered how he would feel if he thought he was going to sink into the water out there where the current ran toward the Gulf Stream, and the Stream was alive—with death.

"This is one time," said the Viscount, with a smile that was invisible in the night, but audible, "when we don't seem to rule the waves, what?"

Then Crunch told him.

The Viscount was not angry. He just said, "Splendid, old man! Then we can still get one of those what-do-you-call-its, eh?"

When Mr. McLaen reached Key Amigo, after flying from Michigan and driving a long way down the Key West road, it was night. He'd had no dinner and he was hungry. Nevertheless he stopped long enough, while his duffle was being unloaded, to look at the thing on the dock. It was like a big bat—fifteen feet from tip to tip. It hung from a block and tackle and had been spread out with spikes. The colored boy who was waiting on him followed his eyes. "That there Crunch Adams and his mate and this Englishman catched it," he said. "In the *Poseidon*. Guess they'd go awhalin' if they was any whales outside. He sure is the harpooninest man! Me, if ah even seen one of them devilfish I'd row right up into the air!"

Mr. McLaen chuckled. "I take it he likes fishing?"

"That Lord Crabbey? Not fishin'! He don't fish! He's a pure proggin' man! He's out right now, Mr. McLaen—tryin' to prog up a 'lectric ray! Ain't rightly got no sense at all. He tells the boss here to tell you he's too busy to talk any more business than to say 'O.K.'—whatever that means."

"I think I understand."

Mr. McLaen grinned in the dark. He followed the boy to his cabin. He tipped him five dollars. It was a record for the man from Michigan.

Out on the broad, smooth bay, near the shore of an island, the *Trident* moved along behind her headlight. Two men stared into the water with breathless concentration. Below them streamed beauty—bizarre beauty, fiendish beauty. They did not talk at all, but it was evident in their gestures and their attitudes that they understood each other extremely well.

The next afternoon was calm. The *Trident* was out to see who could be scared by daylight. Aboard her were Crunch, who was looking at the Viscount with a continual but secret admiration, Mr. McLaen, who was expertly casting a plug into every likely cove, and the man from England himself, who stood in the bow, holding a harpoon, ready for anything. They slowly rounded a bend in Angelfish Creek. It is a favorite mooring place for private boats of all kinds—sheltered, beautiful, and full of fish. Crunch was not surprised, but he was somewhat displeased, to see the *Paloma* anchored there.

The Viscount squinted at it. *"Paloma,"* he said, *"Paloma, Paloma, Paloma!* Isn't that Terry Walm's boat?"

Crunch nodded.

"Let's go over and put aboard, what? I know the young chappie."

Crunch did not seem eager to turn from his course.

"Anything wrong?" the Viscount asked.

"Wrong? Nothing. The people on that ship, though, have a habit of razzing the devil out of the *Trident*."

The Viscount's eyeglass twinkled. "They do, eh? Don't like the

Trident, eh? You know, young Walm owes my company about ten thousand pounds. I wasn't aware he had the *Paloma* in commission. I do think we might stop by. I fancy he'd be quite taken with the *Trident* under the circumstances." He saw Crunch's look of discomfort. "Oh, no mention of the money, old fellow! Not a syllable! I just think we might drift past and solicit the crashing bounder's admiration, don't you? Matter of fact, I insist!"

Crunch grinned then and turned the wheel.

The Truth about Izaak Walton

ED ZERN

It has been said that Ed Zern could turn out a light and amusing exposition on nuclear fission. Anglers, as a group, are inclined to treat angling as a serious matter—they even take themselves seriously. So far as can be determined, Ed Zern has never written a serious word on fishing, yet his angling books have been extremely successful. There must be more lighthearted fishermen than we know.

IF YOU THINK *this* book is dull, go curl up with *The Compleat Angler, or The Contemplative Man's Recreation.* Then try to uncurl.

Of course, Izaak Walton wrote *The Compleat Angler* a long time ago. Even nonfishermen could not spell very good in those days.

The Compleat Angler is all about a character named Piscator. Later, in disgust, he became a stage director.

Izaak Walton pretended to be an expert on fishing. In his introduction, he refers to "the honest Angler." That's how much *he* knew.

The Compleat Angler is chockful of useful information for fishermen. For example, in Part I, Chapter IV, it says: "And next you are to notice, that the Trout is not like the Crocodile." Walton was observant.

In Chapter VIII, he tells of a man who caught a pike by using a mule as bait. Fortunately, for Ike, it was several hundred years before anybody read beyond Chapter I.

499

In the same chapter, he also tells of a pike that bit a Polish girl's foot. Personally, I would prefer this type bait over mules.

I once knew a Polish girl in Hamtramck, Michigan, who —————— ————————————————————————— not once but several times!

Publisher's Note: This is Mr. Zern's first book. He has apparently never heard about postal regulations.

ABOUT THE EDITOR

RAYMOND R. CAMP was born in 1908 in Spring Lake, New Jersey, and educated at the University of Pennsylvania and New York University. From 1929 to 1956 he was a member of the editorial staff of *The New York Times*. He was named outdoor editor of that newspaper in 1936 and began writing the "Wood, Field and Stream" column. This pleasant assignment sent him fishing and hunting over most of the Western Hemisphere and Europe and through part of Africa, with time out for serving as a lieutenant colonel of Infantry in the African and European Theaters during World War II. Currently he is associate editor of *Field and Stream* Magazine.

Mr. Camp is a member of Theta Chi Fraternity, the Anglers Club, Feather-Dusters Club, Andros Yacht Club and the Overseas Press Club. He is married to the former Nancy Ames Bigelow, and they have four children: Nancy, Susan, Raymond and Jonathan. The Camps make their home in Madison, Connecticut.

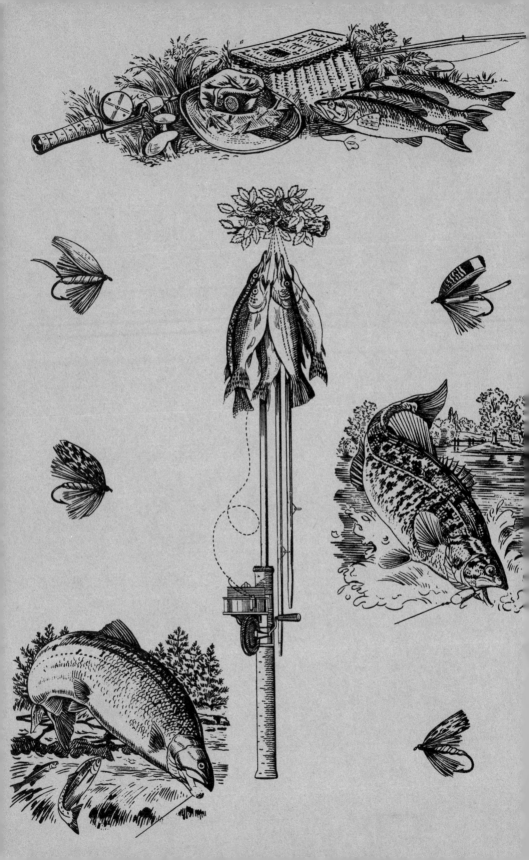